Essential Maths

Book 8H

David Rayner

Elmwood Press

First published 2009 by
Elmwood Press
80 Attimore Road
Welwyn Garden City
Herts. AL8 6LP
Tel. 01707 333232

Reprinted 2010, 2011.

ISBN 9781 902 214 764

Numerical answers are published in a separate book

Typeset and illustrated by Domex e-Data Pvt. Ltd.
Printed and bound in Singapore.

PREFACE

Essential Maths Book 8H has been written for pupils who are working towards National Curriculum Level 7. Level 6 work is consolidated and then developed further.

Although there is no set path through the books, the topics appear in the order suggested in the National Numeracy Strategy guide. Broadly speaking, the book is split into 6 units. Each unit of work can be used during one half-term with appropriate revision material at the end of the unit. Many topics are reviewed later in the book, in line with the NNS guide.

Puzzle activities and mental arithmetic tasks can be found between the units, to be used whenever appropriate. Investigations appear regularly throughout the book. Ideas for discussing and exploring themes from the 'history of mathematics' are included between each pair of units.

The authors believe that children learn mathematics most effectively by *doing* mathematics. Many youngsters who find mathematics difficult derive much more pleasure and enjoyment from the subject when they are doing questions which help them build up their confidence. Pupils feel a greater sense of satisfaction when they work in a systematic way and when they can appreciate the purpose and the power of the mathematics they are studying.

No textbook will have the 'right' amount of material for every class. The authors believe that it is preferable to have too much material rather than too little. Opportunities for functional maths are incorporated into activities throughout the book.

Most work is broken down into two parts. 'M' exercises are aimed at all children at this level. 'E' exercises provide extension work. Pupils may move naturally onto this work after an 'M' exercise or teachers may judge that a number of students should *only* tackle 'E' exercise.

Pupil self-assessment is a very important part of assessment for learning. Regular 'check yourself' sections appear throughout the book. Answers to these parts only are provided at the back of the book for immediate feedback.

David Rayner

CONTENTS

UNIT 1

1.1 Properties of numbers

In section 1.1 you will learn about:

- prime numbers
- factors and multiples
- square numbers
- prime factor decomposition
- cube numbers and higher powers

Prime numbers, factors, multiples

- A *prime* number is divisible by just two different numbers: by itself and by one. Notice that 1 is *not* a prime number.

  Here are some prime numbers: 7 23 11
- The *factors* of 15 divide into 15 exactly.

  1 × 15 3 × 5 The factors of 15 are 1, 3, 5 and 15.
- The first four *multiples* of 6 are 6, 12, 18, 24

  The first four multiples of 11 are 11, 22, 33, 44
- The first four *square* numbers are 1, 4, 9, 16 [ie 1^2, 2^2, 3^2, 4^2]

Exercise 1M

1 Which of these are prime numbers? 21, 5, 49, 81, 13, 65

2 Write down the first ten prime numbers.

3 Make four prime numbers using each of the digits once each.

7	1	2	4
3	5	9	6

4 Find all the factors of

(a) 12 (b) 30 (c) 17 (d) 50

5 7 is a factor of which numbers between 20 and 30?

6 (a) List the factors of 24.
(b) List the factors of 40.
(c) List the common factors of 24 and 40. [i.e. the numbers which are in list (a) and list (b).]

7 (a) List the factors of 28.
(b) List the factors of 36.
(c) List the common factors of 28 and 36.
(d) Write down the highest common factor of 28 and 36.

8 Find the highest common factor of
(a) 24 and 42 (b) 35 and 49

9 Factors occur in pairs. For example $48 = 1 \times 48$, 2×24, 3×16, 4×12, 6×8

Write down all the factor pairs for
(a) 28 (b) 30

10 

(a) From the balls shown, which two balls add up to 24? There are three answers.

(b) Which two prime number balls add up to 18? There are two answers.

11 Answer true or false :

(a) 'All prime numbers are odd.'
(b) 'If the product of two numbers is zero than one of the numbers must be zero.'
(c) 'Every positive integer greater than 20 has an even number of factors.'

12 The number in the square is the product of the two numbers on either side of it. Copy and complete:

(a) 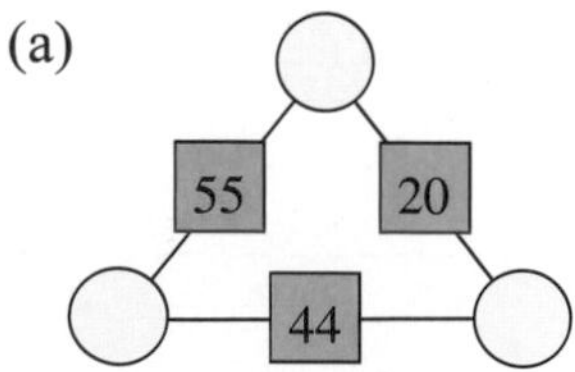

(b) 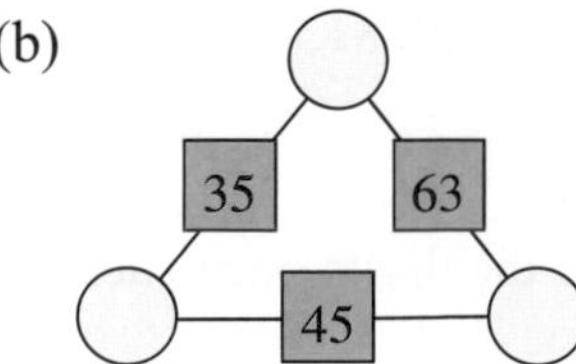

(c) 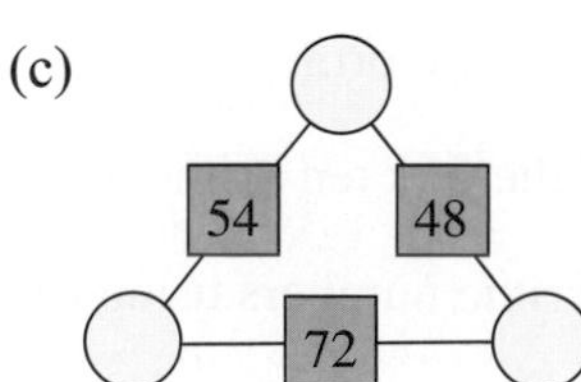

Exercise 1E

1 Write down the first four multiples of

(a) 3 (b) 7 (c) 10 (d) 15

2 Here are the first six multiples of 12 and 15

12:	12	24	36	48	60	72
15:	15	30	45	60	75	90

Write down the lowest common multiple of 12 and 15. [i.e. the lowest number which is in both lists.]

3 Copy and complete the first five multiples of 6 and 8.

6 : 6, 12, ☐, ☐, ☐

8 : 8, ☐, ☐, ☐, ☐

Write down the L.C.M. of 6 and 8

4 The number n is a multiple of 7 between 30 and 40.

The number m is a multiple of 9 between 40 and 50.

Work out $n + m$.

5 Answer true or false:

(a) 'All multiples of 9 are multiples of 3.'

(b) 'All factors of 12 are factors of 6.'

(c) 'All numbers have an even number of different factors.'

6 True or false?

'The total number of cubes in the pyramid is given by $5^2 + 4^2 + 3^2 + 2^2 + 1^2$.'

7 Which of these are prime numbers? 13, 21, 27, 31, 49, 51, 63, 65, 67

8 Add together all the prime numbers less than 16.

9 60 is mid-way between 2 prime numbers. What are they?

10 (a) How many even prime numbers are there?

(b) How many prime numbers have 5 as their last digit?

11 The number 13 is prime. When the digits are reversed we get 31, and 31 is also prime.
Find two more numbers with this property.

12 Here are the first three triangle numbers.

1 3 6

(a) Draw similar diagrams to show the next two triangle numbers.

(b) Show that consecutive pairs of triangle numbers add up to make square numbers.

13 

Traditionally there are 47 matches in a box.

Write the number 47 as

(a) the sum of four square numbers,

(b) the sum of five square numbers.

(c) the sum of a cube number and two square numbers

[you may use any square number more than once.]

Prime factor decomposition

Factors of a number which are also prime numbers are called prime factors. We can find these prime factors using a 'factor tree'. Here are two examples.

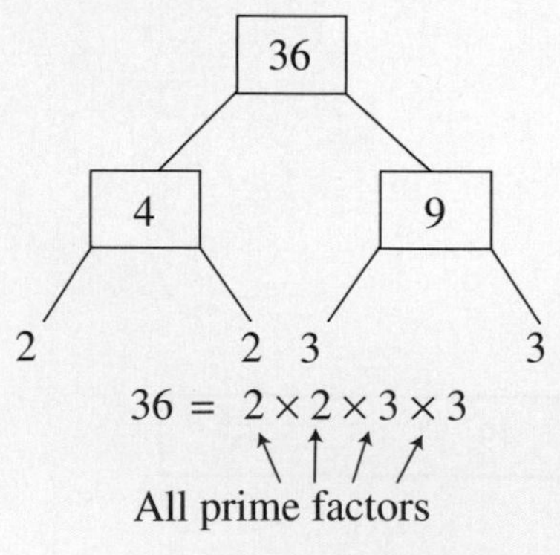

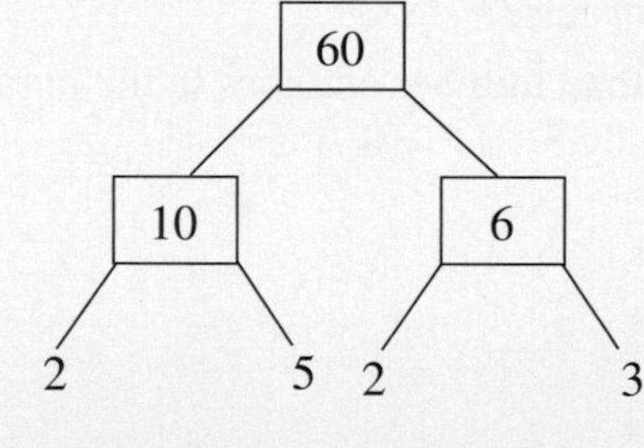

Exercise 2M

1 Draw a factor tree for 108 and for 300. Remember that you only stop when you get to prime numbers.

2 Draw factor trees for the following numbers.

(a) 24 (b) 81 (c) 84 (d) 200

(e) 294 (f) 630 (g) 392 (h) 3960

3 $154 = 2 \times 7 \times 11$ and $1365 = 3 \times 5 \times 7 \times 13$.

Find the highest common factor of 154 and 1365.

[i.e. the highest number that goes into 154 and 1365.]

4 $105 = 3 \times 5 \times 7$ and $330 = 2 \times 3 \times 5 \times 11$.

Find the highest common factor of 105 and 330.

[i.e. the highest number that goes into 105 and 330.]

5 $975 = 3 \times 5 \times 5 \times 13$ and $550 = 2 \times 5 \times 5 \times 11$

Find the highest common factor (H.C.F.) of 975 and 550.

6 (a) $625 = 5 \times 5 \times 5 \times 5$. The square root, $\sqrt{625} = 5 \times 5 = 25$

(b) Given $36 = 2 \times 2 \times 3 \times 3$, find $\sqrt{36}$

(c) Given $2401 = 7 \times 7 \times 7 \times 7$, find $\sqrt{2401}$

7 Write the following numbers as the product of prime factors and then find the square root of each number.

(a) 100 (b) 324 (c) 441

8 Some prime numbers can be written as the sum of 2 square numbers. e.g. $1^2 + 2^2 = 5$.

Find 5 two-digit prime numbers that can be written as the sum of two square numbers. [Hint: start by listing the square numbers.]

9 Find the smallest value of n for which

$1^2 + 2^2 + 3^2 + 4^2 + \ldots\ldots + n^2 > 1000$

10 Find the remainder when these numbers are divided by 6.

(a) 6^2 (b) $6^2 + 2$ (c) $2^2 + 3^2$ (d) $2^2 \times 3^2 \times 6^2$

Cubes and higher powers

- The first three *cube numbers* are: $1^3 = 1 \times 1 \times 1 = 1$

  $2^3 = 2 \times 2 \times 2 = 8$

  $3^3 = 3 \times 3 \times 3 = 27$

- Finding the *cube root* of a number is the inverse function.

  e.g. $\sqrt[3]{27} = 3$ $\qquad \sqrt[3]{8} = 2$

- Higher powers are written in a smilar way

  $3 \times 3 \times 3 \times 3 \times 3$ is written 3^5. 'Three to the power 5'

  $2 \times 2 \times 2 \times 2 \times 2 \times 2$ is written 2^6. 'Two to the power 6'

  To work out 7^4 on a calculator, press $\boxed{7}\,\boxed{x^y}\,\boxed{4}\,\boxed{=}$

Exercise 2E

1 Work out

(a) 4^3 (b) 5^3 (c) 6^3 (d) 10^3

2 Write down a cube number which is also a square number.

3 Work out (a) $\sqrt[3]{27}$ (b) $\sqrt[3]{125}$ (c) $\sqrt[3]{64}$

4 Work out the following, without a calculator.

(a) 3^2 (b) 1^3 (c) 2^5 (d) 7^1 (e) 10^4

(f) 11^2 (g) 100^2 (h) 0.1^2 (i) $(\frac{1}{2})^2$ (j) 10^6

5 Copy and complete with either <, = or > in the box.

(a) $3^2 \square 2^5$ (b) $2^4 \square 4^2$ (c) $5^2 \square 2^5$

(d) $10^2 \square 2^{10}$ (e) $0.9^2 \square 0.9$ (f) $8^7 \square 8^6$

6 Find the missing numbers so that the answer is always 100.

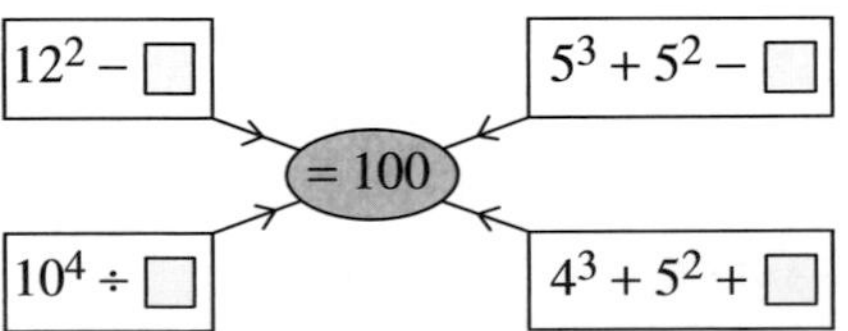

7 Answer true or false:

(a) The only cube number which is also a square number is 1.

(b) If $x^3 = x$, then x must be 1.

(c) 3^x is positive for all values of x.

8 Read the letter which appeared recently in 'The Times' newspaper.

How old was Tony at the time?

In his prime

One of a group of students asked me my age to which I replied that it was currently a prime number and in three years' time would be a perfect square.

Another student said I couldn't possibly be 13 to which another added that I could easily be 97.

The matter was resolved when yet another pointed out that in three years' time my age would also be a perfect cube. Such is the delight of numbers.

TONY HARWOOD

9 Use the $\boxed{x^y}$ key on a calculator to work out

(a) 7^5 (b) 5^6 (c) 0.5^3 (d) 2.1^4

10 *Without* using the cube root key, use a calculator to estimate the following. Give your answers correct to the nearest whole number.

(a) $\sqrt[3]{20}$ (b) $\sqrt[3]{400}$ (c) $\sqrt[3]{111}$

11 Copy and complete the following

(a) If $a = 2^2$ and $b = 2^3$, then $ab = 2^{\square}$

(b) If $p = 3^3$ and $q = 3^4$, then $pq = 3^{\square}$

(c) If $c = 5^2$ and $d = 5^3$, then $cd = 5^{\square}$

(d) If $x = 4^2$, $y = 4^3$, $z = 4^5$, then $xyz = \square^{\square}$

12 Look at the sequence 1, 8, 27, 64, 125,...

Write down (a) the next term

(b) the nth term

13 Substitute four different values for n in the expression $5^n + 3$.

Is the result a multiple of 4 in each case?

14 Find values of n and m such that

(a) $n^2 + 15 = m^3$

(b) $n^2 + 375 = m^3$

15 Find values of a and b such that $a^2 + b^2 = a^3$

1.2 Fractions

In section 1.2 you will learn about

- equivalent fractions
- adding and subtracting fractions
- multiplying fractions
- dividing by a fraction

Equivalent fractions

The diagram shows the *equivalent fractions* $\frac{2}{3}$, $\frac{4}{6}$ and $\frac{6}{9}$.

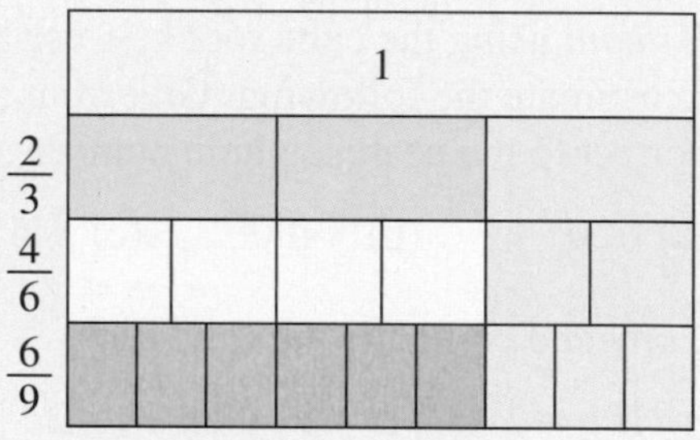

Exercise 1M

1 Find the missing number to make these fractions equivalent.

(a) $\frac{3}{8} = \frac{\square}{16}$ (b) $\frac{1}{4} = \frac{\square}{20}$ (c) $\frac{20}{48} = \frac{\square}{12}$ (d) $\frac{6}{15} = \frac{\square}{5}$

(e) $\frac{5}{9} = \frac{\square}{45}$ (f) $\frac{5}{7} = \frac{\square}{42}$ (g) $\frac{3}{11} = \frac{\square}{44}$ (h) $\frac{18}{21} = \frac{\square}{7}$

2 Write four fractions equivalent to $\frac{2}{5}$.

3 Cancel down each fraction to its simplest terms

(a) $\frac{7}{21}$ (b) $\frac{6}{24}$ (c) $\frac{18}{45}$ (d) $\frac{40}{64}$ (e) $\frac{24}{42}$

(f) $\frac{60}{144}$ (g) $\frac{20}{1000}$ (h) $\frac{34}{40}$ (i) $\frac{33}{121}$ (j) $\frac{30}{75}$

4 Each card has a fraction and a letter. Find the cards which contain equivalent fractions and arrange the letters to make the name of a capital city.

M	A	R	E	O	T		
$\frac{6}{10}$	$\frac{15}{24}$	$\frac{21}{35}$	$\frac{12}{20}$	$\frac{30}{50}$	$\frac{10}{16}$		
S	C	E	M	O	W	A	O
$\frac{9}{21}$	$\frac{33}{77}$	$\frac{9}{24}$	$\frac{27}{63}$	$\frac{24}{56}$	$\frac{60}{140}$	$\frac{15}{45}$	$\frac{6}{14}$

5 $\frac{3}{4}$ is a *proper fraction* because the numerator is less than the denominator.

$\frac{7}{5}$ is an *improper fraction* because the numerator is greater than the denominator.

$2\frac{1}{3}$ is a *mixed number* because it contains a whole number and a fraction.

Change the following improper fractions to mixed numbers.

(a) $\frac{5}{3}$ (b) $\frac{7}{5}$ (c) $\frac{12}{5}$ (d) $\frac{11}{3}$ (e) $\frac{20}{7}$ (f) $\frac{73}{10}$

(g) $\frac{33}{8}$ (h) $\frac{41}{5}$ (i) $\frac{17}{2}$ (j) $\frac{501}{250}$ (k) $\frac{19}{3}$ (l) $\frac{47}{7}$

6 Convert these mixed numbers to improper fractions.

(a) $3\frac{1}{4}$ (b) $2\frac{1}{2}$ (c) $4\frac{3}{4}$ (d) $2\frac{1}{5}$ (e) $5\frac{1}{3}$

(f) $7\frac{1}{3}$ (g) $3\frac{3}{7}$ (h) $2\frac{5}{9}$ (i) $1\frac{1}{11}$ (j) $6\frac{3}{50}$.

Adding and subtracting fractions

Fractions can be added when they have the same denominator.

So, for example, $\frac{1}{5}+\frac{2}{5}=\frac{3}{5}$ and $\frac{1}{8}+\frac{5}{8}=\frac{6}{8}$.

If fractions do not have the same denominator, change them into *equivalent fractions* which do have the same denominator before adding or subtracting.

(a) $\frac{1}{6}+\frac{1}{3}$
$=\frac{1}{6}+\frac{2}{6}$
$=\frac{3}{6}=\frac{1}{2}$

(b) $\frac{7}{8}-\frac{3}{4}$
$=\frac{7}{8}-\frac{6}{8}$
$=\frac{1}{8}$

(c) $\frac{2}{5}+\frac{3}{7}$
$=\frac{14}{35}+\frac{15}{35}$
$=\frac{29}{35}$

cancel the final answer if you can

Exercise 1E

Work out

1 $\frac{2}{5}+\frac{1}{5}$

2 $\frac{3}{11}+\frac{7}{11}$

3 $\frac{1}{8}+\frac{2}{8}+\frac{4}{8}$

4 $\frac{4}{15}+\frac{7}{15}$

5 $\frac{6}{7}-\frac{2}{7}$

6 $\frac{7}{9}-\frac{5}{9}$

7 $\frac{11}{7}-\frac{8}{7}$

8 $\frac{1}{6}+\frac{5}{6}-\frac{3}{6}$

9 Copy and complete

(a) $\frac{3}{10}+\frac{1}{5}$
$=\frac{3}{10}+\frac{\square}{10}=\frac{\square}{10}$

(b) $\frac{5}{8}+\frac{1}{4}$
$=\frac{5}{8}+\frac{\square}{8}=\frac{\square}{8}$

(c) $\frac{7}{12}-\frac{1}{3}$
$=\frac{7}{12}-\frac{\square}{12}=\frac{\square}{12}$

Work out the following

10 $\frac{3}{8}+\frac{1}{4}$

11 $\frac{5}{18}+\frac{1}{9}$

12 $\frac{9}{20}+\frac{3}{10}$

13 $\frac{3}{4}+\frac{1}{8}$

14 $\frac{5}{8}+\frac{1}{16}$

15 $\frac{5}{6}-\frac{2}{3}$

16 $\frac{3}{4}-\frac{1}{2}$

17 $\frac{7}{8}-\frac{1}{2}$

18 $\frac{1}{4}+\frac{1}{3}$

19 $\frac{1}{2}+\frac{2}{5}$

20 $\frac{1}{3}+\frac{2}{5}$

21 $\frac{3}{4}+\frac{1}{5}$

22 $\frac{1}{5}-\frac{1}{6}$

23 $\frac{4}{3}-\frac{5}{4}$

24 $\frac{7}{12}-\frac{1}{8}$

25 $\frac{1}{2}-\frac{2}{11}$

26 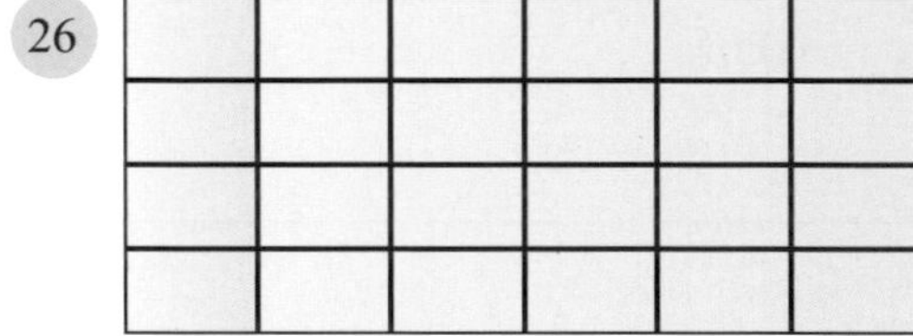

Draw a 4 × 6 rectangle. Divide it into three parts using three different fractions, each with numerator 1.

27 Draw a 4 × 5 rectangle and divide it into four parts using four different fractions, each with numerator 1.

28 A girl read $\frac{3}{8}$ of her book one day and $\frac{2}{5}$ the next day.
How much was there left to read?

29 A blackbird shares 3g of worms between her three chicks. Emily receives $\frac{3}{4}$ g and Brian receives $\frac{5}{8}$ g. How much is left for Lucky, the third chick?

30 A wooden pole is painted in four colours: red, yellow, blue and green. If $\frac{1}{8}$ is red, $\frac{5}{12}$ is yellow and $\frac{1}{16}$ is blue, what fraction of the pole is painted green?

Multiplying fractions

- The pink shaded strip is $\frac{1}{5}$ of the rectangle.
- The grey section is $\frac{1}{4}$ of $\frac{1}{5}$ of the rectangle.

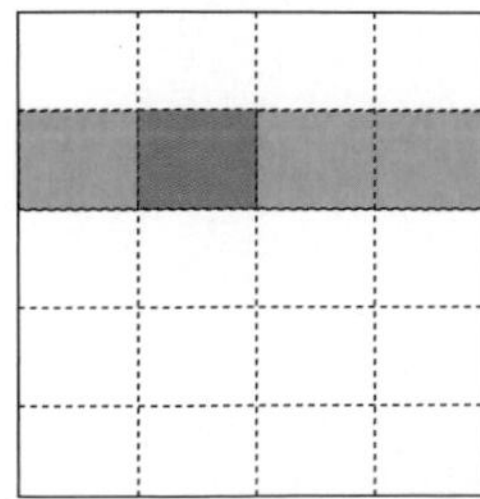

The rectangle on the right is divided into 20 equal parts so the grey section is $\frac{1}{20}$ of the rectangle.

So $\frac{1}{4}$ of $\frac{1}{5}$ of the rectangle = $\frac{1}{20}$ of the rectangle

Notice that $\frac{1}{4} \times \frac{1}{5} = \frac{1}{20}$.

The word 'of' can be replaced by a multiplication.

- Look at these multiplications

(a) $\frac{2}{3} \times \frac{1}{5} = \frac{2}{15}$ (b) $\frac{3}{7} \times \frac{1}{4} = \frac{3}{28}$

(c) $\frac{3}{4} \times \frac{1}{6} = \frac{\cancel{3}^{1}}{\cancel{24}_{8}} = \frac{1}{8}$ (d) $\frac{6}{7} \times \frac{2}{3} = \frac{\cancel{12}^{4}}{\cancel{21}_{7}} = \frac{4}{7}$

Multiply the numerators, multiply the denominators and then cancel down.

- Some people prefer to cancel earlier. For example:

(a) $\frac{5}{\cancel{6}_{3}} \times \frac{\cancel{2}^{1}}{3} = \frac{5}{9}$ (b) $\frac{3}{\cancel{8}_{4}} \times \frac{\cancel{6}^{3}}{7} = \frac{9}{28}$ (c) $\frac{\cancel{5}^{1}}{\cancel{12}_{4}} \times \frac{\cancel{9}^{3}}{\cancel{10}_{2}} = \frac{3}{8}$

Exercise 2M

All fractions should be given in their simplest form.

1 What fractions are these?

(a) $\frac{1}{4}$ of $\frac{1}{3}$ (b) $\frac{1}{5}$ of $\frac{3}{5}$ (c) $\frac{2}{3}$ of $\frac{3}{4}$ (d) $\frac{3}{5}$ of $\frac{1}{4}$

2 Work out

(a) $\frac{2}{5} \times \frac{3}{5}$ (b) $\frac{3}{7} \times \frac{1}{4}$ (c) $\frac{3}{8} \times \frac{2}{5}$ (d) $\frac{3}{4} \times \frac{1}{6}$

(e) $\frac{5}{8} \times \frac{1}{2}$ (f) $\frac{5}{6} \times \frac{3}{4}$ (g) $\frac{2}{7} \times \frac{3}{4}$ (h) $\frac{1}{8} \times \frac{3}{5}$

(i) $\frac{2}{9} \times \frac{3}{5}$ (j) $\frac{3}{11} \times \frac{1}{2}$ (k) $\frac{4}{9} \times \frac{3}{4}$ (l) $\frac{5}{12} \times \frac{8}{10}$

3 The diagram shows a square of side 1 m divided into four rectangles A, B, C and D.
Find the areas of A, B, C and D in m^2.

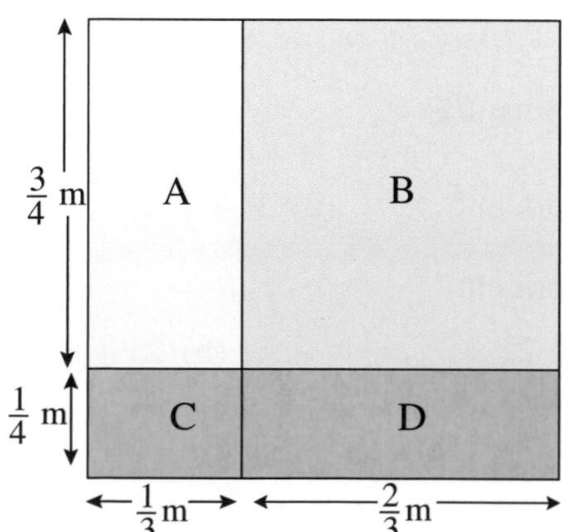

4 Work out

(a) $\frac{3}{4}$ of 16 (b) $\frac{3}{8}$ of 24 (c) $\frac{9}{10}$ of 60 (d) $\frac{5}{6}$ of 36

(e) $\frac{5}{9}$ of 27 km (f) $\frac{2}{3}$ of 63 kg (g) $\frac{5}{7}$ of 63 m (h) $\frac{8}{9}$ of £108

5 

Justin works 54 hours a week and he spends $\frac{5}{6}$ of his time on the phone.

How many hours is that?

6 Find each missing number below.

(a) $\frac{\square}{4}$ of $32 = 24$ (b) $\frac{\square}{7}$ of $21 = 9$ (c) $\frac{3}{\square}$ of $20 = 12$

(d) $\frac{3}{\square}$ of $14 = 6$ (e) $\frac{4}{5}$ of $\square = 16$ (f) $\frac{3}{10}$ of $\square = 18$

We can multiply mixed fractions by changing them to improper fractions ('top heavy fractions').

(a) $2\frac{1}{3} \times \frac{3}{4}$

$= \frac{7}{\cancel{3}_1} \times \frac{\cancel{3}^1}{4}$

$= \frac{7}{4} = 1\frac{3}{4}$

(b) $1\frac{2}{3} \times 1\frac{1}{4}$

$= \frac{5}{3} \times \frac{5}{4}$

$= \frac{25}{12} = 2\frac{1}{12}$

Exercise 2E

1 Work out (a) $3\frac{1}{2} \times \frac{2}{3}$ (b) $2\frac{3}{4} \times \frac{3}{11}$

2 Work out

(a) $2\frac{1}{2} \times \frac{1}{4}$ (b) $2\frac{1}{2} \times \frac{1}{6}$ (c) $3\frac{1}{2} \times \frac{3}{10}$ (d) $1\frac{1}{2} \times \frac{2}{3}$

(e) $3\frac{1}{4} \times \frac{1}{10}$ (f) $\frac{3}{5} \times 4\frac{1}{4}$ (g) $2\frac{1}{2} \times 1\frac{1}{2}$ (h) $3\frac{1}{2} \times 3\frac{1}{2}$

3 A photograph is $3\frac{1}{4}$ inches wide and $2\frac{1}{2}$ inches tall. Calculate the area of the photograph.

4 (a) To find $\frac{5}{9} \times 12$, we can write $\frac{5}{9} \times \frac{12}{1}$.

So $\frac{5}{\cancel{9}_3} \times \frac{\cancel{12}^4}{1} = \frac{20}{3} = 6\frac{2}{3}$

(b) Work out $\frac{3}{8} \times 12$

5 Work out

(a) $\frac{7}{8} \times 12$ (b) $\frac{5}{8} \times 10$

(c) $\frac{7}{12} \times 16$ (d) $\frac{5}{6}$ of 9

(e) $16 \times \frac{1}{24}$ (f) $11 \times \frac{7}{33}$

(g) $\frac{11}{36}$ of 9 (h) $\frac{2}{15} \times 20$

6 A centipede is born with 60 legs. It loses $\frac{1}{5}$ of its legs falling downstairs and a further $\frac{1}{3}$ of the remainder following an argument with a blackbird. How many legs has it left?

7 Find the missing numbers

(a) $2\frac{1}{2} \times \frac{1}{\square} = \frac{5}{8}$ (b) $\frac{\square}{10} \times 3\frac{1}{3} = 3$ (c) $2\frac{1}{2} \times \frac{\square}{\square} = 3$

8 Arrange the fractions $\frac{2}{3}, \frac{11}{18}, \frac{23}{36}, \frac{5}{8}$ in order of size with the smallest first.

9 Copy and complete

(a) $\frac{1}{4} + \square = \frac{5}{12}$ (b) $\square - \frac{3}{7} = \frac{5}{21}$ (c) $\square - \frac{2}{5} = \frac{4}{15}$

(d) $\square - \frac{2}{3} = \frac{1}{6}$ (e) $\frac{4}{9} + \square = \frac{25}{36}$ (f) $\square + \square = \frac{11}{15}$

(ask a friend to check)

10 What fraction of each shape is coloured pink?

(a)

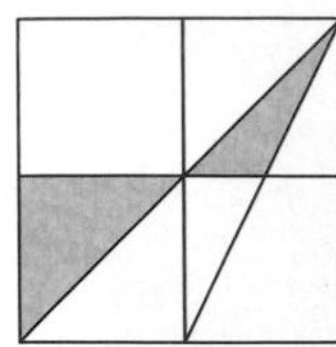

(b)

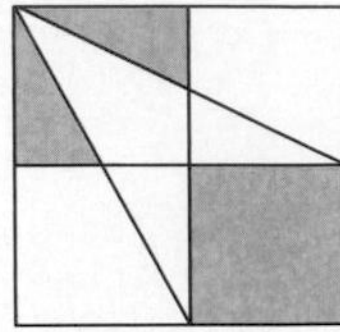

(c)

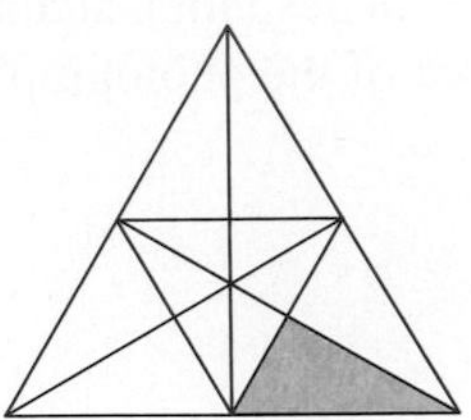

11 Copy and complete the addition square.

+		$\frac{1}{6}$		$\frac{2}{3}$
	$\frac{7}{12}$			1
$\frac{3}{8}$				
			$\frac{7}{10}$	
	$\frac{3}{4}$		1	

12 (a) To work out $2\frac{1}{4} + \frac{1}{3}$, we write $2\frac{1}{4}$ as $\frac{9}{4}$.

Then $\frac{9}{4} + \frac{1}{3} = \frac{27}{12} + \frac{4}{12} = \frac{31}{12} = 2\frac{7}{12}$

(b) Work out $1\frac{3}{4} + \frac{2}{3}$, by writing $1\frac{3}{4}$ as a top-heavy fraction.

13 Work out

(a) $3\frac{2}{5} + \frac{1}{4}$ (b) $2\frac{2}{3} + \frac{3}{4}$ (c) $1\frac{1}{2} + 2\frac{2}{3}$

(d) $3\frac{1}{6} - 2\frac{1}{2}$ (e) $5\frac{1}{4} - 3\frac{2}{3}$ (f) $4\frac{3}{5} + 1\frac{1}{2}$

14 By midday $\frac{3}{4}$ of a group of people have arrived. By two o'clock a further 16 arrived, leaving only 17% of the group still to come.

How many people were in the whole group?

15 Copy and complete the 'magic' squares.

(a)

$\frac{1}{10}$	$\frac{9}{20}$	$\frac{1}{5}$
$\frac{7}{20}$	$\frac{1}{4}$	
	$\frac{1}{20}$	

(b)

		$\frac{3}{8}$
	$\frac{1}{4}$	
$\frac{1}{8}$	$\frac{1}{3}$	$\frac{7}{24}$

Dividing an integer by a fraction

- 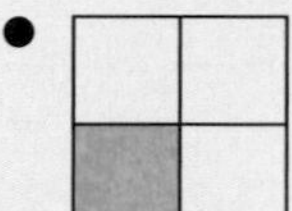 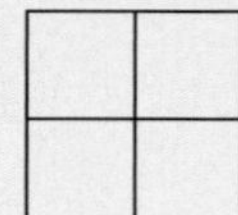 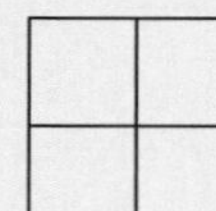 How many quarters are there in 3?
  Answer 12
- $2 \div \frac{1}{3}$ 'How many thirds are there in 2?' Answer: 6
- $5 \div \frac{1}{2}$ 'How many halves are there in 5?' Answer: 10

Exercise 3M

1 (a) How many thirds are there in 1?
(b) How many thirds are there in 2?
(c) How many thirds are there in 4?

How many thirds are there in 33?

2 (a) How many quarters are there in 1?
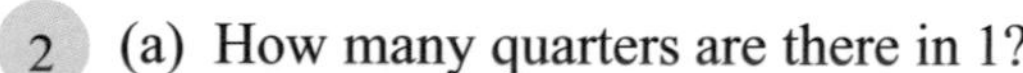
(b) How many quarters are there in 3?
(c) How many quarters are there in 6?

3 (a) How many tenths are there in 2?
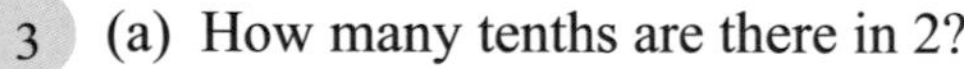
(b) How many fifths are there in 3?
(c) How many sevenths are there in 2?

4 Work out

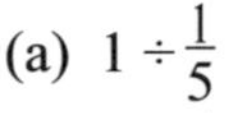
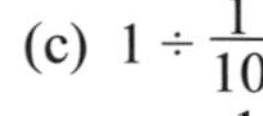

(a) $1 \div \frac{1}{5}$ (b) $3 \div \frac{1}{2}$ (c) $1 \div \frac{1}{10}$

(d) $2 \div \frac{1}{2}$ (e) $9 \div \frac{1}{3}$ (f) $12 \div \frac{1}{3}$

5 Copy and complete this pattern

$60 \times \frac{1}{6} = 10$ $\quad 10 \div \frac{1}{6} = 60$

$30 \times \frac{2}{6} = 10$ $\quad 10 \div \frac{2}{6} = \square$

$20 \times \frac{3}{6} = 10$ $\quad 10 \div \frac{3}{6} = \square$

$15 \times \frac{4}{6} = \square$ $\quad 10 \div \frac{4}{6} = \square$

$12 \times \frac{5}{6} = \square$ $\quad 10 \div \frac{5}{6} = \square$

6 Copy and complete

(a) $10 = \square \times \frac{1}{2}$ (b) $\square \times \frac{1}{3} = 8$ (c) $\square \times \frac{1}{4} = 5$

(d) $\square \times \frac{1}{3} = 2$ (e) $11 = \square \times \frac{1}{2}$ (f) $\square \times \frac{1}{5} = 5$

Dividing a fraction by a fraction

How many $\frac{1}{8}$ s are there in $\frac{1}{2}$?

The answer is 4.

Notice that $\frac{1}{2} \div \frac{1}{8} = \frac{1}{2} \times \frac{8}{1} = 4$.

$\frac{1}{2}$ is shaded

To divide by a fraction, turn the fraction you are dividing by upside down and then multiply.

(a) $\frac{3}{5} \div \frac{1}{4} = \frac{3}{5} \times \frac{4}{1}$
$= \frac{12}{5}$
$= 2\frac{2}{5}$

(b) $\frac{5}{6} \div \frac{3}{4} = \frac{5}{6} \times \frac{4}{3}$
$= \frac{20}{18} = \frac{10}{9}$
$= 1\frac{1}{9}$

Exercise 3E

Work out.

1 $\frac{1}{2} \div \frac{1}{4}$ 2 $\frac{1}{3} \div \frac{1}{2}$ 3 $\frac{3}{4} \div \frac{1}{3}$ 4 $\frac{2}{3} \div \frac{1}{2}$

5 $\frac{1}{5} \div \frac{1}{2}$ 6 $\frac{1}{2} \div \frac{1}{5}$ 7 $\frac{3}{4} \div \frac{4}{5}$ 8 $\frac{1}{2} \div \frac{1}{6}$

9 $\frac{5}{6} \div \frac{1}{3}$ 10 $\frac{2}{5} \div \frac{2}{3}$ 11 $\frac{5}{7} \div \frac{9}{10}$ 12 $\frac{5}{12} \div \frac{1}{8}$

13 $\frac{3}{7} \div \frac{3}{5}$ 14 $\frac{9}{14} \div \frac{6}{7}$ 15 $\frac{11}{15} \div \frac{1}{10}$ 16 $\frac{4}{3} \div \frac{8}{1}$

17 $\frac{2}{5} \div \frac{2}{1}$ 18 $\frac{5}{7} \div \frac{6}{1}$ 19 $\frac{4}{9} \div 6$ 20 $\frac{5}{11} \div 3$

In questions 21 to 25 you must decide whether to multiply or divide.

21 A wine glass holds $\frac{1}{7}$ of a litre of wine. How many times can the glass be filled from a bottle which contains 2 litres of wine?

22 How many pieces of wood, each $5\frac{1}{2}$ cm long, can be cut from a plank 132 cm long?

23 An unfortunate motorist has to fill a five litre petrol can using a mug which takes only $\frac{5}{8}$ of a litre each time. How many times does he have to use the mug?

24 A sum of £20 is divided between several people so that each receives $\frac{2}{5}$ of a pound. How many people receive a share?

25 A sheet of paper is $\frac{1}{10}$ mm thick. How thick is a pad containing 360 sheets of paper?

1.3 Area and Perimeter

In section 1.3 you will:

- learn about rectangles, triangles, parallelograms and trapeziums
- solve a variety of mixed problems

Rectangles and triangles

Exercise 1M

Calculate the area of each shape. The lengths are in cm.
[Reminder: area of triangle = $\frac{1}{2}\, b \times h$]

1
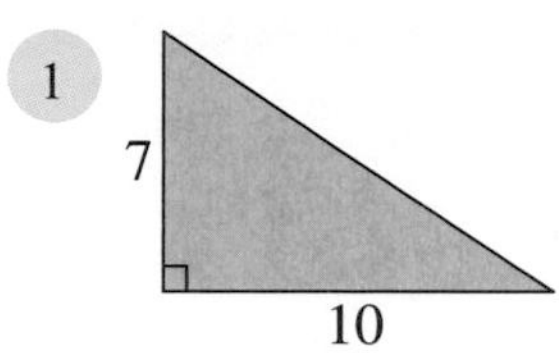

2
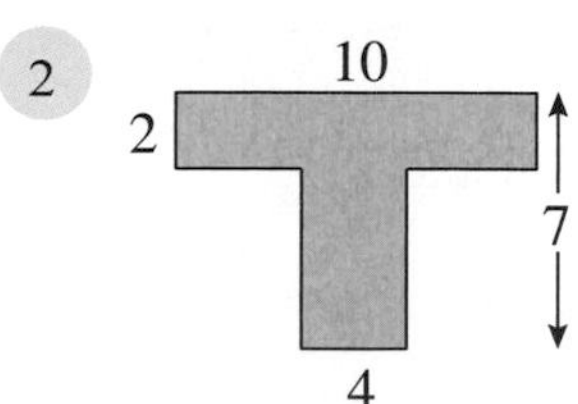

3
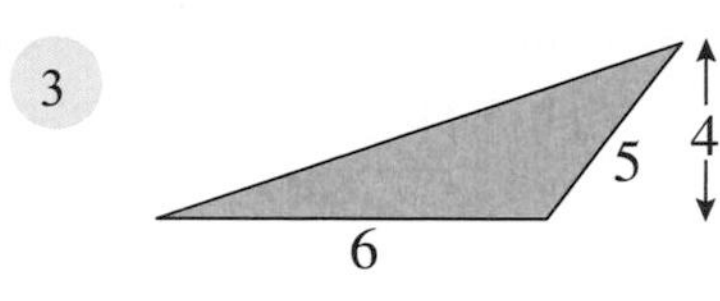

4 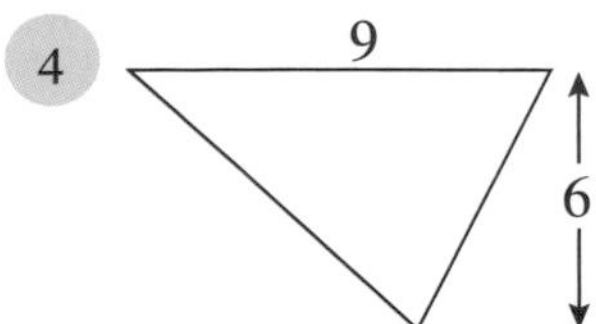

5

3
6
8

6 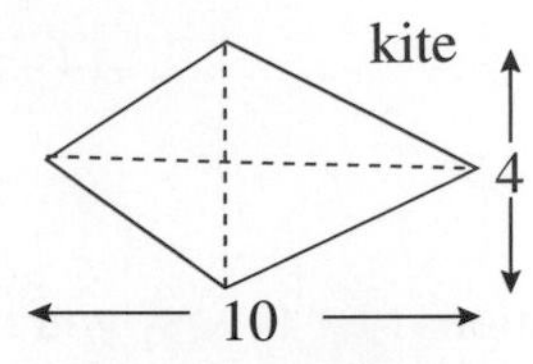

7 What metric unit would you use for the area of:
(a) a tennis court,
(b) the Isle of Man,
(c) a 5p coin?

8 Work out the perimeter of
(a) a regular octagon of side 5 cm
(b) a square of area 100 cm^2.

9 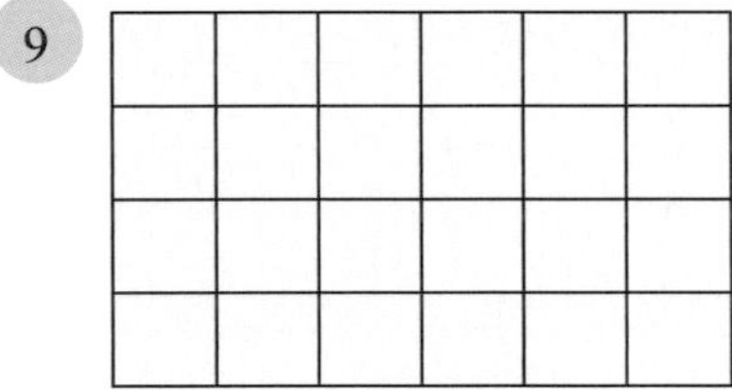

Here is a 4×6 rectangle made using 24 squares. What other rectangles can be made using 24 squares?

10 Suzy has enough squares to make exactly five different rectangles. How many squares does she have?

11 Here are some shapes made with centimetre squares.

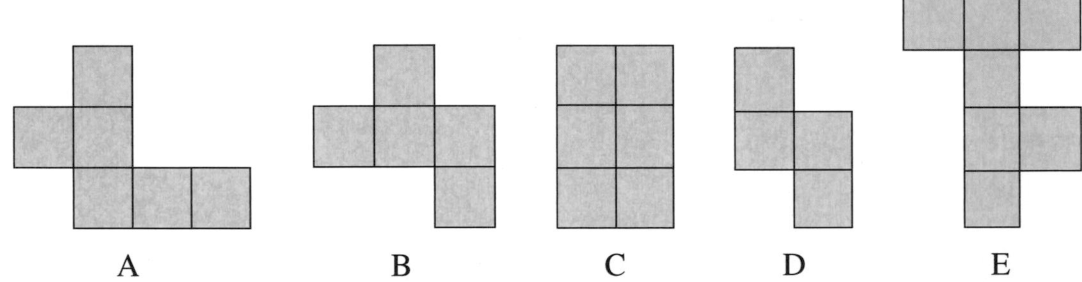

(a) Which shape has an area of 4 cm^2?
(b) Which shape has a perimeter of 12 cm?
(c) Which two shapes have the same perimeter?

12 Draw a shape similar to those in the question above:

(a) with area 7 cm^2 and perimeter 14 cm
(b) with area 11 cm^2 and perimeter 16 cm.

Parallelogram and trapezium

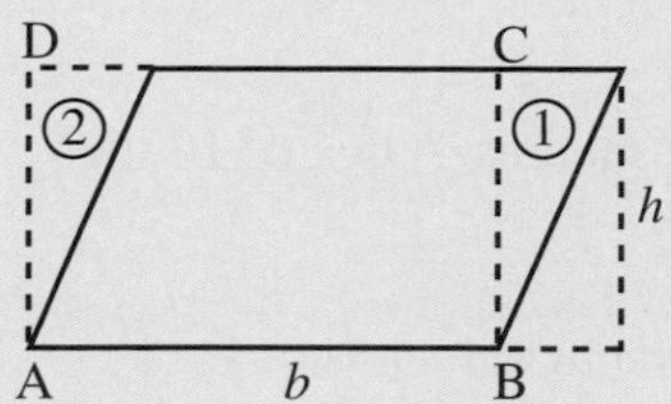

Area of parallelogram
= area of rectangle ABCD + area of Δ 1 – area of Δ2.
But area of Δ1 = area of Δ2

∴ area of parallelogram = $b \times h$

Area of trapezium PQRS = area of ΔPQS + area of ΔSRQ

$= \frac{1}{2}ah + \frac{1}{2}bh$

$= \frac{1}{2}(a+b)h$

area of trapezium = $\frac{1}{2}$ (sum of parallel sides) × height

Exercise 1E

Calculate the area of each shape. The lengths are in cm.

1
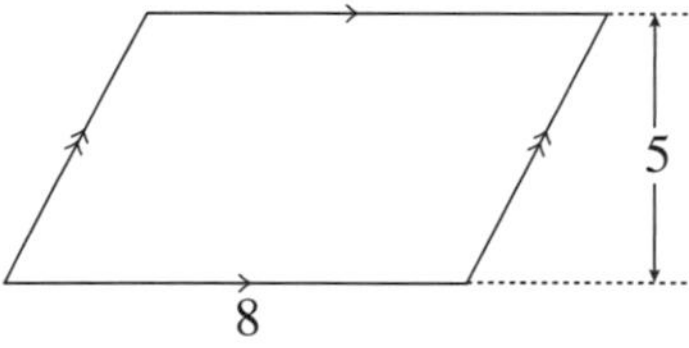

2
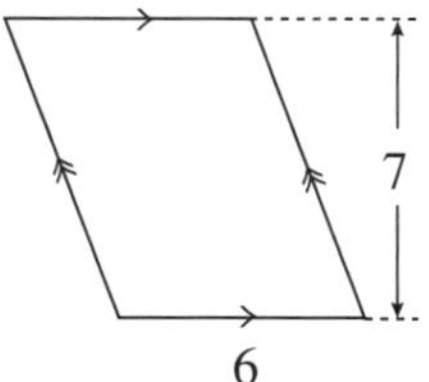

3
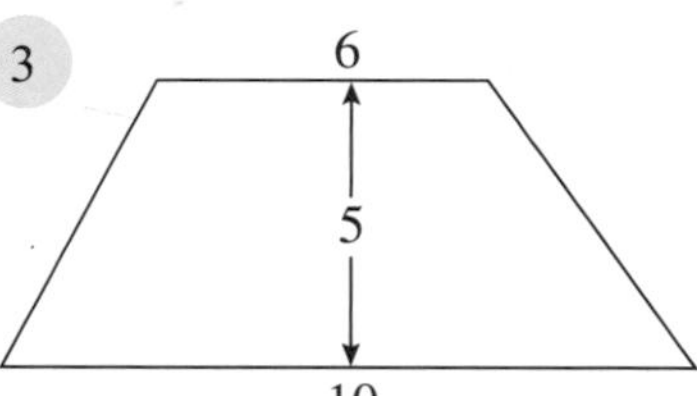

4
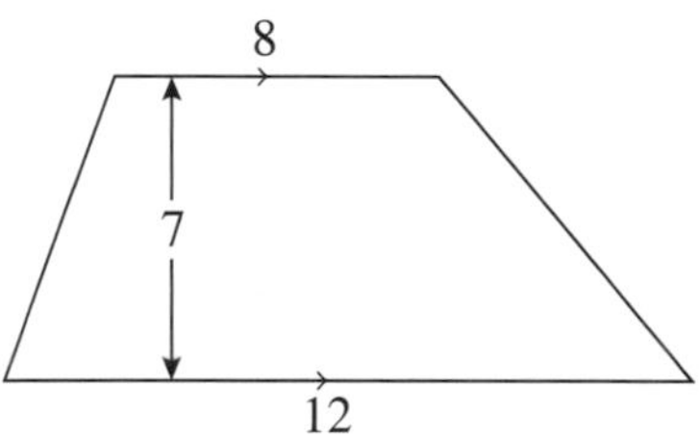

5
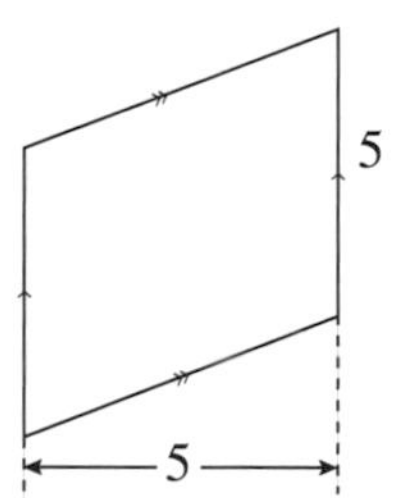

6 Find the shaded area
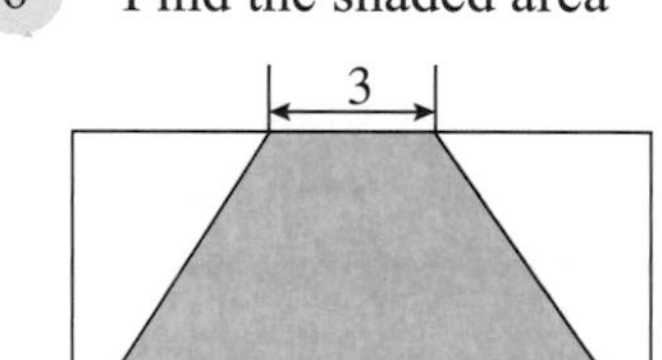

7 Sketch a trapezium with parallel sides of length 5 cm and 7 cm.
The distance between the parallel sides is 4 cm. Calculate the area of the trapezium.

8 A parallelogram has a base of length 10cm and an area of 60cm^2.
Calculate the height of the parallelogram.

9 The area of this triangle is 15cm^2. Find possible values of b and h.

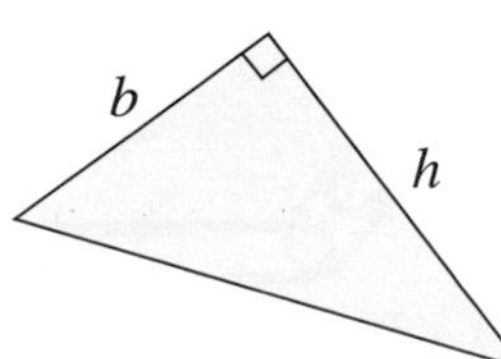

10 (a) How many square centimetres are there in one square metre?
(b) How many square metres are there in one square kilometre?

Mixed problems

Exercise 2M

1 A wall measuring 2m by 6m is covered with tiles which are 20 cm squares. A box of 10 tiles costs £5.95. How much will it cost to buy the tiles for this wall?

2 A rectangular field measures 400m by 1km. Calculate the area of the field in hectares. [1 hectare = 10 000m^2]

3 A square field has an area of 4 hectares. Calculate the perimeter of the field.

4 Here are two shapes *both* with a perimeter of 32cm. Calculate the *area* of each shape.

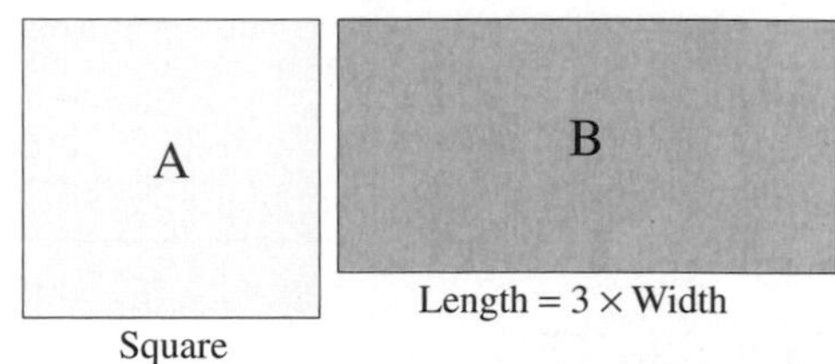

5 Lawn

Pond 2 m 7 m

3 m

8 m

A gardener is spreading fertilizer on his lawn (but not the pond in the middle!). The instructions only say that 2 measures of the fertilizer will treat 10m^2 of lawn. Each measure of fertilizer costs 60p. Find the cost of the fertilizer required.

6 (a) The pentagon is drawn on a 1 cm grid. Calculate its area.

(b) On a 1 cm grid draw an obtuse-angled triangle with an area of (i) 3 cm^2
(ii) 7.5 cm^2

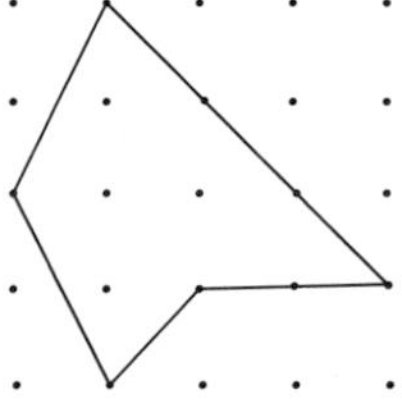

7 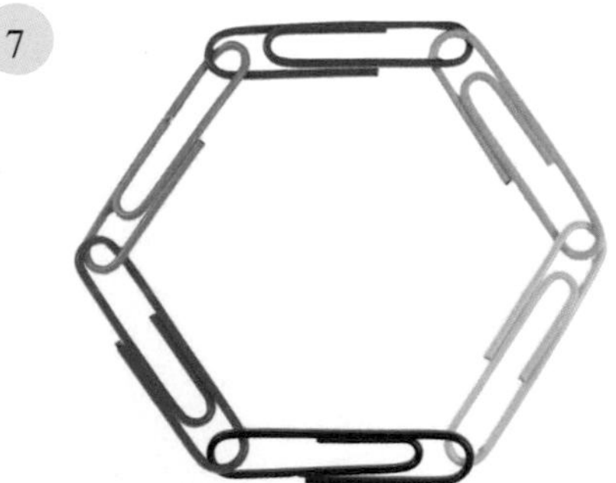

Paper clips are used to make a hexagon. Estimate the area of the hexagon using the wires around the outside of the shape.

8 The diagram shows a garden with two crossing paths.
Calculate the total area of the paths.

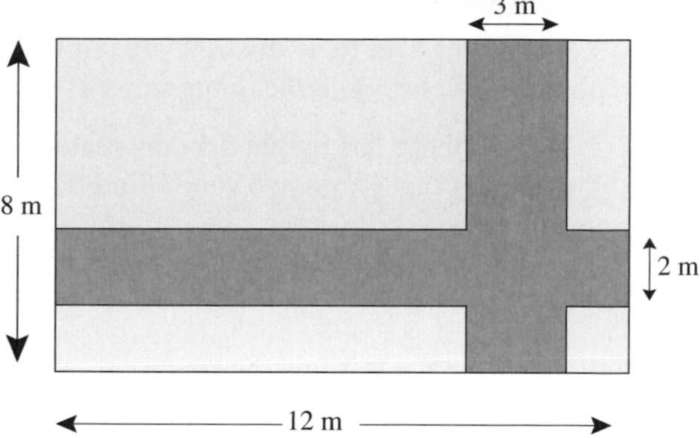

9

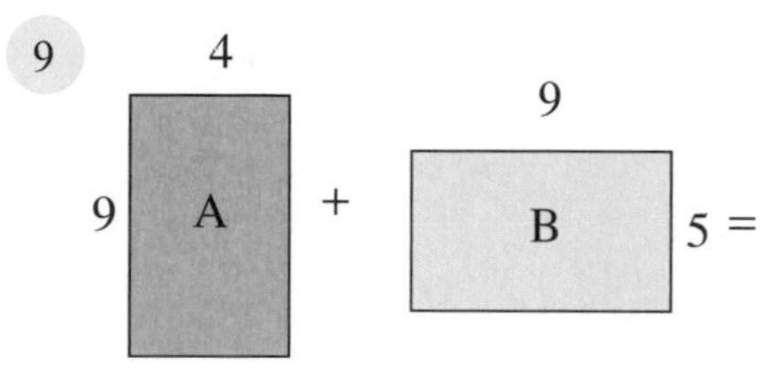

The area of square C is equal to the sum of the areas of rectangles A and B.
How long is the side of square C?
(The lengths are in cm.)

10

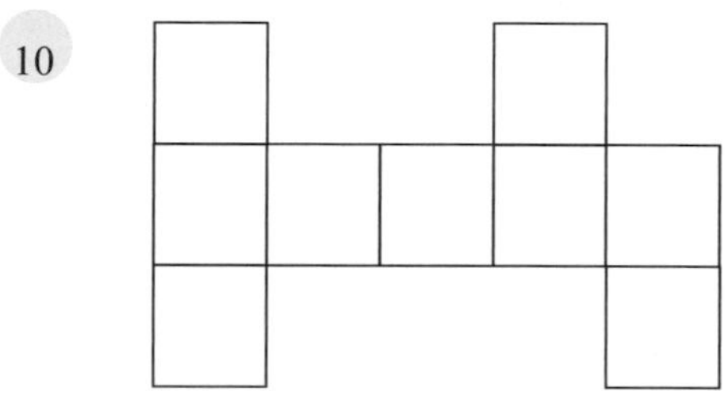

This shape has an area of $225 cm^2$.
Calculate its perimeter.

Exercise 2E

In questions 1 to 6 the area is written inside the shape. Calculate the length of the side x, correct to 1 decimal place where necessary.

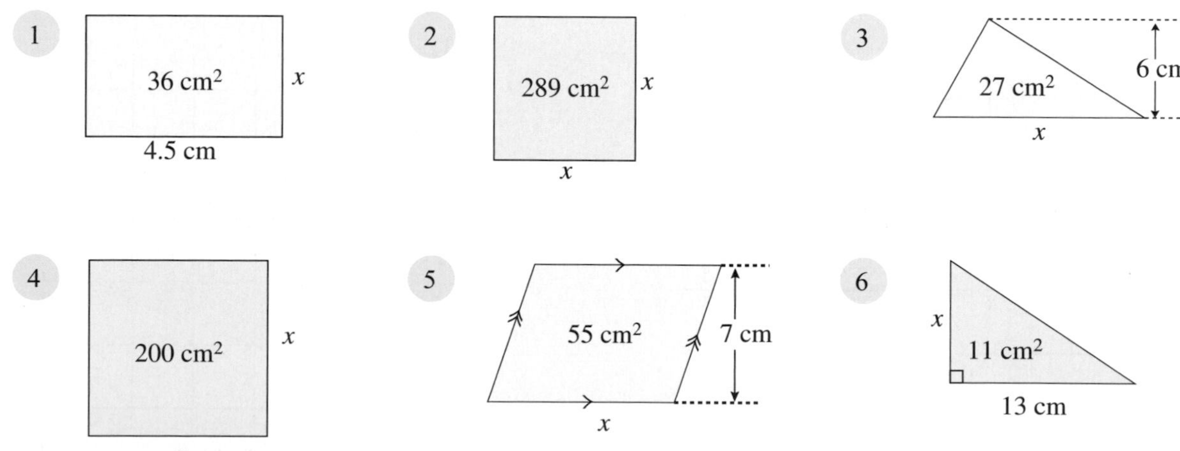

7 (a) This delightful photo of Hannah has height 5 cm greater than its width. The area of the photo is 84 cm^2. Find the dimensions of the photo.

(b) A second photo has height 3.5 cm greater than its width. The area of this photo is 65 cm^2. Find the dimensions of this photo.

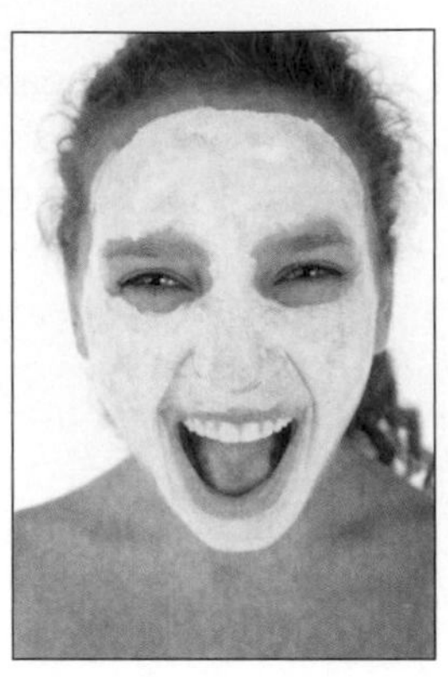

8

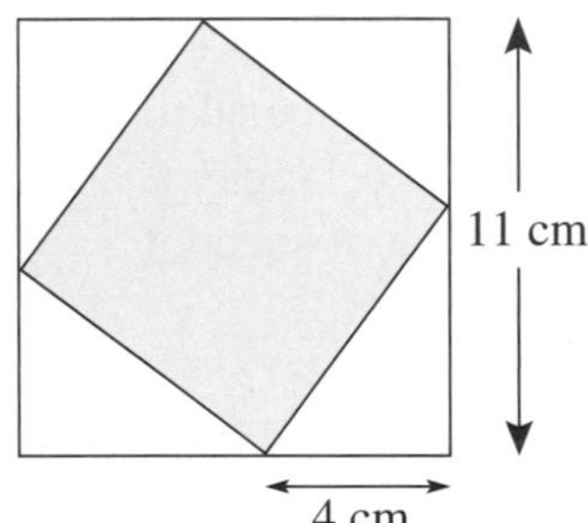

The diagram shows a green square inside a larger square. Calculate the area of the green square.

9 Calculate the area of each shaded shape. Give your answers in square units.

(a)

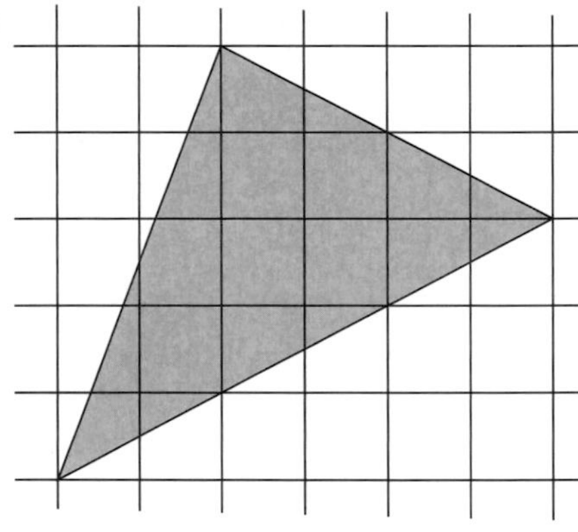

(b)

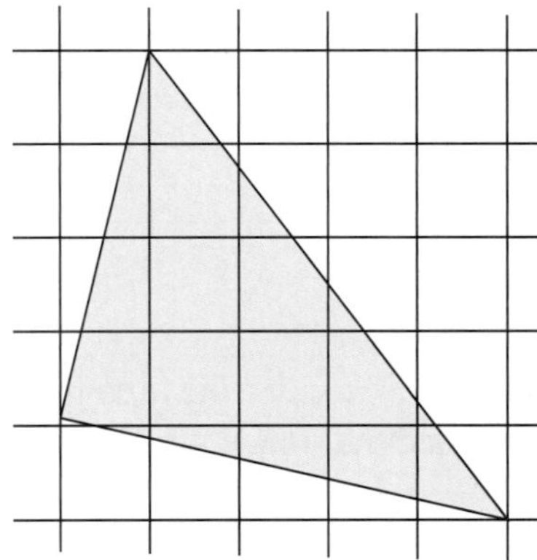

(c)

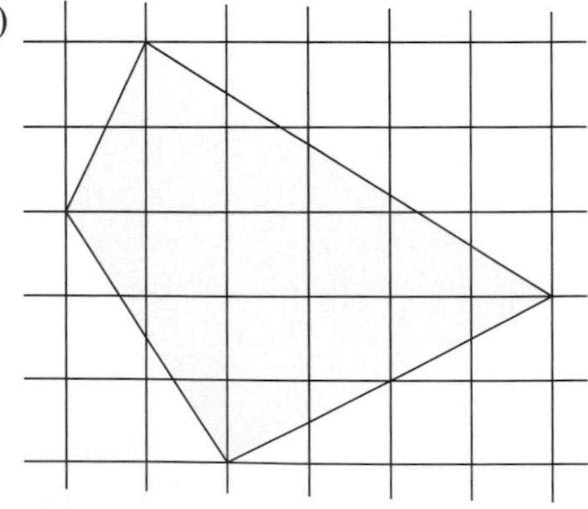

(d)

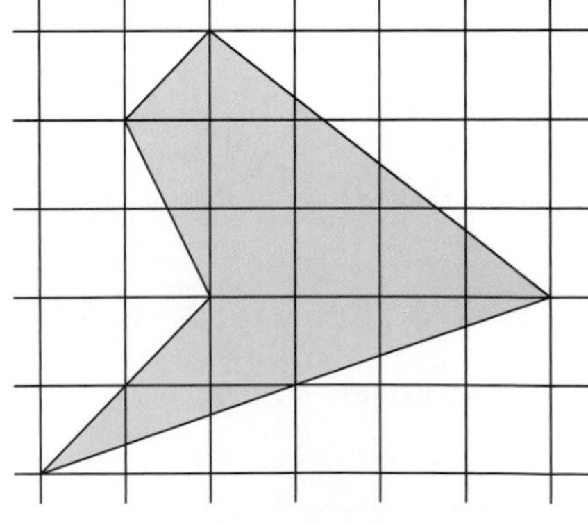

Investigation

Find the connection

You need square 'dotty' paper or ordinary squared paper.

(a) Draw *any* triangle ABC and shade it.

(b) Draw a square on each of the sides of the triagle.

(c) Join PQ to form ΔPQC (marked ①)

Join RS to form ΔRSB (marked ②)

Join UT to form ΔUTA (marked ③).

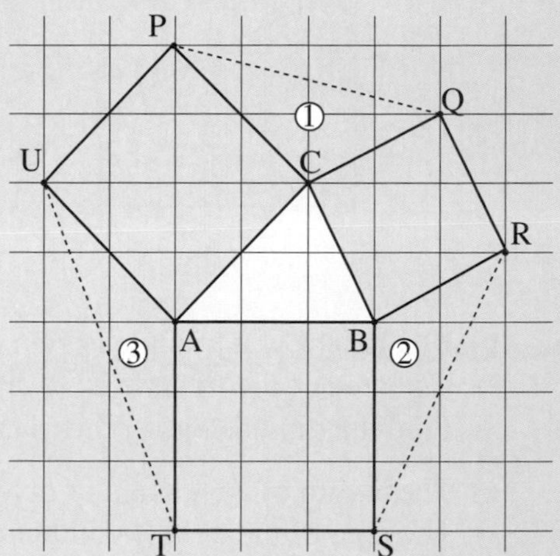

(d) Find the areas of triangles ABC, PQC, RSB, UTA. You may be able to use the formula $\left(\frac{\text{base} \times \text{height}}{2}\right)$ or you may need to draw construction lines as in the questions above.

(e) What do you notice? Draw another triangle and repeat the procedure. Do you get the same result?

CHECK YOURSELF ON SECTIONS 1.1, 1.2 and 1.3

1.1 Prime numbers, factors, multiples

(a) Write down the first nine prime numbers in order of size.
(b) Find two prime numbers whose sum is another prime number.
(c) Find a number less than 30 which has 6 factors.
(d) Write down all the factors of 120.
(e) Write down the first five multiples of 7.
(f) Write the following as the sum of two square numbers
(i) 45 (ii) 106 (iii) 73

(g) Write down the value of each of the following
(i) 3^2 (ii) 2^5 (iii) 10^4 (iv) 100^3

1.2 Calculating with fractions

(a) Work out (i) $\frac{3}{7} + \frac{1}{2}$ (ii) $\frac{5}{12} - \frac{1}{8}$ (iii) $\frac{1}{3} + \frac{3}{4}$

(b) Work out (i) $\frac{3}{5} + \frac{4}{9}$ (ii) $\frac{5}{12} \div \frac{1}{8}$ (iii) $2\frac{1}{2} \times \frac{1}{10}$

1.3 Area and perimeter

(a) Find the area and perimeter of each shape. Lengths are in cm.

(i)

9

15

12

(ii)

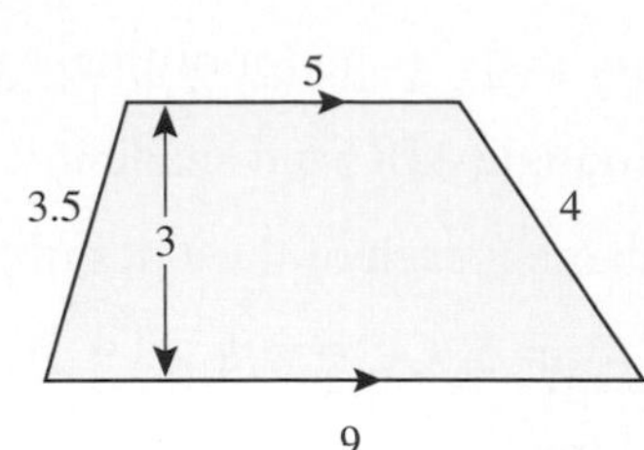

(b) The height of a triangle is 7cm greater than its base.
The area of the triangle is 30 cm^2.
Find the dimensions of the triangle.

(c) The length of a rectangular field is twice the width.
The area of the field is 45000 m^2.

Find the perimeter of the field.

1.4 Negative numbers

In section 1.4 you will

- add and subtract negative numbers
- multiply and divide negative numbers

Adding and subtracting

For adding and subtracting with negative numbers a number line is very useful.

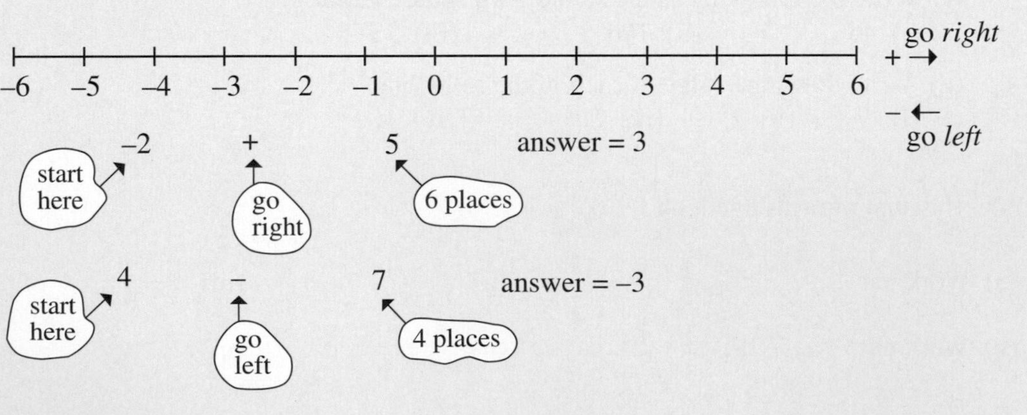

Exercise 1M

1 Use a number line to work out

(a) 4 – 5 (b) –2 + 4 (c) –3 + 6 (d) –2 – 1
(e) 3 – 7 (f) –2 + 5 (g) 4 – 9 (h) –3 + 2
(i) –5 – 1 (j) 7 – 8 (k) 4 – 7 (l) –3 + 8

2 Work out

(a) 6 – 11 (b) –3 – 3 (c) –5 + 4 (d) –3 + 3
(e) 8 – 12 (f) 11 – 13 (g) –4 – 4 (h) 10 – 20
(i) –5 – 15 (j) –3 – 13 (k) 8 – 5 (l) –6 + 20

3 Copy each sequence and fill in the missing numbers.

(a) 9, 6, 3, ☐, ☐ (b) ☐, –1, 3, 7, 11 (c) ☐, ☐, –10, –5, 0, 5

4 Copy and complete the addition squares

(a)

+	7	–1		
		0		–1
–3			1	
2	9			
				3

(b)

+	–5	3		
–1		2		0
			10	
4				
			6	–1

Two signs together

The calculation 8 – (+3) can be read as '8 take away positive 3'.

Similarly 6 – (– 4) can be read as '6 take away negative 4'

It is possible to replace *two* signs next to catch other by *one* sign as follows

+ + = +
– – = +
– + = –
+ – = –

Remember: 'same signs: +' 'different signs: –'

When two adjacent signs have been replaced by one sign in this way, the calculation is completed using the number line as before.

Work out the following

(a) –7 + (–4)
= –7 – 4
= –11

(b) 8 + (–14)
= 8 – 14
= –6

(c) 5 – (+9)
= 5 – 9
= –4

(d) 6 – (–2)
= 6 + 2
= 8

Exercise 1E

1 Work out

(a) $5 + (-2)$ (b) $4 + (-5)$ (c) $6 + (-6)$ (d) $4 + (-8)$

(e) $8 - (+2)$ (f) $7 - (+8)$ (g) $3 - (-1)$ (h) $4 - (-2)$

(i) $6 - (-3)$ (j) $4 - (-4)$ (k) $9 - (+1)$ (l) $10 - (+5)$

2 Work out

(a) $4 - (-2)$ (b) $6 - (-6)$ (c) $8 + (-10)$ (d) $3 + (-2)$

(e) $8 + (+2)$ (f) $7 - (+4)$ (g) $6 - (-5)$ (h) $4 - (-2)$

(i) $10 + (-20)$ (j) $15 + (-16)$ (k) $9 + (-12)$ (l) $-3 - (-4)$

3 At 25000 feet on a mountain the air temperature is –23°C and because of the low air pressure water boils at 71°C (which makes it difficult to make a nice cup of tea).

What is the difference between the air temperature and the temperature of the boiling water?

4 Write down the number exactly halfway between

(a) –1 and 5 (b) –2 and –7 (c) –11 and –12

5 In a 'magic square' you get the same number when you add across each row, add down each column and add diagonally. Copy and completes the following magic squares.

(a)

0		
–1		
4	–3	

(b)

4	–3	2
0		

(c)

–2		–4
	–1	
		0

(d)

	–1		–3
3		9	
		–5	
–6	5	0	7

(e)

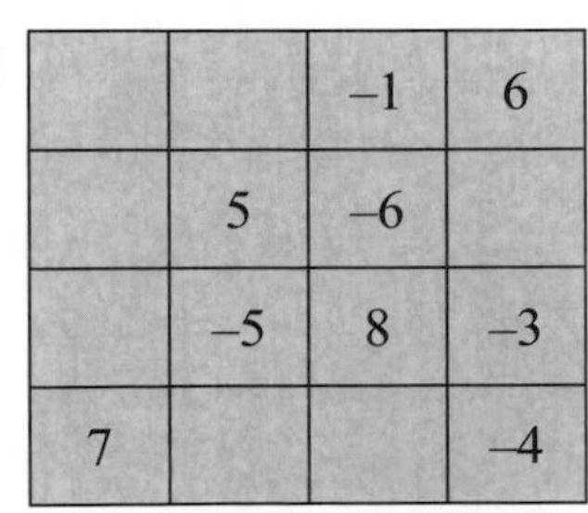

		–1	6
	5	–6	
	–5	8	–3
7			–4

6 You can choose any 3 numbers from

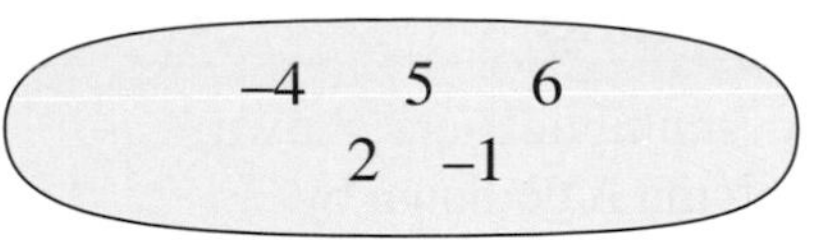

Here is a calculation □ + □ – □ =

(a) What is the largest answer you can get?

(b) What is the smallest answer you can get?

7 Copy and complete the tables

a	9	3	8	3	2	5	4	7		
b	5	5	3	7	–2	–2			4	2
$a–b$	4	–2					–2	–3	–3	–1

a	–3	4	3	5	7	4	6			
b			–3	–1				5	–1	2
$a–b$	–3	–5			8	10	6	2	3	–2

8 Copy and complete these number walls

(a)

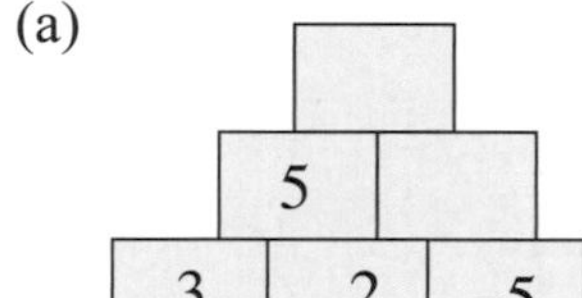

(b)

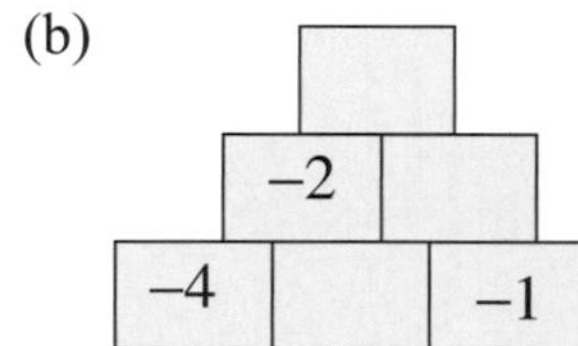

(c)

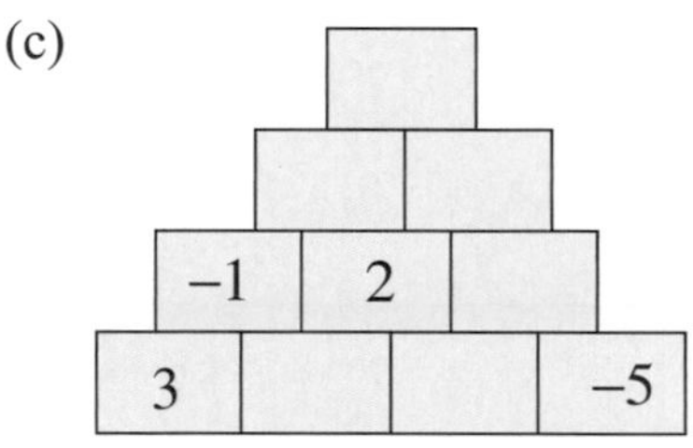

(d)

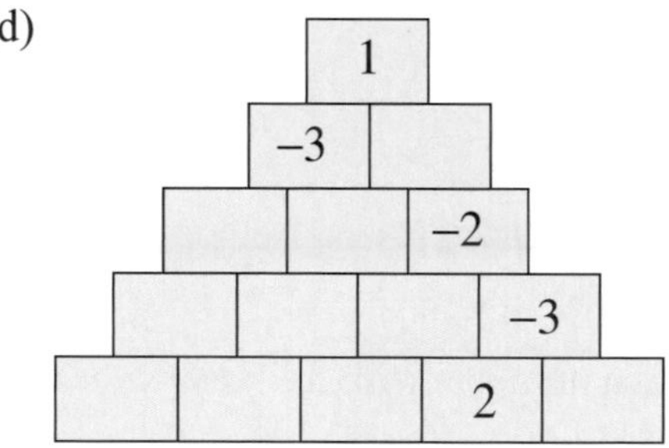

(e)

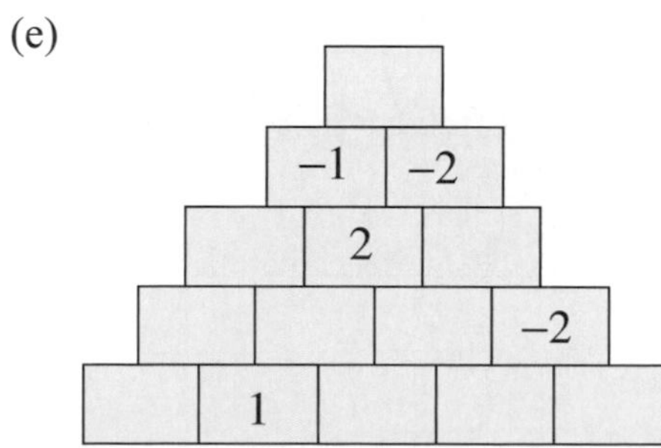

(f)

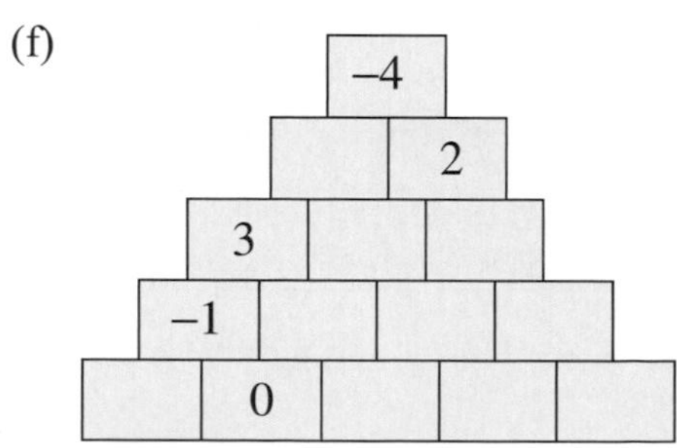

Multiplying and dividing

- In the sequence of multiplications shown, the numbers in column A go down by one each time.
  The numbers in column B go down by five each time

  Continuing the sequence:
  We see that:

$$\begin{array}{rcl} & A & B \\ & \downarrow & \downarrow \\ 5 \times & 3 = & 15 \\ 5 \times & 2 = & 10 \\ 5 \times & 1 = & 5 \\ 5 \times & 0 = & 0 \\ 5 \times & -1 = & -5 \\ 5 \times & -2 = & -10 \\ 5 \times & -3 = & -15 \end{array}$$

> 'When a positive number is multiplied by a negative number the answer is negative'.

- In this sequence the numbers in column C go down by one each time.
  The numbers in column D *increase* by 3 each time.

  Continuing the sequence:

  We see that:

$$\begin{array}{rcl} & C & D \\ & \downarrow & \downarrow \\ -3 \times & 3 = & -9 \\ -3 \times & 2 = & -6 \\ -3 \times & 1 = & -3 \\ -3 \times & 0 = & 0 \\ -3 \times & -1 = & 3 \\ -3 \times & -2 = & 6 \\ -3 \times & -3 = & 9 \end{array}$$

> 'When two negative numbers are multiplied together the answer is positive.'

Summary of rules.

(a) When two numbers with the *same sign are multiplied together, the answer is positive.*

(b) When two numbers with *different signs are multiplied together, the answer is negative.*

(c) For division the rules are the same as for multiplication.

Examples: $-3 \times (-7) = 21$ $\quad 5 \times (-3) = -15$ $\quad -12 \div 3 = -4$

$20 \div (-2) = -10$ $\quad -10 \div (-20) = \frac{1}{2}$ $\quad -1 \times (-2) \times (-3) = -6$

Exercise 2M

Work out

1. $5 \times (-2)$
2. -2×4
3. $7 \times (-2)$
4. $-3 \times (-2)$
5. $-3 \times (-1)$
6. $-4 \times (-1)$
7. -5×2
8. $5 \times (-1)$
9. -4×2
10. $-3 \times (-3)$
11. $6 \times (-3)$
12. $-8 \times (-1)$
13. $12 \div (-2)$
14. $-8 \div (-1)$
15. $6 \div (-2)$
16. $-10 \div (-2)$
17. $-20 \div (-1)$
18. $12 \div (-3)$
19. $-3 \div (-1)$
20. $9 \div (-3)$
21. Work out
    (a) $-7 \times (-2)$ (b) -3×6 (c) $8 \div (-8)$
    (d) $10 \times (-3)$ (e) $-2 \times (-2)$ (f) $-12 \div 3$
    (g) $-5 \times (-4)$ (h) -1×23 (i) $-2 \times (-2)^2$
    (j) $0 \times (-7)$ (k) $(-3)^2$ (l) $-3 \times (-2) \times (-3)$
22. Find the missing numbers
    (a) $-4 \times \square = 12$ (b) $3 \times \square = -12$ (c) $-8 \div -4 = \square$
    (d) $5 \times \square = -5$ (e) $\square \times (-3) = 9$ (f) $12 \div \square = -6$
    (g) $\square \div (-3) = 2$ (h) $\square \div 5 = -4$ (i) $-2 \times \square = 20$
    (j) $-3 \times \square = 6$ (k) $-2 \times \square = 4$ (l) $(-1)^2 = \square$

In questions 23 to 31 the next number in each table is found by multiplying the two numbers before it.

For example

–3	–2	6	–12	–72

Copy and complete each table.

23

3	–1		

24

–5	3		

25

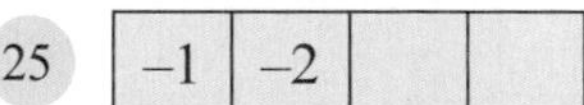

–1	–2		

26

3	–2			

27

–2	–1			

28

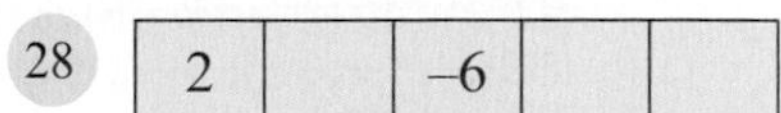

2		–6		

29

			3	–9

30

	4	–4		

31

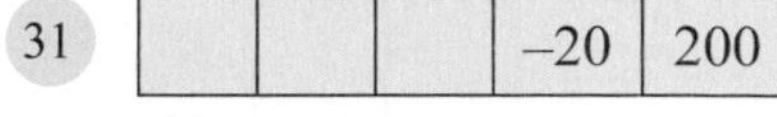

			–20	200

Exercise 2E

This exercise has questions involving addition, subtraction, multiplication and division.

1 Work out

(a) $-7 + 13$ (b) $-5 - (-4)$ (c) -7×4 (d) $-12 \div (-12)$

(e) $-6 + (-3)$ (f) $-10 + 10$ (g) $-8 - 5$ (h) $12 - 60$

(i) $3 \times (-3)$ (j) $(-2)^2$ (k) $5 - (-5)$ (l) $6 \div (-6)$

2 Find the missing numbers

(a) $5 \times \square = -50$ (b) $-2 \div \square = 1$ (c) $\square - 3 = 12$ (d) $\square + (-7) = -9$

(e) $10 - \square = -3$ (f) $\square \div (-3) = -1$ (g) $-7 - 7 = \square$ (h) $\square \times (-7) = 14$

(i) $1 - \square = -9$ (j) $-3 \times \square = 0$ (k) $8 - \square = -8$ (l) $(-1)^3 = \square$

3 Work out

(a) $-3 + (-2)$ (b) $-8 \div 8$ (c) $5 + (-7)$ (d) $-2 \times (-\frac{1}{2})$

(e) $8 \div (-8)$ (f) $-7 - (-2)$ (g) $-12 \div (-2)$ (h) $(-3)^3$

(i) $6 + (-6.5)$ (j) $(-8 + 2)^2$ (k) $(-2)^2 \times (-3)$ (l) $(-3 - (-2))^2$

4 A max/min thermometer records both the highest and lowest temperatures after the time it is reset. Tom reset the thermometer on Tuesday when the temperature was 3C. During the night the temperature fell 7° and then during Wednesday it rose by 8° before falling 9° overnight. On Thursday it rose 11° and fell 4° overnight. On Friday it rose 7° during the day. What were the maximum and minimum temperatures recorded?

5 Copy and complete the addition square shown. The numbers inside the square are found by adding together the numbers across the top and down the side.

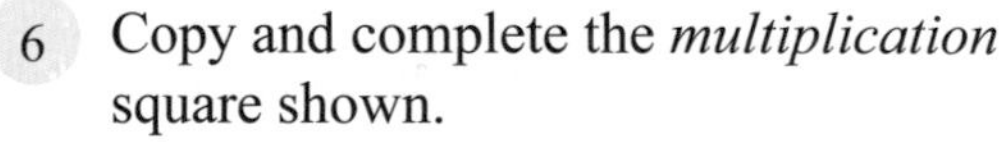

6 Copy and complete the *multiplication* square shown.

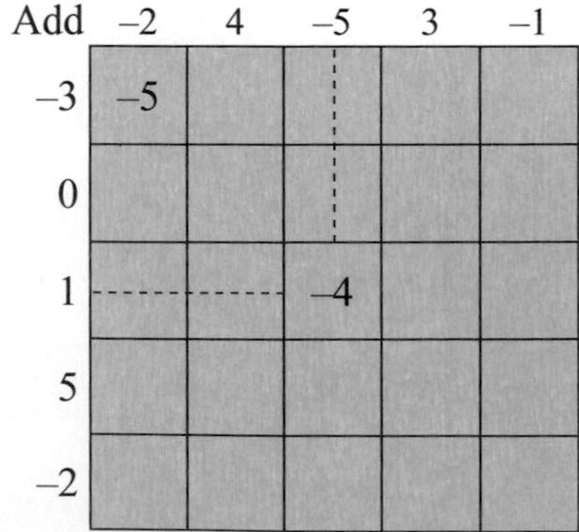

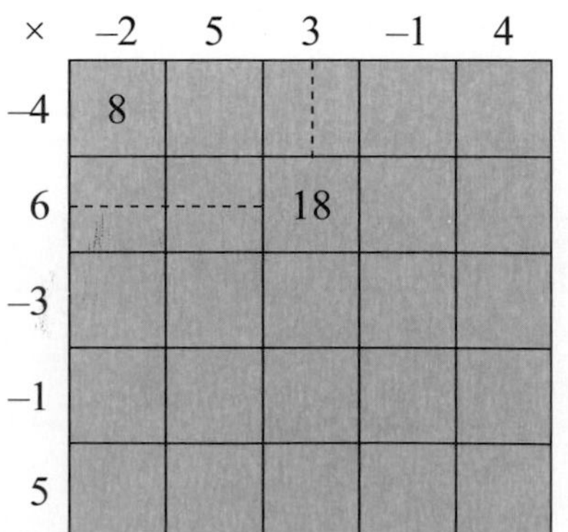

7 The sum of the numbers –3 and 4 is 1 and their product is –12. ('product' means multiplied together)

(a) Find two numbers whose sum is 3 and whose product is –10.

(b) Find two numbers whose sum is –1 and whose product is –12.

(c) Find two numbers whose sum is 4 and whose product is –12.

8 Copy and complete the table.

	Sum	Product	Two numbers
(a)	–7	10	
(b)	–13	30	
(c)	–5	6	
(d)	5	–6	
(e)	–8	12	
(f)	–2	–15	
(g)	–13	42	

Practice tests

Questions on negative numbers are more difficult when the different sorts are mixed together. Do one of these tests every two weeks or so.

Test 1

1 –8 – 8

2 –8 × (–8)

3 –5 × 3

4 –5 + 3

5 8 – (–7)

6 20 – 2

7 –18 ÷ (–6)

8 4 + (–10)

9 –2 + 13

10 +8 × (–6)

11 –9 + (+2)

12 –2 – (–11)

13 –6 × (–1)

14 2 – 20

15 –14 – (–4)

16 –40 ÷ (–5)

17 5 – 11

18 –3 × 10

19 9 + (–5)

20 7 ÷ (–7)

Test 2

1 –10 × (–10)

2 –10 – 10

3 –8 × (+1)

4 –8 + 1

5 5 + (–9)

6 15 – 5

7 –72 ÷ (–8)

8 –12 – (–2)

9 –1 + 8

10 –5 × (–7)

11 –10 + (–10)

12 –6 × (4)

13 6 – 16

14 –42 ÷ (+6)

15 –13 + (–6)

16 –8 – (–7)

17 5 × (–1)

18 2 – 15

19 21 + (–21)

20 –16 ÷ (–2)

Test 3

1 –2 × (+8)

2 –2 + 8

3 –7 – 6

4 –7 × (–6)

5 36 ÷ (–9)

6 –8 – (–4)

7 –14 + 2

8 5 × (–4)

9 11 + (–5)

10 11 – 11

11 –9 × (–4)

12 –6 + (–4)

13 3 – 10

14 –20 ÷ (–2)

15 16 + (–10)

16 –4 – (+14)

17 –45 ÷ 5

18 18 – 3

19 –1 × (–1)

20 –3 – (–3)

Test 4

1 –4 + 4

2 –4 × (+4)

3 –2 – 12

4 –2 × (–12)

5 3 + (–4)

6 4 – (–10)

7 –22 ÷ 11

8 –9 + 7

9 –6 – (–13)

10 –3 × (–11)

11 4 – 5

12 –20 – (+10)

13 4 × (–7)

14 7 – (–12)

15 9 – 18

16 56 ÷ (–7)

17 7 – 6

18 –11 + (+2)

19 –2 × (+8)

20 –8 ÷ (–2)

1.5 Sequences

In section 1.5 you will learn how to:

- find the next term in a sequence
- find and use a rule for a sequence
- solve problems using differences in sequences

Here is sequence 2, 8, 14, 20

- A number sequence is a set of numbers in a given order.
- Each number in a sequence is called a *term*.
- To find the next term in a sequence look at the gaps between terms. You may have to add, subtract, multiply or divide to find the next term.

(a) 4, 11, 18, 25,… the next term is 32 (add 7)

(b) 3, 6, 12, 24,… the next term is 48 (multiply by 2)

(c) 2, 3, 5, 8, 12,… the next term is 17 (add one more each time)

Exercise 1M

Find the next number in each sequence.

1 3, 8, 13, 18,

2 16, 12, 8, 4,

3 2, 5, 8, 11,

4 1, 2, 4, 8,

5 0, 1, 3, 6, 10,

6 0.8, 1, 1.2,

7 $\frac{1}{16}, \frac{1}{8}, \frac{1}{4}, \frac{1}{2},$

8 1, 4, 8, 13,

9 4, 40, 400,

10 11, 7, 3, –1,

11 80, 79, 77, 74,

12 100, 10, 1, 0.1,

13 1, 3, 9, 27,

14 4, 7, 13, 25, 49,

15 –5, –2, 1, 4,

16 Write down the sequence and find the missing numbers

(a) [2] [6] [18] [54] [ ]

(b) [1] [2] [4] [ ] [11]

(c) [9] [5] [ ] [–3] [–7]

(d) [ ] [8] [ ] [ ] [17] [20]

Find the next term in each sequence

17 1, 2, 6, 24, 120,

18 1, 1, 2, 6, 24, 120,

19 $\frac{1}{3}, \frac{2}{6}, \frac{3}{9}, \frac{4}{12},$

20 $\frac{1}{5}, \frac{2}{7}, \frac{3}{9}, \frac{4}{11},$

21 $n, 2n, 3n, 4n,$

22 15, 13, 10, 6,

23 2.01, 2.05, 2.09,

24 5.4, 5.2, 4.9, 4.5,

25 0.4, $\frac{3}{5}$, 0.8,

26 $\frac{1}{4}$, 0.3, $\frac{7}{20}$,

27 Square numbers can be written using consecutive odd numbers

$2^2 = 1 + 3$

$3^2 = 1 + 3 + 5$

$4^2 = 1 + 3 + 5 + 7$

$5^2 = 1 + 3 + 5 + 7 + 9$

(a) Complete the line: $10^2 = 1 + 3 + 5 + \ldots\ldots$

(b) Find the value of n below

$100^2 = 1 + 3 + 5 + \ldots\ldots + n.$

Sequence rules

For the sequence 3, 7, 11, 15, 19,…. the first term is 3 and the term-to-term rule is 'add 4'.

For the sequence 30, 27, 24, 21,…. the term-to-term rule is 'subtract 3'

For the sequence 2, 5, 11, 23,…. the term-to-term rule is 'double and add 1'

Exercise 1E

1 The first term of a sequence is 7 and the term-to-term rule is 'add 11'. Write down the first five terms of the sequence.

2 Write down the term-to-term rule for each sequence.

(a) 11, 13, 15, 17, 19,

(b) 62, 57, 52, 47,

(c) 5, 10, 20, 40,

(d) 81, 27, 9, 3,

3 Write down the rule for each sequence.

(a) 2.3, 2.5, 2.7, 2.9,… (b) 86, 43, 21.5,… (c) 2.5, 2.35, 2.2, 2.05,…

(d) 0.03, 0.3, 3, 30,… (e) 1.6, 0.8, 0.4, 0.2, (f) 4, 1, –2, –5,

4 You are given the first term and the rule of several sequences. Write down the first five terms of each sequence.

	First term	Rule
(a)	17	add 4
(b)	5	subtract 2
(c)	5	double
(d)	8000	divide by 10

5 The rule for the number sequences below is

'double and add 1'

Find the missing numbers

(a) 3 → 7 → 15 → 31 → ☐

(b) ☐ → 9 → 19 → 39 → ☐

(c) ☐ → 7 → ☐ → ☐

(d) ☐ → ☐ → ☐ → 47

6 The rule for the sequences below is

'multiply by 3 and take away 1'

Find the missing numbers.

(a) 1 → 2 → 5 → ☐

(b) ☐ → 8 → 23 → ☐

(c) 4 → ☐ → ☐ → ☐

7 Find the rule for each sequence. Each rule has two operations (similar to the rules in questions 5 and 6 above).

(a) $2 \longrightarrow 7 \longrightarrow 22 \longrightarrow 67$

(b) $3 \longrightarrow 4 \longrightarrow 6 \longrightarrow 10$

(c) $2 \longrightarrow 4 \longrightarrow 10 \longrightarrow 28$

8 In a linear sequence the terms go up or go down in equal steps.

For example 5, 9, 13, 17,… or 20, 17, 14, 11,…

Find the missing numbers in these linear sequences.

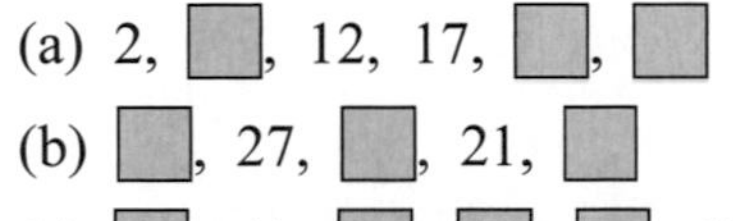

(a) 2, □, 12, 17, □, □

(b) □, 27, □, 21, □

(c) □, 41, □, □, □, 17

9 The following are linear sequences

(a)

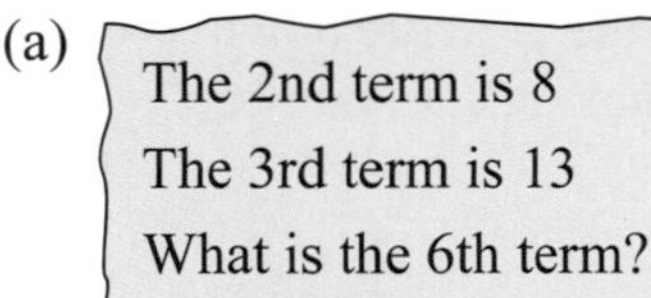

(b)

The 3rd term is 15

The 5th term is 29

What is the 7th term?

(c)

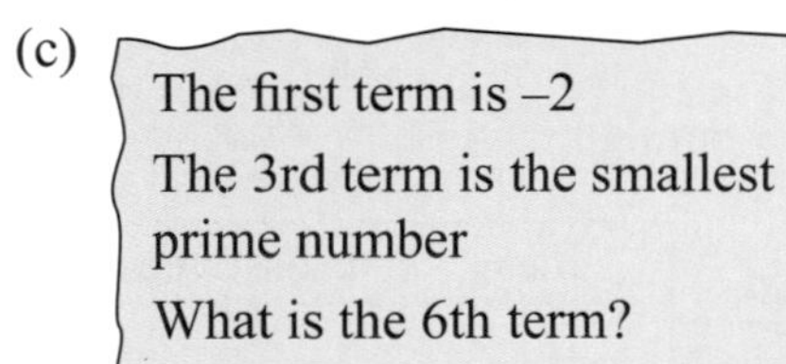

(d)

The 2nd term is 7

The 5th term is four times as large as the 1st term.

What is the 6th term?

10 (a) Copy and complete the following sequence.

$2 \times 99 = 198$

$3 \times 99 = 297$

$4 \times 99 = 396$

$5 \times 99 = \square$

$\square \times 99 = \square$

(b) Find the missing number

$\square \times 99 = 891$

11 Look at this sequence

$3^2 = 9$

$33^2 = 1089$

$333^2 = 110889$

$3333^2 = 11108889$

Write down the value of $33\,333^2$ and the value of $33\,333\,333^2$.

12 (a) What is the next term in the sequence 1, 2, 3, ...?
There is more than one possible answer.
The sequence may continue 1, 2, 3, 4, 5, ... (add 1)
Or it may continue 1, 2, 3, 5, 8, 13, ... (add the last 2 terms)

(b) Look at the sequence which starts 2, 4, 8, ...

Write down the next three terms in *two different* ways so that a consistent rule applies.

13 Write down the first six terms of these sequences

(a) the first term is 5
the rule is 'subtract 1.5'

(b) the second term is 5184
the rule is 'divide by 6'

(c) the fourth term is 2
the rule is 'add 3'

(d) the third term is 7
the rule is 'divide by 10'

(e) the first two terms are 2, 3
the rule is 'add the two previous terms'

(f) the first two terms are 0, 2
the rule is 'add the two previous terms'

(g) the first two terms are 1, 3
the rule is 'multiply the two previous terms'

(h) the first term is 4
the rule is 'write down the next square number'

Differences in sequences

Different numbers of lines are drawn below and the maximum number of crossovers for each is shown.

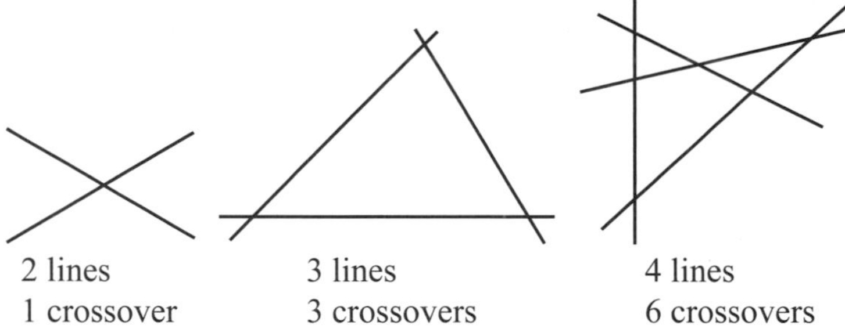

lines	crossovers
2	1
3	3
4	6
5	10

One method for predicting further results is to look at the *differences* between the numbers in the 'crossovers' column.

The differences form an easy pattern so that we can predict that there will be a maximum of 15 crossovers when 6 lines are drawn.

lines	crossovers	differences
2	1	
		2
3	3	
		3
4	6	
		4
5	10	
		5
6	15	

predictions

- In some sequences in the next exercise you may need to find the 'differences of the differences', called the second differences.

[In the table above the second differences are all 1.]

- Consider the sequence below.

2

10

30

68

130

- The first, second and third differences are shown below.

	First difference	Second difference	Third difference
2			
	8		
10		12	
	20		6
30		18	
	38		6
68		24	
	62		(6)
130		(30)	
	(92)		
(222)			

An obvious pattern is seen so that the numbers circled can be predicted.

Exercise 2M

1 Here is a sequence: 3 4 6 9

Write the numbers in a table as shown.

Predict the numbers shown with? marks to find the next two terms in the sequence 3, 4, 6, 9,

terms	differences
3	
	1
4	
	2
6	
	3
9	
	?
?	
	?
?	

2 Below are three sequences. Use differences to predict the next two numbers in each sequence.

(a)	(b)	(c)
6	7	5
7	11	8
9	16	12
12	22	17
16	29	23
?	?	?
?	?	?

3 Predict the next two terms in each sequence.

(a) 10, 12, 15, 19,
(b) 1, 8, 17, 28, 41,
(c) 5, 11, 19, 29, 41,

4 Here is a sequence of matchstick squares

$n = 1$

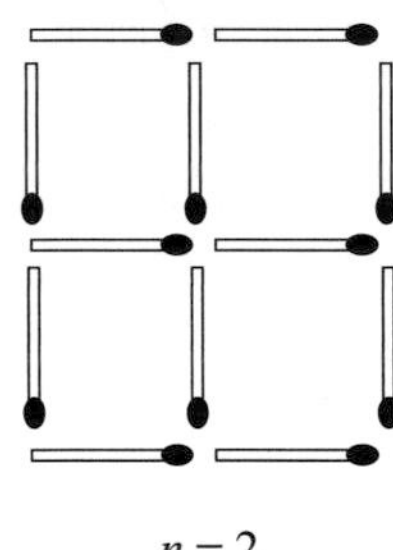

$n = 2$

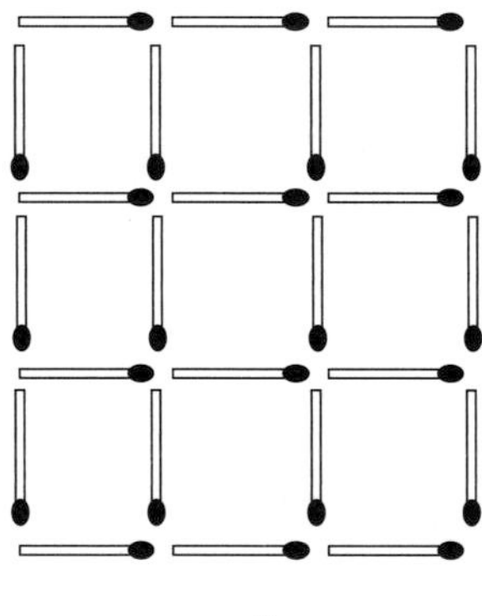

$n = 3$

Shape number, n	No. of matches	Difference
1	4	
		8
2	12	
		12
3	24	
		16
4	40	
5	?	

Use the differences to predict the number of matches in shape number 5.

 39

Exercise 2E

1 Below is a sequence of rectangles where each new diagram is obtained by drawing around the outside of the previous diagram, leaving a space of 1 unit.

diagram 1
3 squares

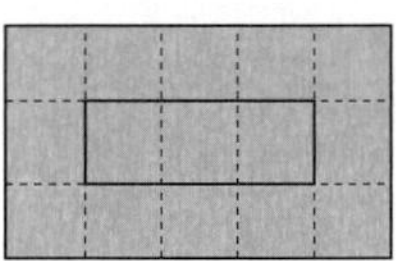

diagram 2
15 squares

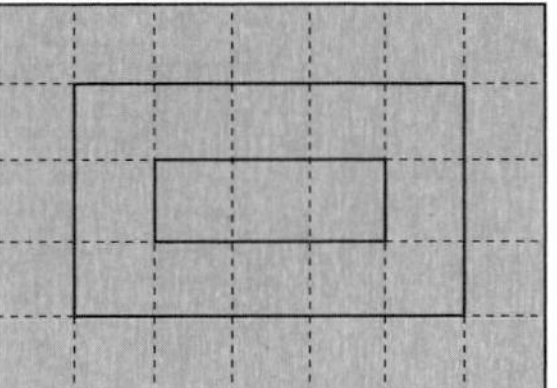

diagram 3
35 squares

(a) Draw diagram 4 and count the number of squares it contains. Enter the number in a table and use differences to *predict* the number of squares in diagram 5.

(b) Now draw diagram 5 to check if your prediction was correct.

diagram	squares	differences
1	3	
		12
2	15	
		20
3	35	
4		

2 Below are the first three members of a sequence of patterns of hexagons made with sticks.

diagram 1

diagram 2

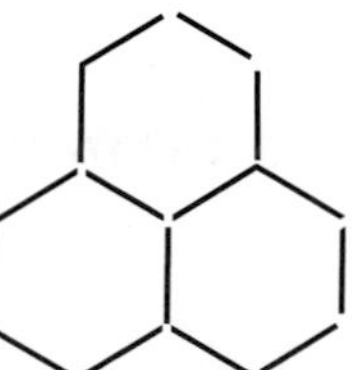

diagram 3

Draw diagram 4 and count the number of sticks it contains. Write your results in a table and then predict the number of sticks needed to make diagram 6.

3 Below are three sequences. Use differences to predict the next two numbers in each sequence.

(a)	(b)	(c)
1	3	11
6	6	14
13	13	22
22	24	35
33	39	53
?	?	?
?	?	?

4 The numbers 1, 2, 3, … 96 are written in a spiral which starts in the centre.

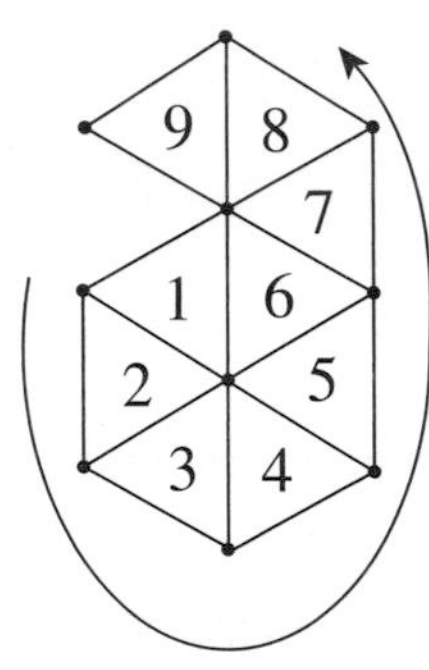

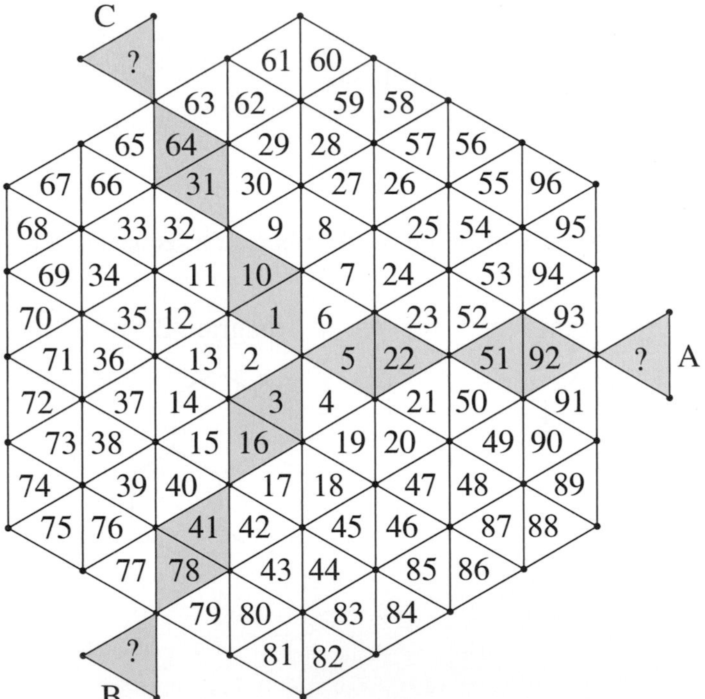

There are, in fact, many sequences in the pattern.

(a) In the row marked A, the numbers are

5 22 51 92.

Predict the next number in this sequence.

(b) Predict the next number in the rows marked B and C.

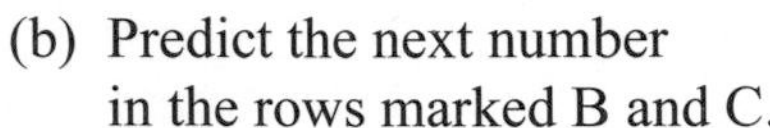

5 (a) This sequence is more difficult

Number	difference
2	
	2
4	
	4
8	
	7
15	
	11
26	

(b) The first differences make no obvious pattern. Work out the second differences and find the missing numbers.

number	difference	second difference
2		
	2	
		2
4		
	4	
		3
8		
	7	
		4
15		
	11	
		?
26		
	?	
?		

6 Use first, second and third differences to predict the next number in each of the sequences below.

(a)	(b)	(c)
2	3	1
5	11	4
13	31	13
28	69	34
52	131	73
87	?	?
?		

7 Playing cards can be used to build (rather unstable!) 'houses'. Simple houses with 1 storey, 2 storeys and 3 storeys are shown below, together with the number of cards required to make each one.

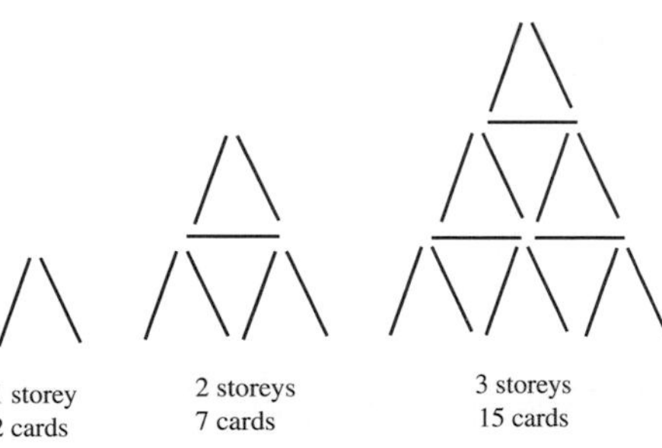

(a) Draw a house with 4 storeys and count the number of cards required.
Write down the sequence of the numbers of cards needed for 1, 2, 3 and 4 storeys.

(b) Ceri has a very steady hand and decides to build a house with as many storeys as possible.
How many storeys will it be possible to build if she has 5 packs of 52 cards?

CHECK YOURSELF ON SECTIONS 1.4 and 1.5

1 Adding and subtracting with negative numbers

(a) Work out

(i) $-7-3$ (ii) $8-22$ (iii) $6+(-19)$ (iv) $40-(-10)$

(v) $-19+100$ (vi) $0.2-1$ (vii) $3-(+10)$ (viii) $-8+(-32)$

(b) Copy and complete the 'magic' square

1		–1
		4
		3

2 Multiply and dividing with negative numbers

(a) Work out (i) $-5\times(-6)$ (ii) $3\times(-4)^2$ (iii) $-12\div(-2)$

(b) Find the missing numbers

(i) $8\times\square=-24$ (ii) $\square\div 7=-4$ (iii) $(-1)^3\times -11=\square$

3 Sequences

(a) Find the next term in each sequence.

(i) 9, 20, 31, 42 (ii) 256, 64, 16, 4 (iii) 34, 3.4, 0.34

(b) Find the first five terms in each sequence.

(i) 2nd term = 10, rule: add 8

(ii) 4th term = 30, rule: divide by 2

(c) Use differences to predict the next two numbers in each sequence.

(i) 6, 9, 13, 18, 24, □, □ (ii) 9, 11, 15, 22, 33, □, □

1.6 Using a calculator

In section 1.6 you will:

- review the correct order of operations in calculations
- learn to use the brackets and fractions buttons
- learn to use the memory and raising to a power buttons

Order of operations

Some people use the word 'BIDMAS' to help them remember the correct order of operations.

Brackets
Indices
Divide
Multiply
Add
Subtract

Here are four examples

- $8 + 6 \div 6 = 8 + 1 = 9$
- $20 - 8 \times 2 = 20 - 16 = 4$
- $(13 - 7) \div (6 - 4) = 6 \div 2 = 3$
- $20 - 8 \div (5 + 3) = 20 - 8 \div 8 = 19$

Exercise 1M

Work out, without a calculator.

1. $5 + 7 \times 2$
2. $9 - 12 \div 2$
3. $24 + 6 \times 2$
4. $(8 + 9) \times 2$
5. $17 - (2 + 5)$
6. $5 \times 8 + 6 \times 3$
7. $5 \times 6 - 8 \div 2$
8. $102 \div (17 - 15)$
9. $18 \div (9 - 12 \div 4)$
10. $2 \times (8 + 4 \times 3) - 7$
11. $(8 + 5) \times (20 - 16)$
12. $14 - 7 - 3 \times 2$

In questions 13 to 24 find the missing signs (+, –, ×, ÷), There are no brackets.

13. 9 3 3 = 18
14. 7 3 11 = 32
15. 6 12 3 = 10
16. 11 4 4 = 10
17. 15 4 5 = 35
18. 8 3 6 = 30
19. 7 6 2 = 10
20. 9 10 5 = 7
21. 6 3 2 4 = 8
22. 10 8 2 = 6
23. 8 4 4 4 = 18
24. 9 2 2 5 = 10

The last twelve questions have brackets.

25. 7 2 3 = 15
26. 4 2 5 = 28
27. 9 3 6 = 36
28. 8 7 3 = 5
29. 20 8 2 = 2
30. 7 2 5 1 = 30
31. 3 11 3 = 42
32. 15 8 9 3 = 3
33. 8 4 10 6 = 1
34. 3 2 4 2 = 20
35. 18 1 2 3 = 12
36. 4 8 6 2 = 20

Exercise 1E

Use a calculator and give the answer correct to two decimal places.

1. 3.4×1.23
2. $20.4 - 5.7412$
3. 0.341^2
4. $0.17 + 2.89 - 1.514$
5. $3.2^2 - 2.8$
6. $4.6 \times 1.9 + 8.05$
7. $0.54 \times 0.87 - 0.1$
8. $8.7 \div 2.73$
9. $12.5 - 0.516 + 1.2$
10. $\frac{8.9}{7.4}$
11. $\frac{20.2}{5.6} + 8.2$
12. $\frac{8.65}{6} - 0.12$

In questions 13 to 30 remember 'BIDMAS'.

13. $2.6 + 2.7 \times 1.9$
14. $8.01 + 0.8 \times 3.2$
15. $7.93 + 5 \div 12$
16. $8.6 \div 0.7 - 5.55$
17. $8 \div 0.55 + 2.33$
18. $8.06 + 1.4 \times 1.5$
19. $3.5 + \frac{8.5}{1.34}$
20. $1.53^2 + 2.53$
21. $6.4 + \frac{1.7}{0.85}$
22. $8.65 + 30 \div 8.2$
23. $5.44 + 1.37^2$
24. $6.4^2 \div 19$
25. $0.751 - 0.14 \times 0.9$
26. 2.3^3
27. $10 + 10 \times 10$
28. $8.9 + \frac{19.6}{15}$
29. $\frac{2.7 + 5.65}{3.3}$
30. $\frac{11.2 - 5.67}{1.9}$

Using brackets

Most calculators have brackets buttons like these [( ], [ )].

Don't forget to press the [=] button at the end to give the final answer.

(a) $8.5 - (1.2 \times 3.6)$

[8.5] [−] [(] [1.2] [×] [3.6] [)] [=]

Answer = 4.18 to 2 d.p.

(b) $\dfrac{9.62}{(8.14 - 0.27)}$

[9.62] [÷] [(] [8.14] [−] [0.27] [)] [=]

Answer = 1.22 to 2 d.p.

Exercise 2M

Work out and give the answer correct to 2 decimal places.

Hint: use the x^2 key

1. $11.52 - (3.14 \times 2.6)$
2. $12.5 + (3.8 \div 6)$
3. $(5.27 + 8.2) \div 2.7$
4. $9.6 + (8.7 \div 11)$
5. $(9.5 \div 7) - 0.44$
6. $13.7 - (8.2 \times 1.31)$
7. $6.31 - \left(\dfrac{8.2}{1.9}\right)$
8. $\left(\dfrac{7.65}{1.5}\right) - 3.06$
9. $\dfrac{3.63}{3.9 + 0.121}$
10. $(2.26 + 3.15 + 8.99) \div 1.45$
11. $5.89 \times (1.8 - 0.633)$
12. $17.8 \div (5.8 - 4.95)$
13. $(11.2 \div 7) \times 2.43$
14. $(3.65 + 1.4 - 2.34) \times 2.6$
15. $35 - (8.7 \times 2.65)$
16. $\dfrac{(9.37 + 8.222)}{2.47}$
17. $\dfrac{11.23}{(9.7 - 6.66)}$
18. $\dfrac{(114 - 95.6)}{14}$
19. $2.7^2 - 1.56$
20. $0.73^2 \times 5.2$
21. $6.6 + 4.1^2$
22. $(1.5 + 2.61)^2$
23. $(8.2 - 6.93)^2$
24. $(2.4 \times 0.15)^2$
25. $8.9 - (1.35)^2$
26. $(2.7^2 - 3.3) \div 5$
27. $2.1^2 + 3.11^2$
28. $\left(\dfrac{4.5}{8}\right) + \left(\dfrac{4.7}{7}\right)$
29. $3.2^2 - \left(\dfrac{4.2}{3.7}\right)$
30. $\dfrac{2.6^2}{(1.4 + 1.91)}$

Fractions

The [$a\frac{b}{c}$] key is used for fractions.

To enter $\frac{3}{4}$, press [3] [$a\frac{b}{c}$] [4]. You see 3 ⌟ 4

To enter $5\frac{1}{3}$, press [5] [$a\frac{b}{c}$] [1] [$a\frac{b}{c}$] [3]. You see 5 ⌟ 1 ⌟ 3

Exercise 3M

Work out

1. $\frac{2}{3}+\frac{1}{4}$
2. $\frac{5}{6}+\frac{1}{3}$
3. $\frac{8}{9}+\frac{1}{3}$
4. $\frac{4}{15}+\frac{1}{2}$
5. $\frac{3}{5}-\frac{1}{2}$
6. $\frac{7}{8}-\frac{1}{16}$
7. $\frac{5}{7}-\frac{1}{2}$
8. $\frac{5}{6}-\frac{1}{5}$
9. $\frac{9}{10}+\frac{1}{20}$
10. $\frac{11}{12}-\frac{3}{4}$
11. $\frac{4}{9}\times\frac{1}{2}$
12. $\frac{3}{11}\times\frac{1}{4}$
13. $2\frac{1}{4}+\frac{2}{3}$
14. $3\frac{2}{3}-1\frac{1}{2}$
15. $4\frac{1}{2}+\frac{5}{8}$
16. $\frac{1}{6}+3\frac{3}{4}$
17. $3\frac{1}{5}\times 1\frac{1}{2}$
18. $4\frac{1}{2}\div\frac{3}{4}$
19. $3\frac{1}{2}\div\frac{2}{5}$
20. $21\div 5\frac{1}{4}$
21. Copy and complete.

    (a) $1\frac{1}{4}+2\frac{1}{5}=\square$ (b) $\square+3\frac{1}{3}=4\frac{1}{2}$ (c) $\square+\frac{5}{6}=1\frac{3}{4}$

    (d) $\square-\frac{3}{7}=\frac{3}{4}$ (e) $\square\div\frac{2}{3}=2$ (f) $\square\times 1\frac{2}{5}=\frac{1}{2}$

Work out: $\left(\frac{2}{3}-\frac{1}{4}\right)\times\frac{6}{7}$

Press the keys

[( ] [2] [$a\frac{b}{c}$] [3] [−] [1] [$a\frac{b}{c}$] [4] [ )] [×] [6] 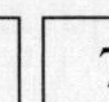 [7] [=]

Answer $=\frac{5}{14}$

Exercise 3E

Work out

1. $\left(\frac{3}{5}+\frac{1}{8}\right)\times\frac{1}{2}$
2. $\left(\frac{5}{6}-\frac{1}{9}\right)\times\frac{3}{4}$
3. $\left(\frac{4}{5}-\frac{1}{2}\right)^2$
4. $\left(1\frac{2}{3}+\frac{1}{4}\right)\div\frac{2}{3}$
5. $\frac{5}{8}\div\left(\frac{1}{3}+\frac{1}{2}\right)$
6. $2\frac{3}{4}\times\left(\frac{2}{5}+\frac{1}{10}\right)$
7. Copy and complete.

(a)

+		$\frac{3}{5}$		$1\frac{3}{4}$
	$\frac{5}{8}$		$\frac{5}{6}$	
$\frac{1}{4}$				
$2\frac{1}{2}$	$2\frac{5}{8}$			
			$\frac{11}{15}$	

(b)

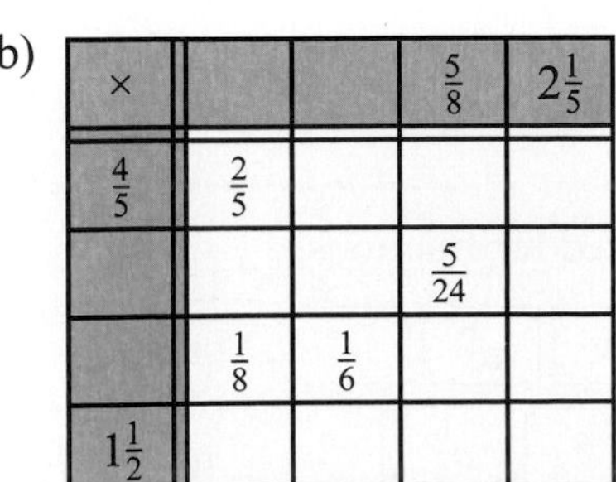

×			$\frac{5}{8}$	$2\frac{1}{5}$
$\frac{4}{5}$	$\frac{2}{5}$			
			$\frac{5}{24}$	
	$\frac{1}{8}$	$\frac{1}{6}$		
$1\frac{1}{2}$				

Work out.

8 $\left(1\frac{2}{3}\right)^2 - \frac{5}{9}$

9 $\left(\frac{1}{3} - \frac{1}{4}\right) \times \frac{6}{7}$

10 $\frac{8}{9} - \left(\frac{2}{3}\right)^3$

11 $\frac{5}{8} \div 1\frac{7}{8} - \frac{1}{15}$

12 $\dfrac{\left(2\frac{3}{5} - 1\frac{3}{4}\right)}{\left(\frac{1}{5} - \frac{1}{6}\right)}$

13 $\frac{14}{15} \times \frac{3}{7} - \frac{7}{10} + \frac{1}{15}$

Copy and complete.

14 $\frac{2}{3} \div \square - \frac{1}{4} = \frac{31}{36}$

15 $\left(\square + \frac{2}{3}\right) \times \frac{3}{5} = \frac{26}{35}$

16 $\left(1\frac{1}{4} + \square - \frac{3}{8}\right) \div \left(2\frac{1}{2}\right)^2 = \frac{27}{50}$

Negative numbers

On a calculator the [(–)] button is used for negative numbers.

On a calculator work out:

(a) –5.2 + 7.81

Press the keys

[(–)] [5.2] [+] [7.81] [=]

Answer = 2.61

(b) 7.5 ÷ (–0.04)

[7.5] [÷] [(–)] [0.04] [=]

Answer = –187.5

Notice that we do not *need* the brackets buttons. You may use them if you prefer.

Exercise 4M

Work out the following. Give the answer correct to one decimal place where appropriate.

1 –7 × 3

2 –5 × (–2)

3 8 ÷ (–4)

4 10 × (–4)

5 –2 × (–2)

6 –12 ÷ 3

7 –3.4 × (–2.5)

8 –0.5 × 6.8

9 12.5 – (–2.5)

10 –1.1 × (–1.1)

11 –8 ÷ (–0.25)

12 –6.8 ÷ 0.1

13 $\dfrac{-8 \times (-3)}{4}$

14 $\dfrac{12}{(3 \times (-2))}$

15 $\dfrac{20}{(-2)} + 8$

16 –11.4 + 1.71

17 –9.2 – 7.4 + 15.2

18 –4.74 – (–13.08)

19 $82 - 9.2^2$

20 $101 - (-6.4)^2$

21 $8 + (-3.5)^2$

22 $\dfrac{-8.5 \times (-6.2)}{-0.2}$

23 $\dfrac{3^2 - 5^2}{(-4.6 + 2.1)}$

24 Copy and complete.

(a) 5.6 ÷ (–0.2) = $\square$

(b) –8.4 × $\square$ = 27.72

(c) 4.6 – $\square$ = 11.61

Other useful buttons

M +	Adds the number to the current memory. This key is useful when several numbers are to be added together.
^ or x^y	Raises the number to a power.
Ans	The 'answer' button can be used as a 'short term memory'. It holds the answer from the previous calculation.

(a) $15.2 - (1.2 + 0.71)^4$

15.2 | − | (| 1.2 | + | 0.71 |) | ^ | 4 | =

Answer = 1.89 to 2 d.p.

(b) $1.2^5 + 0.9^6$

1.2 | ^ | 5 | + | 0.9 | ^ | 6 | =

Answer = 3.02 to 2 d.p.

Exercise 5M

Work out correct to 1 decimal place, unless told otherwise.

1. $(1.3 \times 2.4) + (5.3 \times 0.7) + (8.6 \times 0.61) + 11.7$
2. $(0.8 \times 0.7) + (1.1 \times 3.5) + 6.23 + (1.9 \times 0.8)$
3. $(1.8 \times 1.9 \times 3.1) + (0.91 \times 5.6) + (4.71 \times 1.9)$
4. $(8.9 \times 1.5) + 7.1^2 + 5.3^2 + 31.4$
5. $8.21 + (9.71 \times 2.3) + (8.2 \times 1.4) + 2.67$
6. $(8.9 \times 1.1) + (1.2 \times 1.3 \times 1.4) + (0.76 \times 3.68)$

In questions 7 to 10 find the total bill, correct to the nearest penny.

7. 7 balloons at 69p each
   5 tins at 42p each
   48 eggs at £1.55/dozen
   3 packets of tea at £1.19 each
   4 grapefruit at 33p each

8. 14 bolts at 22p each
   30m of cable at 15p/metre
   3 sacks of fertilizer at £5.35 each
   200 tiles at £2.30 for 10
   5 plugs at 49p each

9 200g of cheese at £5.20/kg
1 bottle of ketchup at £1.19
3 jars of coffee at £2.45 each
4 lemons at 29p each
8 lb potatoes at 32p/lb

10 1 tube of glue at £1.35
3 tins of paint at £4.20 each
100 m of wire at 11p/metre
100 g of nails at £8/kg
3 boxes of seed at £3.35 each

Exercise 5E

Give answers correct to 1 decimal place.

In questions 1 to 9 use the x^y button, where needed.

1 3.7^3

2 2.1^4

3 $3.1^5 + 112$

4 1.64^5

5 $(1.81 + 2.43)^4$

6 $19.8 + 1.96^3$

7 $1.7^3 + 2.4^3$

8 $200 - 3.7^4$

9 $3.2 + 3.2^2 + 3.2^3$

In questions 10 to 24 think ahead and use your calculator as efficiently as possible.

10 $\dfrac{5.65}{1.21+3.7}$

11 $\dfrac{8.7}{13} + \dfrac{4.9}{15}$

12 $14.6 - (3.9 \times 2.62)$

13 $12.94 - \sqrt{8.97}$

14 $\dfrac{5.41+7.82}{9.82-3.99}$

15 $\sqrt{\dfrac{100.9}{9.81+56}}$

16 11.2% of 9.6^3

17 $\frac{2}{7}$ of $\left(\dfrac{4.2}{1.95-0.713}\right)$

18 $\frac{1}{6} + \frac{1}{7} + \frac{1}{8} + \frac{1}{9}$

19 $\dfrac{\sqrt{8.74} + \sqrt{7.05}}{\sqrt{3.14} + \sqrt{2.76}}$

20 $\dfrac{900}{101 - 2.9^4}$

21 $(15\% \text{ of } 22.36)^3$

22 18% of 9.1% of 1150

23 $2.8^5 - \sqrt{\dfrac{9.7}{11.4}}$

24 $\frac{2}{3}$ of $\left(\dfrac{9.81}{1.25^2}\right)^3$

25 $\dfrac{(-8.23) \times (-1.24)}{3.6}$

26 $\dfrac{(-5.1) \times (-1.42)}{(-1.7)}$

27 $\dfrac{(-2.3) \times (-2.8)}{(-3.5)}$

Crossword Puzzle

The crossword puzzle below is made from words on a calculator.
For example the number 804 on a calculator makes
the word HOB when the calculator is turned upside down.

Copy the crossword grid and complete it using the clues.

1		2			3	4
				5		
6			7			
			8			
	9	10				
		11				
12					13	

Across

1 $277 + (7 \times 8 \times 9 \times 10)$

3 $1 + 2 + 3 + 4 + 2^2$

5 $8.5 \times 8.6 \times 10 - 94$

6 $11^3 + 2^2 - 5^4$

7 $10^4 - (47\frac{1}{8} \times 48)$

8 Capital City

9 $0.2^2 + (0.2^3 \div 100)$

11 Short for 'Australia'

12 $(13 \times 77 \times 3) + (21 \div 0.5)$

13 $20 \div 0.2 - 2 \times 3 \times 11$

Down

1 $19^3 + 2 \times (11^2 + 2.5\% \text{ of } 80)$ [backwards]

2 $(3^3)^2 + 0.2^2 \times 100$

3 $0.8 - (2 \times 0.0133)$

4 $8 \div 100 - (3^2 \div 10^4)$

5 $41 \times 42 \times 43 + 491$
The letters can be rearranged to make something you find at the seaside]

7 $(3 \times 10^3 + 13 \times 77) \times 8$

10 last three digits of $10 \div 0.1^2$

CHECK YOURSELF ON SECTION 1.6

1 Order of operations

Work out

1. $15 + 9 \div 3$
2. $3.5 \times (6 + 14)$
3. $19 - 20 \times 0.5$

Copy and complete

4. $\square \div (5 \times 2) = 8$
5. $(\square \times 8) - 3 = 37$
6. $3 \times \square - 12 = 960 \div (16 \div 2)$

2 Using a calculator

Work out and give your answer correct to 1 decimal place.

(a) $27.7 \div (0.97 \times 35.4)$ (b) $\dfrac{17.1}{(8.2 - 7.57)^2}$ (c) $4\frac{2}{5} - 1\frac{5}{6}$

(d) $\dfrac{8.7}{1.4} + \dfrac{11.92}{2.6}$ (e) $\left(\dfrac{4.2}{1.6 + 0.791}\right) \times (8.6 \div 3.7)$

(f) $\dfrac{-3.61 \times (-2.4)}{4.5}$ (g) $16.5 - (-3.91)^2$ (h) $84.6 + 3.6^4$

UNIT 1 MIXED REVIEW

Part one

1. Which of these are prime numbers?

   11 91 39 37 51 19

2. Write down all the factors of

   (a) 15 (b) 24 (c) 30

3. Find the next number in each sequence.

   (a) 2, 20, 200 (b) 3, 6, 12, 24 (c) 50, 49, 47, 44

   (d) 3.3, 3.2, 3.1, 3 (e) 500, 50, 5 (f) 5, 7, 11, 17, 25

4 The rule for the sequences below is *'double and add 3'*. Find the missing numbers.

(a) $1 \rightarrow 5 \rightarrow 13 \rightarrow \square$

(b) $2 \rightarrow \square \rightarrow \square$

(c) $\square \rightarrow 9 \rightarrow \square$

5 Write down the rule for each sequence.

(a) $1\frac{1}{2}, 2, 2\frac{1}{2}, 3,$

(b) $3\frac{1}{2}, 7, 14, 28,$

(c) 3, 2.8, 2.6, 2.4,

6 Use differences to find the next number in each of the following sequences.

(a)	(b)	(c)
3	2	7
5	4	9
9	12	17
15	26	37
23	46	75
?	?	137
		?

7 Maggie has been working very hard! On Monday she worked from 0830 till 1800, on Tuesday from 0700 till 1845 and on Wednesday from 0615 till 2145. Each day she had a break of 30 minutes. How many hours and minutes did she work in those three days?

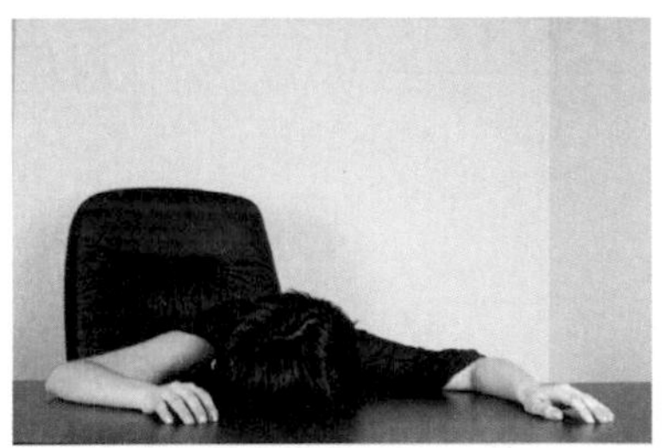

8 Work out

(a) $-2 - 3$ (b) $6 - 9$ (c) -2×4 (d) $-3 \times (-2)$

(e) $-4 + 10$ (f) $6 \times (-2)$ (g) $-7 + 7$ (h) $2 - 20$

9 Copy and complete the magic squares

(a)

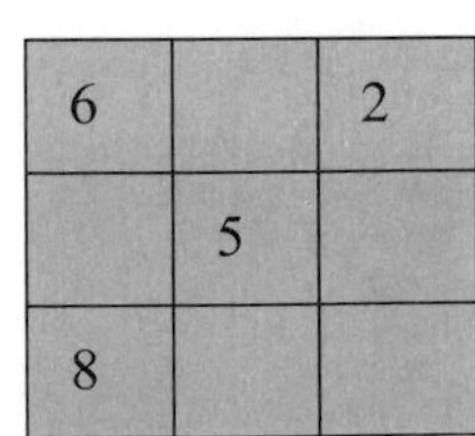

6		2
	5	
8		

(b)

–4	3	–5
	–7	0

10 Work out

(a) $1 \div \frac{1}{5}$ (how many fifths are there in 1?) (b) $2 \div \frac{1}{10}$

(c) $1 \div \frac{1}{8}$ (d) $3 \div \frac{1}{3}$

11 Find the area of each shape. All lengths are in cm.

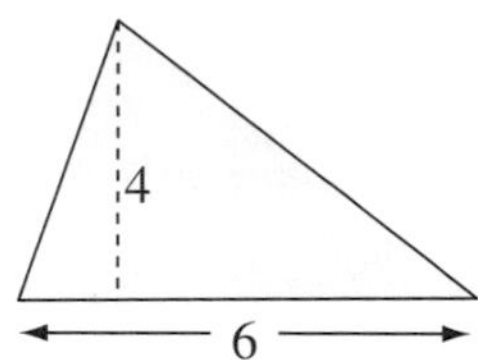

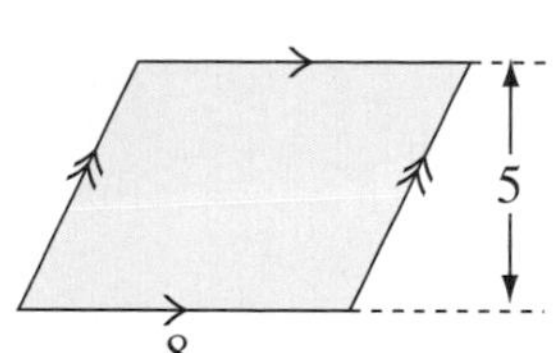

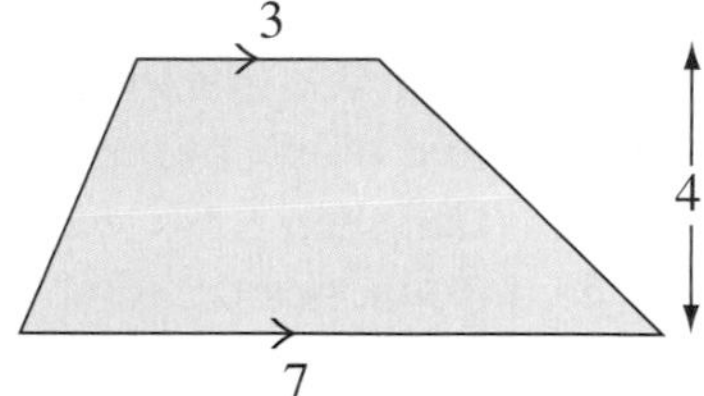

12 The perimeter of a rectangle is 24 cm. The sides of the rectangle are in the ratio 2:1. Calculate the area of the rectangle.

13 Work out

(a) $\frac{1}{4} + \frac{1}{8}$ (b) $\frac{1}{8} + \frac{3}{4}$ (c) $\frac{1}{10} + \frac{1}{5}$ (d) $\frac{2}{3} - \frac{1}{6}$

(e) $\frac{2}{3}$ of 60 (f) $\frac{3}{5}$ of 40 (g) $\frac{4}{7}$ of 350 (h) $\frac{1}{4} + \frac{2}{3}$

14 Work out the following (remember 'BIDMAS')

(a) $40 - 9 \times 2$ (b) $25 + 4^2$ (c) $(7 - 2)^2$

(d) $4 \times (3 \times 3 - 1)$ (e) $15 - 12 \div 3$ (f) $(3^2 - 5)^2$

15 Use a calculator to work out the following. Give your answers correct to 1 decimal place or as a fraction.

(a) $18.3 - (1.91 \times 2.62)$ (b) $\dfrac{5.23}{(9.2 - 7.63)}$ (c) $3\frac{2}{5} + \frac{1}{2}$

(d) $\dfrac{8.91}{1.6} + \left(\dfrac{1.54}{0.97}\right)$ (e) $\left(\dfrac{1.4 + 0.761}{1.76}\right)^2$ (f) $2\frac{1}{4} \div \frac{3}{4}$

Part two

1 Calculate the area of the pink region.

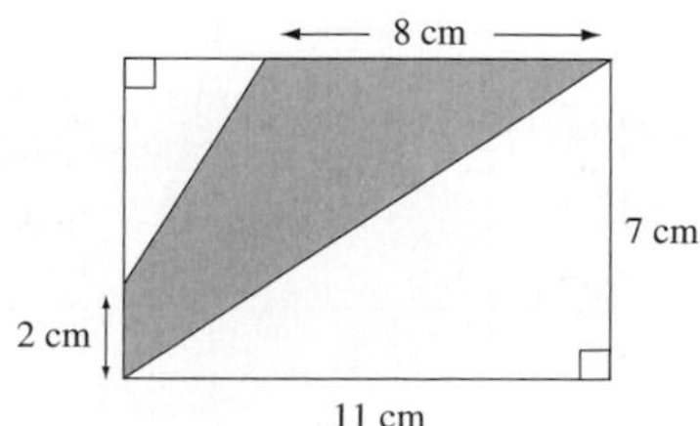

2 Work out, without a calculator:

(a) 4^2 (b) 2^3 (c) 1^5 (d) $10^3 - 5^3$

3 Use a calculator to find the square roots, correct to 1 decimal place.

(a) $\sqrt{15}$ (b) $\sqrt{7}$ (c) $\sqrt{135}$ (d) $\sqrt{8.21}$

4 In 2008 a survey in a town in America showed that only $\frac{3}{7}$ of the population thought that their town was 'friendly'. As a consequence the town council put up street signs and in a similar survey one year later $\frac{3}{5}$ of the population thought that the town was friendly. The population of the town was 7350. How many *more* people thought the town was friendly in the second survey than in the first survey?

5 Here is a sequence of squares surrounded by dots.

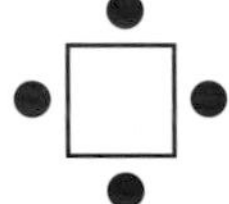 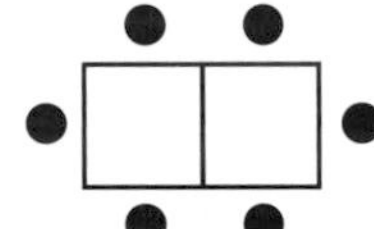 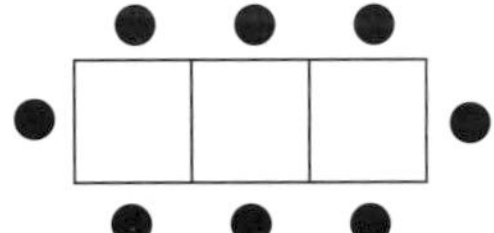

(a) How many small dots will surround the diagram with a row of 10 squares?
(b) How many squares are in the diagram which has 104 dots?

6 Match each calculation with its value on the right

3×2^4 2^5 $3^2 \times 5$ 3×10^2

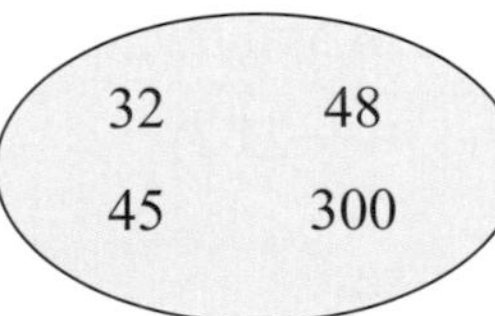

7 Find the missing numbers $2^{\square} \times 3^{\square} = 324$

8 Copy the triangle on squared paper. Find the area of the triangle, giving your answer in square units.

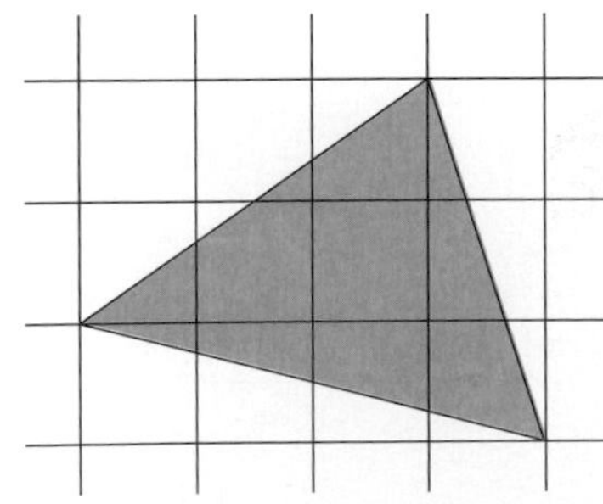

9 Copy and complete the crossnumber puzzle

1		2		3
		4	5	
6	7			
	8			9
10		11		

Across

1 $11^2 \times 2$

4 5×3^3

6 $7^2 - 5^2 - 5$

8 $3^5 \div 3$

10 $6^2 - 3^3$

11 $2^{10} - 20^2$

Down

1 $10^3 \div 2^2 + 1^4$

2 $2^2 + 4^2 + 1^2$

3 $4^3 + (125 \div 5^3)$

5 $2^6 \div 2$

7 $9^2 + 2^4 + 1^5$

9 $2^8 - 202$

10 There were 4 candidates in a class election. Mary got $\frac{1}{3}$ of the votes, George got $\frac{1}{3}$ of the votes, Henry got $\frac{1}{6}$. What fraction did Sheena, the 4th candidate get?

11 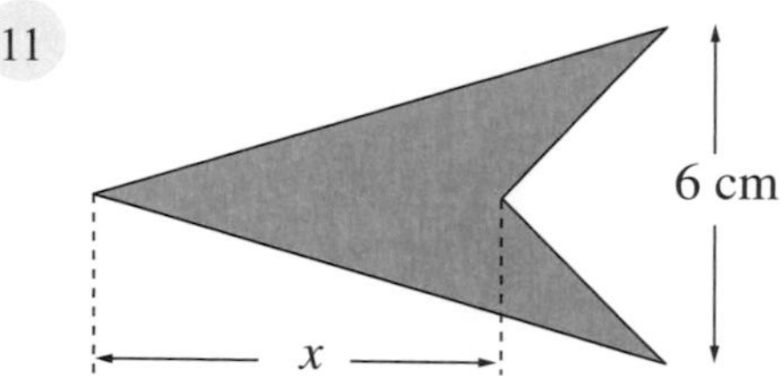

The arrowhead has an area of 42 cm^2.
Find the length x.

12 A rectangular field of area 4.2 hectares has a length of 350 m.
How wide is the field?

13 Work out, without a calculator.

(a) $\frac{5}{6} \times \frac{2}{3}$ (b) $\frac{3}{4} \div \frac{1}{2}$ (c) $\frac{3}{7} - \frac{1}{3}$

(d) $1\frac{3}{4} \div \frac{1}{3}$ (e) $2\frac{1}{2} \times 1\frac{1}{4}$ (f) $\frac{8}{11} - \frac{1}{4}$

14 

The area of this shape is 176 cm^2.
Work out the perimeter of the shape.

Puzzles and Problems 1

Cross numbers

Make three copies of the pattern below and complete the puzzles using the clues given. To avoid confusion it is better not to write the small reference numbers 1, 2, . . .19 on your patterns.
Write any decimal points on the lines between squares.

1				2			3
		4				5	
6				7	8		
		9	10				
	11						12
13		14		15		16	
		17					
18					19		

Part A

Across

1. 15% of 23
2. Next prime number after 23
4. One-third of 2409
5. Solve the equation $\frac{x}{5} = 3.8$
6. Area of a circle of diameter 30 cm (to 3 s.f.)
7. $(71.6)^2 - (\frac{1}{2} + \frac{3}{50})$
9. $245^2 - (3^3 \times 2^2)$
13. $7 + 7^2 + 7^3$
15. $\frac{1}{4} + 3 \times 13$
17. Last 3 digits of (567×7)
18. 50 m written in cm
19. $75 \div 6$

Down

1. Volume of a cube of side 15 cm
2. One minute to midnight on the 24 hour clock
3. $\frac{5.2}{0.21} + \frac{17}{0.31}$ to 1 d.p.
5. $(11\frac{1}{4})^2$ to the nearest whole number
8. $12 - \frac{1}{100}$
10. Prime number
11. $2^5 - 3$
12. $\frac{3}{7}$ of 3675
13. North-west as a bearing
14. $\frac{3}{4}$ of 11% of 12 000
16. Number of minutes between 1313 and 1745.

Check: There should be 5 decimal points in the puzzle.

Part B

Across

1. $(0.5 \div \frac{1}{2}) \times 123$
2. $1001 \div 77$
4. $200 - (4 \div 0.5)$
5. $(2^3 - 1)^2$
6. $33\frac{1}{3}\%$ of 2802
7. $8.14 - (1.96 \times 0.011)$ to 3 d.p.
9. 7391×11
13. $1^1 + 2^2 + 3^3 + 4^4$
15. $10^4 - [2 \times 20^2 + 9 \times 7]$
17. Number of minutes between 0340 and 1310.
18. $80^2 + 9^2 + 1^2$
19. $19 + \frac{3}{20} + \frac{1}{4}$

Down

1. (1 across) × (2 across)
2. $\frac{1}{2} + \frac{1}{3} + \frac{1}{4} + \frac{1}{5}$ to 3 d.p.
3. $20^2 - \sqrt{4}$
5. $42.2 - (8.1 \times 0.13)$ to 1 d.p.
8. 143×7
10. Inches in a foot.
11. $(2^3 \times 3^2) + 2^2 + 2$
12. Number of hours in a leap year.
13. 13% of £22.80, to the nearest penny
14. Next in the sequence 0.858, 8.58, 85.8, . . .
16. 113×0.3

Check: There should be 6 decimal points in the puzzle.

Part C

Across

1. South-west as a bearing.
2. Inches in a yard
4. Last three digits of $(11^2 + 2^2)^2$
5. 4 score plus ten
6. $(26\frac{1}{2})^2$, to the nearest whole number
7. $\frac{24.3}{1.9} + \frac{357}{24} + \frac{87.04}{3.7}$, correct to 2 d.p.
9. $(13 \text{ across})^2 + (5 \text{ across})^2 + 103$
13. $800 - 694$
15. Last three digits of $(407 \times 21 \times 11)$
17. $\frac{2}{3} + \frac{3}{4} + \frac{4}{5} + \frac{5}{6}$
18. $\frac{392.2}{(4.97 + 2.66)}$, correct to 2 d.p.
19. Next in the sequence 3, 5, 9, 17, 33, 65

Down

1. Solve the equation $\frac{555}{x} = 2$
2. 11% of £323.11, to the nearest penny
3. $\frac{1.23}{1.4 - 0.271}$, correct to 2 d.p.
5. $30 \times 31 - 11$
8. Area, in cm², of a rectangle measuring 1.2 m by 11 cm
10. (A square number) – 1
11. 80% of 50
12. $\sqrt{(4 \text{ across})} \times (13 \text{ across}) + (10 \text{ down})$
13. Angle in degrees between the hands of a clock at 2.30
14. A quarter share of a third share of a half share of £152.16
16. $76.8 \div 0.4$

Check: There should be 7 decimal points in the puzzle.

Mental Arithmetic Practice

Here is a set of mental arithmetic questions. Ideally a teacher will read out each question twice, with pupils books closed. The test of 30 questions should take about 20 minutes.

1. Add together 15, 25 and 70.
2. How many millimetres are there in a kilometre?
3. Find the length of the perimeter of a regular hexagon of side 20 cm.
4. Find the change from £10 when you buy two magazines for 75p each.
5. Give a rough estimate for the square root of 405.
6. Find the cost of 60 eggs at £1 per dozen.
7. A car is travelling at a steady speed of 30 m.p.h. How far does it go in 30 minutes?
8. Find the difference between $8\frac{1}{2}$ and 20.
9. Work out $1 + 2^2 + 3^3$.
10. Through what angle does the minute hand of a clock move between 8.50 and 9.00?
11. Work out roughly the area of a circle of radius 10 cm.
12. A bridge was built in Paris in 1780. How many years ago was that?
13. What is 40% as a fraction?
14. How many items costing £25 each can you buy with £200?
15. What five coins make 75p?
16. Calculate the length of the perimeter of a rectangular field measuring 110 m by 80 m.
17. Work out 0.03 multiplied by 1000.
18. Increase a price of £700 by 1%.
19. Answer true or false: $(\frac{1}{3})^2$ is greater than $\frac{1}{3}$.
20. A large brick weighs 1 kg. Roughly what does it weigh in pounds?
21. Work out 1% of £150.
22. A plant grows 5 cm every day. How many days will it take to grow 60 cm?
23. A charity collection is made into a pile of 1000 20p coins. How much was collected?
24. Add together 67 and 77.
25. True or false: At a steady speed of 30 m.p.h. you go 1 mile every 2 minutes.
26. Glen has one of each of the coins from 1p to 1 pound. What is their total value?
27. Three angles of a quadrilateral are 80°, 120° and 60°. What is the fourth angle?
28. How many inches are there in a foot?
29. A pie chart has a pink sector representing 25% of the whole chart. What is the angle of the sector?
30. Write down the next prime number after 31.

A long time ago! 1

The Eye of Horus

In Ancient Egypt, Horus was represented as the falcon-headed god. He was the ultimate god of mathematics.

All Egyptian fractions were unit fractions like $\frac{1}{2}$, $\frac{1}{3}$ and $\frac{1}{8}$.

The eye of Horus represented the sacred unit fractions. The 'eye of Horus' symbol was used to protect from evil.

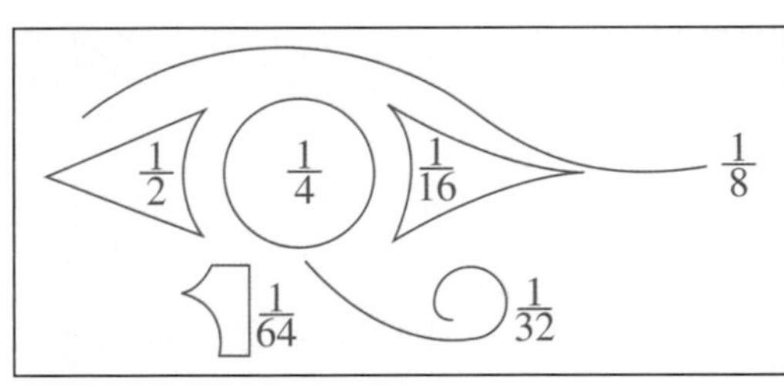

The eye of Horus.

Each symbol represents the fraction shown.

By adding together different parts of the eye, other fractions are created.

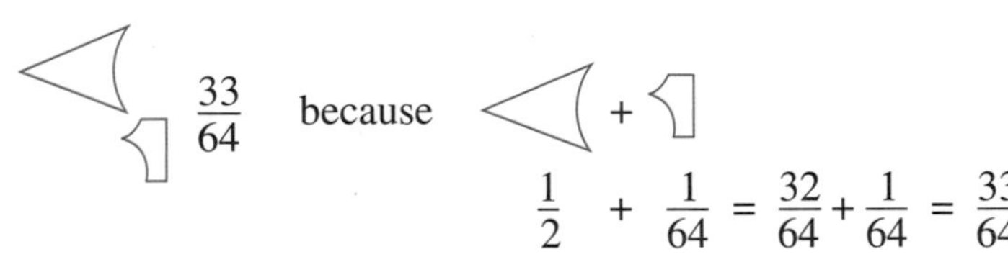

$\frac{33}{64}$ because

$$\frac{1}{2} + \frac{1}{64} = \frac{32}{64} + \frac{1}{64} = \frac{33}{64}$$

$\frac{9}{32}$ because

$$\frac{1}{4} + \frac{1}{32} = \frac{8}{32} + \frac{1}{32} = \frac{9}{32}$$

Exercise

1 Work out the value of each of these fractions.

(a) (b)

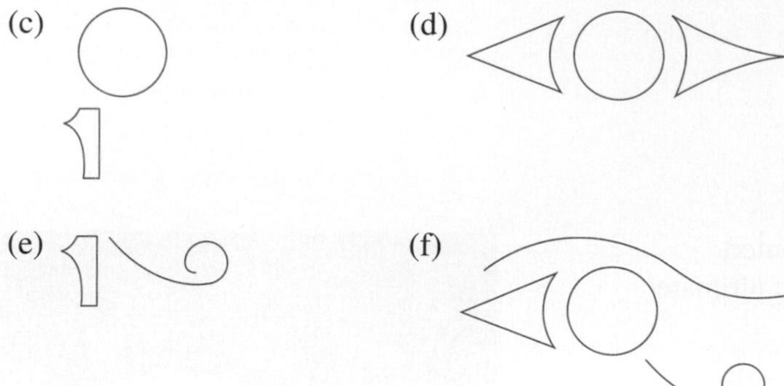

2 Use the symbols from the eye of Horus to show the following fractions.

(a) $\frac{1}{16}$ (b) $\frac{3}{16}$ (c) $\frac{3}{4}$ (d) $\frac{7}{8}$

3 (a) What is the total of all the fractions in the eye of Horus?

(b) What extra fraction is needed to make the total equal to 1?

4 **RESEARCH:**

(a) Find out more about the god Horus.

(b) Find out how the Egyptians represented the fraction $\frac{1}{3}$.

(c) What system did the Egyptians use to multiply numbers?

UNIT 2

2.1 Written calculations

In section 2.1 you will:

- review paper and pencil calculations with whole numbers and decimals
- practise reading number scales
- learn to multiply by decimal numbers
- learn to divide by decimal numbers

(a) $453 - 26$

$$\begin{array}{r} 4\,\overset{4}{\cancel{5}}\,{}^{1}3 \\ -\ \ 2\,6 \\ \hline 4\,2\,7 \end{array}$$

(b) 305×8

$$\begin{array}{r} 3\,0\,5 \\ \times\ \ \ 8 \\ \hline 2\,4\,4\,0 \end{array}$$

(c) $18 - 7.2$

$$\begin{array}{r} 1\,\overset{7}{\cancel{8}}.\,{}^{1}0 \\ -\ 7.\,2 \\ \hline 1\,0.\,8 \end{array}$$

(d) $93.8 \div 7$

$$\begin{array}{r} 1\ \ 3\,.\,4 \\ 7\,\overline{)\,9\ {}^{2}3\,.\,{}^{2}8} \end{array}$$

(e) $32.9 \div 100$

$= 0.329$

(f) 24×300

$= 24 \times 3 \times 100$

$= 7200$

Exercise 1M

Work out, without a calculator

1. $607 + 848$
2. $6275 + 49$
3. $2900 - 1484$
4. 5.25×1000
5. 217×6
6. 0.93×9
7. 214×8
8. 315×7
9. $0.6 \times 100\,000$
10. $0.72 - 0.067$
11. 17×1000
12. 5.62×10
13. 73×40
14. $5.48 \div 4$
15. $8.3 \div 10$
16. $219 \div 1000$

17 14 490 ÷ 3

18 26 × 300

19 124 × 200

20 5184 + 2787

21 0.0924 ÷ 2

22 284 + 19 + 564

23 316 × 5

24 56 000 ÷ 20

25 19.2 – 5.8

26 11 + 5.2 – 8.4

27 173 × 8

28 868 ÷ 7

29 98.7 ÷ 7

30 0.38 – 0.252

31 73.2 ÷ 100

32 5.1 × 100

Exercise 1E

1 I think of a number. If I add 5 and then multiply the result by 10 the answer is 67. What number was I thinking of?

2 Tom and three of his friends go to see a film. The tickets cost £23 altogether. How much does each person pay?

3 Ordinary pencils cost 35p but a special 'knotted' pencil costs £1.50. Cherie buys eleven ordinary pencils and five knotted pencils. How much change does she get from £20?

4 How many of the 'knotted' pencils in question **3** could you buy with £100?

Work out

5 42 + 0.72 + 5.3

6 5.48 ÷ 4

7 2900 – 1573

8 0.95 × 9

9 14490 ÷ 6

10 4000 – 264

11 5.24 × 0.5

12 8.52 ÷ 4

13 52 × 100

14 234 + 23.4

15 0.612 ÷ 6

16 5.2 × 2000

17 0.0924 ÷ 4

18 0.72 – 0.065

19 73 × 30

20 5.7 ÷ 100

21 Write as a decimal fraction what fraction of each shape is coloured.

(a)

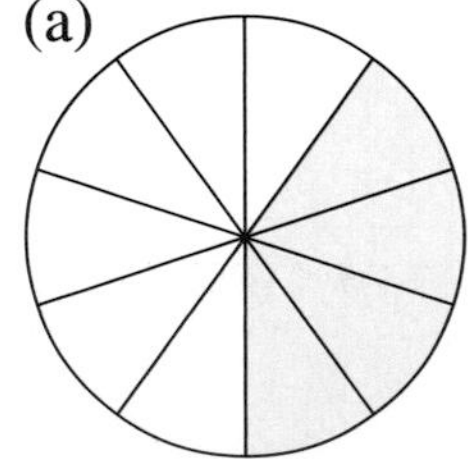

(b)

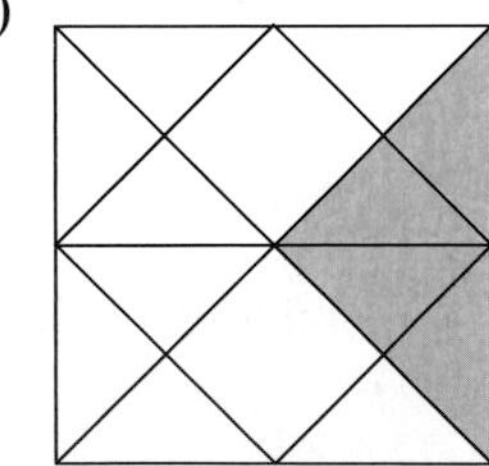

22 Copy and complete.

(a) 35.8 ÷ ☐ = 0.358

(b) ☐ + 1.4 = 7.63

(c) ☐ – 0.35 = 0.08

(d) 14 × ☐ = 2800

(e) 0.67 ÷ 100 = ☐

(f) 8 – ☐ = 2.62

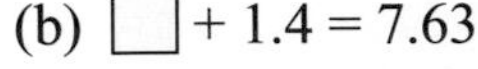

Scale reading and place value

Exercise 2M

For each of the scales work out the measurement shown by each arrow.

1

2
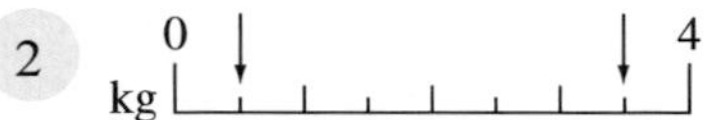

3 10 50 kg

4 0.6 0.7 m

5 0.5 1.0 m

6 9 13 kg

7 40 60 g

8 0.21 0.22 kg

9
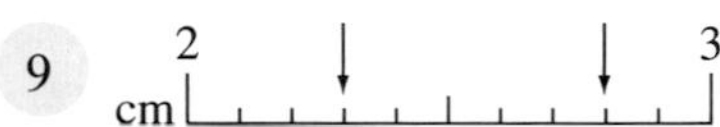

10
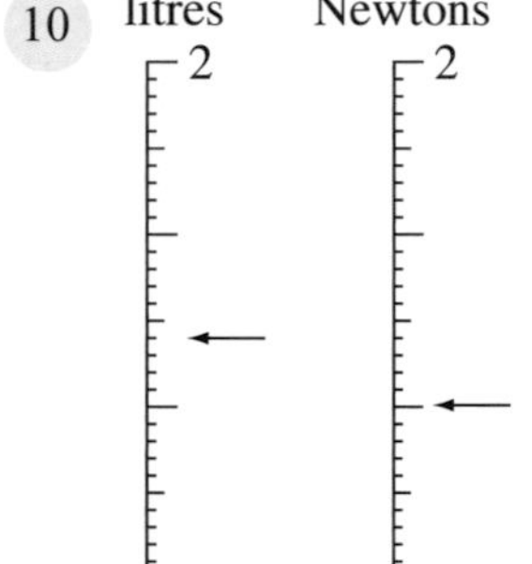

11
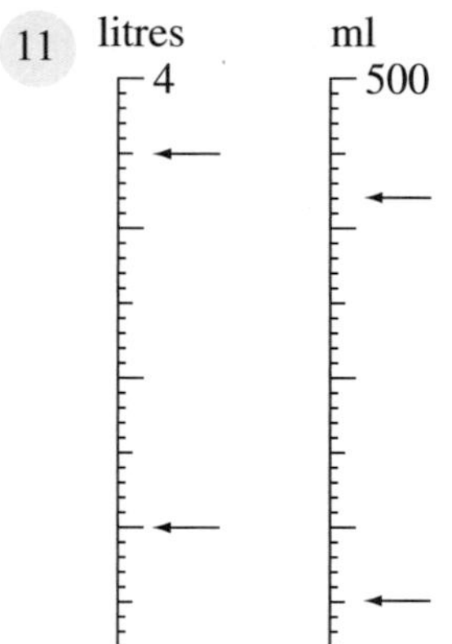

12
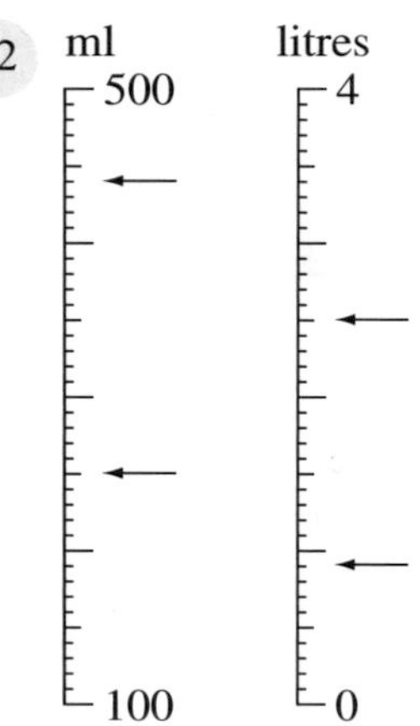

13

14

15
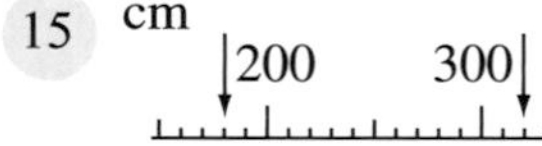

16 kg 1 2

17
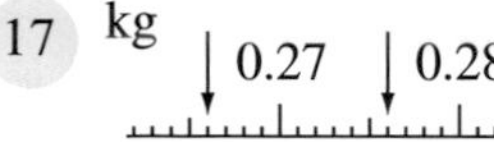

18 kg 0.9 1.0

19 6 10

20
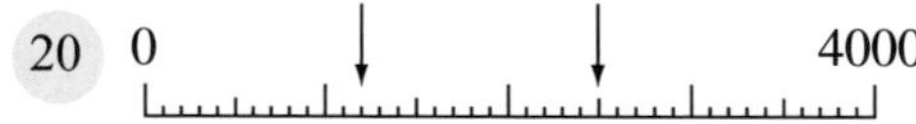

21 Copy the line and locate the numbers.

2.03 2.05 1.95 1.97 2.07

1.9 2.1

22 Copy the line and locate the numbers.

1.98 1.935 1.915 1.94

1.9 2.0

Write 1.41, 1.4, 1.141, 1 in ascending order.

Write in column.	Put in zeros.	Arrange in Order.
1.41	1.410	1
1.4	1.400	1.141
1.141	1.141	1.4
1	1.000	1.41

Exercise 2E

1. Arrange in order of size, smallest first.
   (a) 0.73, 0.718, 0.7 (b) 0.405, 0.5, 0.41
   (c) 0.3, 0.035, 0.029 (d) 0.06, 0.058, 0.0511

2. Write the number half way between:
   (a) 0.2 and 0.8 (b) 0.4 and 0.5 (c) 0.02 and 0.08
   (d) 0.1 and 0.2 (e) 0.06 and 0.07

3. Write each statement with either >, < or = in the space.
   (a) 0.032 □ 0.004 (b) 0.728 □ 0.73 (c) 0.3 cm □ 3mm
   (d) 0.005 □ 0.0006 (e) 0.6 m □ 55 cm (f) 0.09 □ 0.1

4. (a) What is 0.01 more than 3.29?
   (b) What is 0.001 more than 0.628?
   (c) What is 0.01 less than 6.4?
   (d) What is 0.001 less than 0.426?

5. Copy each sequence and fill in the spaces.
   (a) 2.67, 2.68, 2.69 □, □ (b) 1.52, 1.51, 1.5, □, □
   (c) 3.6, 3.8, 4, □, □ (d) □, 5, 5.01, 5.02, □

6. What has to be added or subtracted to change:
   (a) 3.24 to 3.26 (b) 0.714 to 0.712
   (c) 0.142 to 0.152 (d) 0.599 to 0.6?

7. Arrange in order of size, smallest first.
   (a) 0.002 km, 30 cm, 4.1 m, 180 mm, 0.00035 km
   (b) 585 mm, 0.62 m, 118 cm, 0.008 km, 50 000 mm

Multiplying by 0.1 and 0.01

- Multiplying by 0.1 is the same as dividing by 10. Eg. $5 \times 0.1 = 5 \div 10 = 0.5$
- Multiplying by 0.01 is the same as dividing by 100. Eg. $4 \times 0.01 = 4 \div 100 = 0.04$

Exercise 3M

Work out

1 8×0.1	2 3×0.1	3 12×0.1	4 26×0.1
5 0.4×0.1	6 0.7×0.1	7 0.9×0.1	8 0.24×0.1
9 8×0.01	10 6×0.01	11 15×0.01	12 7×0.01
13 52×0.01	14 63×0.01	15 0.6×0.001	16 5.2×0.01
17 11×0.1	18 9×0.1	19 23×0.01	20 0.5×0.1

21 Copy each chain of numbers and fill in the empty boxes with the correct operation.

(a) 3.6 → ☐ → 360 → ☐ → 0.36 → ☐ → 3.6 → ☐ → 0.036

(b) 670 → ☐ → 67 → ☐ → 6.7 → ☐ → 670 → ☐ → 6.7

(c) 83.2 → ☐ → 8320 → ☐ → 832 → ☐ → 8.32 → ☐ → 0.832

(d) 5 → ☐ → 0.05 → ☐ → 0.005 → ☐ → 50 → ☐ → 0.5

Multiplying decimal numbers

5×0.3 is the same as $5 \times \frac{3}{10}$. Work out $(5 \times 3) \div 10 = 15 \div 10 = 1.5$

4.2×0.2 is the same as $4.2 \times \frac{2}{10}$. Work out $(4.2 \times 2) \div 10 = 8.4 \div 10 = 0.84$

21.4×0.05 is the same as $21.4 \times \frac{5}{100}$. Work out $(21.4 \times 5) \div 100 = 107 \div 100 = 1.07$

Here is a final check:
When we multiply two decimal numbers together, the answer has the same number of figures to the right of the decimal point as the total number of figures to the right of the decimal point in the question.

Examples:

(a) 0.3×0.4

$(3 \times 4 = 12)$

So $0.3 \times 0.4 = 0.12$

(b) 0.7×0.05

$(7 \times 5 = 35)$

So $0.7 \times 0.05 = 0.035$

Exercise 3E

1	17 × 0.2	2	8 × 0.3	3	12 × 0.2	4	5 × 0.03
5	0.7 × 3	6	23 × 0.02	7	0.9 × 0.5	8	6 × 0.06
9	12 × 0.05	10	0.7 × 0.7	11	8 × 0.1	12	14 × 0.3
13	15 × 0.03	14	0.4 × 0.04	15	0.001 × 0.6	16	33 × 0.02
17	1.2 × 0.3	18	3.2 × 0.2	19	1.4 × 0.4	20	2.1 × 0.5
21	3.61 × 0.3	22	2.1 × 0.6	23	0.31 × 0.7	24	0.42 × 0.02
25	0.33 × 0.02	26	3.24 × 0.01	27	8.11 × 0.07	28	16.2 × 0.8
29	5.06 × 0.05	30	30.9 × 0.3	31	0.22	32	0.42

33

You are given that £1 = $1.95 and £1 = €1.25

(a) How many euros do you get for £40?

(b) How many dollars do you get for €50?

(c) How many dollars do you get for €1000?

34 Copy and complete.

(a) 0.6 × 3 = ▭ (b) 0.7 × ▭ = 4.2

(c) ▭ × 0.6 = 0.18 (d) 265 ÷ ▭ = 2.65

(e) ▭ × 0.03 = 0.066 (f) $▭^2$ = 0.0009

12.2 × 27 is approximately 10 × 30 = 300

12.2 × 27 = (12.2 × 10 × 27) ÷ 10
= (122 × 27) ÷ 10

```
              277
            × 27
122 × 20     2440
122 × 7       854
             3294
```

Answer: 3294 ÷ 10 = 329.4

18.4 × 3.2 is approximately 20 × 3 = 60

18.4 × 3.2 = (18.4 × 10 × 3.2 × 10) ÷ 100
= (184 × 32) ÷ 100

```
              184
            × 32
184 × 30     5520
184 × 2       368
             5888
```

Answer: 5888 ÷ 100 = 58.88

Exercise 4M

Work out, after finding an approximate answer first.

1 6.2×2.1
2 5.3×32
3 4.7×15
4 3.8×17
5 11.4×15
6 21.4×21
7 15.2×13
8 23.6×25
9 2.3×1.2
10 3.5×1.5
11 4.3×2.3
12 2.4×1.8
13 13.2×1.4
14 14.5×3.3
15 21.2×2.4
16 31.5×1.5
17 35.6×1.9
18 42.3×2.7
19 8.64×4.7
20 0.332×42
21 0.32×5.6
22 1.52×1.7
23 0.35×0.13
24 0.51×0.24

Dividing by 0.1 and 0.01

- $1 \div 0.1 = 1 \div \frac{1}{10} \ldots$ How many $\frac{1}{10}$s are there in 1? Answer: 10

  $7 \div 0.1 = 7 \div \frac{1}{10} \ldots$ How many $\frac{1}{10}$s are there in 7? Answer: 70

  $13 \div 0.01 = 13 \div \frac{1}{100} \ldots$ How many $\frac{1}{100}$s are there in 13? Answer: 1300

- We see that: dividing by 0.1 is the same as multiplying by 10,
  dividing by 0.01 is the same as multiplying by 100.

$3 \div 0.1 = 3 \times 10$
$= 30$

$14 \div 0.1 = 14 \times 10$
$= 140$

$7 \div 0.01 = 7 \times 100$
$= 700$

Exercise 5M

1 $5 \div 0.1$
2 $9 \div 0.1$
3 $11 \div 0.1$
4 $6 \div 0.1$
5 $32 \div 0.1$
6 $0.7 \div 0.1$
7 $0.9 \div 0.1$
8 $1.3 \div 0.1$
9 $3 \div 0.01$
10 $11 \div 0.01$
11 $4 \div 0.01$
12 $0.3 \div 0.01$
13 $0.8 \div 0.01$
14 $57 \div 0.01$
15 $1.9 \div 0.01$
16 $0.42 \div 0.01$

17 Find the missing numbers

(a) $12 \div 0.1 = \square$
(b) $7 \div \square = 70$
(c) $3 \div \square = 300$
(d) $\square \div 0.1 = 20$
(e) $1.2 \div 0.01 = \square$
(f) $1.7 \div \square = 17$

18 Copy each chain of numbers and fill in the boxes with *divisions*.

(a) 5.2 → ☐ → 52 → ☐ → 0.52 → ☐ → 520 → ☐ → 5200

(b) 640 → ☐ → 6.4 → ☐ → 64 → ☐ → 0.64 → ☐ → 64

(c) 0.7 → ☐ → 7 → ☐ → 700 → ☐ → 70 → ☐ → 0.07

(d) 130 → ☐ → 13000 → ☐ → 1300 → ☐ → 1.3 → ☐ → 130

19 (a) Write 10 pence in pounds as a decimal.

(b) Write 1 penny in pounds as a decimal.

(c) How many 10ps are there in £12.70?

(d) How many 1ps are there in £8.05?

Dividing by any decimal number

To divide by any decimal number we transform the calculation into a division by a *whole number*.

Examples $3.6 \div 0.2 = 36 \div 2 = 18$ [Multiply 3.6 and 0.2 by 10.]

$1.5 \div 0.03 = 150 \div 3 = 50$ [Multiply 1.5 and 0.03 by 100.]

Since both numbers are multiplied by 10 or 100 the answer is not changed.

Exercise 5E

Work out, without a calculator

1 $1.46 \div 0.2$
2 $2.52 \div 0.4$
3 $0.942 \div 0.3$
4 $0.712 \div 0.2$
5 $0.375 \div 0.5$
6 $0.522 \div 0.6$
7 $6.54 \div 0.2$
8 $1.944 \div 0.6$
9 $0.1368 \div 0.04$
10 $0.228 \div 0.04$
11 $0.498 \div 0.06$
12 $5.04 \div 0.7$
13 $3.744 \div 0.09$
14 $0.1685 \div 0.005$
15 $0.2846 \div 0.2$
16 $0.0585 \div 0.09$
17 $0.0257 \div 0.005$
18 $1.872 \div 0.08$
19 $0.268 \div 0.4$
20 $0.39 \div 0.006$
21 $0.42 \div 0.03$
22 $7.041 \div 0.01$
23 $0.1638 \div 0.001$
24 $15.33 \div 0.07$
25 $0.993 \div 0.3$
26 $1.05 \div 0.6$
27 $8.4 \div 0.02$
28 $7.52 \div 0.4$
29 $4.006 \div 0.002$
30 $17.4 \div 0.2$
31 $54 \div 0.3$
32 $32 \div 0.4$

33 A bottle of water contains 1 litre. How many glasses can be filled from this box if each glass holds 0.2 litres?

34 Asda sell 200g of red currants for £1.75.
An average red currant weighs 0.8 g.
(a) How many red currants are there in a 200 g pack?
(b) Work out the cost of one red currant.

35 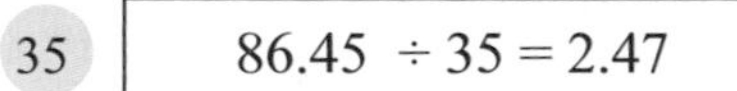
86.45 ÷ 35 = 2.47

Use the calculation above to work out:

(a) 864.5 ÷ 35 (b) 0.8645 ÷ 35
(c) 86.45 ÷ 3.5 (d) 864.5 ÷ 0.35

Exercise 6E

(a) Start in the top left box.
(b) Work out the answer to the calculation in the box.
(c) Find the answer in the top corner of another box.
(d) Write down the letter in that box.
(e) Repeat steps (b), (c) and (d) until you arrive back at the top left box. What is the message?

START

- 10000 — 5×25
- 9 — E — 260×0.01
- 1.25 — T — $\sqrt{400}$
- 2.5 — I — 0.16×100
- 0.55 — N — 1% of 10^6
- 180 — O — $2314 - 586$
- 20 — H — $17 - 3.6$
- 219 — M — $3133 \div 13$
- 1728 — N — $2.7 \div 0.3$
- 55 — N — $5^3 \times 0.01$
- 70.4 — O — $0.6 - \frac{1}{20}$
- 90 — Y — 0.6×0.7
- 0.42 — O — $385 \div 7$
- 125 — I — $3^3 + 3$
- 16 — S — $756 \div 9$
- 241 — O — 22×3.2
- 30 — T — 5% of 50
- 2.6 — L — $1.8 \div 0.02$
- 84 — L — $18 \div 0.1$
- 13.4 — E — $15.33 \div 0.07$

2.2 Estimating and checking answers

In section 2.2 you will:

- estimate the value of a calculation
- check answers to see that they are 'about the right size'
- round numbers to one or two decimal places

Estimating

(a) Look at the calculations

3×5, 3×50, 30×50, 30×500.

$3 \times 5 = 15$

$3 \times 50 = 150$

$30 \times 50 = 1500$

$30 \times 500 = 15000$

(b) Work out a rough estimate for 278×13

Instead of 278 use 300

Instead of 13 use 10

So 278×13 is roughly 300×10, which is 3000.

Exercise 1M

1 Work out.

(a) 40×2 (b) 40×20 (c) 40×2000 (d) 4×200

(e) 3×70 (f) 30×700 (g) 50×3 (h) 500×30

(i) 50×50 (j) 40×800 (k) 8×3000 (l) 90×20

2 Work out a rough estimate for the following.

(a) 11×48 (b) 22×19 (c) 708×2 (d) 96.2×21

(e) 976×2.9 (f) 97×3.04 (g) $197 \div 2$ (h) 611×0.106

3 Petrol costs €1.09 per litre in Spain.
Estimate the total cost of 48 litres.

4 We know that $48 \div 6 = 8$. Use this fact to work out the following

(a) $4.8 \div 8$ (b) $0.48 \div 8$

(c) 0.8×6 (d) 0.06×8

(e) $4.8 \div 6$ (f) $0.48 \div 6$

(g) 0.08×0.6 (h) $480000 \div 0.6$

5 Do not use a calculator Decide, by estimating, which of the three answers is closest to the exact answer. Write the calculation and the approximate answer for each question (use ≈).

	Calculation	A	B	C
(a)	97.9 × 11.3	90	500	1000
(b)	6.73 × 9.65	30	70	300
(c)	1.03 × 60.6	6	60	200
(d)	2.3 × 96	200	90	20
(e)	18.9 × 21.4	200	400	4000
(f)	5.14 × 5.99	15	10	30
(g)	811 × 11.72	8000	4000	800
(h)	99 × 98	1 million	100 000	10 000
(i)	1.09 × 29.6	20	30	60
(j)	81 413 × 10.96	8 million	1 million	800 000
(k)	601 ÷ 3.92	50	100	150
(l)	402 ÷ 4.97	8	0.8	80
(m)	58.4 ÷ 0.98	60	300	600
(n)	0.2 × 111.3	10	20	180
(o)	217 ÷ 201.4	0.2	1	10
(p)	88.4 + 95 + 141	300	100	3000
(q)	9.83% of (2567.3 + 1.92)	250	400	2500
(r)	$\frac{1}{5}$ of (20.27 × 20.11)	16	80	160
(s)	$\frac{9}{19}$ of 1% of 6060	30	60	300
(t)	$\frac{2}{3}$ of 24.8% of $\frac{1}{2}$ of 2403.62	20	200	2000

6 Answer true or false (the sign ≈ means 'is roughly equal to').

(a) 27.8 × 3.2
= 30 × 3
= 90

(b) 904 × 23
= 900 × 20
= 180 000

(c) 4267 ÷ 38
= 4000 ÷ 40
= 100

7

What's in the boot, then?

A MOTORIST who was stopped for a routine police check in Colchester, Essex, was found to be wearing Wellington boots filled with baked beans in tomato sauce.

Officers warned him to choose more suitable footwear.

(a) Estimate the number of tins required to fill a pair of Wellington boots.

(b) A tin of Heinz baked beans costs 49p. Estimate the cost of the beans needed to fill the boots.

Exercise 1E

Do not use a calculator for these questions.

1 Ten elastic bands weigh 11 grams. Estimate the weight of a ball containing 985 elastic bands.

2 Daily disposable contact lenses cost 96p per pair. Find the approximate cost of 2 years supply of lenses.

3 A cut-price video was sold at £6.95 per copy. Estimate the total cost of 42 copies.

4 The rent for a flat is £95 per week. Estimate the total spent on rent in one year.

5 2105 people share the cost of hiring a cruise boat. Roughly how much does each person pay, if the total cost was half a million pounds?

6 A boxer earned a fee of $5 million for a fight which lasted 1 minute 35 seconds. Estimate the money he earned per second of the fight.

In questions 7 and 8 there are six calculations and six answers. Write down each calculation and insert the correct answer from the list given. Use estimation.

7 (a) 5.9×6.1 (b) $19.8 \div 5$ (c) 32×9.9

(d) $0.89 + 14.7$ (e) 4.5×44 (f) $4141 \div 40$

Answers:	198, 35.99, 103.5, 15.59, 316.8, 3.96

8 (a) $102.8 \div 5$ (b) $11.2 \div 98.6$ (c) 3×0.41

(d) 34×2.9 (e) 51×3.9 (f) $238.6 \div 4.7$

Answers:	50.76, 20.56, 1.23, 198.9, 98.6, 0.114

9 Write the decimal point in the correct place.

(a) length of a football pitch 9572 m

(b) weight of an 'average' new born baby 3124 kg

(c) width of this book 1831 mm

(d) area of the classroom floor 560 m^2

(e) weight of a packet of sugar 100 kg

(f) diameter of a football 3140 cm

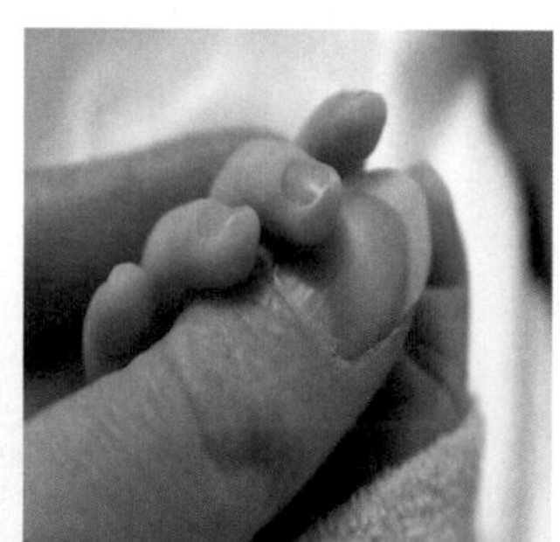

10 At a fun fair, customers pay 95p for a ride on a giant spinning wheel. The operator sells 2483 tickets during the weekend and his costs for electricity and rent were £114. Estimate his profit over the weekend.

11 A quick way of adding lots of figures on a shopping bill is to round every number to the nearest pound.

So £2.43 becomes £2, £0.91 becomes £1, £0.24 becomes £0 and so on.

(a) Use this method to estimate the totals below:

(i)	WSKAS COCKTAIL	0.85	(ii)	PLN BAGUETTE	0.49
	H/EATING MINCE	3.95		FOIL	0.65
	HAWAIIAN CRN	1.85		LETTUCE ROUND	0.24
	PAIN AU CHOC	0.54		JW TUNA MAYO	0.75
	PAIN AU CHOC	0.54		SOYA MILK	0.47
	PAIN AU CHOC	0.54		SOYA MILK	0.47
	BUTTER	0.89		ORNGE MRMLDE	0.74
	BUTTER	0.89		YOGHURT	0.99
	EGGS	0.78		SPGHTI/HOOPS	0.26
	PORK/CHICK/PIE	2.03		CHEESE	1.34
	MED.MAT.CHDR.	1.21		WHISKAS	0.45
	HOT PIES	1.47		WHISKAS	0.45
	POT. WAFFLES	1.39		VINEGAR	0.68
	WHOLE BRIE	1.01		KING EDWARDS.	0.99
	MUFFINS	0.49		UHT H/FAT MILK	0.26
	BACON RASHERS	0.65		APPLES	1.89
	BEETROOT	0.99		WHISKAS	0.45
	LOOSE CHEESE	0.99		PEACHES	0.24
	LASAGNE	3.29		FROM. FRAIS	0.72
	PINEAPPLE JUICE	1.99		WINE	3.55
	EGGS	0.95		LAMB LEG	4.45
	CURRY PASTE	1.49		SALT	0.89
	LETTUCE	0.99		SAUSAGES	1.75
	AVOCADO	1.68		PIZZA	2.79

(b) Use a calculator to work out the exact total for part (i). Compare the answer with your estimate above.

12 (a) In 1989 thousands of people formed a human chain right across U.S.A., a distance of about 4300 km. Estimate the number of people in the chain.

(b) Estimate the number of people needed to form a chain right around the equator. (Assume you have enough people volunteering to float for a while in the sea.) The distance right around the equator is about 40 000 km.

13 Estimate:

(a) the number of times your heart beats in one day (24 h),

(b) the thickness of one page in this book.

14 Give an estimate for each of the following calculations

(a) $\frac{62.4 \times 19.3}{10.7}$ (b) $\frac{3198 - 207}{93.7}$ (c) 52% of £987.50

(d) $30.23^2 - 112$ (e) $\frac{2}{3}$ of 589 m (f) $\frac{407.5 + 2.794}{15.6 + 24.7}$

Checking answers

Here are five calculations followed by appropriate checks, using inverse operations.

(a) $22.5 \div 5 = 4.5$ check $4.5 \times 5 = 22.5$

(b) $29.5 - 1.47 = 28.03$ check $28.03 + 1.47$

(c) $78.5 \times 20 = 1570$ check $1570 \div 20$

(d) $\sqrt{11} = 3.31662$ check 3.31662^2

(e) $14.7 + 28.1 + 17.4 + 9.9$ check $9.9 + 17.4 + 28.1 + 14.7$
[add in reverse order]

Exercise 2M

1 Work out the following and check using inverse operations

(a) $83.5 \times 20 = \square$ check $\square \div 20$

(b) $104 - 13.2 = \square$ check $\square + 13.2$

(c) $228.2 \div 7 = \square$ check $\square \times 7$

(d) $\sqrt{28} = \square$ check $\square^2$

(e) $11.5 + 2.7 + 9.8 + 20.7$ check $20.7 + 9.8 + 2.7 + 11.5$

2 (a) Will the answer to 64×0.8 be larger or smaller than 64?

(b) Will the answer to $210 \div 0.7$ be larger or smaller than 210?

(c) Will the answer to 17.4×0.9 be larger or smaller than 17.4?

3 Copy and complete with either $>$ or $<$ in the boxes.

(a) 520×1.02 ☐ 520

(b) 18.6×0.83 ☐ 18.6

(c) $27 \div 1.4$ ☐ 27

(d) $85 \div 0.92$ ☐ 85

4 Here are the answers obtained by six children. Some are correct but some are clearly impossible or highly unlikely.

Decide which answers are 'OK' and which are 'impossible' or 'highly unlikely'.

(a) Top speed of winning snail = 10 m/sec

(b) Time taken to walk 1 mile to school = 21 minutes

(c) The height of Mrs Brown's washing machine = 315 cm

(d) Number of bricks needed to build a 2 bedroom house = 1 million

(e) The mean value of the numbers 32, 35, 31, 36, 32 = 37.8

(f) One per cent of the UK population = 60 000 people.

5

Some time ago a rather aggressive shark attacked a house in Oxford. Estimate the following.

(a) The length of the shark.

(b) The cost of repairing the damage to the house.

(c) How far the shark jumped from the sea to strike the house.

Rounding off

- Using a calculator, $\sqrt{11} = 3.3166248$

  We can *round off* this number to either 1 or 2 decimal places.

- Rounding to one decimal place.
  If the figure in the 2nd decimal place is *5 or more*, round up. Otherwise do not

  2.761 = 2.8 to 1 d.p.
  ↑

  13.45 = 13.5 to 1 d.p.
  ↑

  0.337 = 0.3 to 1 d.p.
  ↑

- Rounding to two decimal places.
  If the figure in the 3rd decimal place is *5 or more*, round up. Otherwise do not.

  1.4281 = 1.43 to 2 d.p.
  ↑

  0.0742 = 0.07 to 2 d.p.
  ↑

  8.555 = 8.56 to 2 d.p.
  ↑

Exercise 2E

1 Round off these numbers correct to one decimal place.

(a) 8.24 (b) 7.166 (c) 0.762 (d) 11.27
(e) 0.352 (f) 8.741 (g) 11.518 (h) 0.648

2 Round off these numbers correct to two decimal places.

(a) 1.246 (b) 8.043 (c) 11.222 (d) 3.084
(e) 0.1355 (f) 22.456 (g) 0.8592 (h) 6.097

3 Work out these answers on a calculator and then round off the answers correct to two decimal places.

(a) $11.21 \div 7$ (b) 0.54×8.1 (c) $4216 \div 214$ (d) 12.6×0.071
(e) $\sqrt{13}$ (f) $\sqrt{8.5}$ (g) 1.36^2 (h) 0.97^2
(i) 0.77×0.78 (j) $11.82 \div 13$ (k) 2.4×0.716 (l) $\sqrt{(4.2 \times 3.5)}$

4 

Measure the height and width of this photo. Work out the area and give your answer in cm^2 correct to one decimal place.

5 Round off these numbers to the nearest hundred.

(a) 1741 (b) 22 483 (c) 807.1 (d) 15 255
(e) 562.8 (f) 2222 (g) 3552 (h) 1027

6 Work out these answers on a calculator and then round off the answers to the nearest whole number.

(a) $618 \div 24$ (b) 1.4×1.99 (c) $2384 \div 111$ (d) 12.7×0.78

(e) $\sqrt{69.7}$ (f) $\frac{8.4 + 7.21}{3.2}$ (g) $\frac{11.6}{3.4} + 14$ (h) $\frac{\sqrt{77}}{9} + 11.7$

(i) $\frac{7 \times 0.7 \times 13}{4.7}$ (j) $\frac{8.4}{11} + \frac{4.21}{0.5}$ (k) $\frac{8.06 - 1.7}{\sqrt{3.3}}$ (l) $0.6 \div 0.023$

Estimating game

- This is a game for two players. On squared paper draw an answer grid with the numbers shown.

  Answer grid

198	1089	99	100	360	18
180	450	22	440	155	1980
1240	200	45	62	100	550
40	620	495	279	800	55
2000	80	220	10	891	250
4950	1550	1000	3960	3069	341

- The players now take turns to choose two numbers from the question grid below and multiply them on a calculator.

  Question grid

2	5	9
11	20	31
40	50	99

  The number obtained is crossed out on the answer grid using the player's own colour.

- The game continues until all the numbers in the answer grid have been crossed out. The object is to get four answers in a line (horizontally, vertically or diagonally). The winner is the player with most line of four.
- A line of *five* counts as *two* lines of four.

  A line of *six* counts as *three* lines of four.

CHECK YOURSELF ON SECTIONS 2.1 AND 2.2

1 Written calculations

Work out, without a calculator.

(a) 185×8 (b) $0.082 + 17 + 5.09$ (c) $4466 \div 7$ (d) $10^4 - 2387$ (e) $0.81 \div 5$

2 Multiplying and dividing by decimals

Work out.

(a) 19×0.1 (b) 7×0.01 (c) $1.2 \div 0.1$ (d) $8.64 \div 0.4$
(e) 0.32×0.03 (f) $(5.6 \times 0.2) \div 0.05$

3 Estimating and rounding off

(a) Work out an estimate for the following.

(i) 12×79 (ii) 611×1.92 (iii) $396 \div 1.97$ (iv) $\frac{61 \times 28.5}{10.55}$

(v) 74% of £801 (vi) $\sqrt{1010}$

(b) Estimate the length of the Great Wall of China.
Give your answer in kilometres.

(c) Round off to one decimal place.

(i) 16.37 (ii) 8.455 (iii) 0.339

2.3 Geometrical reasoning

In section 2.3 you will learn how to:

- find angles using a wide range of angle properties
- prove results in geometry

Triangles, quadrilaterals and parallel lines

Reminders

b
c
a
d

$a + b + c + d = 360°$

b
a

$a = b$ (corresponding angles)

q
p

$p = q$ (alternate angles)

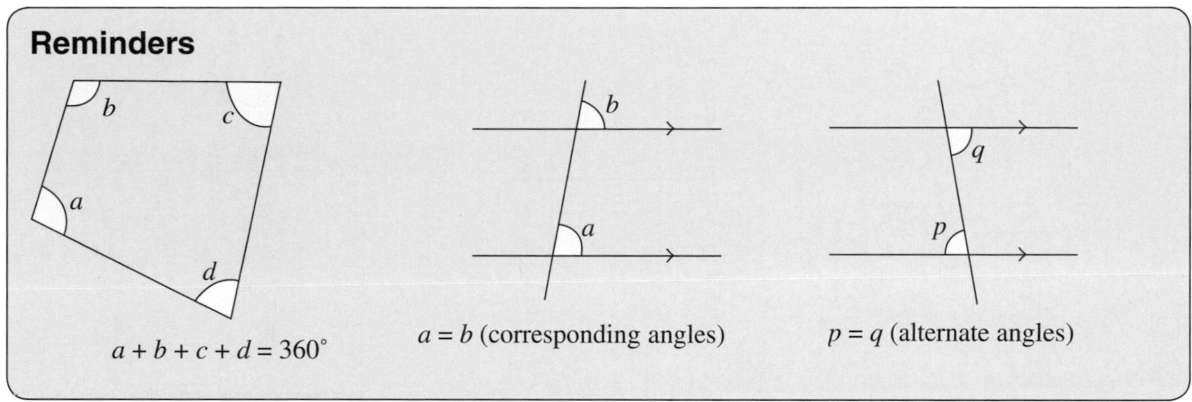

Exercise 1M

This exercise contains a mixture of questions which require a knowledge of all parts of this section.

Find the angles marked with letters.

1

74°
42°
a

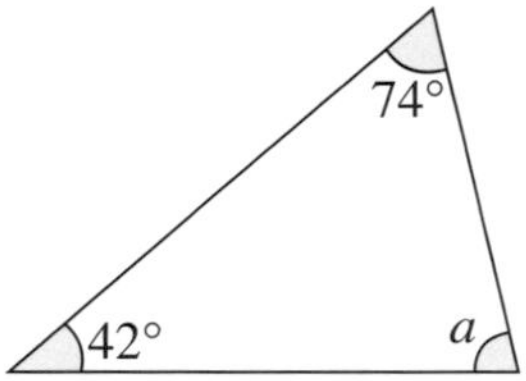

2

b
44°
51°

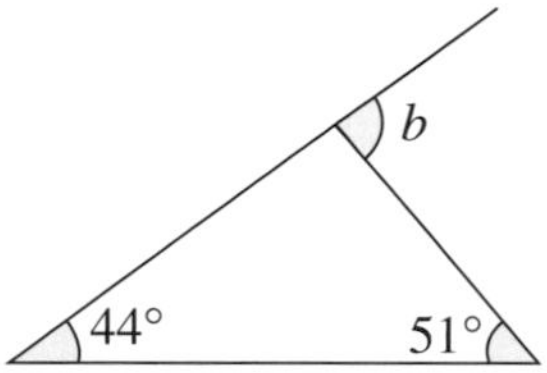

3

65°
c

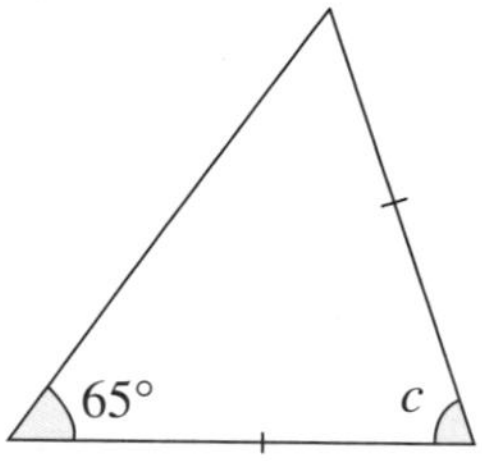

4

e
d
85°

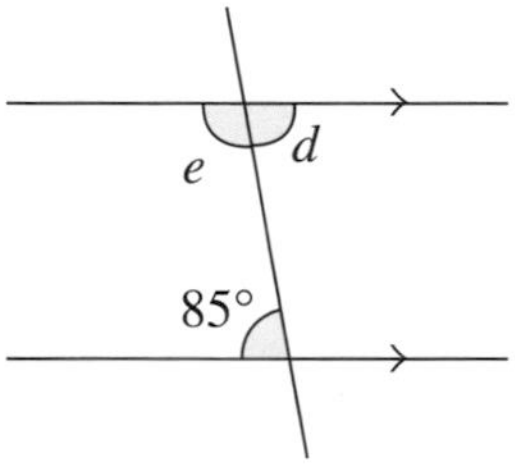

5

a
100°
82°
b

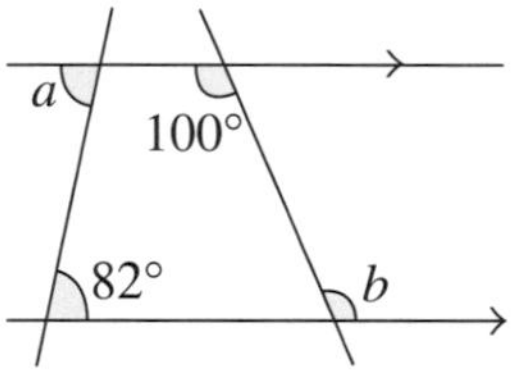

6

114°
c

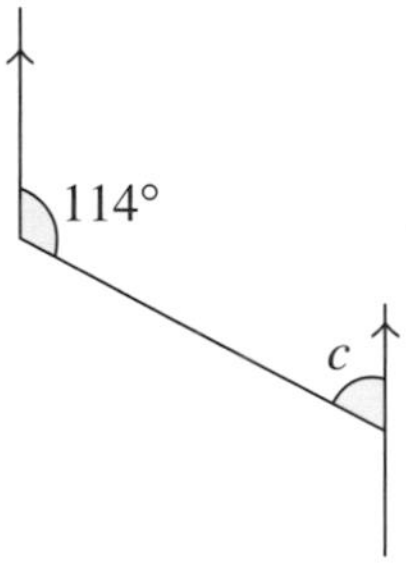

7

120°
x
x
x

8

Q
b
b
40°
P
b
b
b

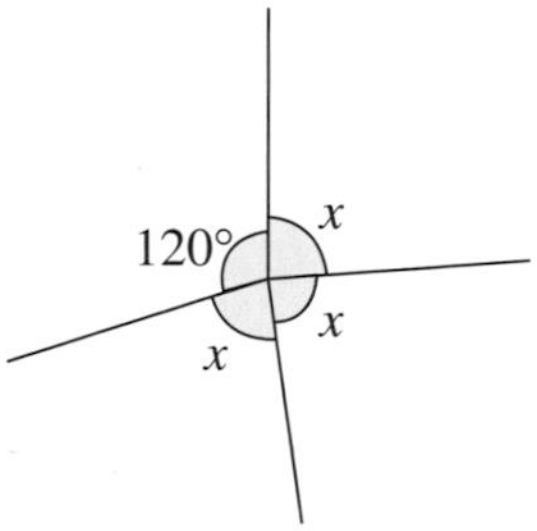

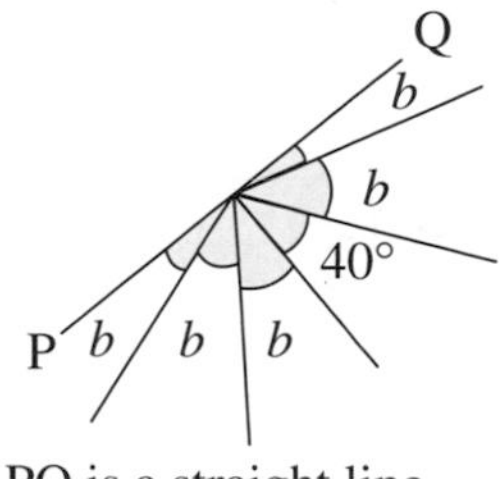

PQ is a straight line

9

90°
108°
y
94°

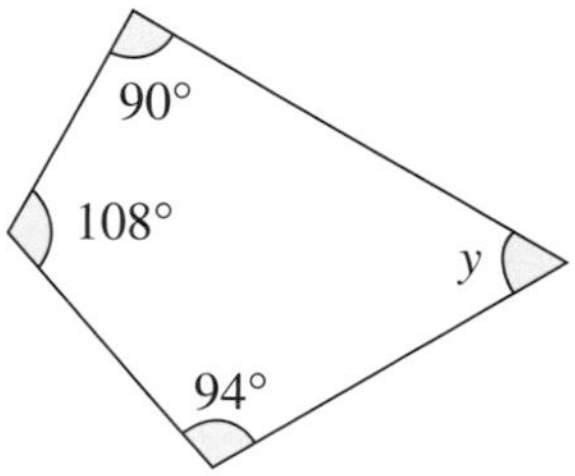

Find the angles marked with letters. Draw each diagram and show your working.

10
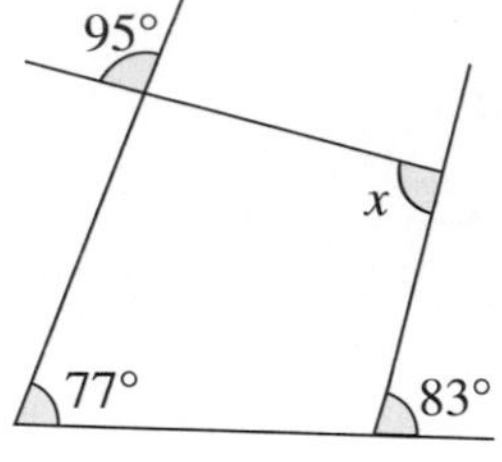

11
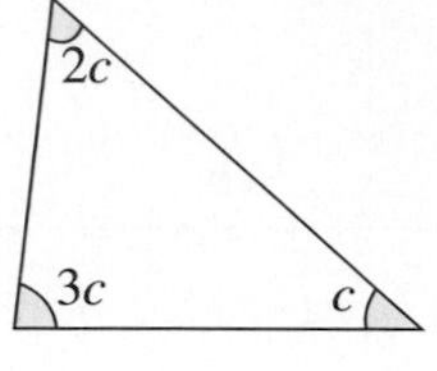

12
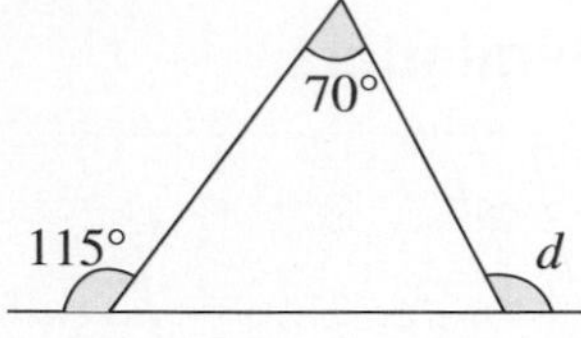

13
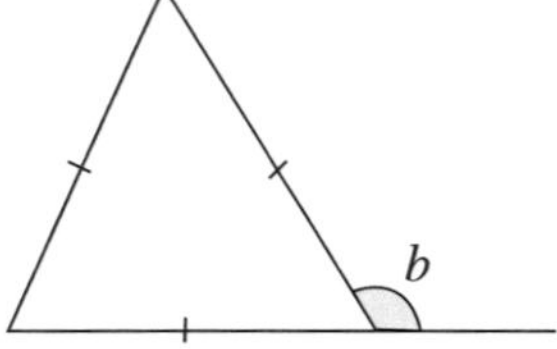

14
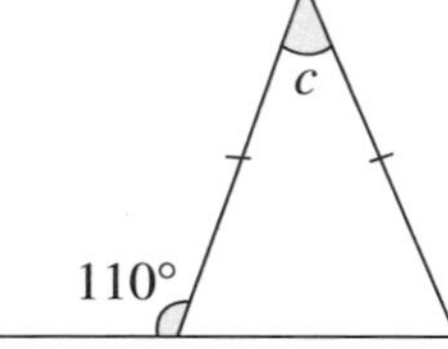

15
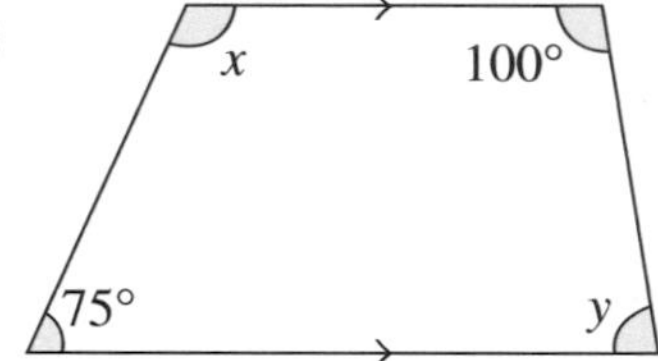

16
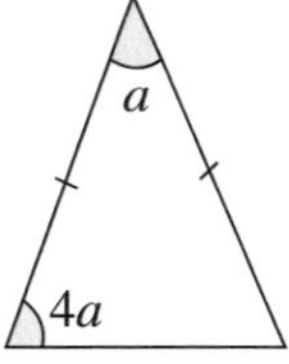

17
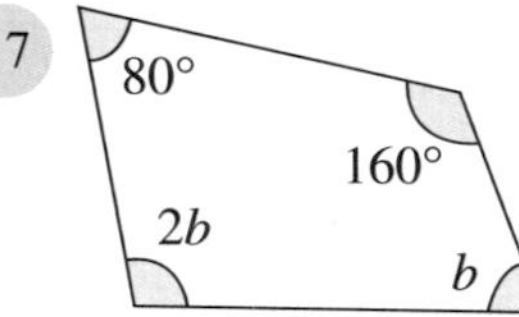

18
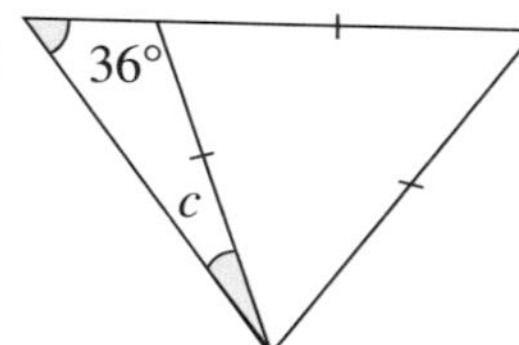

19
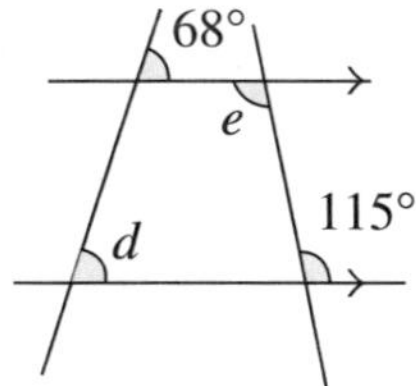

20
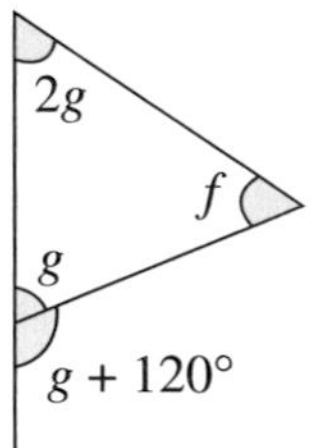

21
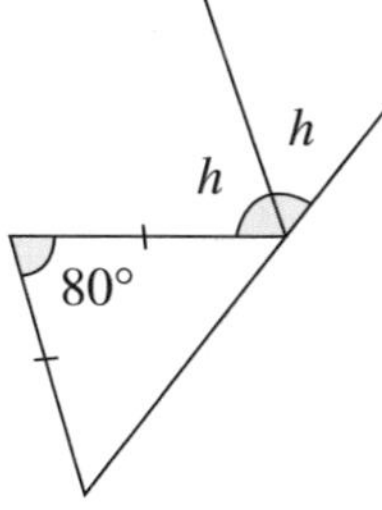

22
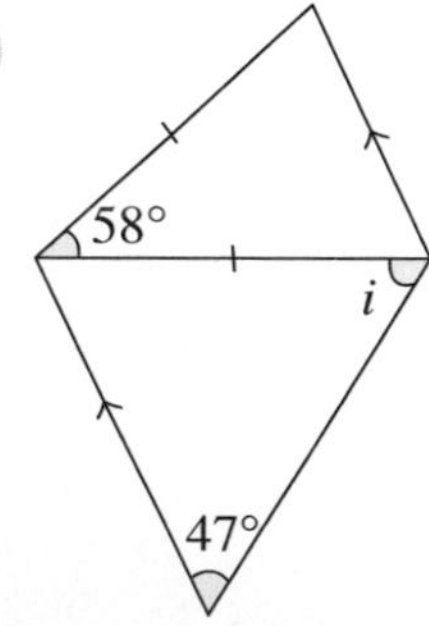

23
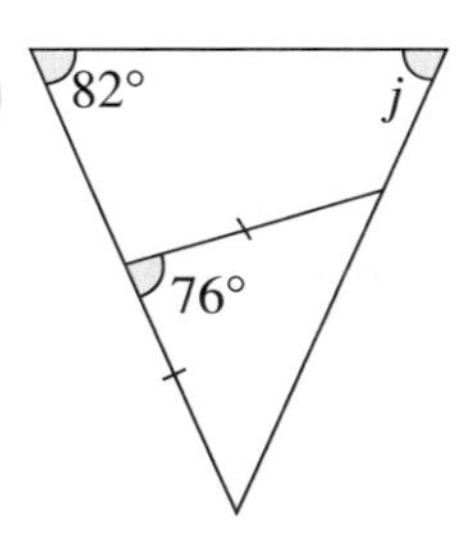

24
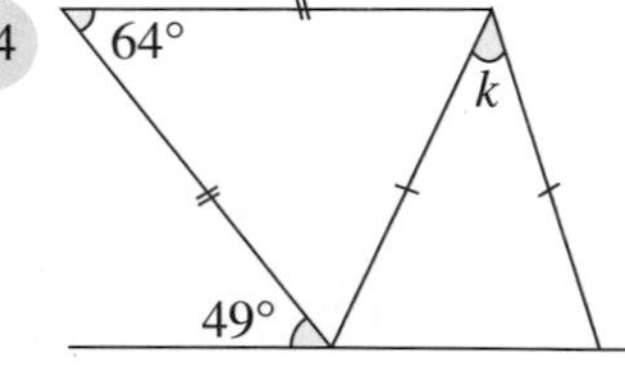

Find the angles marked with letters.

$a = 68°$ (corresponding angles)

$b = 68°$ (alternate angles)

$e = 60°$ (angles on a straight line)

$a + c + e = 180°$ (angles in a triangle)

$68 + c + 60 = 180$

$c = 180° - 128° = 52°$

$d = 60°$ (alternate angles)

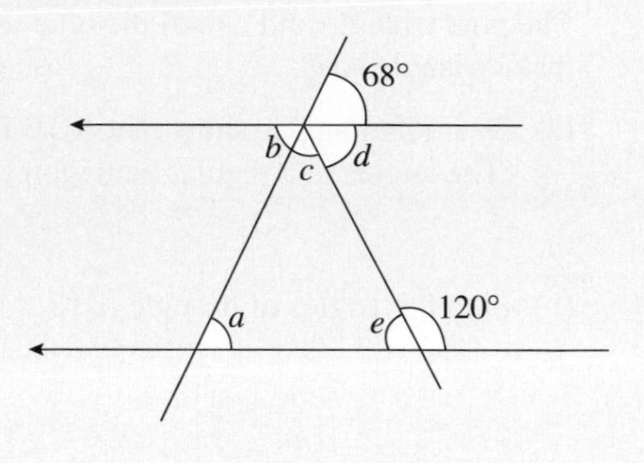

Exercise 1E

Find the angle x in each diagram. Show your working.

1

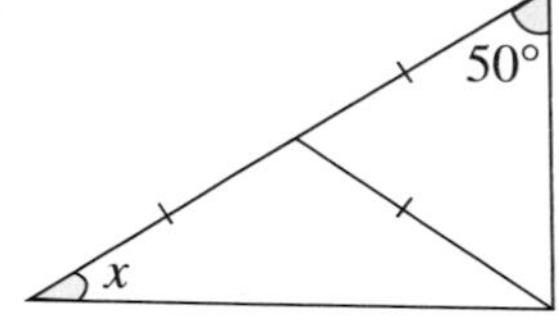

2

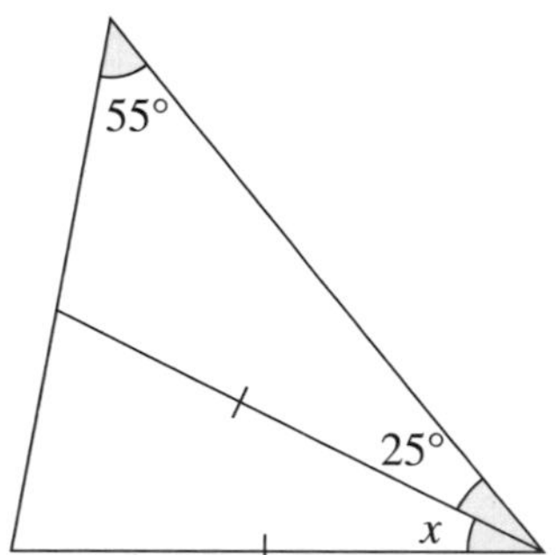

3

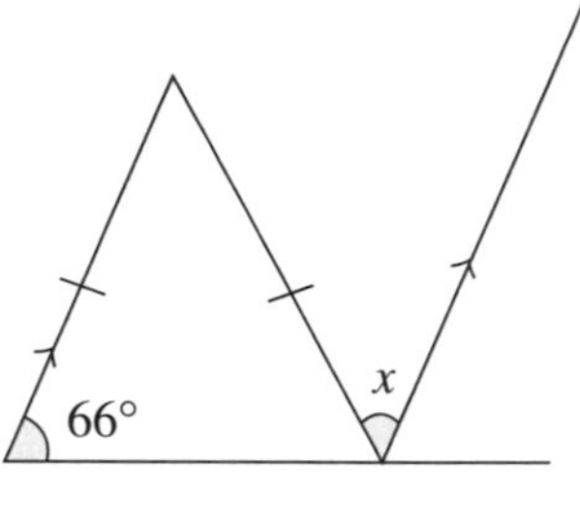

4

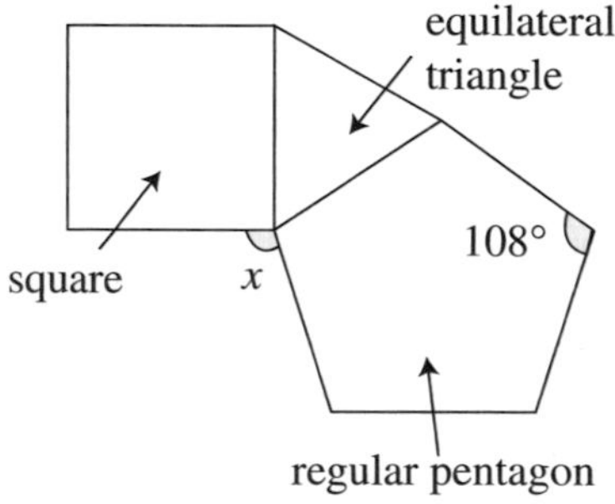

5 The diagram shows two equal squares and a triangle. Find the size of angle x.

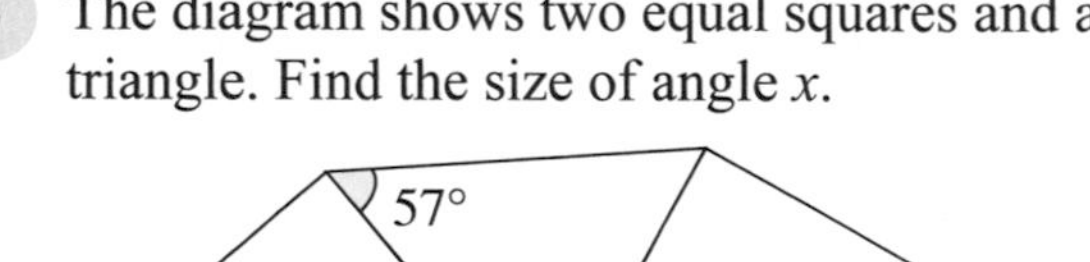

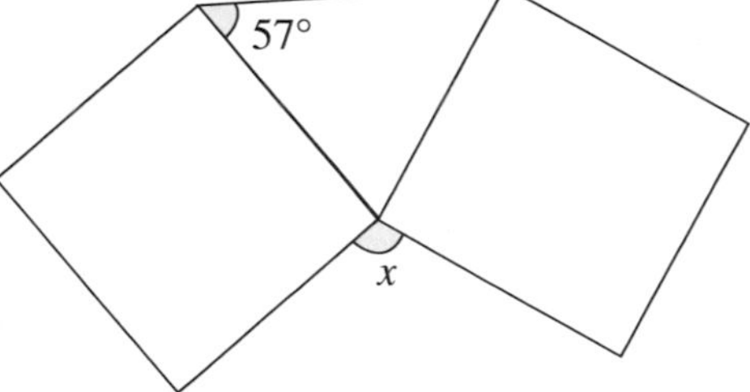

6

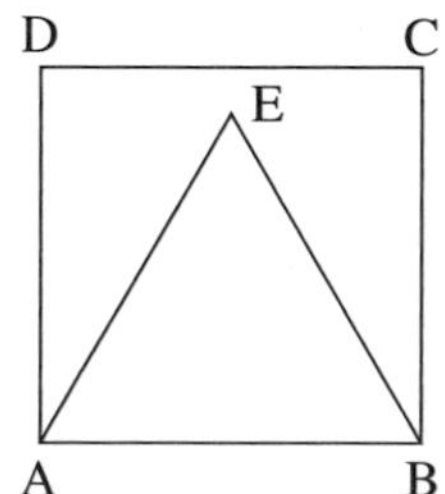

ABE is an equilateral triangle drawn inside square ABCD. Calculate the size of angle DEC.

7 The diagram shows a regular pentagon cut into three triangles. The pink triangle and one of the blue triangles are joined to make triangle ABC.

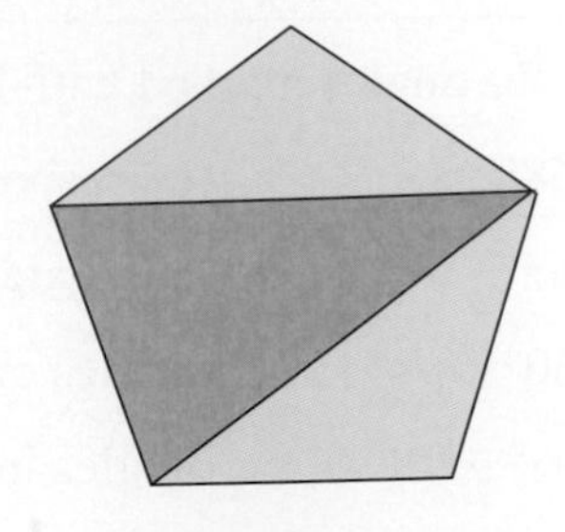

(a) By finding angles show that ADB is a straight line. (The angles in a regular pentagon are each 108°.)

(b) Find the angles of triangle ABC.

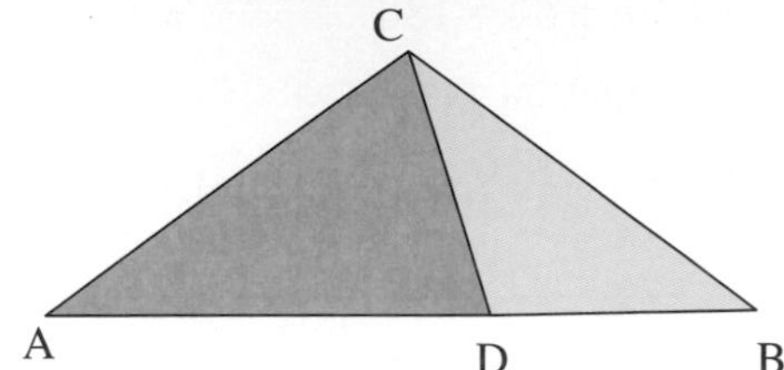

Exercise 2M

Begin each question by drawing a diagram.

1 Calculate the acute angle between the diagonals of the parallelogram shown.

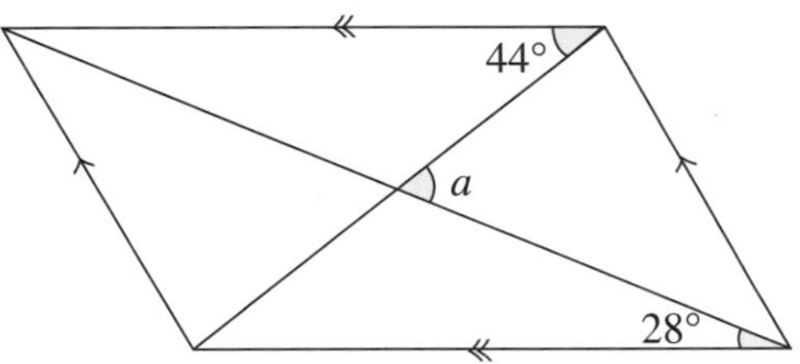

2 In the parallelogram PQRS line QA bisects (cuts in half) angle PQR. Calculate the size of angle RAQ.

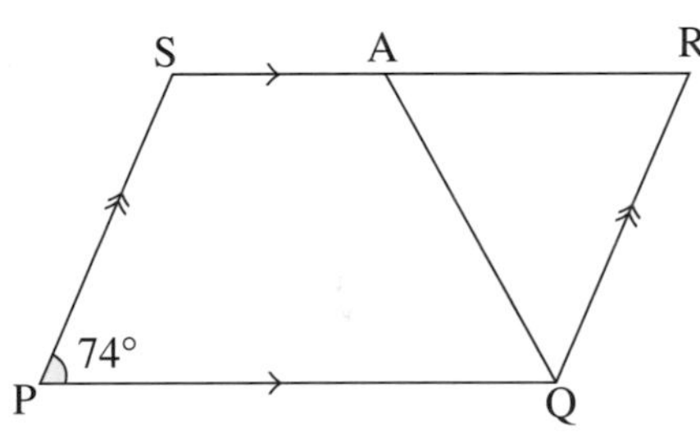

3 The diagram shows two equal squares and a triangle. Find the size of angle a.

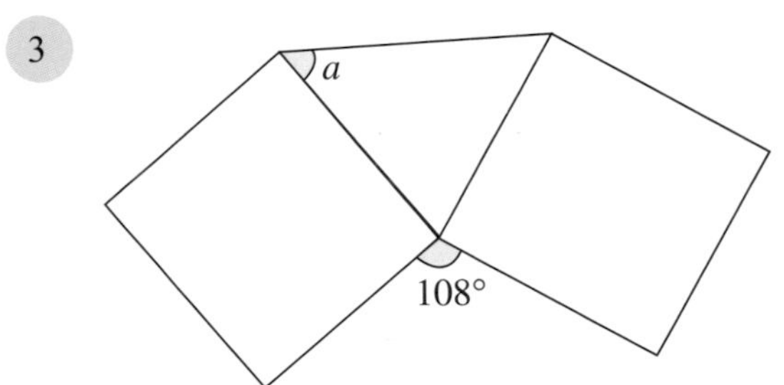

4 In the diagram KL is parallel to NM and LJ = LM.
Calculate the size of angle JLM.

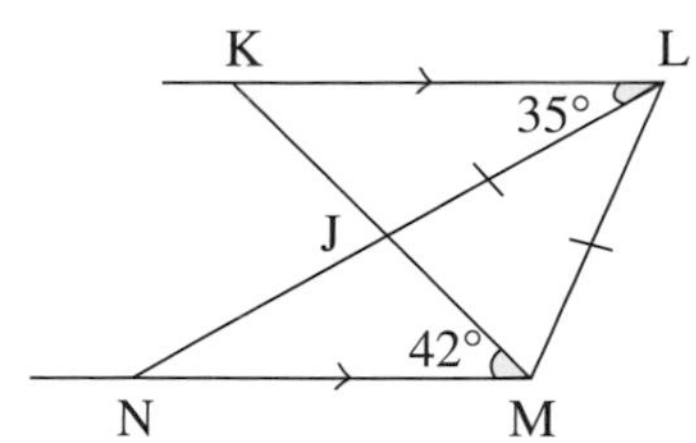

5 The diagram shows a series of isosceles triangles drawn between two lines.
Find the value of x.

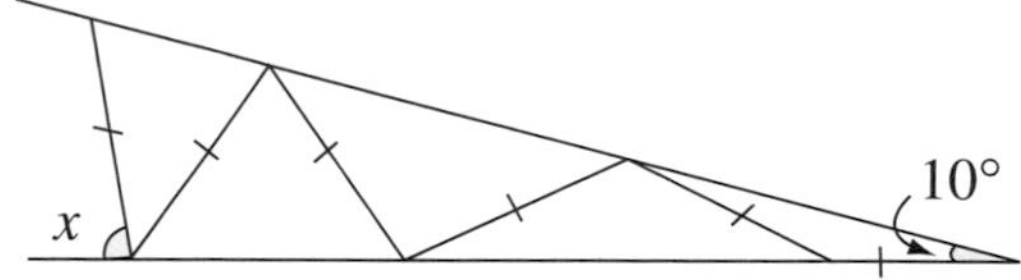

6 Draw a sketch of an isosceles triangle ABC with AB = AC.
Point D lies on AC so that $A\hat{D}B = 90°$. If $B\hat{A}C = 40°$, calculate the size of $C\hat{B}D$.

7 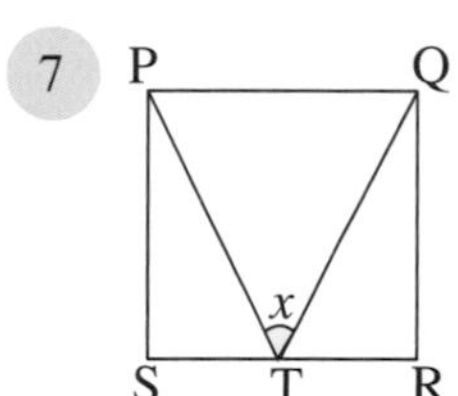

Triangle PQT is drawn inside square PQRS. $P\hat{T}S = 2 \times S\hat{P}T$ and $R\hat{Q}T = 22.9°$
Calculate the size of angle x.

8 Draw a sketch of triangle KLM with KL = KM and $K\hat{M}L = 78°$.
Point N lies on KM and LN bisects $K\hat{L}M$.
Calculate the size of angle LNM.

9 In the diagram AC bisects $B\hat{A}D$ and DE = AE.
Find the angles a and x.

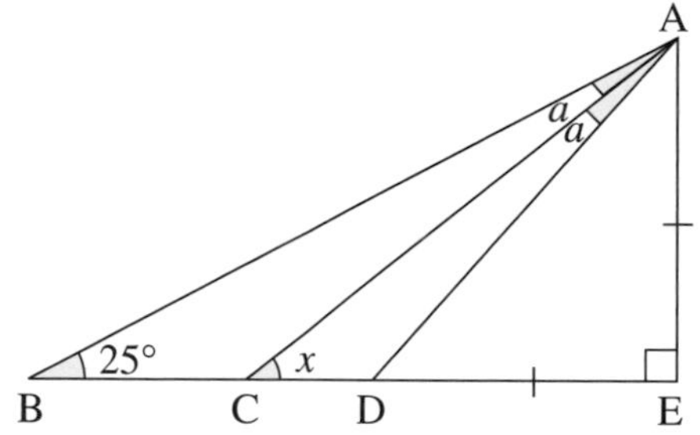

Proving results

So far we have *demonstrated* that the sum of the angles in a quadrilateral is 360°, by cutting out the angles and rearranging them. A demonstration like this might not work for every conceivable quadrilateral. When we *prove* results it means that the result is true for every possible shape. We often prove one simple result and then use that result to prove further results (and so on).

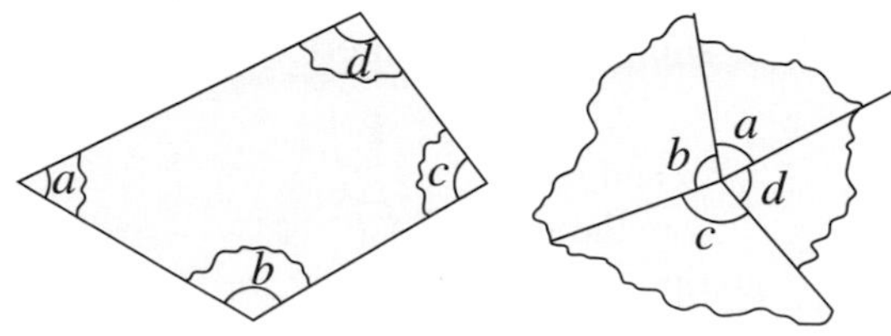

Example

When straight lines intersect, opposite angles are equal.
By definition, the angle on one whole turn is 360°.
So $a + b + a + b = 360°$
$\therefore\ a + b = 180°$

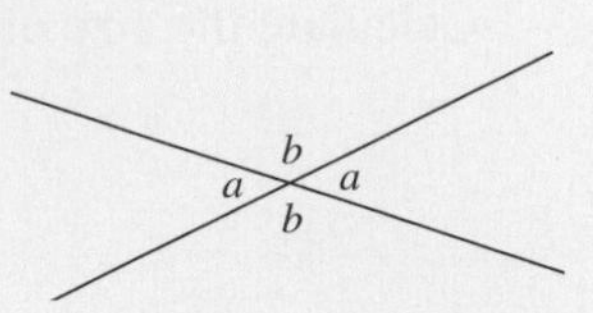

This proves that the sum of the angles on a straight line is 180°.

Exercise 2 E

1 Copy and complete this proof for the sum of the angles in a triangle.

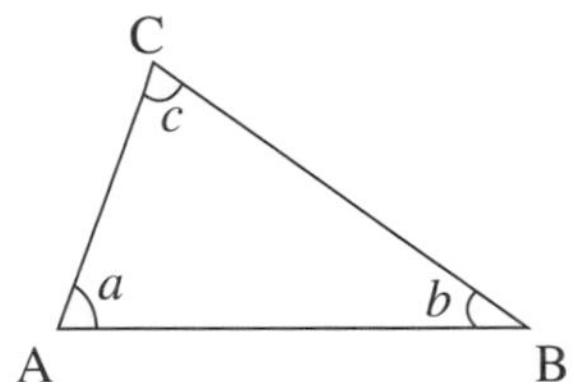

Here is ΔABC.

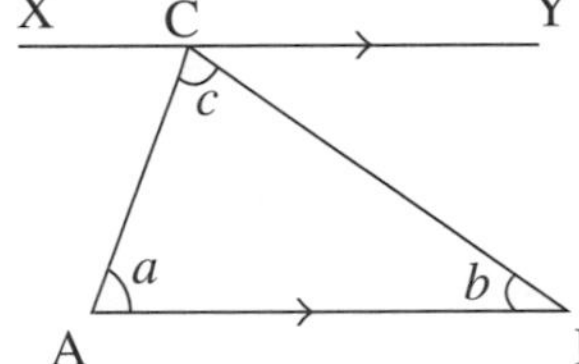

Draw line XCY parallel to AB.

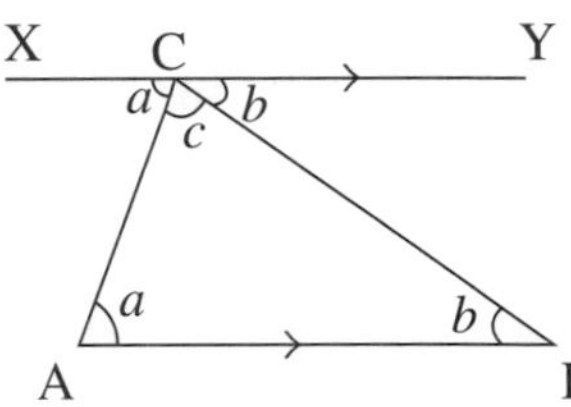

$A\hat{B}C = Y\hat{C}B$ (alternate angles)

$B\hat{A}C = \square$ (alternate angles)

$a + b + c = \square$ (angles on a straight line)

$\therefore$ angles in a triangle: $a + b + c = 180°$

2 Copy and complete this proof for the sum of the angles in a quadrilateral.

Draw any quadrilateral ABCD with diagonal BD.

Now $a + b + c = \square$ (angles in a Δ)

and $d + e + f = \square$ (angles in a Δ)

$\therefore\ a + b + c + d + e + f = \square$

This proves the result.

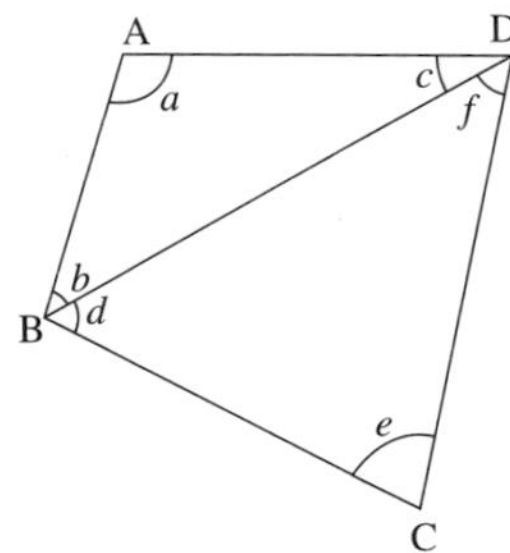

3 To prove that the exterior angle of a triangle is equal to the sum of the two interior opposite angles.

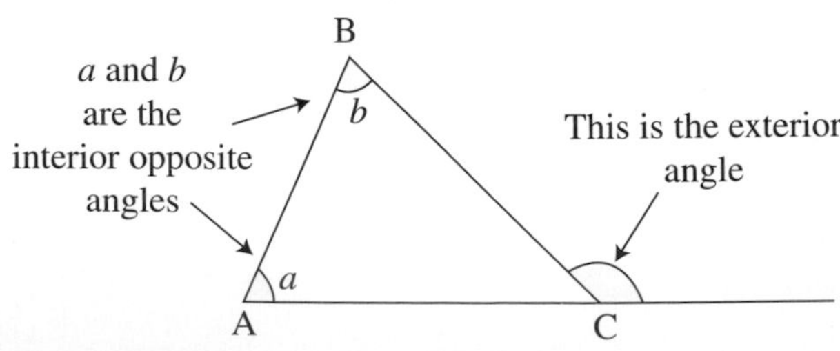

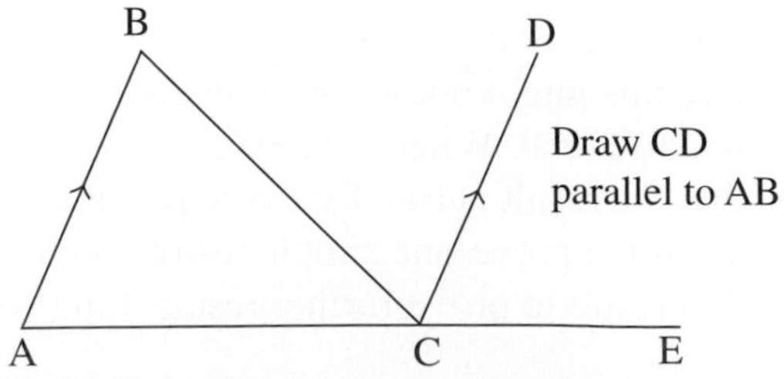

Copy and complete the proof:

$B\hat{A}C = D\hat{C}E$ (corresponding angles) ('F' angles)

$A\hat{B}C =$ ☐ (alternate angles) ('Z' angles)

$\therefore$ ☐ = ☐ + ☐

4 Explain why opposite angles of a parallelogram are equal. [Use alternate and corresponding angles.]

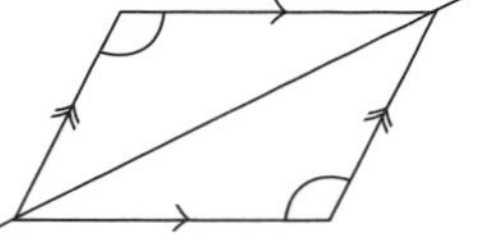

2.4 Using algebra

In section 2.4 you will:

- learn about the rules of algebra in expressions
- introduce algebra to solve problems

Rules of algebra

- An algebraic *expression* is formed from letter symbols and numbers. For example $3n$, $4n + 5$ and $1 - 2x$ are all expressions. Notice that there is no equals sign in an expression.
- In an *equation* like $2n - 1 = 15$, n is one particular unknown number.
- In the *formula* $A = LB$, A, L and B are variable quantities, related by the formula. If we know the values of L and B we can calculate the value of A.

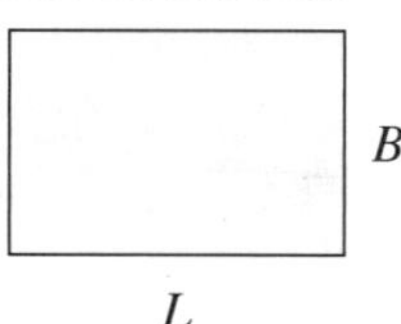

- In the *function* $y = 2x + 7$, the value of y can be found for any chosen value of x.

Like terms can be added:

$3n + 2 + 5n = 8n + 2$

$x^2 + 2x^2 - x = 3x^2 - x$

$m + mn - 3mn = m - 2mn$

Cancelling fractions:

$\frac{\cancel{4} \times 3}{\cancel{4}} = 3$ $\quad$ $\frac{2 \times \cancel{n}}{\cancel{n}} = 2$

$\frac{\cancel{n} \times n \times n}{\cancel{n}} = n^2$

Brackets:

$3(2x - 1) = 6x - 3$

$n(3n + 4) = 3n^2 + 4n$

$a(4 + b) + b(2 - 3a) = 4a + ab + 2b - 3ab$

$= 4a + 2b - 2ab$

Exercise 1M

1 Simplify the following.

(a) $3m + 2n + 5m$ (b) $5x + y + 3y + x$ (c) $4p + 4p + q$ (d) $2n + 4m - 2n + m$

(e) $6a + 3b - 5a - b$ (f) $10e + f + 4f$ (g) $w + 5 + 5w - 2$ (h) $7x - 3 + 4x + 10$

2 Simplify the following.

(a) $8 + a - 11 + a$ (b) $6m + 16m - n + n$ (c) $3t + r - 2t + 6r$

(d) $u + 2u + 3u + 4u$ (e) $1 - 8x + 2 - 13x$ (f) $2a + 4b + c - b + 2c$

(g) $19 - 3a + 1 + 2a + b$ (h) $5a + 7 + 3b - 5a + 10b$

3 State whether each part is an *expression*,
an *equation* or
a *formula*.

A $3x + 1 = 7$ **B** $x + 3 + 2x - 1$ **C** $1 + 2a = 4$

D $P = 3Q + N$ **E** $x + y + s$ **F** $7 = 3x - 10$

G $3(a + 2b + c)$ **H** $a + 2c + a$ **I** $W = 2(X + Y)$

4 Find three matching pairs

A $2a + 3 - a$ B $b + 3 + a + 1$ C $a + 2b + 3 - b$

D $3b + 3 + a - 2b$ E $3 + a$ F $a + 4 + b$

5 Multiply out the brackets.

(a) $2(a + 4)$ (b) $5(m + 2)$ (c) $3(2x + 1)$ (d) $3(x + y)$ (e) $6(w - 3)$

(f) $7(p - 3)$ (g) $6(2a - 1)$ (h) $5(2x - 2)$ (i) $6(a + 2b)$

6 Multiply out the brackets and simplify.

(a) $5(a + 1) + 2(a - 3)$ (b) $3(2x + 4) + 4(x - 2)$

(c) $7(2x - 1) + 5(x + 2)$ (d) $6(x + y + 1) + 2(x - y - 2)$

(e) $3(a + 2b - 3) + (b - a)$ (f) $10(a - 2b + c) + 3(a + b + c)$

7 Copy and complete the following.

(a) $4(n + 1) = 4n + \square$ (b) $5(\square - 2) = 5a - 10$

(c) $\square(a + 2b) = 3a + 6b$ (d) $7(x - \square) = 7x - 28$

8 Which two expressions below are *equivalent* (this means they give the same answer when thc like terms are collected).

(a) $5a - 2b + 3 + 6b + a$ (b) $3b + 6 + 4a - 2 + 3b$ (c) $4b + 7 + 4a + 2b - 3$

9 Write down an expression for the perimeter of each shape below. Collect like terms where possible.

(a)

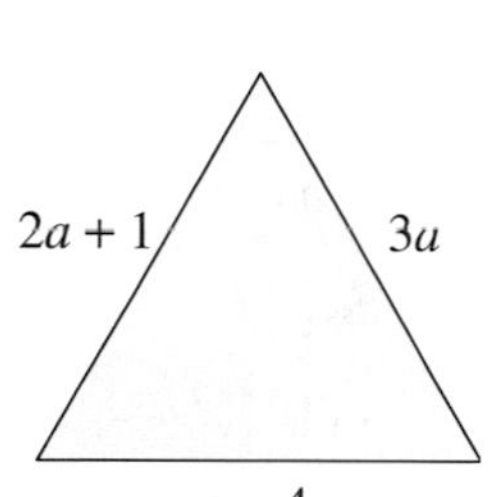

(b)

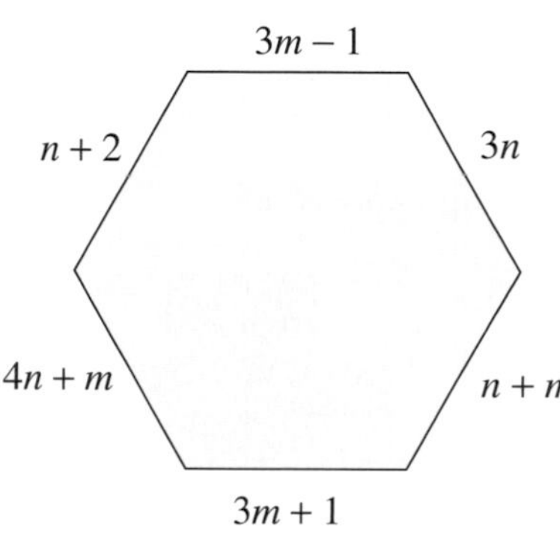

(c)

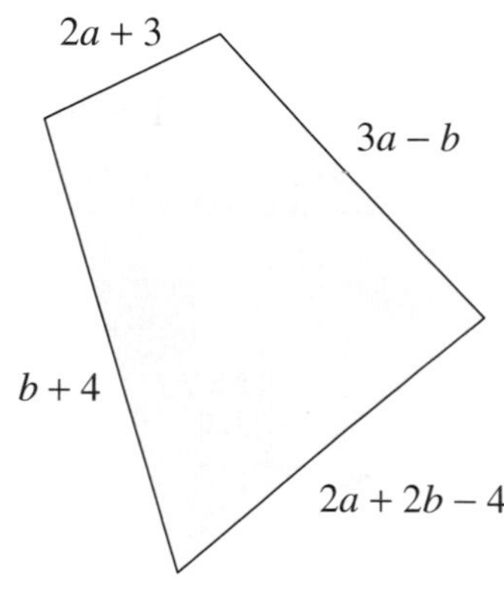

Exercise 1E

In questions 1 to 15 answer 'true' or 'false'.

1 $5 \times n = 5 + n$

2 $a \times a = a^2$

3 $a + b = b + a$

4 $t \times t \times t = 3t$

5 $h \times 3 = 3h$

6 $p - q = q - p$

7 $a + A = 2a$

8 $a + a^2 = a^3$

9 $n \times n \times n = n^3$

10 $4n - n = 4$

11 $a \div 5 = \frac{a}{5}$

12 $(a + b) \div n = \frac{a + b}{n}$

13 $m \div 4 = 4 \div m$

14 $\frac{n + n}{n} = 2$

15 $a \times b \times a = a^2b$

16 Here are some cards.

$3n$	$n + 2$	$n + n$	n
n^2	$2n \div 2$	n^3	
$n - 2$	$3n - n$	$2 \div n$	$n \times n$

(a) Which cards will always be the same as $2n$?

(b) Which card will always be the same as $n \times n \times n$?

(c) Which card will always be the same a $\frac{2}{n}$?

(d) Draw a new card which will always be the same as $2n + 2n$.

17 In number walls each brick is made by adding the two bricks underneath it.

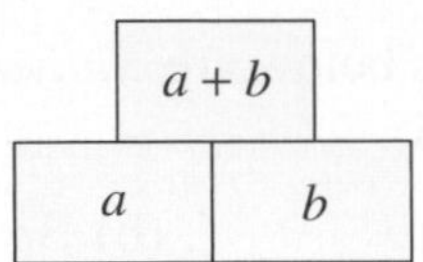

Draw the walls below and fill in the missing expressions.

(a)

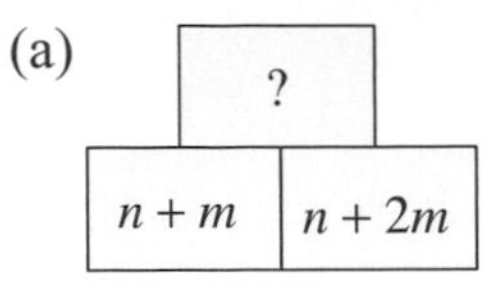

(b)

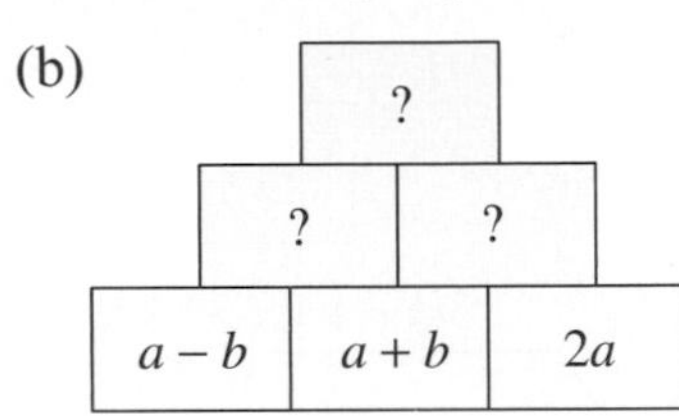

(c)

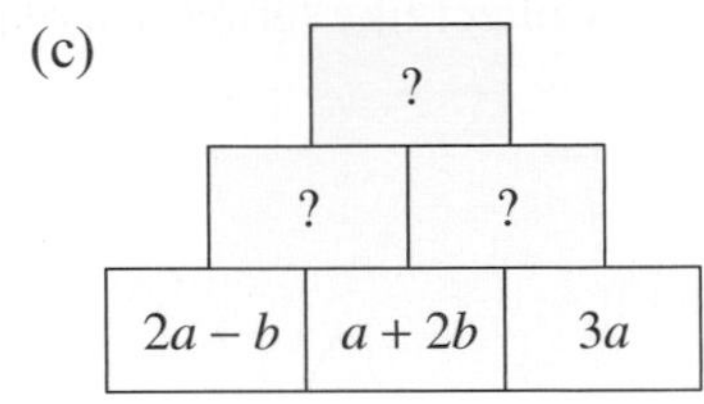

18 Draw the walls and fill in the missing expressions.

(a)

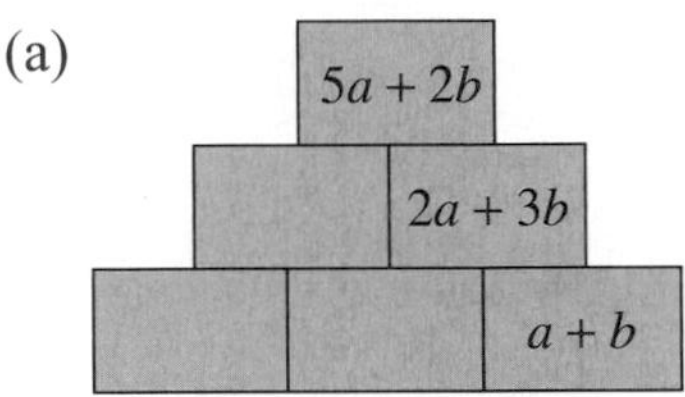

(b)

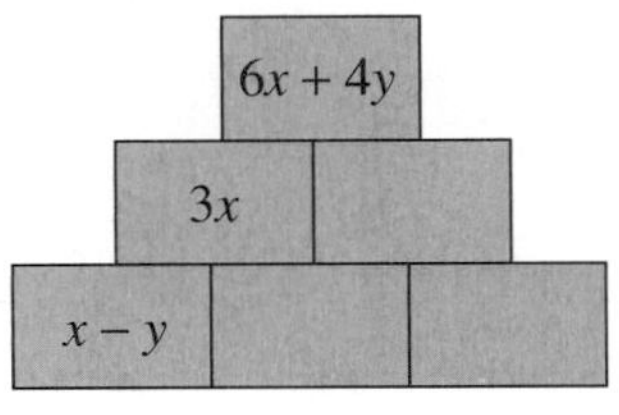

(c)

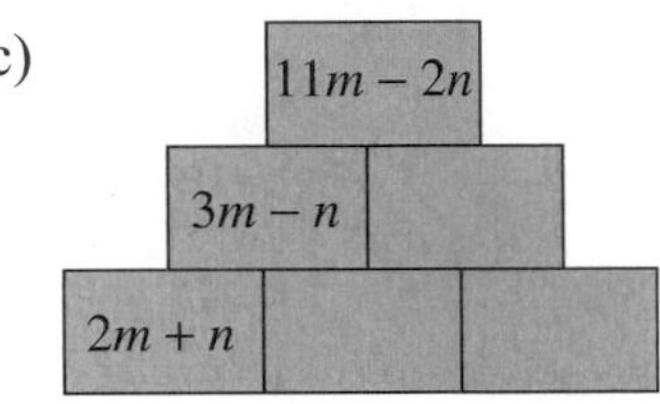

(d)

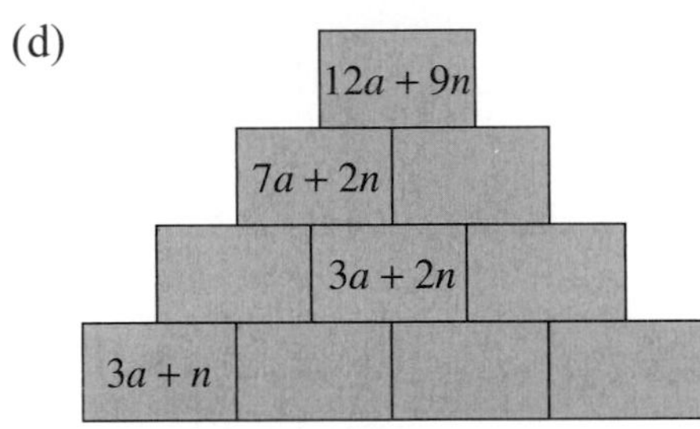

(e)

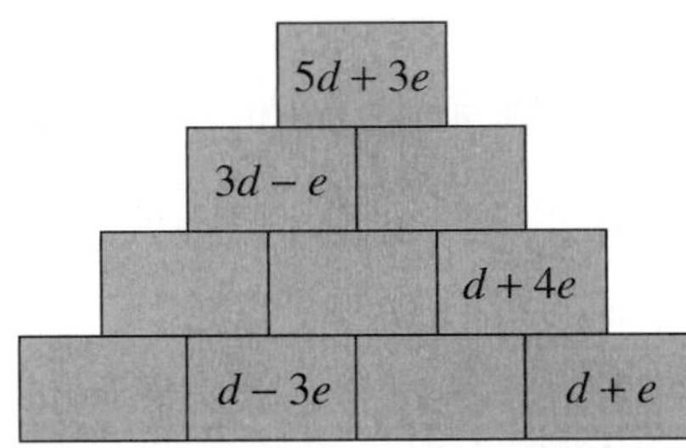

19 For (a) and (b) use the six bricks to make a number wall.

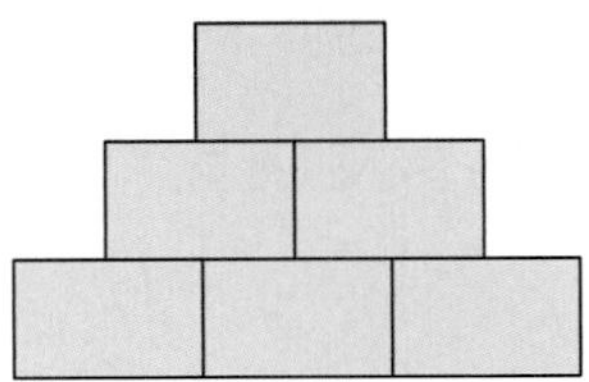

(a)

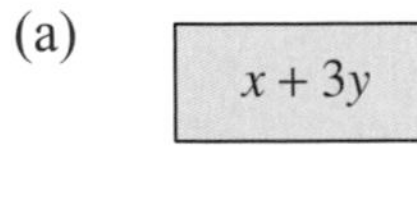

$9x + 6y$

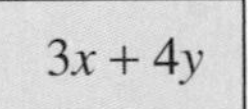

$5x - y$

$6x + 2y$

$2x + y$

(b)

$6a - b$

$2a - b$

$a - 2b$

$4a$

$3a - b$

$a + b$

Exercise 2M

1 Draw your own addition square like the one shown here.

	1	2	3	4	5	6	7	8	9
1	2	3	4	5	6	7	8	9	10
2	3	4	5	6	7	8	9	10	11
3	4	5	6	7	8	9	10	11	12
4	5	6	7	8	9	10	11	12	13
5	6	7	8	9	10	11	12	13	14
6	7	8	9	10	11	12	13	14	15
7	8	9	10	11	12	13	14	15	16
8	9	10	11	12	13	14	15	16	17
9	10	11	12	13	14	15	16	17	18

2 In this 2 by 2 square, taken from the main square, the smallest number is 8. Draw the square and fill in the missing numbers.

8	?
?	?

3 (a) Here is a 2 by 2 square. The top left number is x.

x	

The other three main numbers are shown

x	$x + 1$
$x + 1$	$x + 2$

(b) Draw the three squares shown and use xs to write down the other 3 numbers in each square.

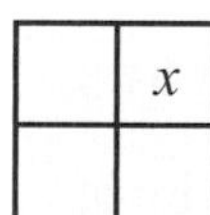
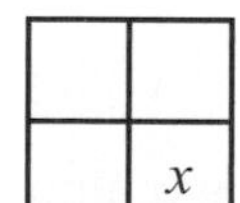
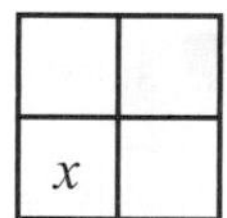

4 Draw the squares shown and use xs to fill in the other 8 numbers

x		

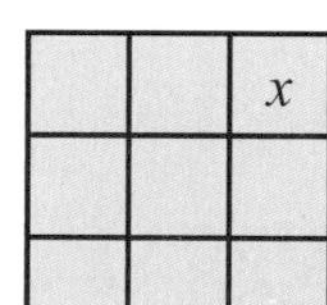
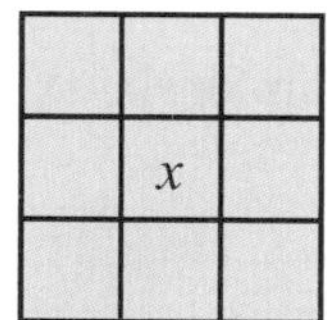

5 Draw each of the shapes below and fill in the missing numbers using the letters given.

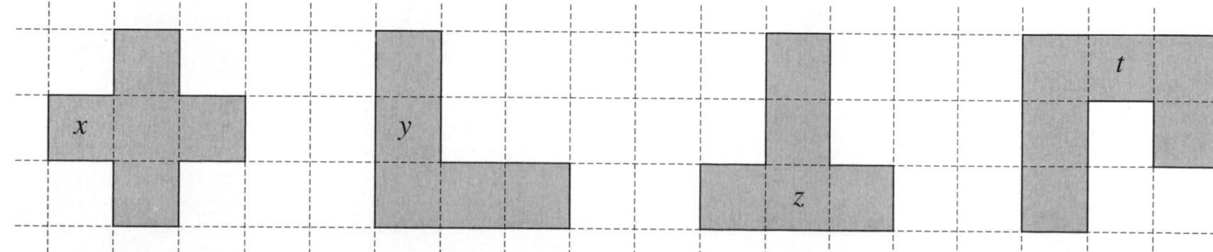

Using letters for numbers

Find the expressions you are left with.

(a) Start with n, multiply by 5 and then add 8. $n \to 5n \to 5n + 8$

(b) Start with a, subtract b and then add 10. $a \to a - b \to a - b + 10$

(c) Start with p, add 3 then multiply the result by 4. $p \to p + 3 \to 4(p + 3)$

(d) Start with m, subtract t and then square the result. $m \to m - t \to (m - t)^2$

Exercise 2E

Write down the expression you get. If any of your answers contain brackets, do not remove them.

1 Start with n, multiply by 5 then add x.

2 Start with n, add x and then multiply the result by 5.

3 Start with h, multiply by 6 and then subtract t.

4 Start with h, subtract t and then multiply the result by 6.

5 Start with b, add x and then multiply the result by 5.

6 Start with b, multiply by a and then add x.

7 Start with y, square it and then multiply the result by 3.

8 Start with n, multiply by d and then subtract 3.

9 Start with h, subtract H and then multiply the result by 5.

10 Start with x, subtract 8 and then multiply the result by 5.

11 Start with a, double it and then add A.

12 Start with y, double it and then subtract 3.

13 Start with x, square it and then add 2.

14 Start with a, add 10 and then square the result.

15 Here is flow diagram for the expression $2(3n + 7)$

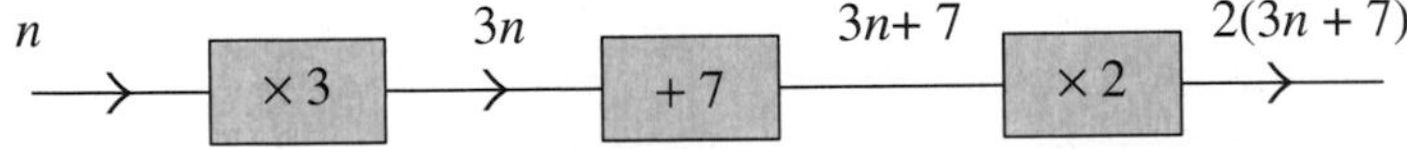

Find the expression you obtain for each of the following flow charts:

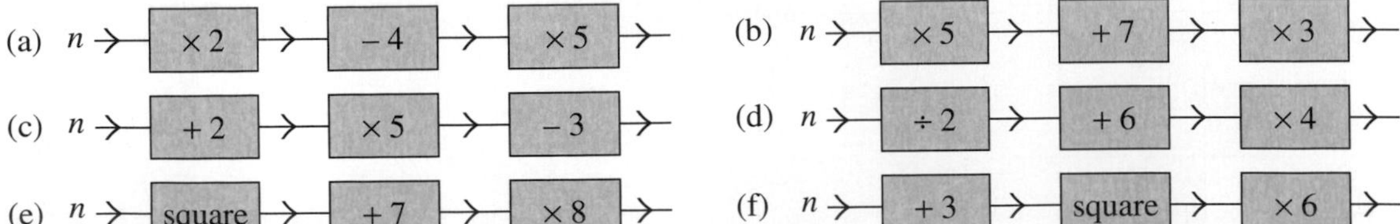

(g) $n \rightarrow$ [$+2$] $\rightarrow$ [$\div 5$] $\rightarrow$ [square] $\rightarrow$ [-7] $\rightarrow$ [$\times 3$] $\rightarrow$

(h) $n \rightarrow$ [square] $\rightarrow$ [-8] $\rightarrow$ [$\times 3$] $\rightarrow$ [$+1$] $\rightarrow$ [$\div 7$] $\rightarrow$

16 Draw the flow diagram for the following expressions.

(a) $2n + 7$ (b) $3(5n - 3)$ (c) $\frac{6n + 1}{5}$

(d) $n^2 - 3$ (e) $(n + 5)^2$ (f) $3(n^2 - 1)$

17 Draw the flow diagram for the expression $2\left[\frac{3n^2 - 1}{5} + 7\right] + 100$

In questions 18 to 32 simplify the expressions.

18 $\frac{n}{n}$ 19 $\frac{5a}{a}$ 20 $\frac{n^2}{n}$

21 $2n^2 - n^2$ 22 $a + b + c + a$ 23 $m - 3 + 3m$

24 $pq + pq$ 25 $\frac{n \times n \times n}{n}$ 26 $\frac{a + a + a}{a}$

27 $\frac{4x}{2}$ 28 $\frac{a^2}{a^3}$ 29 $\frac{n}{2} + \frac{n}{2}$

30 $3p - 1 - 3p + 2$ 31 $8n \div 8$ 32 $a^2 \times a$

Exercise 3M

1 Alex has a large number of cards. Altogether there are $4n + 12$ cards.

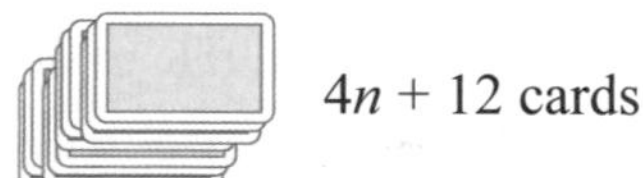

(a) Alex sorts the cards into two piles. One pile has $n + 7$ cards. Write an expression for the number of cards in the second pile.

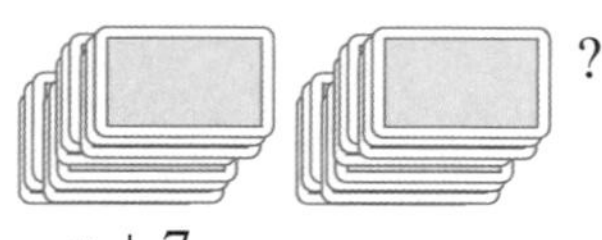

(b) Now Alex takes all the cards and puts them in two equal piles. How many cards are in each pile?

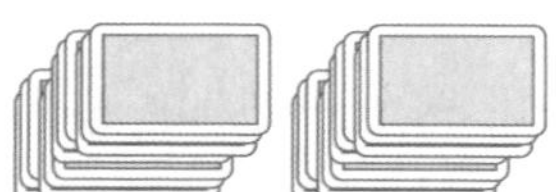

(c) Alex puts the $4n + 12$ cards into two piles so that one pile has three times as many cards as the other. How many cards are in each pile?

(d) Finally Alex puts the cards into two piles as shown. There are 18 cards in the first pile. How many cards are in the second pile?

first pile second pile

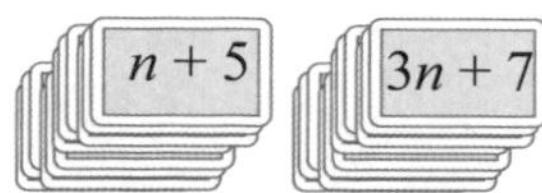

2 A machine makes x chocolates every minute. It runs for 5 minutes, after which 7 of the chocolates are rejected. How many good chocolates did the machine make in the 5 minutes?

3 A small bag of peanuts contains y nuts, and a large bag contains 5 times as many. If a boy buys a large bag and then eats 9 nuts, how many are left in his bag?

4 Bill used to earn £d per week. He then had a rise of £6 per week. How much will he now earn in 7 weeks?

5 A tile weighs t kg. How much do n tiles weigh?

6 In a butcher's shop: chickens weigh m kg each;
ducks weigh x kg each;
turkeys weigh z kg each.

Find the total weight of
(a) n chickens, y ducks and t turkeys.
(b) v ducks, 8 turkeys and p chickens.

7 The height of a balloon increases at a steady rate of x metres in t hours.
How far will the balloon rise in one hour?
How far will the balloon rise in t hours?

8 Unleaded petrol costs z pence per litre, which is x pence per litre less than 4 star.
How much do I pay for n litres of 4 star?

9 The diagram shows a rectangle cut into sections. Write an expression for the total area shaded green.

	x	3
y	(shaded)	
2		(shaded)

Exercise 3E

1 Phil has 3 bags of coins.

Each bag has n coins inside.

Write an expression to show the total number of coins in Phil's 3 bags after the following.

(a) Phil took 4 coins out of *one* bag.

(b) Phil took 1 coin out of *each* bag.

(c) Phil took 3 coins out of each of *two* of the bags and *none* out of the other bag.

(d) Phil took 5 coins out of one bag and 2 coins out of each of the other two bags.

2 Write an expression for each of the missing lengths in these rectangles.

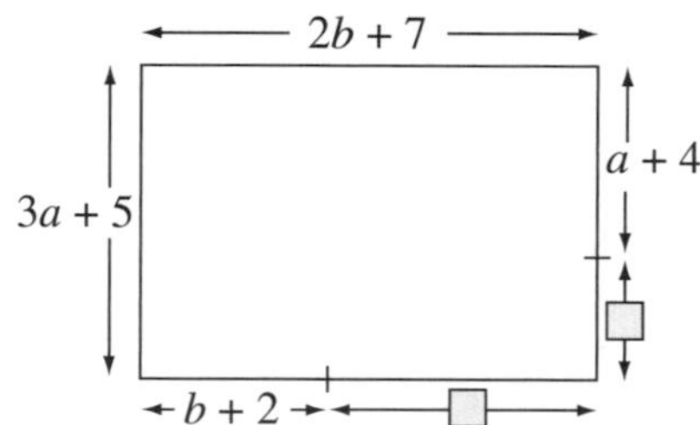

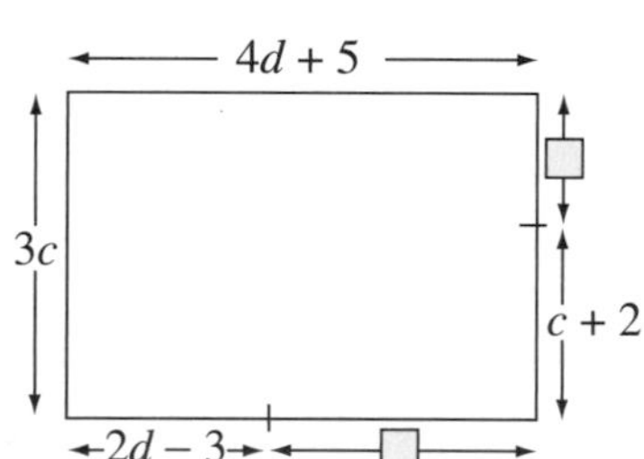

3 Selmin has found a sequence for square numbers:

$$2^2 = 1^2 + 1 + 2$$

$$3^2 = 2^2 + 2 + 3$$

$$4^2 = 3^2 + 3 + 4$$

(a) Write down the line that starts '$5^2 =$......'

(b) Using ns, write down the line that starts '$n^2 =$......'

4 Leila has a different sequence:

$$2^2 = 1 \times 3 + 1$$

$$3^2 = 2 \times 4 + 1$$

$$4^2 = 3 \times 5 + 1$$

(a) Write down the line that starts '$5^2 =$.....'

(b) Write down the line that starts '$n^2 =$....'

5 Here is sequence for square numbers using consecutive odd numbers.

$$2^2 = 1 + 3$$

$$3^2 = 1 + 3 + 5$$

$$4^2 = 1 + 3 + 5 + 7$$

Similarly, $n^2 = 1 + 3 + 5 + 7 + \ldots\ldots + k$.

Express k in terms of n. Write $k = \ldots\ldots$

6 'Think of a number'. Ask someone to follow these instructions:

(a) Think of a number.

(b) Add 3 to the number.

(c) Multiply the answer by 5.

(d) Subtract 7 from the new number.

(e) Double the answer.

(f) Subtract 6 from the last number.

(g) Read out the final answer.

You can now work out the original numbers as follows:

'Subtract 10 and divide by 10'

[E.g. if the final answer is 370, the original number was $(370 - 10) \div 10$. It was 36.]

Try this a few times and then explain why it works by using algebra. [Hint: Think of a number x.....].

*7 Here is a magic square in which the numbers in each row, column and diagonal add up to the same number, in this case 18.

9	4	5
2	6	10
7	8	3

Copy and complete these magic squares.

(a)

7		
	6	4
		5

(b)

9		8
	6	
$n + 2$		3

(c)

8	1	6
	n	
	$2n - 1$	

(d)

1	12	7	14
n	3	16	$n-5$
15			4

(e)

	10		
14	15		8
	4	18	
16	13	n	$n-1$

8 Copy and complete these magic squares in terms of a and b.

(a)

$9+6a$	$4-4a$	$5+a$
$7+a$		

(b)

		$8a-b$
$11a+2b$		$3a-2b$
		$10a+3b$

CHECK YOURSELF ON SECTIONS 2.3 AND 2.4

1 Finding angles

Find the angles marked with letters.

(a) 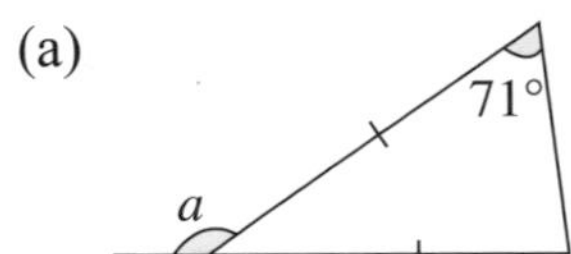

(b) 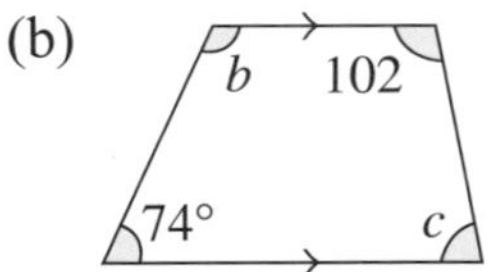

(c) 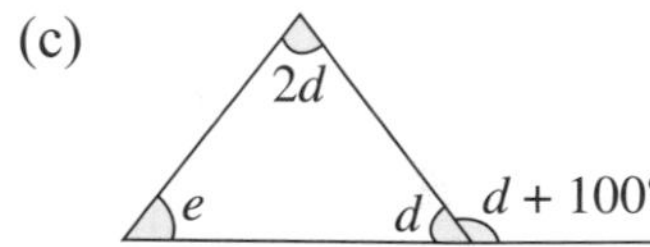

(d) 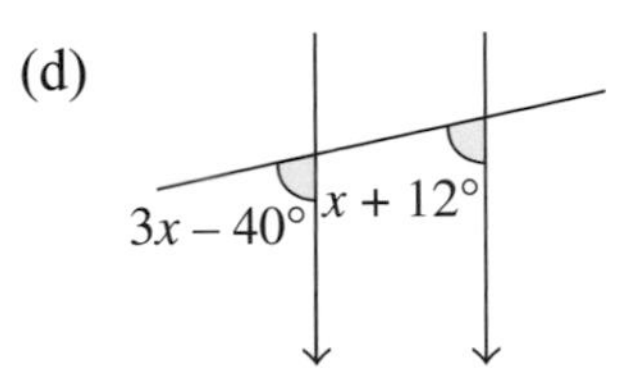

(e) 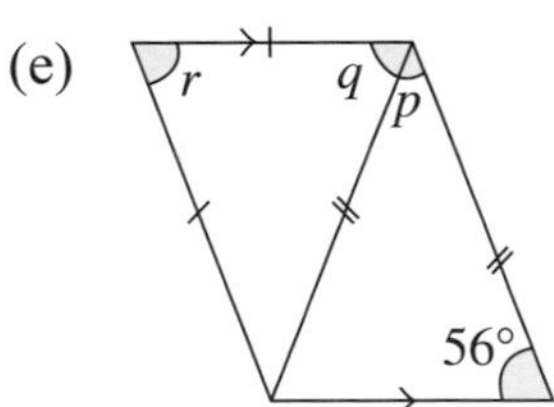

2 Rules of algebra

Simplify the following.

(a) $3n - 6 + n$ (b) $4(c - 3) + 10$ (c) $n(3n - 1) - n$

(d) $xy + 2xy$ (e) $m^2 \times m$ (f) $e(e + 2e + 3e)$

(g) $\frac{n^3}{n^2}$ (h) $\frac{t + 4t - 3t}{2}$ (i) $\frac{1}{m} + \frac{2}{m}$

2.5 Applying mathematics in a range of contexts 1

In section 2.5 you will:

- solve problems in a range of contexts

Exercise 1M

1 Answer true or false.

(a) $0.3 = \frac{1}{3}$ (b) $30\text{p} = £0.3$ (c) $0.08 > 0.085$

(d) $(-3)^2 = -9$ (e) $4\% = \frac{1}{25}$ (f) $\frac{1}{2} - \frac{1}{3} = \frac{1}{6}$

2 A human skeleton was fitted with various motors and sensors so that it could 'run' at a speed of 50 miles per hour for up to three hours. How long would it take to run 16 km?
[Use 1 km = $\frac{5}{8}$ mile]

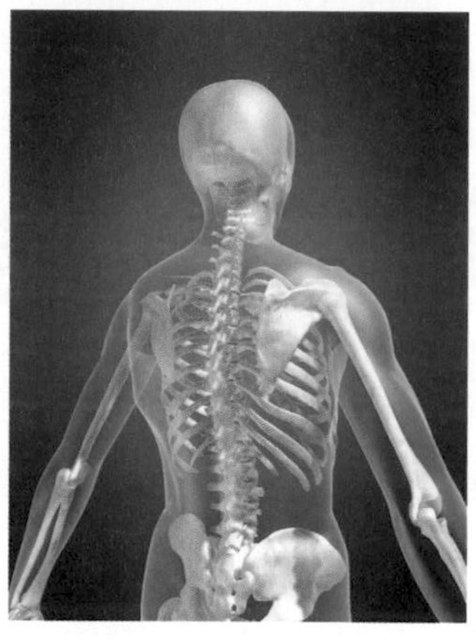

3 Jill is 8 years older than Gary. In 5 years time she will be twice Gary's age. How old is Jill now?

4 Work out the missing numbers

(a) $0.1 \times 100 = \square$ (b) $(\square)^2 = 400$ (c) $15 \div 100 = \square$

(d) $\square \times 4 = 204$ (e) $9 \times \square = 2.7$ (f) $0.1 \times 0.2 = \square$

5 'Ants can move objects 50 times their own weight.'

(a) If one ant weighs 0.016 grams, find the largest mass it can move.

(b) If ants work together efficiently, how many ants would be needed to move a bag of crisps weighing 32 g?

6 Find the number indicated by the arrow on the scales below.

(a) 0 — 0.4 (b) 0 — 0.2 (c) 8 — 12

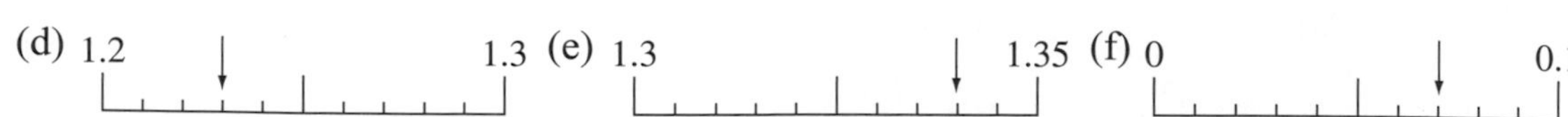

(d) 1.2 — 1.3 (e) 1.3 — 1.35 (f) 0 — 0.1

7 Look at these number cards

[−3] [0] [+2] [−5] [+4] [−6] [+3]

(a) Choose a card to give the answer 2.

[+4] + [−5] + [ ] = 2

(b) Choose a card to give the *lowest* possible answer.

[−3] + [ ] = [ ]

(c) Choose a card to give the *highest* possible answer.

[−5] − [ ] = [ ]

8 The pattern 24680 24680 24680 ….. is continued to form a number with one hundred digits. What is the sum of all one hundred digits?

9 Write each sentence with the number you think is most likely.

(a) The width of an adult hand is [ ]. (4 inches, 4 cm, 0.5 m)

(b) This book weighs about [ ]. (2 kg, 200 g, 800 g)

(c) The classroom door is [ ] high. (80 cm, 2 m, 3 feet)

10 The square ACDE is cut into seven pieces.

Find the area, in square units, of

(a) triangle EDI

(b) square BJIG

(c) parallelogram FGHE.

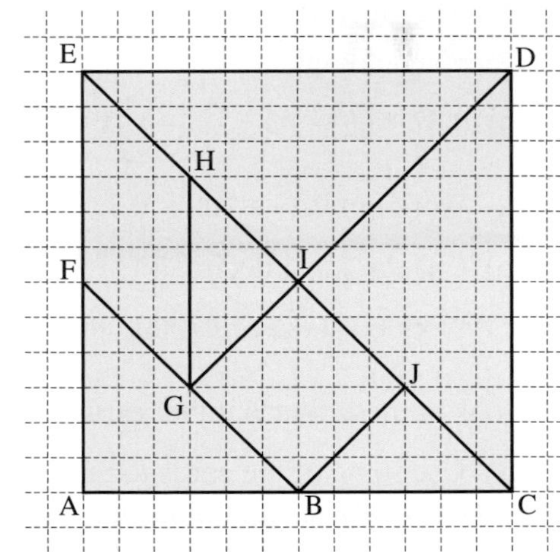

Exercise 2M

1 Copy and complete

(a) $33 + 34 = 100 - \square$

(b) $8 \times 80 \times 100 = 8^2 \times \square$

(c) $240 - 90 = 15000 \div \square$

(d) $0.6 \times 100 = 180 \div \square$

(e) $21 + 22 + 23 = 2 \times 3 \times \square$

(f) $1^1 + 2^2 + 3^3 = 2^{\square}$

2 Look at these numbers.

12	18	30	35	51	70	80

(a) Which numbers divide exactly by 7?

(b) Which numbers divide exactly by both 5 and 2?

(c) Which numbers are multiples of 3?

3 Look at the pattern of paving stones and count the number of stones in the first three rings around the centre stone.

Assuming the pattern continues, how many stones will there be altogether in a circular pattern of seven rings around the centre stone?

4 You are given that $4.2 \times 15 = 63$

Copy and complete:

(a) $0.42 \times \square = 63$

(b) $\square \times 150 = 630$

5 (a) Work out $0.1^2 \times 100 \times 0.23$

(b) Change $\frac{3}{8}$ to a decimal.

(c) Work out 11% of £7000.

6 Look at these four number cards **2** **7** **4** **9**

(a) Use some of the cards to make numbers that are as *close as possible* to the numbers below. You must *not* use the same card more than once in each number.

[For example: 300 **2** **9** **7**]

(i) 50 (ii) 70 (iii) 800 (iv) 7000

(b) Use the cards to make the largest possible *odd* number.

7

The photo shows a mini chain reaction with dominoes.

It takes 4.2 seconds to topple 21 dominoes.

How long will it take to topple a huge pattern with 63 000 dominoes in a line?

8 Work out: (a) A half of 199

(b) A third of 66 303 000

(c) A quarter of 50 000

(d) A fifth of 0.1

9 Fill in the operations to make the answer correct.

You may use any of these signs: + – × ÷

(a) 32 ☐ 5 ☐ 10 = 64

(b) 99 ☐ 2 ☐ 2 = 200

10 This article was in a newspaper in January 2000.

What will be the first date from now made up entirely of *odd* numbers?

How odd

Next Wednesday will be the first time for 1,112 years that date will be made up entirely of even numbers. 2/2/2000 is the first all-even date since 28/8/888.

Exercise 3M

1 Work out

(a) $-3 \times (-5)$ (b) $5 - 22$ (c) $6 - (-10)$

(d) $24 \div (-3)$ (e) $-11 - 10$ (f) $-3 + (-8)$

(g) $\dfrac{4 \times (-3)}{(-2)}$ (h) $6 - 10 - 20$ (i) $\dfrac{36}{-3} - (6 - 10)$

(j) $\dfrac{[10 + (-3)] \times (-4)}{(-1)}$ (k) $55 - 7 - 21 + (-2) - (-20) + (-2)$

2 A climber raises £200 for charity for every metre he climbs up a rock face.
How much does he raise if he climbs 0.81 km?

3 (a) How long does it take the minute hand of a clock to move 360°?

(b) How long does it take the hour hand to move 90°?

(c) How long does it take the seconds hand to move 720°?

4 A Boeing 767 leaves Boston at 08:00 and arrives in London at 11:40.
A plane flying at half the speed of the Boeing leaves Boston at 08:40.
When should it arrive in London?

5 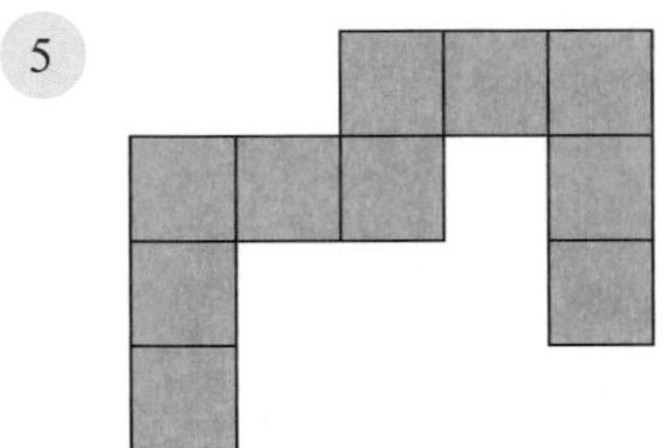

The area of this shape is 14.4 cm^2. Work out the length of the perimeter of this shape.

6 Write 250 billion pence in pounds and pence.

7 Rio has the same number of 20p and 50p coins. The total value of the coins is £7. How many of each coin does he have?

8 The skateboard sequence was taken by a camera with a delay of 0.14 seconds between pictures.
How long did the jump take?

9 A map has a scale of 1 to 200 000. Calculate the actual length of a railway line which is 6 cm long on the map.

10 In a magic square each row, column and both main diagonals have the same total.
Which of the following numbers should replace n in this magic square [2, 4, 6]?

		7
4		14
		n

Exercise 4M

1 I am a two digit prime number.
I am a factor of 434.
What number am I?

2 Copy each calculation and find the missing numbers.

(a)

	6	7	□
	3	□	2
+	□	1	9
□	8	7	5

(b)

	□	0	7	3
	1	□	6	2
+	4	5	□	2
	8	2	1	□

3 Every year the Government spends about £8.8 billion paying teachers (who deserve every penny they get). A wad of fifty £10 notes is about 5 mm thick.

As a publicity stunt, the Minister of Education decides to make a single pile of £10 notes of total value £8.8 billion. How high would the pile be? [1 billion = 1000 million]

4 Dawn has lots of 36p and 27p stamps and she wants to waste as little money as possible when posting 3 packets. Which stamps should she use if the required postage is:

(a) 80p (b) 150p (c) £2?

5 Peter Gibson's paintings became very fashionable in 2009. His masterpiece titled 'Now' was sold for £65 000. The painting was bought by its previous owner in 1998 for £400. Calculate the price increase in euros. [£1 = €1.25]

6 Without a calculator work out which is the largest of:

$\sqrt{555}$ $5\sqrt{55}$ $55\sqrt{5}$

7 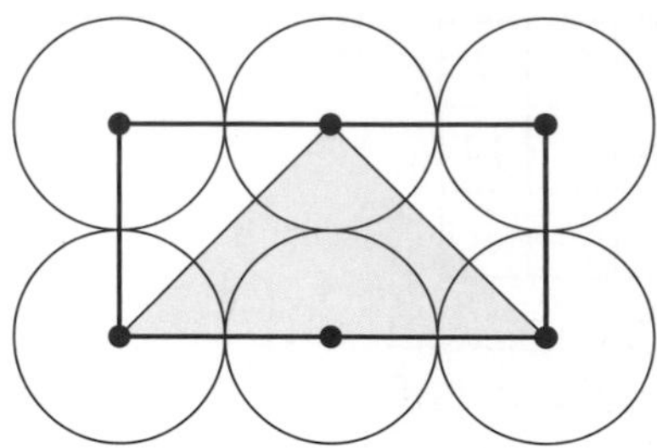

Six touching circles of radius 5 cm are shown. Calculate the area of the triangle shaded green.

8 Four 6s can be used to make 1: $6 + \frac{6}{6} - 6$

(a) Use three 9s to make 2

(b) Use three 7s to make 11

(c) Use four 5s to make 7

(d) Use four 5s to make 3

(e) Use four 8s to make 4

9 The lawn weedkiller 'Verdone' is used with a dose of 15 ml in a bucket of water. The whole bottle of 'Verdone' contains 0.4 litres. How many 15 ml doses can you get from a whole bottle?

10 It costs 35p per minute to hire a powerful computer. How much will it cost to hire the computer from 07:40 to 08:15?

Exercise 5E

1 A jar has a mass of 310 g when empty. When it is full of cereal the total mass is 1.26 kg. What is its mass when it is 30% full?

2 Work out (a) $5^1 + 4^2 + 3^3 + 2^4 + 1^5$

(b) $(1 \times 0.1) + (2 \times 0.02) + (3 \times 0.003)$

(c) $\frac{1}{10} \times \frac{10}{11} \times \frac{11}{12} \times \frac{12}{13}$

3 (a) Convert of speed of 60 km/h into m/s.

(b) A car accelerates from 0 to 60 km/h in 5 seconds.

Work out the acceleration of the car in m/s/s.

4 (a) The number n has 6 factors, including 1 and n. Two of its factors are 2 and 5. What is n?

(b) The number N has 8 factors, including 1 and N. Two of its factors are 10 and 14. What is N?

5 One square metre of the paper used in this book weighs 90 g. The card used for the cover weighs 300 g per square metre. Measure the size of this book and hence calculate its total weight. Check how accurate you were by weighing the book on an accurate set of scales.

6 The pupils in a school were given a spelling test.

Some of the results are given in the table

(a) Copy and complete the table with the missing entries.

(b) What percentage of the boys passed the test?

	Passed	Failed	Total
Boys		311	589
Girls		257	
Total		568	914

7 A women gives a total of £6 to her two children so that her daughter receives three times as much as her son. How much does her daughter receive?

8 Answer 'true' or 'false'

(a) $\frac{1}{6} < 0.2$ (b) $(-3)^2 > 2^3$ (c) $12.5\% = \frac{1}{8}$

(d) 3p = £0.3 (e) $\frac{1}{3} + \frac{1}{6} > \frac{1}{2}$ (f) $(2-5)^2 = 9$

9 Work out these questions using a calculator. Convert your answer into a number with a fraction: either halves, quarters, fifths, tenths or hundredths. For example: instead of '6.4' write '$6\frac{2}{5}$'.

(a) $237 \div 4$ (b) $678 \div 12$ (c) $48 \div 15$ (d) $238 \div 200$

(e) $478 \div 20$ (f) $76 \div 16$ (g) $408 \div 80$ (h) $403.2 \div 8$

10 

Show how this rectangle can be cut into two pieces which can be rearranged to make a 9×2 rectangle.

Exercise 6E

1 On a map of scale 1: 100 000 000 the distance from London to Athens is 2.5 cm. What is the actual distance between these two cities?

2

5	8	14	37	296	323	529

From the list of numbers above, write down

(a) three prime numbers

(b) a square number

(c) a cube number

(d) a number obtained by multiplying together two other numbers in the list.

3 The test results of some students are shown below

Mark	7	8	9	10	11	12
Frequency	3	6	7	18	9	7

What percentage of the students scored 10 marks or more?

4 (a) Work out one tenth of one half of 5% of the square root of one million.

(b) Work out one third of 8% of three quarter of the cube root of one million.

5 (a) Calculate the total surface area of a solid cuboid with dimensions 5 cm × 8 cm × 3 cm.

(b) How many of these cuboids could be painted on all faces, using a tin containing enough point to cover an area of 5 m^2?

6 The symbols O, Δ, □, ∗ represent numbers. Use the clues in (a), (b) and (c) to answer part (d)

(a) O + Δ = ∗

(b) O = Δ + □

(c) O + O + Δ = ∗ + □ + □ + □

(d) Δ = how many □s?

7 (a) Use a calculator to work out (i) $350 \div 99$

(ii) $350 \div 999$

(iii) $350 \div 9999$

(b) Use your answers to *predict* the answer to (i) $350 \div 99999$, correct to 9 decimal places.

(c) Predict the answer to $350 \div 999999$, correct to 11 decimal places.

8 Our cat likes to hide but does not seem to realise that a white towel does not provide good camouflage. When resting he likes to think about numbers.

One day he thought of a 3 digit number that was a multiple of 37. The sum of its digits was 9. What number was he thinking of?

9 (a) In 2009 Ian was paid £368 per week and 18% of his pay was deducted for tax. What was his 'take home pay' in 2009?

(b) In 2010 Ian received a pay rise of 6% but, in the budget, taxes were raised so that 20% of his pay was deducted. What was his take home pay in 2010?

10 Using a calculator, express the following as decimals correct to 4 decimal places:

(a) $2\frac{4}{11}$ (b) $\frac{5}{7} - \frac{4}{9}$

2.6 Circles

In section 2.6 you will learn about

- the circumference of a circle and perimeters of other shapes
- the area of a circle

Circumference

- The perimeter of a circle is called *circumference*

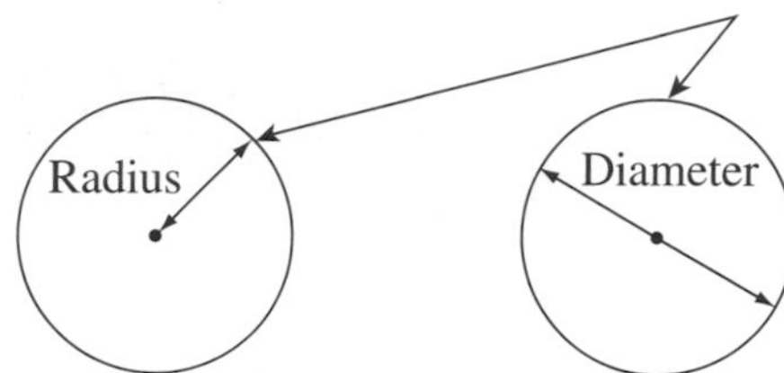

Pi

- For any circle, the exact value of the ratio $\left(\frac{\text{circumference}}{\text{diameter}}\right)$ is a number denoted by the Greek letter π.

  Since $\frac{c}{d} = \pi$, we can write $c = \pi \times d$. Learn this formula.

  Most calculators have a $\boxed{\pi}$ button, which will give the value of π correct to at least 7 significant figures: 3.141593.

- The number π has fascinated mathematicians for thousands of years. The Egyptians had a value of 3.16 in 1500 BC. In about 250 B.C. the Greek mathematician Archimedes showed that π was between $3\frac{10}{71}$ and $3\frac{10}{70}$. He considered regular polygons with many sides. As the number of sides in the polygon increased, so the polygon became nearer and nearer to a circle.

  Ludolph Van Ceulen (1540–1610) obtained a value of π correct to 35 significant figures. He was so proud of his work that he had the number engraved on his tombstone.

  In more recent times a book was published, imaginatively titled 'pi'. The book consisted of the first one million decimal places of pi, calculated by computer.

  The book was not a best seller.

(a) Calculate the circumference of the circle shown.

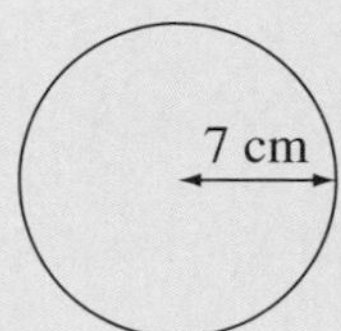

radius = 7 cm

$\therefore$ diameter = 14 cm

circumference = $\pi \times 14$

= 44.0 cm (to 1 d.p.)

(b) A circular tin of diameter 9 cm rolls along the floor for a distance of 3 m. How many times does it rotate completely?

circumference = $\pi \times 9$

= 28.274334 cm

3 m = 300 cm

Number of rotations = $\dfrac{300}{28.274334}$

= 10.61

The tin makes 10 *complete* rotations.

Exercise 1M

In questions 1 to 8 calculate the circumference of the circle. Use the 'π' button on a calculator or take $\pi = 3.142$. Give the answers correct to 1 decimal place unless told otherwise.

1 13 cm

2 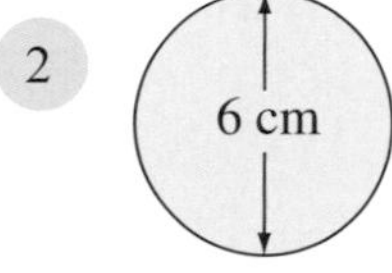

3 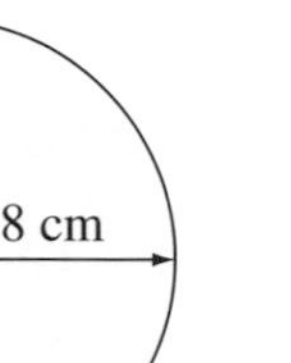

4 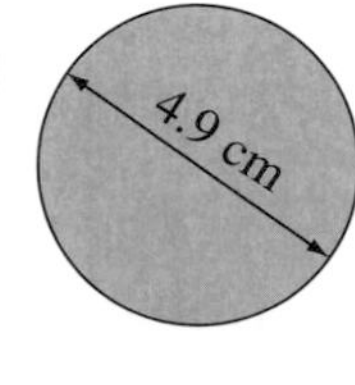

5 3.2 cm

6 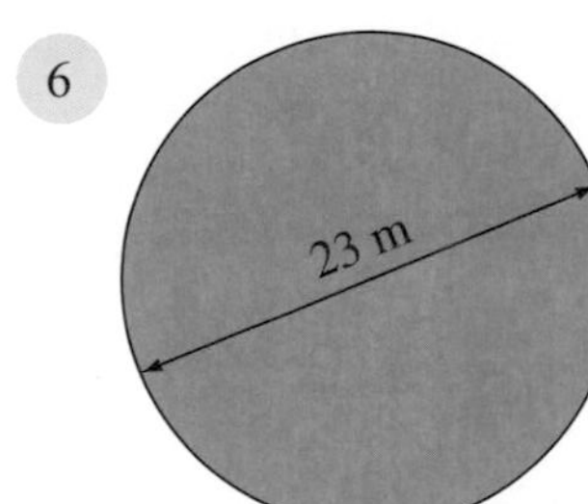

7 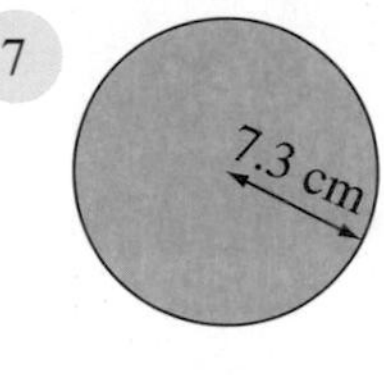

8 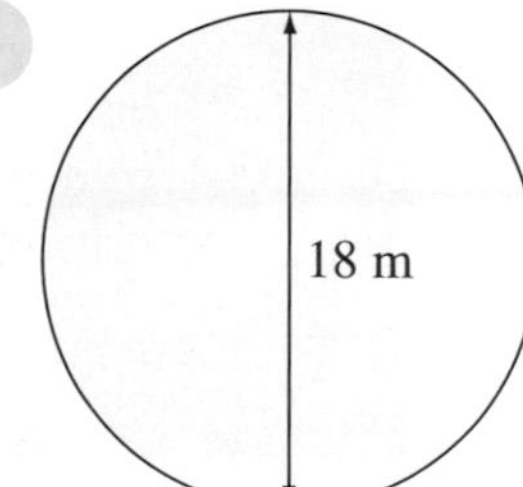

9 Which has the longer perimeter and by how much: an equilateral triangle of side 10 cm or a circle of diameter 10 cm?

10 

The knuckle of a bride's ring finger has width 19 mm. Find the internal circumference of the ring which will just fit.

11 The tip of the minute hand of a clock is 8 cm from the centre of the clock face. Calculate the distance moved by the tip of the minute hand in one hour.

12 A tin can of diameter 8 cm makes 20 complete rotations as it rolls forward in a straight line.

Find the circumference of the can and work out how far the can moves forward.

13 A tennis ball of diameter 7 cm and a golf ball of diameter 4.25 cm roll in a straight line so that each ball makes 10 complete revolutions. Which ball will go further and by how much? Give your answer to the nearest cm.

14 In 1897 politicians in Indiana, USA displayed a complete lack of mathematical understanding when they passed a local law stating that the value of pi was to be taken as 4.

(a) Calculate the circumference of a circle of radius 3.5 cm in Indiana.

(b) Calculate the circumference of the same circle everywhere else in the world.

P. S. The law was soon discarded!

Exercise 1E

1 

The top ring of the Olympic Stadium has a diameter of 234 m.
Find the circumference of the ring, correct to the nearest metre.

2 A tin of tomatoes has diameter 7.5 cm. The tin is wrapped in a paper cover which is long enough to allow 1 cm overlap for fixing. How long is the cover?

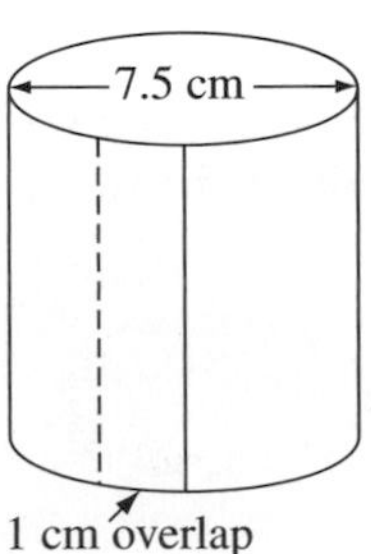

3 The wheels on Gill's bike have a diameter of 62 cm. Gill rolls forward a distance of 1200 cm. Calculate how many times the wheels go round *completely*.

4 In a coin rolling competition Gemma rolls a one pound coin on its edge a distance of 4.2 m. A one pound coin has diameter 2.2 cm. How many times did the coin rotate completely?

5 A newt walks around the edge of a circular pond at a speed of 2 cm/s. How long will it take to walk all the way round if the radius of the pond is 1.3 m?

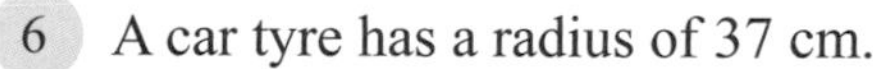

6 A car tyre has a radius of 37 cm.

(a) How long is its circumference in cm?

(b) How many complete rotations will the tyre make if the car travels 2 km?

7 A trundle wheel can be used for measuring distances along roads or pavements. A wheel of circumference one metre is pushed along and distance is measured by counting the number of rotations of the wheel. Calculate the diameter of the wheel to the nearest mm.

8 A push chair has wheels of diameter 66 cm at the back and wheels of diameter 18 cm at the front. The pushchair travels in a straight line and the rear wheels rotate completely 84 times.

(a) How far in metres does the chair travel?

(b) How many complete rotations do the front wheels make?

9 The perimeter of a circular pond is 11.7 m. Calculate the diameter of the pond to the nearest cm.

10 The tip of the minute hand of Big Ben is 4.6 m from the centre of the clock face. Calculate the distance, in km, moved by the end of the minute hand in one year (365 days).

Perimeters

Calculate the perimeter of the shape.

The perimeter consists of a semicircle and 3 straight lines.

Length of semicircle $= \frac{\pi \times 10}{2}$

$= \pi \times 5$ cm

$\therefore$ Perimeter of shape $= (\pi \times 5) + 4 + 10 + 4$

$= 33.7$ cm (to 1 d.p.)

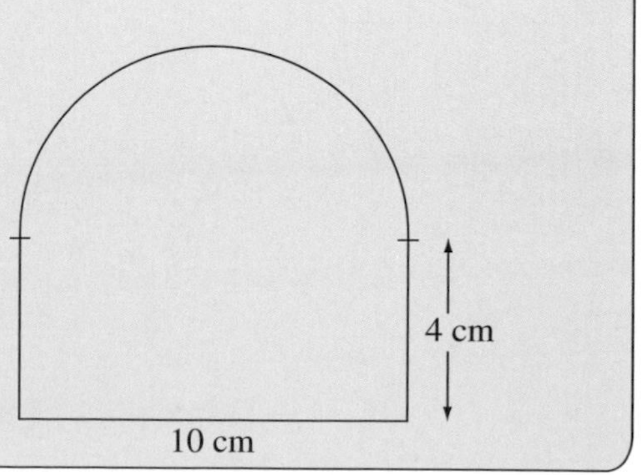

Exercise 2M

Calculate the perimeter of each shape. All arcs are either semicircles or quarter circles.
Give answers correct to 1 d.p.

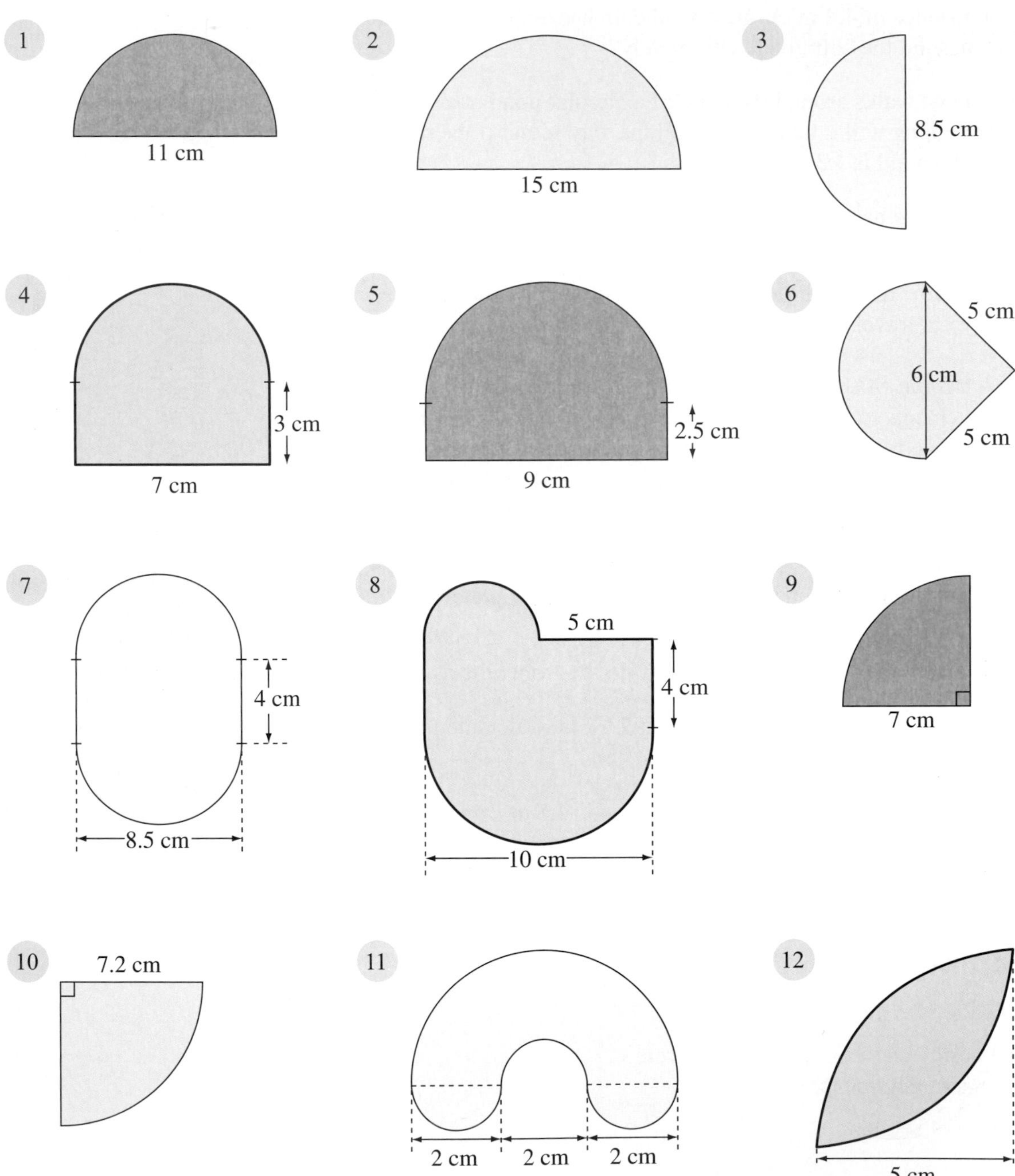

Area of a circle

In *Essential Maths* book 7H we demonstrated the formula for the area of a circle of radius r

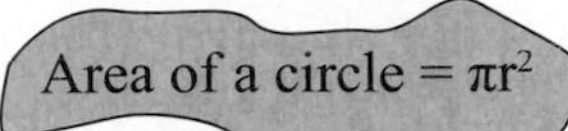

Learn this formula.

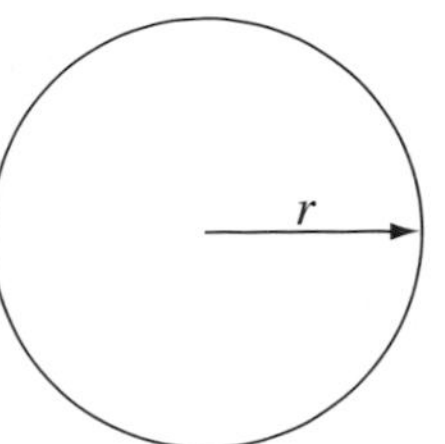

Note: πr^2 means $\pi(r^2)$.

Find the area of each shape.

(a)

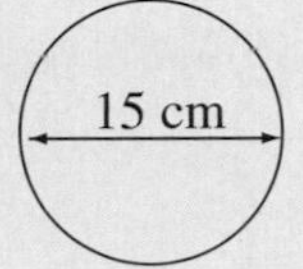

radius = 7.5 cm

area $= \pi r^2$

$= 176.7$ cm^2 (1 d.p.)

On a calculator, press:

7.5 × 7.5 × π =

(b)

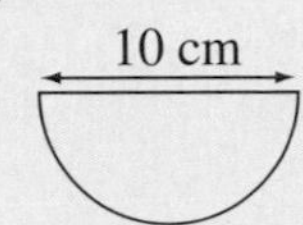

The shape is a semicircle

area $= \dfrac{\pi(5)^2}{2}$

$= 39.3$ cm^2 (1 d.p.)

On a calculator, press:

5 × 5 × π ÷ 2 =

Exercise 3M

In questions **1** to **8** calculate the area of each circle correct to 1 d.p.

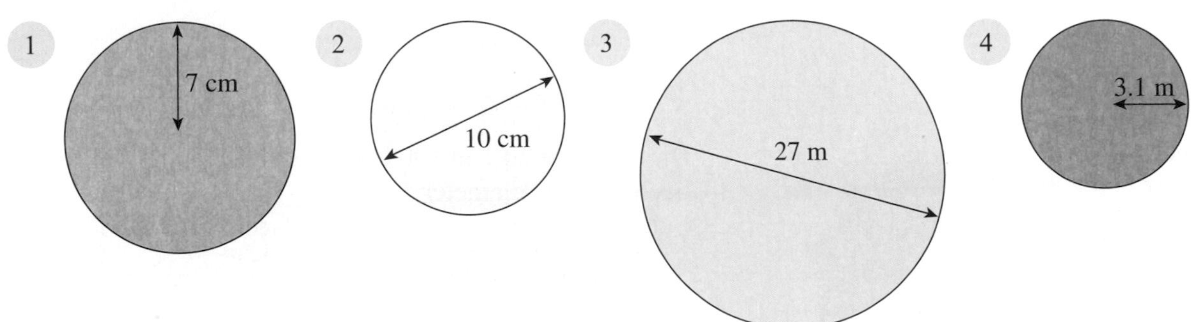

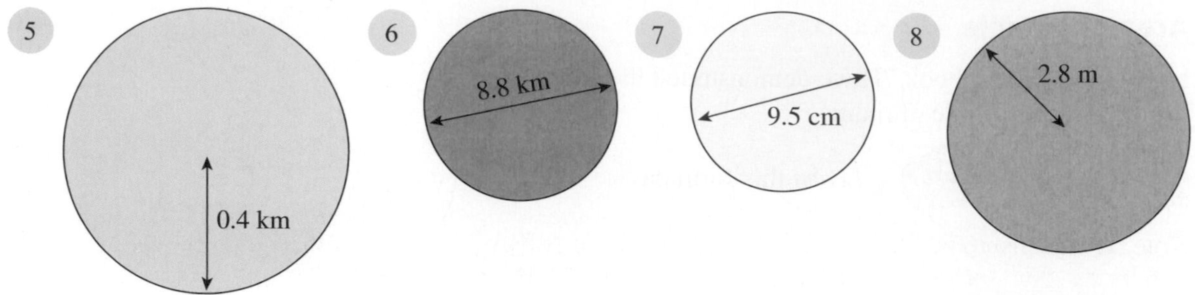

In questions **9** to **15** give your answers correct to 1 d.p., where necessary.

9 When hunting for food, an eagle flies over a circular region of radius 3.5km. What is the area of this region in km^2?

10 A carton of 'Verdone' weedkiller contains enough weedkiller to treat an area of 100 m^2. A circular lawn at Hampton Court has a radius of 16.5 m. How many cartons of weedkiller are needed to treat this lawn?

In questions **11** to **14** find the area of each shape. All arcs are either semicircles or quarter circles and the units are cm.

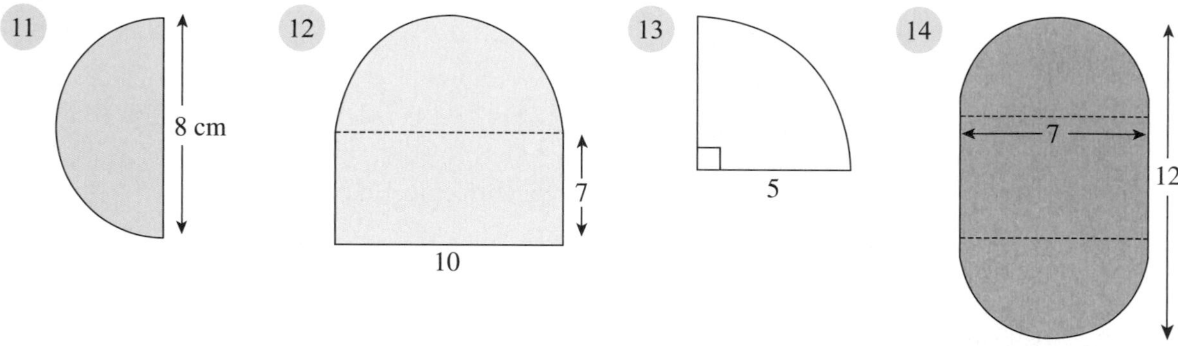

15

Discs numbered 1 to 100 are used for bingo.
Each disc has diameter 3.2 cm.
Calculate the total area of the top faces of all the discs.

Exercise 3E

1 In this stained glass window the circle has diameter 3 m and the outer square is of side 4.5 m. Calculate the area which is outside the circle.

2 The diameters of 1p, 5p and 10p coins are 2 cm, 1.8 cm and 2.4 cm respectively. Calculate the total area of the top faces of the five coins used to make 18p.

In questions **3** to **8** find the shaded area. Lengths are in cm.

3 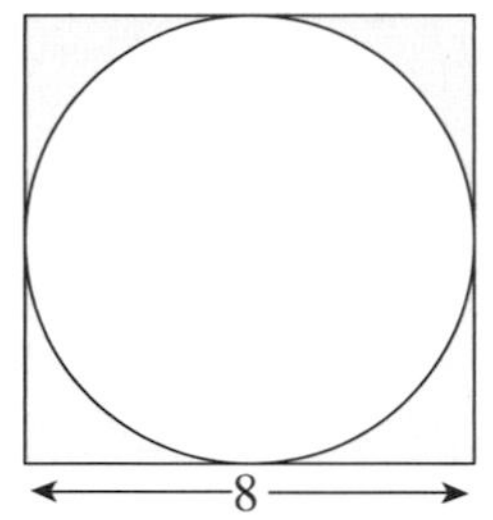

4 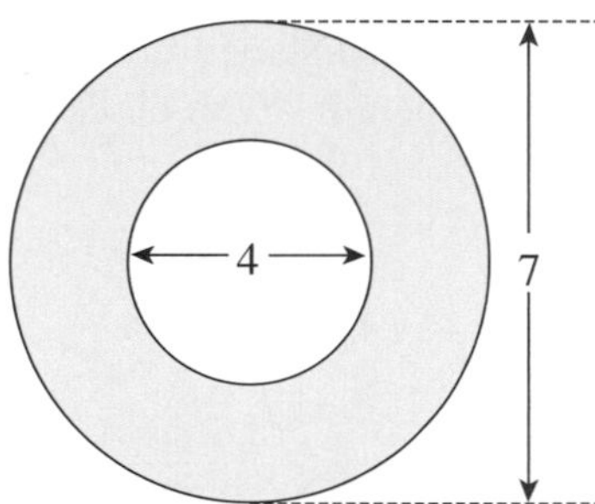

5 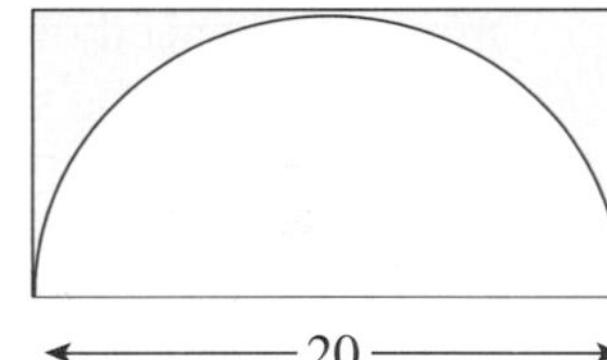

6 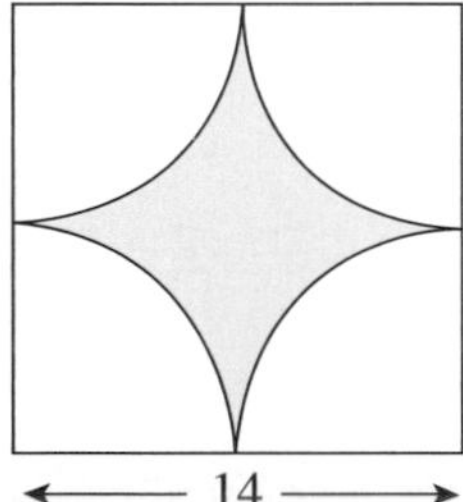

7 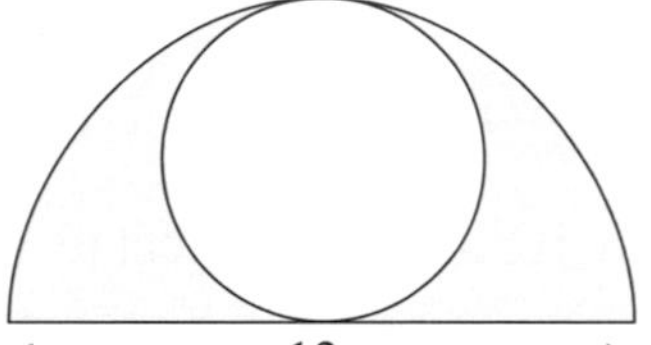

8 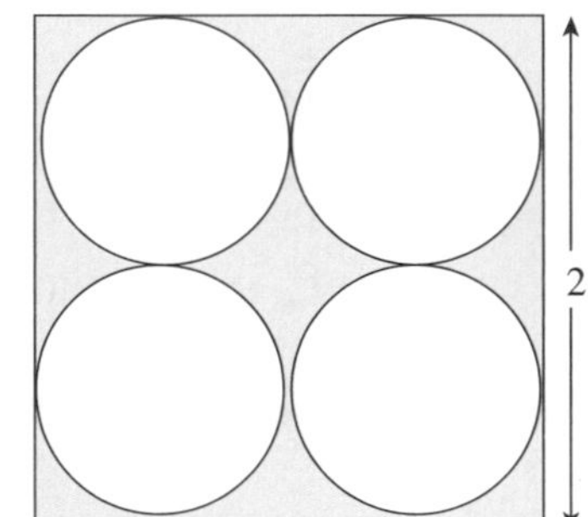

9 

The ice is melting fast so that the iceberg on which this penguin is now standing is of radius 90 cm.

(a) Calculate the surface area of the iceberg.

(b) Where are penguins found in the world?

10 An old fashioned telephone dial has the dimensions shown. The diameter of each finger hole is 1 cm.

Calculate the shaded area.

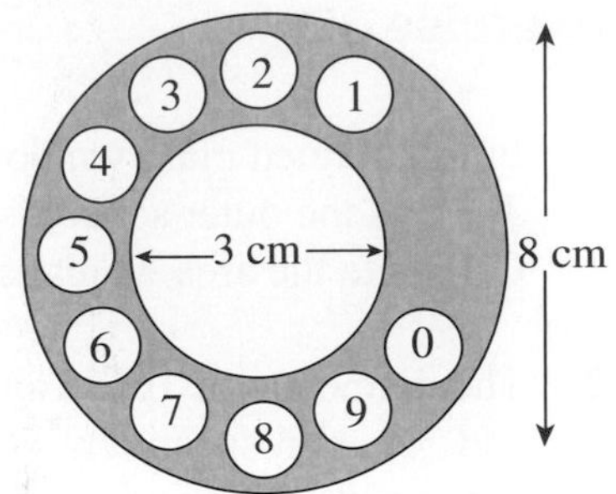

11 A circular pond of radius 3.6 m is surrounded by a concrete path 70 cm wide.

Calculate the area of the surface of the path.

12 A cycling track is a circle of diameter 150 m. The wheels of a bicycle have a diameter 82 cm. How many times will the wheels of the bicycle rotate completely when the bicycle travels ten times around the track?

13 The tip of the second hand of an electric clock moves at a speed of 1 cm/s. Calculate the distance x, from the tip of the second hand to the center of the clock.

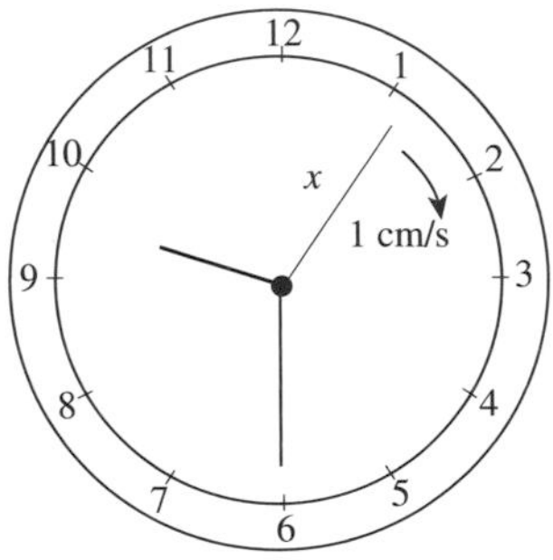

CHECK YOURSELF ON SECTION 2.6

1. Circumference of a circle and perimeters

Calculate the perimeter of each shape. Give answers correct to 1 d.p.

(a)

5.2 cm

(b)

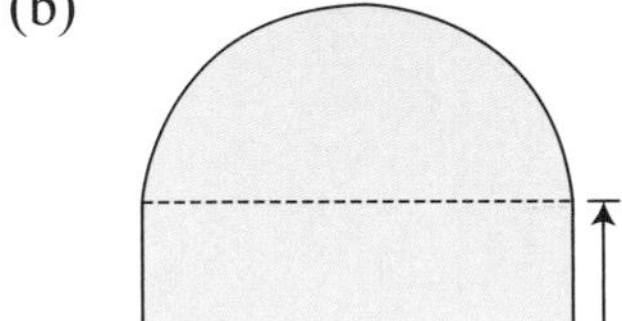

2 cm

6 cm

(c)

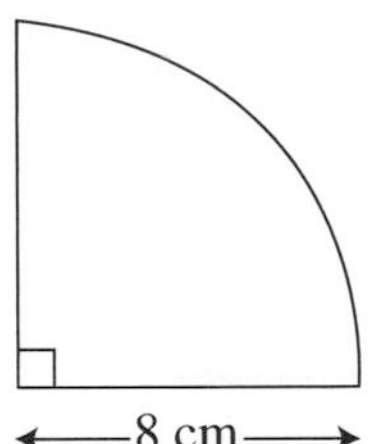

2. Area of a circle

Calculate the area of each shape above.

UNIT 2 MIXED REVIEW

Part one

1 Find the angles marked with letters

(a)

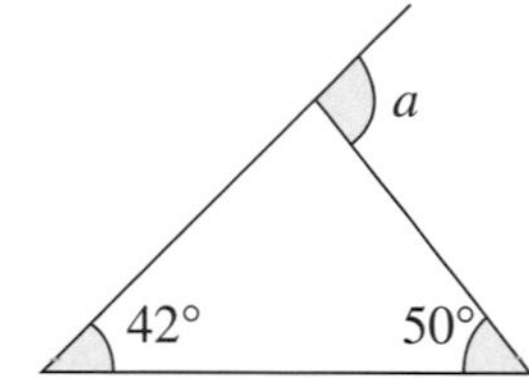

(b)

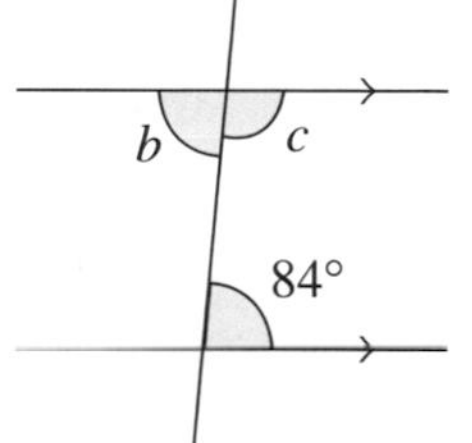

(c)

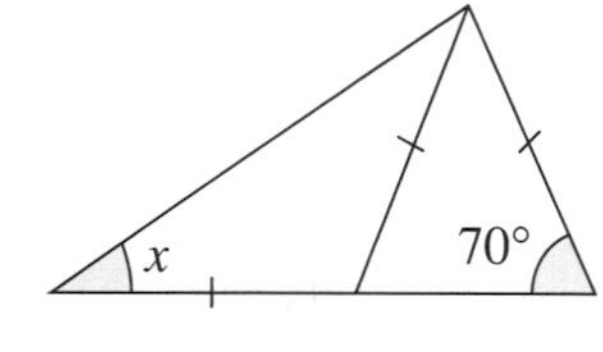

2 A clock shows the time is 4.14. What was the time half an hour ago?

3 Work out without a calculator. Show your working.

(a) $3217 - 609$ (b) 427×5 (c) $1645 \div 7$

(d) 3.7×0.6 (e) $84.6 \div 0.3$ (f) $0.2 \times (1.06 - 0.85)$

4 Copy and complete the table

a	b	$a - b$	$(a - b) \times (-3)$
7	3		
5	10		
2.7	3.7		
–3	–5		
6	–2		

5 Ai Ping earns £894.65 each month.
Estimate how much she earns in one year.

6 Here are six calculations and six answers. Write down each calculation and insert the correct answer from the list below. Use estimation.

(a) $79.6 \div 4$ (b) $145 \div 150$ (c) $288.2 \div 6$

(d) $52.2 + 47.6$ (e) $10.4 \div 97$ (f) $416 \div 1.97$

Answers: 0.97, 99.8, 19.9, 0.11, 211.2, 48.0

7 For each circle, calculate the circumference correct to one decimal place.

(a) 12 cm

(b) 8 m

(c) 3 cm

8 Calculate the angles marked with letters

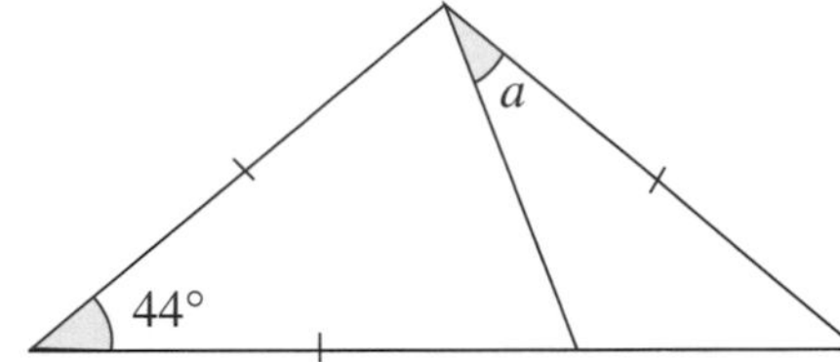

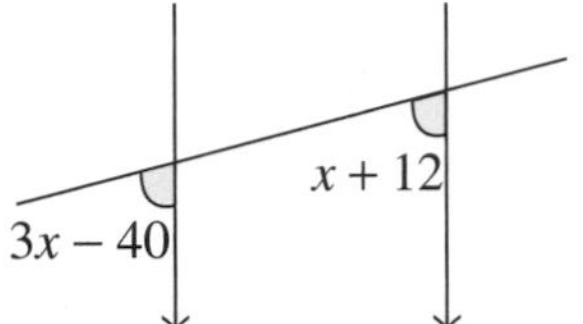

9 Work out the value indicated by the arrow.

(a) 0 1

(b) 7 8

(c) 1 2.5

(d) 17 18

(e) 2 2.04

(f) 0 0.1

(g) 3 6

(h) 0.4 0.5

(i) 0.7 1.1

10 The radius of the outer circle is 6 cm.
Calculate the shaded area.

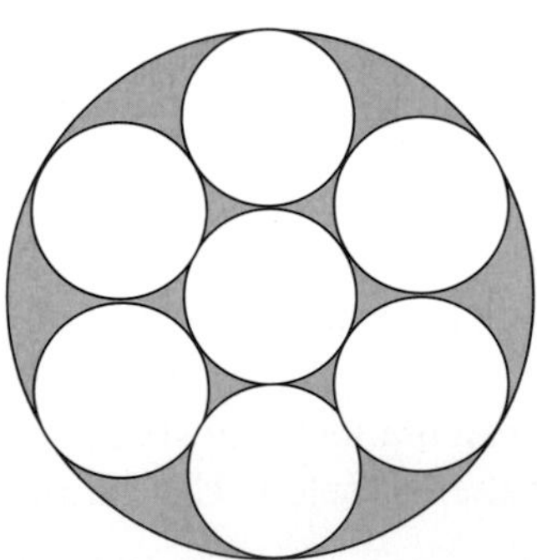

11 Work out without a calculator. Show your working.

(a) $\frac{3}{8} + \frac{1}{5}$

(b) $11.4 \div 0.4$

(c) $17 + 5.01 - 3.98$

(d) $5 \times (-3) - (-7)$

(e) $\frac{2}{3}$ of 5% of a quarter of £24 000

Part two

1 The mean weight of the apples in the pyramid is 109.7 g.
Estimate the total weight of all the apples.

2 (a) Increase 8.621 by $\frac{1}{10}$ (b) Decrease 20.05 by $\frac{1}{10}$

(c) Decrease 12.659 by $\frac{1}{100}$ (d) Increase 3.269 by $\frac{1}{1000}$

3 *Estimate* the answers to the following. Do not use a calculator.

(a) 47.53×102.5 (b) $\dfrac{207.4 - 3.69}{18.2 + 1.63}$ (c) $875.2 \div 9.11$

(d) $\sqrt{38.96 \times 11.32}$ (e) 9.3% of £198.75

4 Calculate the area of each shape. All the arcs are semicircles.

(a)

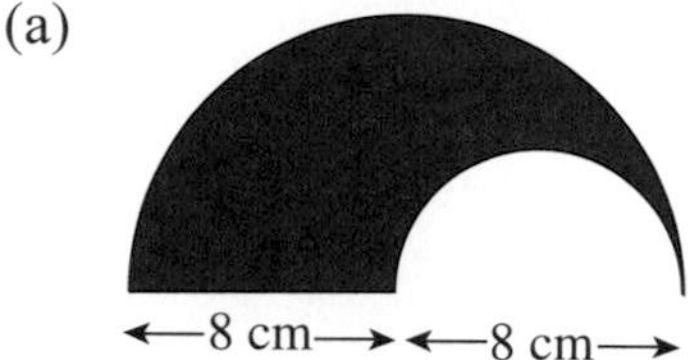

(b)

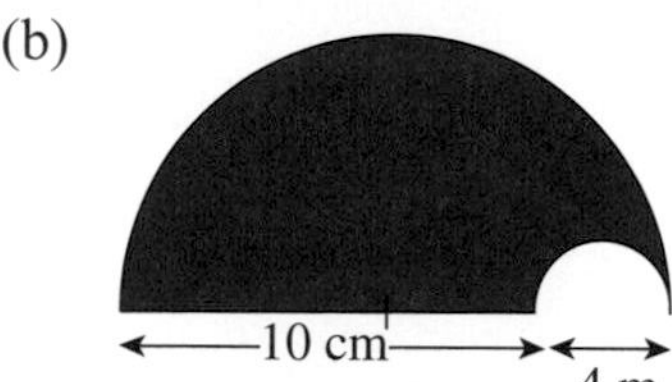

5 Write down the number shown at each arrow.

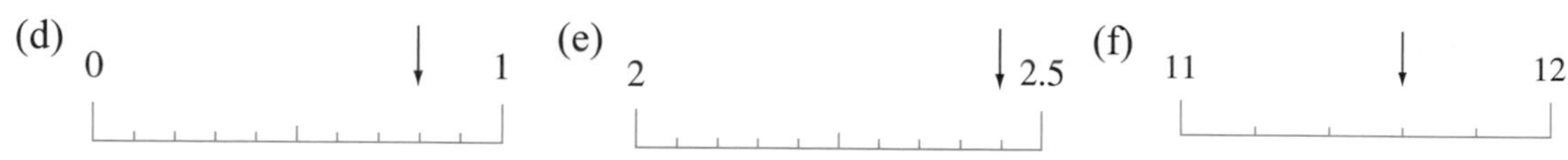

(d) 0 1 (e) 2 2.5 (f) 11 12

(g) 0.2 0.5 (h) 3.1 3.15 (i) 0.325 0.326

6

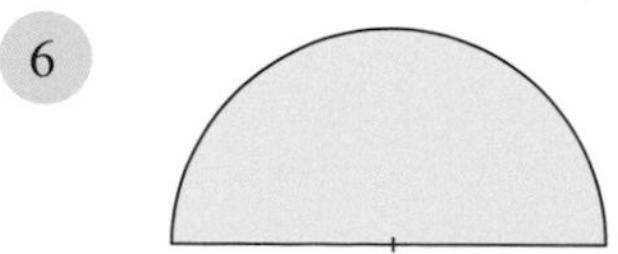

Calculate the perimeter of the semicircle. Give your answer in terms of π.
(Leave π in your answer)

7 Michelle was on her computer one day and it would not do what she wanted. She rather lost her temper with the machine and shouted at it. She did not expect the computer to strike back! The repairs to the computer cost £105 and her dentist bill was £208.50. Calculate the total cost of this dispute when VAT is added at 15%.

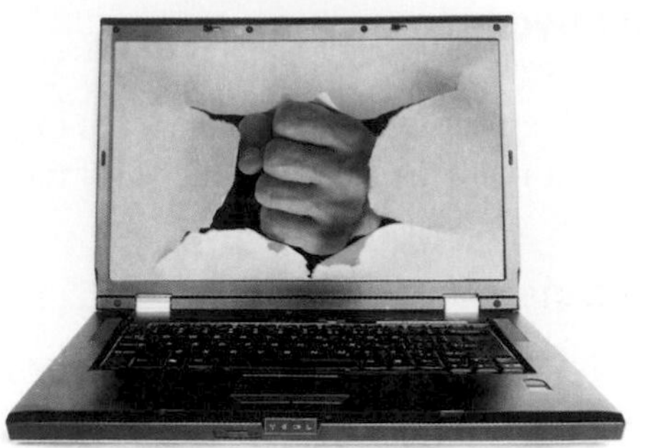

8 A circular lake has a radius of 120 m. Steve runs five times around this lake at a speed of 10 km/h. How long will it take? Give your answer to the nearest minute.

9 Find the angles marked by letters.

(a)

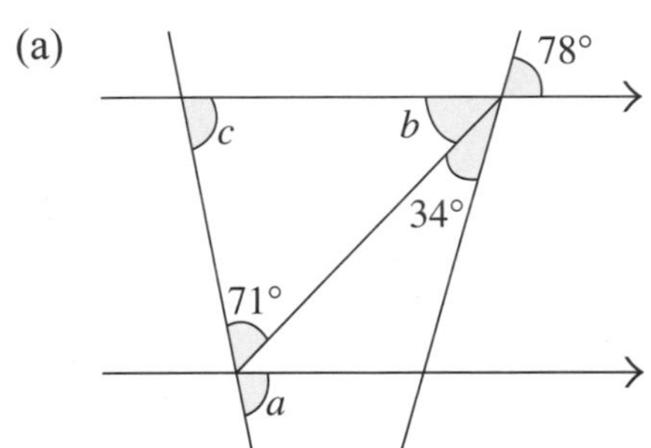

(b)

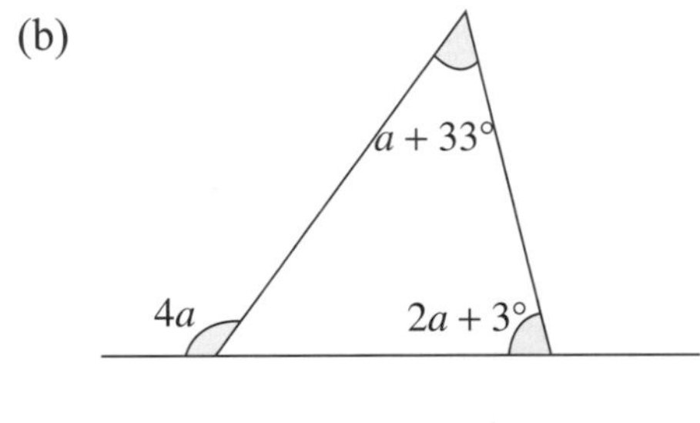

10 Copy each calculation and decide by estimation which is the correct answer from the list given. To obtain any marks you must show the working you used to obtain your estimate.

(a) 3.9×5.2 (b) 10.3×9.8 (c) $36.96 \div 4$

(d) $3.62 \div 18.1$ (e) $20.2 \div 0.101$ (f) 1.1×2.7

Answers (not in order): 2.97, 0.2, 100.94, 20.28, 200, 9.24

11 A bucket weighs 1.2 kg when it is empty, and 6.6 kg when it is full of water. What will it weigh when it is half full?

12 Use estimation to choose the odd one out.

315×9.7; $5874 \div 1.983$; 152.7×2.01; $30\,908 \div 10.2$

13 The trapezium, the square and the circle below all have the same area.

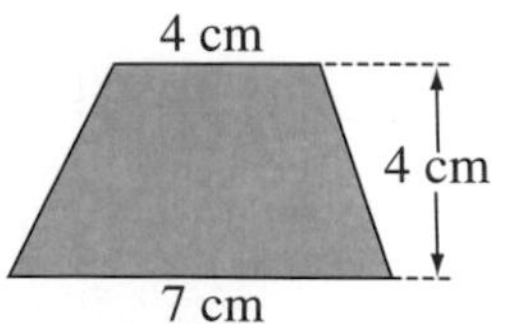

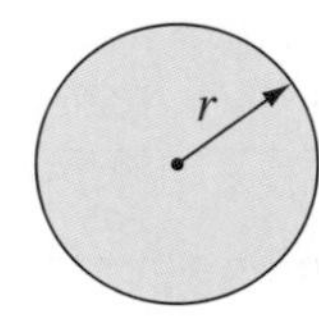

Calculate the values of x and r.

Puzzles and Problems 2

Calculator words

- When you hold a calculator display upside down some numbers appear to form words: 4506 spells "Gosh"

  0.70 spells "Old"

  (ignoring the decimal point)

Translate this passage using a calculator and the clues below:

'(1) ______ !', (2) ______ , (3) ______ , climbing out of (4) ______ . 'It's raining. I can't take (5) ______ and (6) ______ for a walk now.' (7) ______ and (8) ______ were her (9) ______ and they loved to (10) ______ up the (11) ______ and roll about, covering their (12) ______ (13) ______ in mud.

From the window of her small (14) ______ , she saw a lady coming down the (15) ______ . '(16) ______ (17) ______ !' said (18) ______. 'It's (19) ______ , come to (20) ______ her (21) ______ (22) ______ . I'll ask her in for a chat.' '(23) ______ , (24) ______ . (25) ______ ! I'm wetting your floor,' (26) ______ (27) ______ , taking off her coat and (28) ______ and giving (29) ______ the basket of (30) ______ (31) ______ (32) ______ . 'I'll (33) ______ the eggs now', said (34) ______. 'Do you want some?'

'Yes please' smiled (35) ______ . 'I'll eat anything that is (36) ______ .' 'Did you know that the (37) ______ of the (38) ______ garage was ill and (39) ______ so the garage is closed until it is (40) ______ to someone (41) ______ .' '(42) ______ . The (43) ______ (44) ______ are ready.' 'Is that a new (45) ______ in your garden?' asked (46) ______ .

Gardening was one of (47) ______ (48) ______ and she could (49) ______ away hours with her plants and her pet (50) ______ . As it wasn't raining anymore she decided to let the (51) ______ (52) ______ in the garden.

(53) ______ had to go, so she put on her (54) ______ (55) ______ and coat. Picking up her basket, (56) ______ (57) ______,

'My basket has so many (58) ______. It doesn't (59) ______ (60) ______ properly anymore. It (61) ______.'

With that (62) ______ left, saying (63) ______, just in time to (64) ______ another downpour.

Clues to passage

1 : $2 \times 2 \times 2 \times 5$

2 : $0.4 - 0.05085$

3 : $22 \times 23 \times 24 \times 25 + 15\,230$

4 : $0.6^2 + (2 \times 0.1 \times 0.1)$

5 : 0.3×0.5

6 : $(9 \times 10 \times 11) - (2 \times 7 \times 13)$

7 : $0.4^2 - 0.1^2$

8 : $(10^2 + 1) \times 2^3$

9 : $1234 + 5678 - 1012$

10 : $(5 \times 6 \times 5 \times 6) + (1 + 2 + 3 + 4)$

11 : $203 \times 7 \times 5$

12 : $1000 - (3^4 + 1)$

13 : $728 \times 729 + 8 \times 37$

14 : $3 \times 13 \times 10^3 + (3.5 \div 0.5)$

15 : $2570 + 2571 + 2572 + 1^{74}$

16 : $10^3 \div 5^2$

17 : $9 \div 1000$

18 : $333333 - 12345 - 2158$

19 : $(67 \times 68 \times 69) + (34 \times 35) - (2^4)$

20 : $5 \times 7 \times (11 \times 20 + 1)$

21 : $5 \times 5 \times 5 \times 5 \times 2 \times 2 \times 2 \times 7 + 9$

22 : $6000 - 7$

23 : $0.1234 + 0.65$

24 : $11 \times 2 \times 8 \times 3 \times 23 \times 5^2 + (2 \times 7615)$

25 : $(3^2 - 1^2) \times 5$

26 : $5 \times 3 \times 23$

27 : $0.38 - 0.000081$

28 : $123 \times 432 - 91$

29 : $320\,000 - 1170$

30 : $30 \times 200 - 8 + 1$

31 : $567 + 345 - 567$

32 : $0.7 + 0.004 + 0.03$

33 : 1777×2^2

34 : $321\,123 - 2293$

35 : $561 \times 562 + 2^8$

36 : $377\,777 + 321 + 5$

37 : $33\,048 \div (4.7 + 1.3)$

38 : $12345 + (5 \times 13 \times 10^3)$

39 : $0.31 + 0.00034$

40 : $0.047 \times 5 \times 3$

41 : $60^2 - 3^2$

42 : $68 \times 69 \times 70 + (22 + 45) \times 100$

43 : $0.61^2 - 0.00102$

44 : $10^4 - 4007$

45 : $(23 \times 5 \times 3) \div 1000$

46 : $105\,180 + 105\,181 + 105\,177$

47 : $47 \times 48 \times 49 \times 50 - 208\,370$

48 : $(23 \times 10^2 \times 209 \times 11) + 31\,104$

49 : $503 \times \sqrt{(108 \div 3)}$

50 : $448 \times 449 \times 450 - 79\,366$

51 : $41\,300 \div (0.32 + 0.61 + 6.07)$

52 : $(0.7 \div 0.1) + (5 \times 7 \times 10^3)$

53 : $16^2 + 562 \times 561$

54 : $0.33333 + 0.04001$

55 : $(10^4 + 609) \times 5$

56 : $(4^2 - 1^2) \times (30 - 7)$

57 : $0.6^2 - 0.1^2 - 0.00085$

58 : $(999 - 40) \times 2^3 \times 7$

59 : $0.011 \times \sqrt{4096}$

60 : $5678 + 630 \div 2$

61 : $1 - 0.3 + 0.000551$

62 : $315\,513 + (10^3 \div 40)$

63 : $146 \times 147 \times 148 + (3 \times 1211)$

64 : $[1001 \div (7 \times 11)] \times 10^3 \times 3$

Mental Arithmetic Practice

Here is a set of mental arithmetic questions. Ideally a teacher will read out each question twice, with pupils' books closed. The test of 30 questions should take about 20 minutes.

1 Which of these fractions is the larger: $\frac{2}{3}$ or $\frac{3}{4}$?

2 True or false: a weight of 5 stones is less than 50 kg.

3 Work out 1% of £45.

4 Write in words the answer to $10 \times 100 \times 1000$.

5 Add together 5, 6, 7 and 8.

6 A car travels 30 miles in 30 minutes. How far will it travel at this speed in $\frac{3}{4}$ hour?

7 Sam spends 40% of his money on tapes and 50% of his money on clothes. If he had £5 left, how much did he have at first?

8 Write as a decimal: $\frac{1}{5}$ plus $\frac{1}{10}$.

9 A bucket contains 2 litres of milk. How much is left, in ml, after 100 ml is removed?

10 How many hours and minutes is it from 8.15 a.m. until noon?

11 One bag weighs 250 g. How many bags weigh 5 kg?

12 If 20 drinks cost £28, find the cost of 5.

13 A magazine costing 47p was paid for with a £1 coin. Which three coins were given as change?

14 What is the number which is 200 less than 2000?

15 Find the change from a £5 note after buying 3 pounds of apples at 20p per pound.

16 A girl faces West and turns clockwise through 1 right angle. In which direction is she now facing?

17 A film, lasting $1\frac{1}{2}$ hours, starts at 6.20. When does it finish?

18 Work out $100 - 4.9$.

19 Name the date which is 4 months before the 1st of February.

20 Write down the next prime number after 20.

21 Write $\frac{9}{10}$ as a percentage.

22 Of the people in a room, a half were French, ten per cent were German and the rest were Irish. What percentage were Irish?

23 In January, Steve weighs 70 kg. By July his weight is reduced by 10%. What does he weigh in July?

24 Find the total surface area of a cube of side 1 cm.

25 Work out 98 + 67.

26 Write 1.6 recurring correct to one decimal place.

27 A 10 p coin is 1.7 mm thick. What is the height of a pile of coins worth £1?

28 Estimate the length of a side of a square of area 50 cm^2.

29 Work out $\frac{2}{3}$ of £120.

30 True or false: 15 cm is about 6 inches.

A long time ago! 2

Binary numbers

Decimal numbers use 10 digits:

0, 1, 2, 3, 4, 5, 6, 7, 8, 9

Binary numbers use only 2 digits: 0 and 1

A binary number uses powers of 2 to give its value.

$2^0 = 1$ $\quad$ $2^1 = 2$ $\quad$ $2^2 = 4$ $\quad$ $2^3 = 8$

What is the decimal value of the binary number 1101?

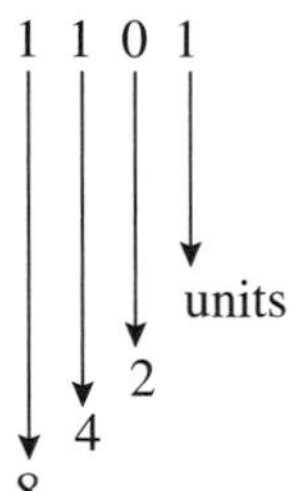

= 8 + 4 + 0 + 1 = 13

A switch can be 'on' or 'off'. The digit 1 can be used for 'on' and the digit 0 for 'off' so circuits could be built using binary numbers.

George Boole in the 19th century developed a 'true' or 'false' logic system called Boolean algebra.

Without binary numbers, there might never have been any computers then where would we be?

The first mention of binary numbers was more than two thousand years ago by an Indian called Pingala.

Exercise

1 Look at the example above then change these binary numbers into decimal numbers.

(a) 101 (b) 11 (c) 110 (d) 1001
(e) 10 (f) 1010 (g) 1100 (h) 1111

2 What is the decimal value of the binary number 10000?

3 Write 32 as a binary number.

4 Write 64 as a binary number.

5 Write the following numbers in binary form.

(a) 17 (b) 24 (c) 4 (d) 14 (e) 44

6 Add these binary numbers to get a binary answer.

(a) $\begin{array}{r} 101 \\ +\ 11 \\ \hline \\ \hline \end{array}$ (b) $\begin{array}{r} 1011 \\ +\ 1001 \\ \hline \\ \hline \end{array}$ (c) $\begin{array}{r} 1010 \\ +\ 1111 \\ \hline \\ \hline \end{array}$

7 Subtract these binary numbers to get a binary answer.

(a) $\begin{array}{r} 1101 \\ -\ 111 \\ \hline \\ \hline \end{array}$ (b) $\begin{array}{r} 1110 \\ -\ 1001 \\ \hline \\ \hline \end{array}$ (c) $\begin{array}{r} 11001 \\ -\ 1101 \\ \hline \\ \hline \end{array}$

8 **RESEARCH:**

(a) Find out what hexadecimal numbers are.
(b) Find out more about George Boole and Boolean algebra.

UNIT 3

3.1 Reflection

In section 3.1 you will learn how to:

- draw reflections on squared paper
- draw reflections using coordinates
- investigate reflections in other situations

Reflections are quite common in everyday life.

Think of examples of reflections:

- in the classroom
- at home
- anywhere

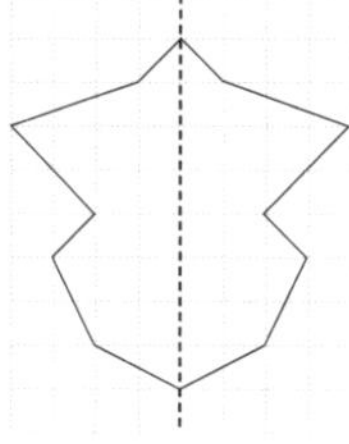

The shape on the left has line symmetry. This can be checked by either paper folding, using tracing paper or by using a mirror.
In a mathematical reflection we imagine a line of symmetry which acts like a double-sided mirror.

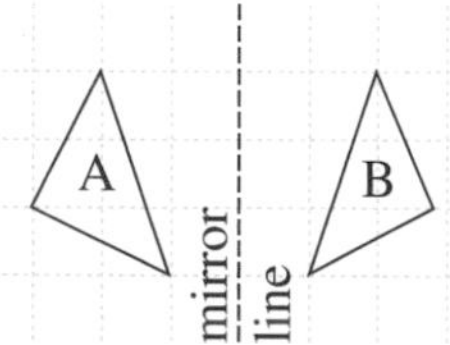

- Triangle B is the image of triangle A under reflection in the mirror line. Similarly triangle A is the image of triangle B under reflection in the same line.

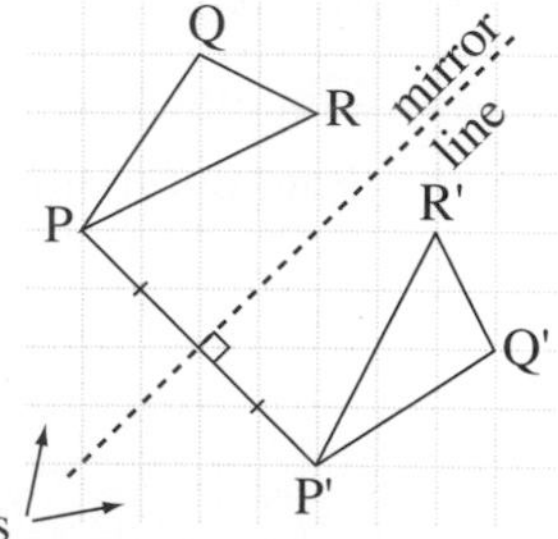

- Extra care is required when the mirror line lies along a diagonal. Notice that the line PP′ is perpendicular to the mirror line.

- The mirror line can pass through the shape which is being reflected, as shown here.

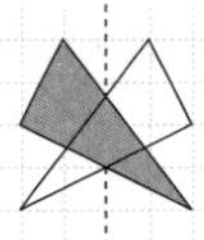

Exercise 1M

Copy each shape on squared paper and draw the image after reflection in the broken line.

1 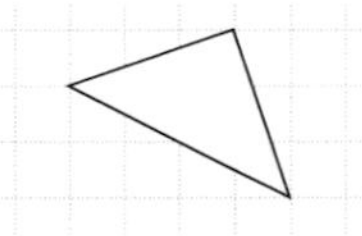

2 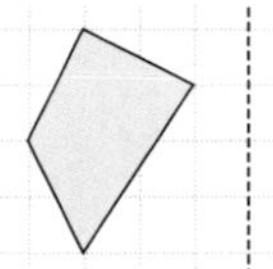

3 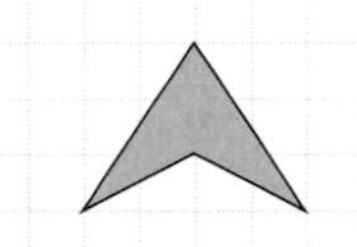

4 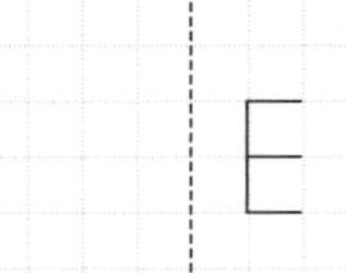

5 

6 

7 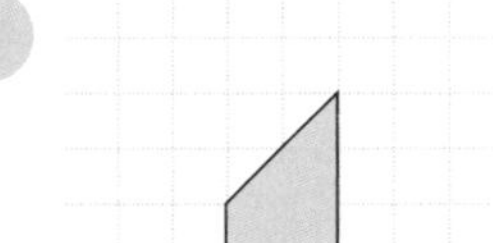

8 

9 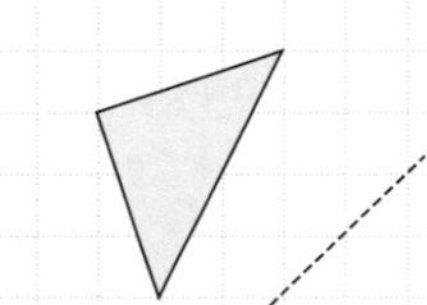

10 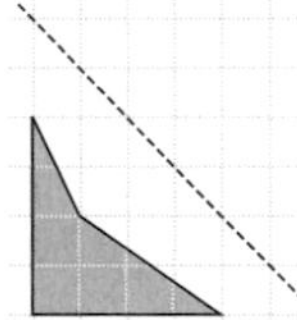

11 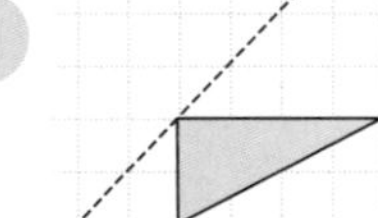

12 

13 Write your own name in capital letters and then reflect the letters in a horizontal line.

14 Draw any shape of your own design (not too complicated!) and then reflect it in either a horizontal, vertical or diagonal line.

Exercise 1E

In questions 1 to 3 first reflect the shape in line 1 and then reflect the image in line 2.

1 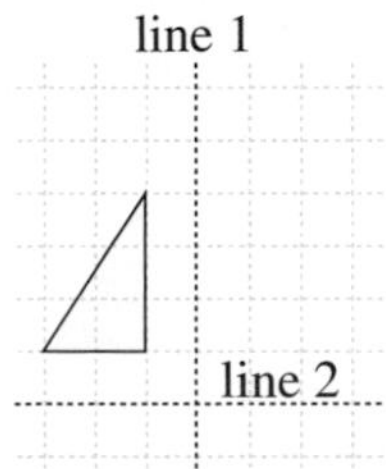

2 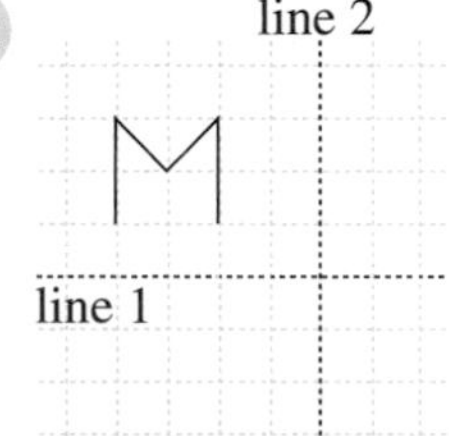

3 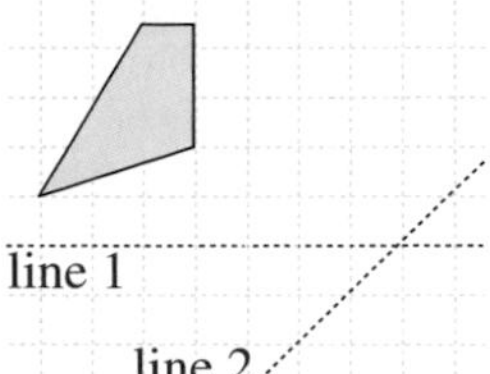

Questions 4 to 6 are more difficult reflections. Copy each shape and draw the image after reflection in the broken line.

4

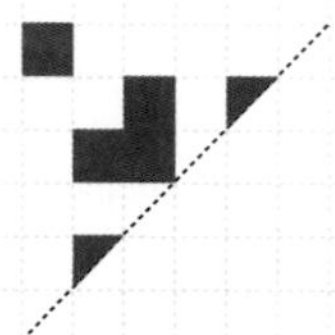

5

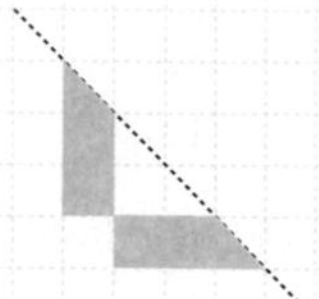

6

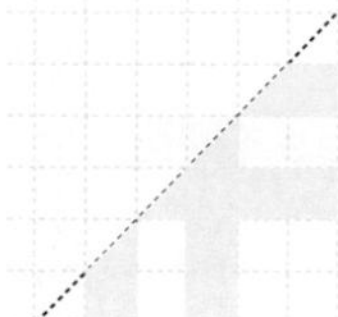

7 The photo shows the captain of a ship holding a clock as his ship is slowly sinking.

A clock face has just twelve marks to show the hours. Draw the clockface, showing the hands as they would appear when looked at in a mirror, when the time was

(a) 2.30

(b) 5.45.

8 Draw the shapes on triangular dotty paper and then draw the image of each shape after reflection in the broken line.

(a)

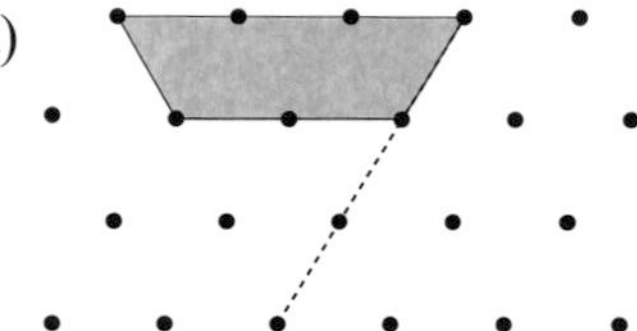

(b)

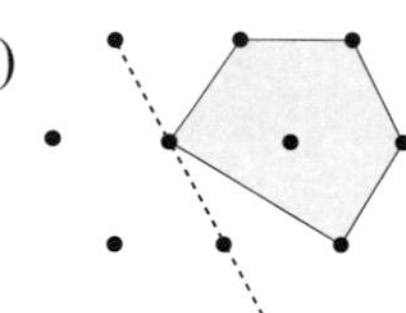

(c)

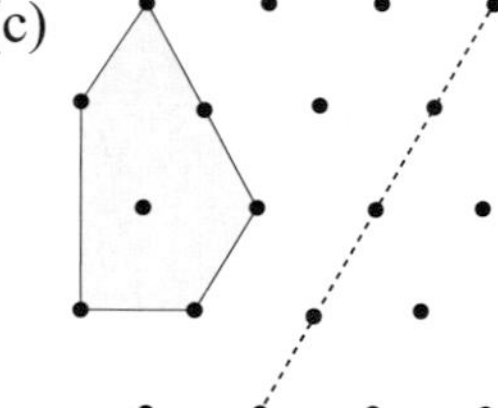

Using coordinates

(a) Triangle 2 is the image of triangle 1 under reflection in the *x axis*. We will use the shorthand 'Δ' for 'triangle'.

(b) $\Delta 3$ is the image of $\Delta 2$ under reflection in the line $x = -1$.

(c) $\Delta 4$ is the image of $\Delta 1$ under reflection in the line $y = x$.

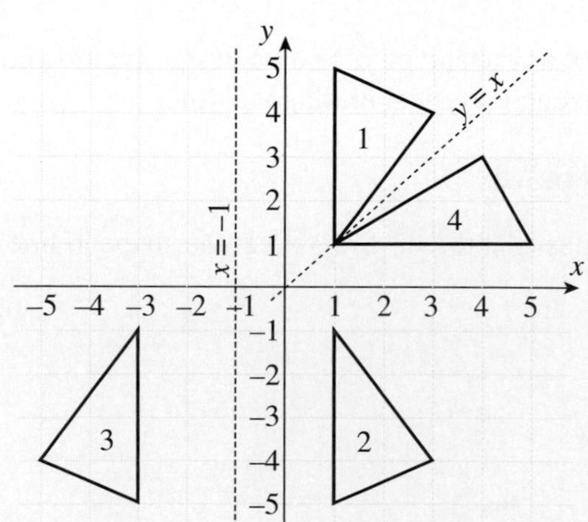

Exercise 2M

1 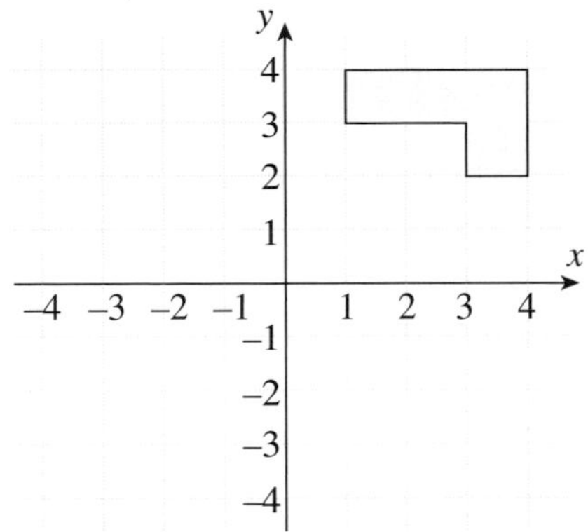

Copy the diagram.

(a) Reflect the shape in the x axis. Label the image A.

(b) Reflect the shape in the y axis. Label the image B.

2 Copy the diagram onto squared paper.

(a) Reflect the blue triangle in $y = 2$. Label the image A.

(b) Reflect the blue triangle in $x = 1$. Label the image B.

(c) Reflect the blue triangle in the x axis. Label the image C.

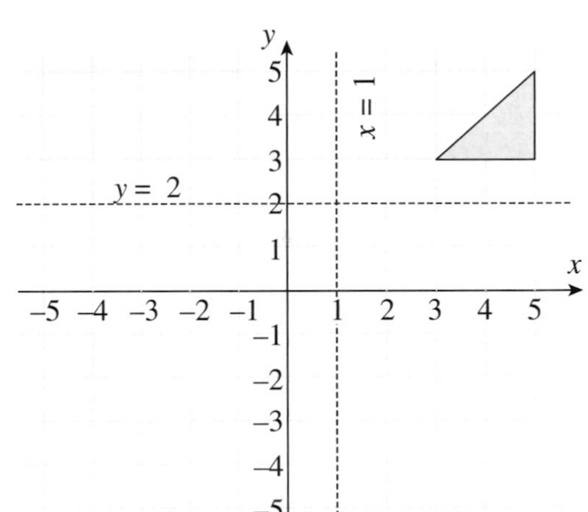

3 Copy the diagram onto squared paper.
Draw the image of the pink triangle under reflection in:

(a) $y = 1$, label it ΔA

(b) $x = -1$, label it ΔB

(c) $y = x$, label it ΔC

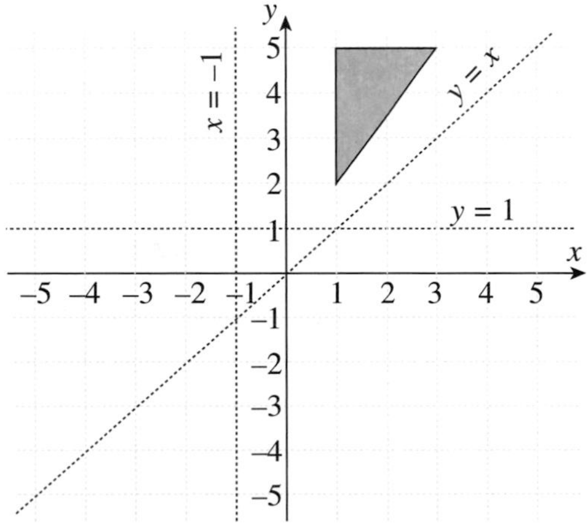

4 (a) Draw x and y axes with values from –6 to +6 and draw shape A which has vertices at (3, 1), (5, 3), (5, 1), (4, 0)

(b) Reflect shape A in the x axis onto shape B.

(c) Reflect shape A in the y axis onto shape C.

(d) Reflect shape A in the line $y = x$ onto shape D.

5 (a) Draw x and y axes with values from –6 to +6 and draw shape A which has vertices at (1, –2), (3, –3), (3, –4), (1, –6)

(b) Reflect shape A in the y axis onto shape B.

(c) Reflect shape B (not shape A!) in the line $y = x$ onto shape C.

(d) Reflect shape C in the line $y = 1\frac{1}{2}$ onto shape D.

(e) Write down the coordinates of the vertices of shape D.

6 (a) Draw x and y axes with values from –6 to +6 and draw shape P which has vertices at (–4, 2), (–4, 3), (–3, 5), (–3, 2).

(b) Reflect shape P in the line $y = 2$ onto shape Q.

(c) Reflect shape Q in the y axis onto shape R.

(d) Reflect shape R in the line $y = x$ onto shape S.

(e) Write down the coordinates of the vertices of shape S.

7 Write down the equation of the mirror line for the following reflections:

(a) $\Delta A \rightarrow \Delta C$

(b) $\Delta A \rightarrow \Delta B$

(c) $\Delta D \rightarrow \Delta G$

(d) $\Delta F \rightarrow \Delta E$

(e) $\Delta F \rightarrow \Delta D$

Remember:

The x axis is also the line $y = 0$.
The y axis is also the line $x = 0$.

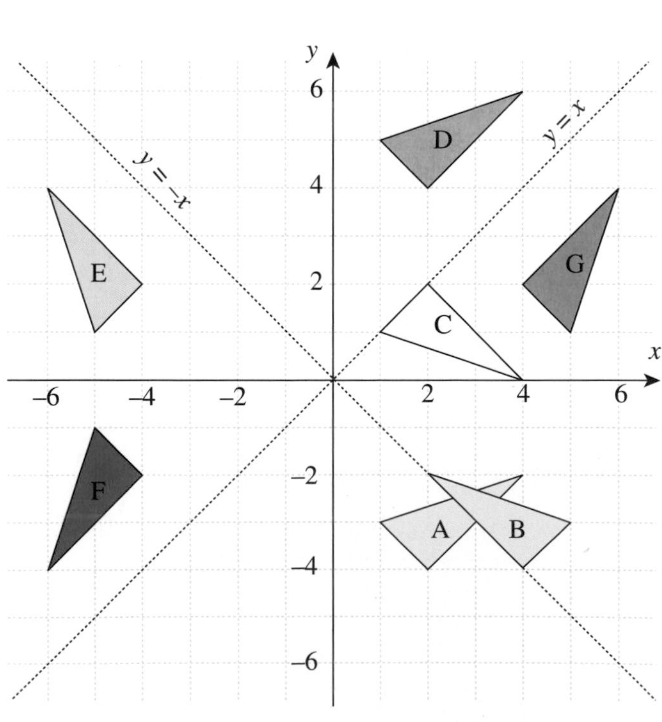

Exercise 2E

1 (a) Draw x and y axes with values from –6 to +6 and draw $\Delta 1$ with vertices at (3, 1), (6, 1), (6, 3).

(b) Reflect $\Delta 1$ in the line $y = x$ onto $\Delta 2$.

(c) Reflect $\Delta 1$ in the y axis onto $\Delta 3$.

(d) Reflect $\Delta 2$ in the y axis onto $\Delta 4$.

(e) Find the equation for the reflection $\Delta 3$ onto $\Delta 4$.

2 (a) Draw $\Delta 1$ with vertices at (–4, 4), (–4, 6), (–1, 6).

(b) Reflect $\Delta 1$ in the line $x = -\frac{1}{2}$ onto $\Delta 2$.

(c) Reflect $\Delta 2$ in the line $y = x$ onto $\Delta 3$.

(d) Reflect $\Delta 1$ in the line $y = x$ onto $\Delta 4$.

(e) Find the equation for the reflection $\Delta 3$ onto $\Delta 4$.

3 The yellow shape is reflected so that the image of A is A′.

(a) Copy the diagram and find the mirror line for this reflection.

(b) Draw the image of the yellow shape after reflection in the mirror line.

(c) Draw a new mirror line at right angles to the first mirror line. Draw the image of the yellow shape in this new mirror line.

4 (a) In what country did Napoleon live? Write your answer in "mirror writing".

(b) Whose statue is on top of a column in Trafalgar Square?

(c) Which famous mathematician made a discovery after an apple fell on his head?

5 The word 'AMBULANCE' is to be printed on the front of an ambulance so that a person in front of the ambulance will see the word written the right way round, when viewed in the driver's mirror. How should the word be printed on the front of the ambulance?

6 Draw a circle, with radius about 4 cm, and mark any three points A, B and C on the circumference. Draw lines through AB, BC and CA as shown.

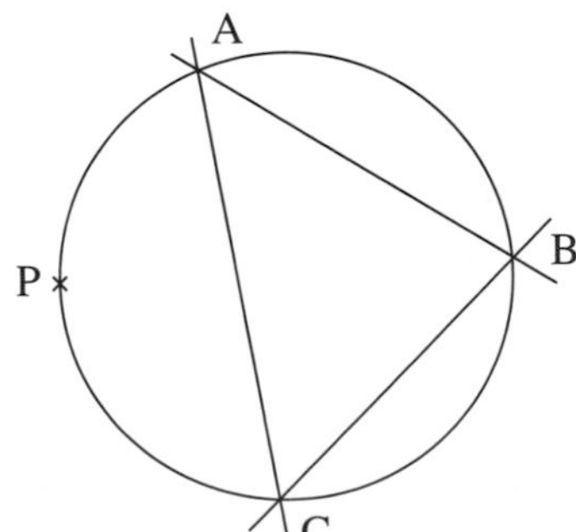

Mark a fourth point P anywhere on the circumference. Use a set square and ruler to find the images of P after reflection in the lines through AB, BC and CA.

What do you notice? Compare your result with that of other people.

7 (a) Find the image of the point (1, 6) after reflection in the line:

(i) $x = 5$ (ii) $x = 50$ (iii) $y = 2$ (iv) $y = 200$ (v) $y = x$ (vi) $y = -x$.

(b) Find the image of the point (63, 207) after reflection in the line:

(i) $y = x$ (ii) $y = -x$.

(c) Find the image of the point (a, b) after reflection in the x axis.

(d) Find the image of the point (a, b) after reflection in the y axis.

8 The line segment AB can be made into a 2 × 2 square using three successive reflections as shown below.

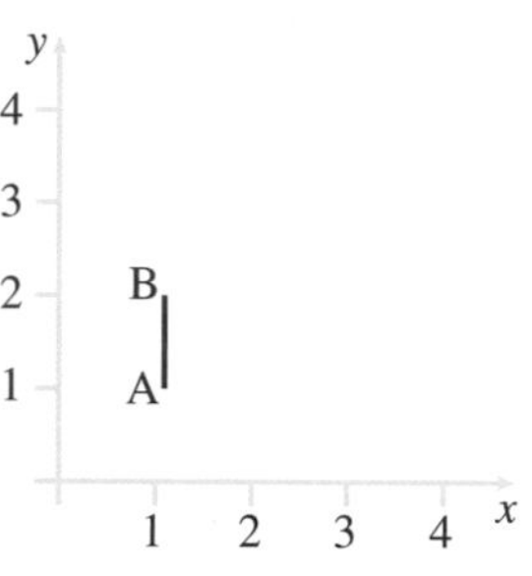

(a) reflect in $y = 2$

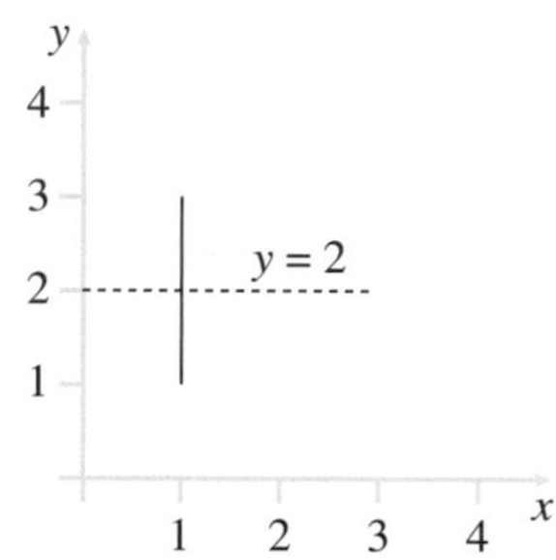

(b) reflect in $x + y = 4$

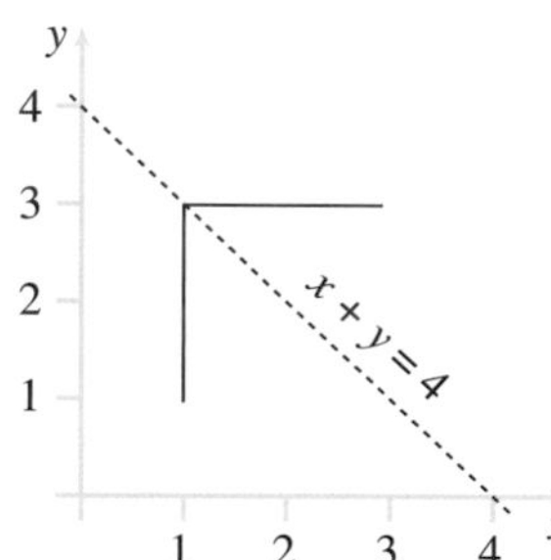

(c) reflect in $y = x$

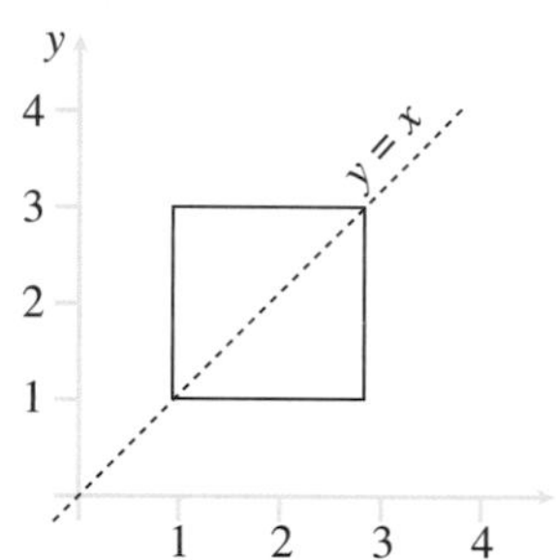

Show how the same line segment AB can be made into a 3 × 3 square with four successive reflections. Give the equations for all the mirror lines.

Investigation – two reflections

Make three copies of the diagram below:

Triangle P can be reflected, in two vertical parallel lines, onto triangle Q.

(a) Draw possible positions for the mirror lines on your three diagrams.

(b) What do you notice each time?

(c) Do you obtain the same connection if one of the mirror lines is to the left of triangle P?

(d) What if both mirror lines are to the left of triangle P? Are the two mirror linesn still connected in the same way?

3.2 Describing data

In section 3.2 you will learn about:

- the mean, median, mode and range of a set of data
- comparing sets of data
- finding averages from frequency tables
- stem and leaf diagrams

The mean

All the data is added and the total is divided by the number of items. In everyday language the word 'average' usually stands for the mean.

The median

When the data is arranged in order of size, the median is the one in the middle. If there are two 'middle' numbers, the median is in the middle of these two numbers [i.e. the mean of the two numbers].

The word 'average' is used to describe a typical or representative member of a set of data.

The mode

The mode is the number or quality (like a colour) which occurs most often. Sometimes a set of data will have no mode, two modes or even more and this is a problem which we cannot avoid.

Range

The range is not an average but is the difference between the largest value and the smallest value in a set of data. It is useful in comparing sets of data when the *spread* of the data is important.

The marks in a spelling test were: 7, 8, 6, 6, 5, 3, 9, 8

(a) mean mark $= \frac{7+8+6+6+5+3+9+8}{8} = \frac{52}{8} = 6.5$

(b) arrange marks in order: 3 5 6 6 7 8 8 9

the median is the half way number $= \frac{6+7}{2} = 6.5$

(c) there are two modes 6 and 8

(d) range $= 9 - 3 = 6$

Exercise 1M

1 (a) Find the mean of 1, 3, 4, 7, 8.
(b) Find the median of 1, 3, 3, 4, 5, 7, 8, 11, 14, 14, 16.
(c) Find the mode of 3, 3, 3, 3, 4, 4, 5, 6, 6, 6, 7, 7.
(d) Find the range of 7, 8, 11, 14, 26, 30.

2 (a) Find the mean of the numbers 4, 13, 5, 7, 9, 6, 5.
(b) Find the median of the numbers 6, 20, 1, 16, 2, 12, 6, 3, 8, 6, 8.
(c) Find the mode of the numbers 13, 2, 11, 2, 10, 4, 5, 10, 8, 10.

3 The digits from 0 to 9 are made using 5p coins.
(a) Count the number of coins in each digit. (For the zero count the last one.)
(b) What is the median number of coins used in a digit?
(c) Work out the mean value of the coins used in a digit when the number 6 5 4 is formed.

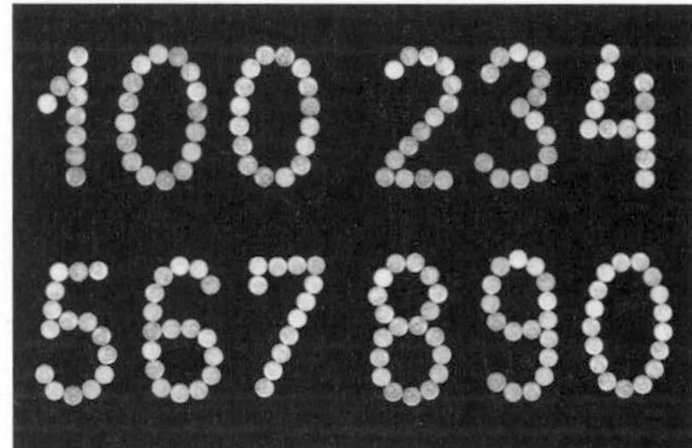

4 In several different shops the price of a certain DVD was £5.95, £3.99, £2.99, £4.75, £3.50, £2.95, £6.50. What is the median price of the DVD?

5 Six girls have heights of 1.48 m, 1.51 m, 1.47 m, 1.55 m, 1.40 m and 1.59 m.
(a) Find the mean height of the six girls.
(b) Find the mean height of the remaining five girls when the tallest girl leaves.

6 The temperature at midnight in nine towns were, in °C,

1°, 0°, –3°, –4°, 3°, –6°, 2°, –2°, –1°.

What was the median temperature?

7 The test results for a class of 30 pupils were as follows:

Mark	3	4	5	6	7	8
Frequency	2	5	4	7	6	6

What was the modal mark?

8 A park in Hatfield has trees which were planted in the years:

1940 1940 1965 1968 1972 1980

1986 1986 1986 1990 1992 1994

Work out the mean age of the trees

(a) in 2009, (b) in 2030.

9 Find the range of the following sets of numbers:

(a) 4, 11, 3, 8, 22, 5, 7, 30, 18

(b) 9, 18, 100, 64, 11, 26

(c) 4, –2, 6, 4, 5, 10, 3.

10 The mean of the numbers 4, 7, 12, 8 and N is 8.
Find the value of N.

11 The median of the numbers 5, 7, 2, 12, 11 and x is 8.
Find the value of x.

Exercise 1E

1 Lauren has five cards. The five cards have a mean of 7 and a range of 4.
What are the missing numbers?

7	7	7		

2 For the set of numbers below, find the mean and the median.

1, 3, 3, 3, 4, 6, 99.

Which average best describes the set of numbers?

3 The heights of the people shown are, in m

1.82 1.71 1.74 1.69 1.73

1.64 1.8 1.77 1.84

(a) Find the median height of these people.

(b) Two more people of heights 1.61 m and 1.7 m join this group. What is the median height of this new group of eleven people?

4 In a history test, Andrew got 62%. For the whole class, the mean mark was 64% and the median mark was 59%. Which 'average' tells him whether he is in the 'top' half or the 'bottom' half of the class?

5 The range for nine numbers on a card is 60.
One number is covered by a piece of blu-tac.
What could that number be?
[There are two possible answers.]

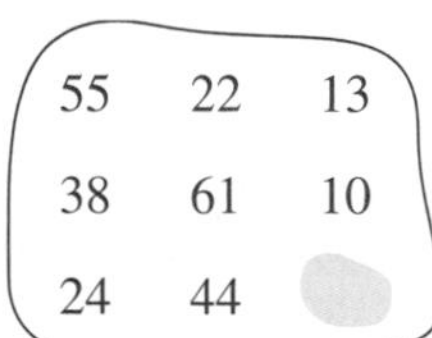

6 Thirteen children took a test. Their marks were:

64 47 56 52 48 63 72

59 68 35 70 ☐ ☐

The mean mark was 58 and the range was 40. What are the missing marks?

7 Write down five numbers so that:

the mean is 7

the median is 6

the mode is 4.

8 The mean of the eight numbers 6, 6, 9, 3, 8, 11, 5, 2 is $6\frac{1}{4}$.

When a number x is added, the new mean of the nine numbers is 7. Find x.

9 Tom and Wendy both do three tests and their marks have the same mean.

The range of Tom's marks is twice the range of Wendy's marks.

Copy and complete the table.

Tom's marks		60	
Wendy's marks	55	60	65

10 The mean age of three people is 22 and their median age is 20.

The range of their ages is 16. How old is each person?

11 Here are 4 cards and you are told that x is a positive whole number.

(a) Find, in terms of x,

(i) The range of the 4 cards.

(ii) The median of the 4 cards.

(iii) The mean of the 4 cards.

(b) The mean is 2 greater than the median.

Find the value of x.

$x - 1$ | $5x + 1$ | $x + 9$ | $x + 3$

12 Here are 9 cards and n is a positive whole number.

(a) Find, in terms of n.

(i) The median of the 9 cards.

(ii) The mode of the 9 cards.

(iii) The mean of the 9 cards.

(b) The range of the cards is 47.
Find the value of n and hence find the mean value of the cards.

n | $n - 7$ | $n - 2$ | $n + 6$ | $4n + 1$ | $n + 3$ | $n + 2$ | $n - 10$ | $n - 2$

13 The mean height of n people is h cm. One person of height x cm leaves the group and one person of height y cm joins the group. Find an expression for the new mean height.

Comparing sets of data

To compare 2 sets of data, always write at least 2 things:

1 Compare an average (i.e. mean, median or mode).

2 Compare the range of each set of data (this shows how spread out the data is).

Exercise 2M

1 The heights in metres of the children in year 8 classes in two schools were recorded.

School A	1.60	1.59	1.63	1.57	1.64	1.58	1.57	1.62	1.57	1.64
School B	1.55	1.42	1.65	1.48	1.50	1.64	1.44	1.69	1.41	1.40

(a) Work out the mean height and the range for school A.
(b) Work out the mean height and the range for school B.
(c) Write a sentence to compare the heights of the children in the two schools.

2 The weights of the tigers in a safari park in Spain are as follows:

65 kg, 71 kg, 72 kg, 85 kg, 91 kg, 92 kg, 94 kg, 101 kg

(a) Find the mean weight of these tigers and the range of their weights.

At another park in Portugal the mean weight of the tigers was 96 kg and the range of their weights was 120 kg.

(b) Write one or two sentences to compare the weights of the tigers at these two parks.
(c) Suggest a possible explanation for the differences you observe.

3 

In an experiment firstly red ants and then black ants were released at the dot in a maze. The time they took to escape was recorded.

Here are the results. The times are in seconds

Red ants:	7	9	10	13	13	22	23	26	30
Black ants:	8	8	11	12	13	13	14	15	17

(a) Write a sentence to compare the times taken to escape for the red and black ants.
(b) Time yourself to see how long it takes you to escape. How did you or your friends compare with the ants?

4 Leila did a survey of the number of people living in the houses in a street in Luton.

(a) Write down the modal number of people in these houses.

People in house	tally	frequency
0	|	1
1	𝍸 |	6
2	𝍸 𝍸	
3	𝍸 𝍸 ||	
4	𝍸 𝍸 𝍸	
5	𝍸 |||	
6	||	

Stephen did a similar survey in a street in Stevenage. His results are below

Number of people	0	1	2	3	4	5	6
Frequency	0	13	11	5	1	0	1

(b) Write a sentence to compare the number of people living in the houses in these two towns.

(c) Suggest a possible reason for the difference you observe.

Frequency tables

When a set of data consists of many numbers it is convenient to record the information in a frequency table. It is possible to find the mean, median and mode directly from the table as shown in the example below.

The frequency table shows the number of goals scored in 15 football matches.

number of goals	0	1	2	3	4	5 or more
frequency	2	5	4	3	1	0

(a) We *could* find the mean as follows:

$$\text{mean} = \frac{(0+0+1+1+1+1+1+2+2+2+2+3+3+3+4)}{15}$$

A better method is to multiply the number of goals by the respective frequencies.

$$\text{mean} = \frac{(0 \times 2) + (1 \times 5) + (2 \times 4) + (3 \times 3) + (4 \times 1)}{15}$$

mean = 1.73 goals (correct to 2 d.p.)

(b) The median is the 8th number in the list, when the numbers are arranged in order. The median is, therefore, 2 goals.

(c) The modal number of goals is 1, since more games had 1 goal than any other number.

Exercise 2E

1 The frequency table shows the weights of 30 eggs laid by the hens on a free range farm.

weight	44 g	48 g	52 g	56 g	60 g
frequency	5	6	7	9	3

Find the mean weight of the eggs.

2 The frequency table shows the weights of the 40 pears sold in a shop.

weight	70 g	80 g	90 g	100 g	110 g	120 g
frequency	2	7	9	11	8	3

Calculate the mean weight of the pears.

3 The frequency table shows the price of a Mars bar in 30 different shops.

price	49p	50p	51p	52p	53p	54p
frequency	2	3	5	10	6	4

Calculate the mean price of a Mars bar.

4 The marks, out of 10, achieved by 25 teachers in a spelling test were as follows:

mark	5	6	7	8	9	10
frequency	8	7	4	2	3	1

mite	✗
might	✓
goal	✓
gole	✗
paralel	✗
thay	✗

Find (a) the mean mark

(b) the median mark

(c) the modal mark.

5 A golfer played the same hole 30 times with the following results.

score	3	4	5	6	7	8
frequency	2	11	5	5	3	4

(a) Find his mean score, median score and modal score on the hole.

(b) Which average best represents the data? Explain why.

6 The table shows the weights of 50 coins. Find the weight x if the mean weight of the 50 coins is 1 gram more than the median weight.

weight	frequency
2 g	4
4 g	7
5 g	16
x	10
9 g	13

7 The number of bedrooms in the houses in a street is shown in the table

(a) If the mean number of bedrooms is 3.6, find x.

(b) If the median number of bedrooms is 3, find the largest possible value of x.

(c) If the modal number of bedrooms is 3, find the largest possible value of x.

number of bedrooms	frequency
2	5
3	12
4	x

8 The weights of 20 ear-rings were measured. Copy and complete the table so that the mean weight is 6.3 g, the median weight is 6 g and the modal weight is 7 g.

weight of ear-ring	5 g	6 g	7 g	8g
frequency	5			2

Stem and leaf diagrams

Data can be displayed in groups in a stem and leaf diagram.

Here are the marks of 20 girls in a science test.

47	53	71	55	28	40	45	62	57	64
33	48	59	61	73	37	75	26	68	39

We will put the marks into groups 20–29, 30–39….70–79.

We will choose the tens digit as the 'stem' and the units as the 'leaf'.

The first four marks are shown [47, 53, 71, 55]

Stem (tens)	Leaf (units)
2	
3	
4	7
5	3 5
6	
7	1

The complete diagram is below....and then with the leaves in numerical order:

Stem	Leaf
2	8 6
3	3 7 9
4	7 0 5 8
5	3 5 7 9
6	2 4 1 8
7	1 3 5

Stem	Leaf
2	6 8
3	3 7 9
4	0 5 7 8
5	3 5 7 9
6	1 2 4 8
7	1 3 5

The diagram shows the shape of the distribution. It is also easy to find the mode, the median and the range.

Exercise 3M

1 The marks of 24 children in a test are shown

41	23	35	15	40	39	47	29
52	54	45	27	28	36	48	51
59	65	42	32	46	53	66	38

Stem	Leaf
1	
2	3
3	5
4	1
5	
6	

Draw a stem and leaf diagram. The first three entries are shown.

2 Draw a stem and leaf diagram for each set of data below

(a)

24	52	31	55	40	37	58	61	25	46
44	67	68	75	73	28	20	59	65	39

Stem	Leaf
2	
3	
4	
5	
6	
7	

(b)

30	41	53	22	72	54	35	47
44	67	46	38	59	29	47	28

3 Here is the stem and leaf diagram showing the masses, in kg, of some people on a bus.

(a) Write down the range of the masses.

(b) How many people were on the bus?

(c) What is the median mass?

Stem (tens)	Leaf (units)
3	3 7
4	1 2 7 7 8
5	1 6 8 9
6	0 3 7
7	4 5
8	2

4 In this question the stem shows the units digit and the leaf shows the first digit after the decimal point.

Draw the stem and leaf diagram using the following data:

2.4	3.1	5.2	4.7	1.4	6.2	4.5	3.3
4.0	6.3	3.7	6.7	4.6	4.9	5.1	5.5
1.8	3.8	4.5	2.4	5.8	3.3	4.6	2.8

Key

3|7 means 3.7

Stem	Leaf
1	
2	
3	
4	
5	
6	

(a) What is the median?

(b) Write down the range.

CHECK YOURSELF ON SECTIONS 3.1 AND 3.2

1 Reflecting shapes

(a) Copy the diagram

(b) Draw the image of $\Delta 1$ after reflection in the line

(i) $x = -1$

(ii) $y = 1$

(c) Write down the equation of the mirror line for the reflection of:

(i) $\Delta 1$ onto $\Delta 2$

(ii) $\Delta 1$ onto $\Delta 3$

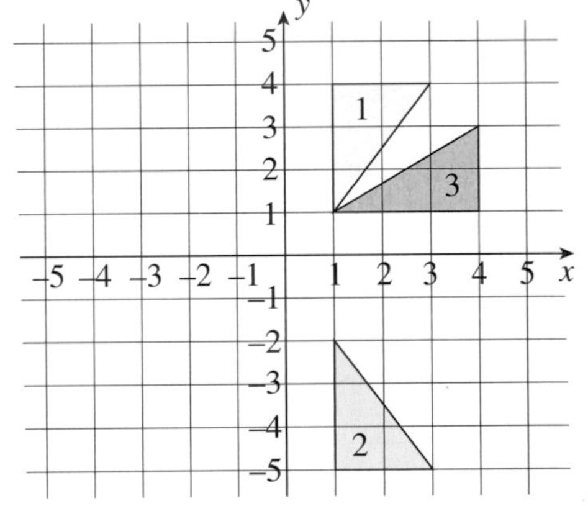

2 Finding averages and range

(a) The mean of the numbers 2, 5, 8, 7 and n is 6.6. Find n.

(b) The distances flown by a variety of paper aircraft are shown in the table.

distance	3 m	4 m	5 m	6 m	7 m	8 m	9 m
frequency	1	4	5	4	3	1	2

Calculate the mean distance flown.

3.3 Mental Calculations

In section 3.3 you will

- practise adding, subtracting and doubling numbers
- perform mental calculations in a range of contexts
- answer questions similar to those on KS3 mental arithmetic tests

Mental calculation strategies

Here are three methods for adding numbers in your head.

A 'Easy-to-add' numbers

$16 + 57 + 24 = 16 + 24 + 57 = 40 + 57 = 97$

$23 + 68 + 7 = 23 + 7 + 68 = 30 + 68 = 98$

$45 + 108 + 35 = 45 + 35 + 108 = 80 + 108 = 188$

B Splitting numbers

$33 + 48$: $30 + 40 = 70$ and $3 + 8 = 11$

So $33 + 48 = 70 + 11 = 81$

$264 + 38$: $260 + 30 = 290$ and $4 + 8 = 12$

So $264 + 38 = 290 + 12 = 302$

C Add/subtract 9, 19, 29… 11, 21, 31…, adjusting by one

$57 + 19 = 57 + 20 - 1 = 77 - 1 = 76$

$109 + 39 = 109 + 40 - 1 = 149 - 1 = 148$

$65 - 29 = 65 - 30 + 1 = 35 + 1 = 36$

$111 - 59 = 111 - 60 + 1 = 51 + 1 = 52$

Exercise 1M

Work out in your head.

A

1. $7 + 13 + 49$
2. $18 + 57 + 12$
3. $25 + 37 + 25$
4. $31 + 55 + 29$
5. $28 + 2 + 67$
6. $55 + 99 + 25$
7. $17 + 13 + 68$
8. $64 + 16 + 27$
9. $42 + 56 + 8$
10. $23 + 25 + 17$
11. $16 + 9 + 44$
12. $91 + 54 + 9$

B

1 $23 + 35$	2 $51 + 37$	3 $44 + 37$	4 $32 + 69$
5 $57 + 59$	6 $67 + 27$	7 $108 + 58$	8 $124 + 33$
9 $63 + 74$	10 $125 + 62$	11 $45 + 68$	12 $53 + 84$

C

1 $55 + 19$	2 $64 + 39$	3 $87 + 9$	4 $55 + 31$
5 $27 + 41$	6 $74 + 29$	7 $25 + 61$	8 $84 - 19$
9 $74 - 59$	10 $93 - 61$	11 $87 - 29$	12 $113 - 81$

New strategies

D Doubling large numbers: work from the left

- double 63 = double 60 + double 3 = 120 + 6 = 126
- double 79 = double 70 + double 9 = 140 + 18 = 158
- double 127 = double 100 + double 20 + double 7 = 200 + 40 + 14 = 254
- double 264 = double 200 + double 60 + double 4 = 400 + 120 + 8 = 528

E (a) Multiplying by doubling and then halving:

- 23×5 $\quad 23 \times 10 = 230$ $\quad 230 \div 2 = 115$
- 7×45 $\quad 7 \times 90 = 630$ $\quad 630 \div 2 = 315$
- 11×15 $\quad 11 \times 30 = 330$ $\quad 330 \div 2 = 165$

36 × 25

36 × 100 = 3600

3600 ÷ 4 = 900

(b) To multiply by 50, multiply by 100, then halve the result.

- 23×50 $\quad 23 \times 100 = 2300$ $\quad 2300 \div 2 = 1150$
- 38×50 $\quad 38 \times 100 = 3800$ $\quad 3800 \div 2 = 1900$

(c) To multiply by 25, multiply by 100, then divide by 4

- 44×25 $\quad 44 \times 100 = 4400$ $\quad 4400 \div 4 = 1100$
- 56×25 $\quad 56 \times 100 = 5600$ $\quad 5600 \div 4 = 1400$

F Multiplying by 19 or 21… or by 49 or 51… or by 99 or 101

- $15 \times 21 = (15 \times 20) + 15 = 300 + 15 = 315$
- $14 \times 51 = (14 \times 50) + 14 = 700 + 14 = 714$
- $23 \times 101 = (23 \times 100) + 23 = 2300 + 23 = 2323$
- $17 \times 19 = (17 \times 20) - 17 = 340 - 17 = 323$
- $16 \times 49 = (16 \times 50) - 16 = 800 - 16 = 784$
- $19 \times 99 = (19 \times 100) - 19 = 1900 - 19 = 1881$

Exercise 1E

Work out in your head.

D

1 double 54
2 double 38
3 double 67
4 double 73
5 double 28
6 double 79
7 double 115
8 double 126
9 double 87
10 double 66
11 double 237
12 double 342

E

1 22×50
2 32×50
3 24×25
4 16×25
5 8×35
6 8×15
7 7×45
8 9×35
9 14×50
10 13×20
11 18×50
12 12×25

F

1 7×21
2 9×51
3 11×41
4 23×31
5 9×19
6 6×29
7 7×99
8 15×99
9 12×101
10 55×101
11 23×1001
12 15×999

KS3 tests

The next 2 tests are written in the form of the Key Stage 3 mental arithmetic tests.

Each question will be repeated once. You have 5 seconds to answer questions 1 to 6, 10 seconds to answer questions 7 to 20 and 15 seconds to answer the remaining questions. You will be told to put down your pen after the correct time interval for each question.

Work out the answer to each question in your head and write down only the answer. Sometimes other useful information, such as the numbers used in the question, has been written down to help you.
Teacher's note: Answer sheets for these tests may be photocopied from the Answer Book.

Test 1

- Time: 5 seconds

1 Look at the numbers on your answer sheet. What is half their total?

2 Change one hundred and forty millimetres into centimetres.

3 What is sixty-three divided by nine?

4 Look at the equation. Write down the value for n.

5 Your answer sheet shows a fraction. Write the fraction in its simplest form.

6 Write four fifths as a decimal number.

- Time: 10 seconds

7 Look at the expression. What is its value when x equals six?

8 A TV film starts at five minutes to seven. It lasts forty-five minutes. At what time does the film finish?

9 What is one hundred and forty minus eighty?

10 On a coach there are fifty pupils. Thirty of the pupils are girls. A pupil is chosen at random. What is the probability that a girl is chosen?

11 Look at your answer sheet. Work out the answer.

12 Ten per cent of a number is eight. What is the number?

13 A pond is fifteen feet long. About how many metres is that?

14 Write the number two and a half million in figures.

15 Look at the equation. Use it to work out the value of $2x$.

16 Estimate the size of this angle in degrees.

17 Estimate the value of fifty-two per cent of sixteen pounds ninety pence.

18 How many halves are there altogether in four and a half?

19 What is five hundred minus forty-five?

20 n stands for a number. Write an expression for the following: 'add six to n, then multiply the result by three'.

- Time: 15 seconds

21 Pete and Bob share some money in the ratio of one to two. Pete's share is fifteen pounds. How much money is Bob's share?

22 What is one quarter of two hundred thousand?

23 Write two consecutive numbers that add up to thirty-five.

24 Use the calculation on your answer sheet to help you to work out how many seventeens there are in two thousand two hundred and ten.

25 Divide twenty-two pounds between four people. How much money does each person get?

26 Write an approximate answer to the calculation on your answer sheet.

27 Find n, if two times n minus one equals eleven.

28 Your answer sheet shows the marks by four pupils in a test. What is the mean mark?

29 Work out three plus four plus five all squared.

30 A man's heart beats 80 times in 1 minute. How many times does it beat in one hour?

Test 2

- Time: 5 seconds

1. Write the number one thousand, five hundred and sixty-seven to the nearest hundred.
2. What is five point two multiplied by one thousand?
3. Work out five per cent of four hundred.
4. Simplify the expression on your answer sheet.
5. What is the sum of the numbers on your answer sheet?
6. What is one tenth of half a million?

- Time: 10 seconds

7. Look at the expression. What is its value when x equals four?
8. Tim's height is one point seven metres. Greg's height is one hundredth of a metre more than Tim's height. What is Greg's height?
9. Twenty per cent of a number is eleven. What is the number?
10. Two angles in a triangle are each sixty-five degrees. What is the size of the third angle?
11. In a group of sixty-three children, twenty-eight are girls. How many are boys?
12. What is the area of this triangle?
13. The value of four x plus y is sixteen. Write the value of eight x plus two y.
14. Divide two by nought point one.
15. Michelle got thirty out of fifty on a test. What percentage did she get?
16. Work out one plus two plus three plus four all squared.
17. Look at the inequalities on your answer sheet. Write down one possible value for x.
18. How many twelfths are there in three quarters?
19. Multiply six point nought two by one thousand.
20. On the answer sheet find the missing number.

- Time: 15 seconds:

21. What is the cost of three items at two pounds ninety-nine pence each?
22. Look at these numbers. Put a ring around the smallest number.
23. Write an approximate answer to the calculation on your answer sheet.
24. Each side of a square is thirty-two centimetres. What is the perimeter of the square?

25 Look at these pairs of numbers. Between which pair of numbers does the square root of thirty-three lie? Put a ring around the correct pair.

26 Look at the calculation on your answer sheet. What is thirty-two multiplied by thirty-eight?

27 A map has a scale of one to ten thousand. What is the actual length of a path which is 8 cm long on the map?

28 Look at the expression on your answer sheet. Write down the value of the expression when x equals nought.

29 Which has the longer perimeter: a square of side 10 cm or an equilateral triangle of side 15 cm?

30 A film started at eight fifty p.m. and ended two and a quarter hours later. When did it finish?

3.4 Using formulas and expressions

In section 3.4 you will

- substitute values into a range of formulas
- evaluate expressions of increasing complexity

Substituting into a formula

(a) In the formula $s = ut, s, u$ and t are variable quantities.

s is for distance.

u is for speed.

t is for time taken.

When $u = 3$ and $t = 10$, $s = ut$

$$s = 3 \times 10 = 30$$

(b) The pulse rate, p, of a cowboy, the mass of the bull, m, and the speed of the bull, s, are connected by the formula $p = \frac{m}{25} + \frac{s}{3}$

when $m = 2000$ and $s = 12$,

$$p = \frac{2000}{25} + \frac{12}{3} = 84$$

Exercise 1M

In questions 1 to 10 you are given a formula. Find the value of the letter required in each case.

1 $x = 3y + 2$
Find x when $y = 4$

2 $a = 4b + 1$
Find a when $b = 5$

3 $c = \frac{d}{5} + 3$
Find c when $d = 15$

4 $e = \frac{f}{2} - 4$
Find e when $f = 8$

5 $g = 8h + 7$
Find g when $h = 6$

6 $i = 5j - 3$
Find i if $j = 7$

7 $k = \frac{l}{3} + 4$
Find k when $l = 21$

8 $m = \frac{n}{4} - 2$
Find m when $n = 32$

9 $p = 6q + 5$
Find p when $q = 13$

10 $r = \frac{s}{6} - 8$
Find r when $s = 66$

11 When the wind velocity is v, the cost of damage, £C, is given by the formula

$C = 500\,v + 20\,000$

Find the cost of damage when $v = 110$.

12 $t = \frac{4u + 3}{5}$
Find t when $u = 3$

13 $v = 3(5w - 6)$
Find v when $w = 2$

14 $m = n^2 - 55$
Find m when $n = 9$

15 $a = 100 - 5e$
Find a when $e = 21$

16 $t = \frac{12 - 7x}{10}$
Find t when $x = 1$

17 $u = 3(60 - h^2)$
Find u when $h = 7$

(a) $h = 24 + 5n$

Find h when $n = -6$

$h = 24 + 5 \times (-6)$

$= 24 - 30$

$= -6$

(b) $p = (u + v)(8 - w)$

Find p when $u = 10$, $v = -7$, $w = 7.5$

$p = (10 - 7)(8 - 7.5)$

$= 3 \times 0.5$

$= 1.5$

Exercise 1E

1 Below are several different formulas for z in terms of x. Find the value of z in each case.

(a) $z = 10x - 6,\quad x = 5.5$

(b) $z = \frac{5x + 3}{2},\quad x = 3$

(c) $z = 3(2x + 5),\quad x = 2$

2 In the formulas below t is given in terms of n and a. Find the value of t in each case.

(a) $t = 5a + 2n$; $a = 3$, $n = 4$

(b) $t = 6a + 3n - 10$; $a = 2$, $n = 1$

(c) $t = an + 7$; $a = 5$, $n = 2$

3 The probability p of a driver having an accident is $p = \frac{5}{a} + \frac{s}{1000}$, where a is the age of the driver and s is the speed at which the car is driven.

Find the value of p when $a = 20$ and $s = 80$.

4 Using the formula $q = 85 + 3x$, find the value of q when

(a) $x = 14$ (b) $x = -11$ (c) $x = \frac{1}{3}$

5 Using the formula $h = n(60 - y)$, find the value of h when

(a) $n = -4$, $y = 35$ (b) $n = \frac{1}{10}$, $y = -20$

6 Here are some polygons.

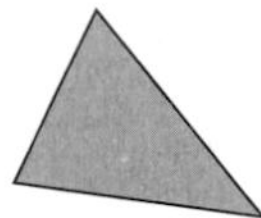

Number of sides:	3	4	5
Sum of angles:	180°	360°	540°

The sum of the angles in a polygon with n sides is given by the formula, sum of angles = $(n - 2) \times 180°$

(a) Find the sum of the angles in a hexagon (6 sides).

(b) Find the sum of the angles in a polygon with 102 sides.

(c) Show that the formula gives the correct answer for the sum of the angles in a pentagon (5 sides).

7 Suppose you add the numbers from 1 to 50: $1 + 2 + 3 + \ldots + 49 + 50$.

The answer is $\frac{50 \times 51}{2} = 1275$.

If you add the numbers from 1 to any number n the answer is given by the formula $\text{Sum} = \frac{n(n+1)}{2}$.

(a) Use the formula to find the sum of the numbers from 1 to 10. (i.e. $1 + 2 + 3 + \ldots + 9 + 10$).

[P.T.O]

(b) Check your answer by adding the numbers in the normal way.

(c) Use the formula to find the sum of the numbers from 1 to 99.

8 Here is a sequence of shapes made from sticks

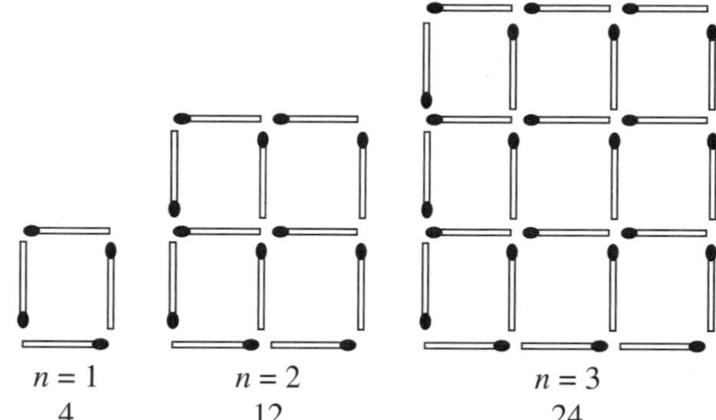

Shape number:	$n = 1$	$n = 2$	$n = 3$
Number of sticks:	4	12	24

The formula for the number of sticks in shape number n is

number of sticks $= 2n^2 + 2n$. (Note: $2n^2 = 2(n^2)$)

(a) Check that the formula gives the correct answer for $n = 1$ and for $n = 2$.

(b) Use the formula to find the number of sticks in shape number 10.

9 An estimate for the volume of a cylinder of radius r and height h is given by the formula $V = 3r^2h$.

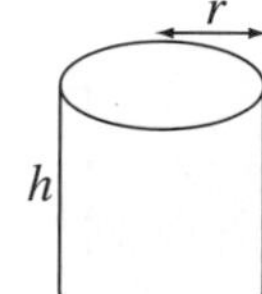

(a) Find the value of V when $r = 10$ and $h = 2$.

(b) Find the value of V when $r = 5$ and $h = 4$.

10 Find the value of c using the formulas and values given.

(a) $c = mx + 7$; $m = 5$, $x = -1$

(b) $c = 2t + t^2$; $t = 3$

(c) $c = 2pq + p^2$; $p = 3$, $q = 2$

(d) $c = (a + b^2)$; $a = 5$, $b = -2$

11

The weight w of the brain of a parrot is connected to its age, A, and its intelligence quotient, I, by the formula

$$w = \frac{A^2 + I/A}{5000}$$

Find w, when $A = 20$ and $I = 2$.

12 From a point h metres above the sea, the distance to the horizon is d km. The formula connecting d and h is

$$d = 3.58\sqrt{h}$$

(a) A sailor in the crow's nest of a ship is 20 m above the sea. How far can he see to the horizon?

(b) How tall is a lighthouse from which the horizon is 19 km away?

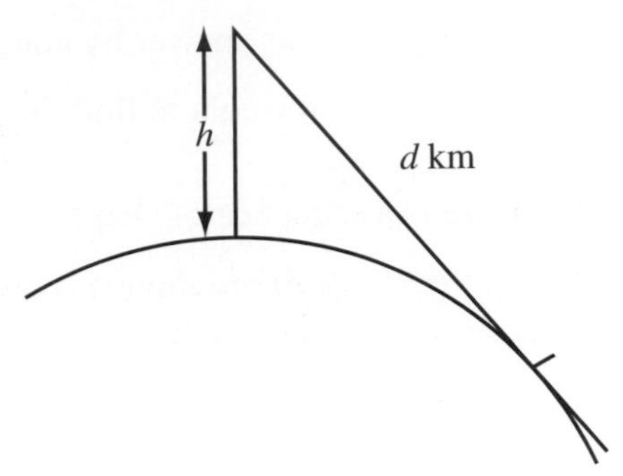

13 In the polygons below, diagonals are drawn from one vertex.

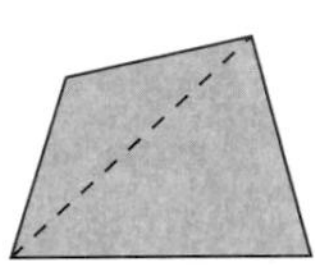

$n = 4$ sides
$d = 1$ diagonal

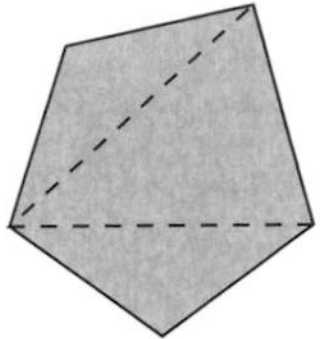

$n = 5$ sides
$d = 2$ diagonals

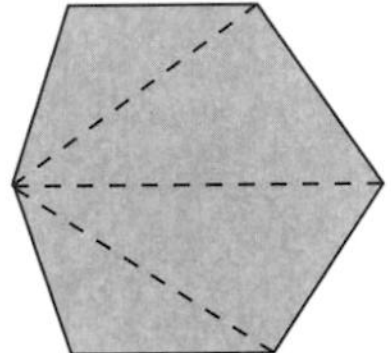

$n = 6$ sides
$d = 3$ diagonals

Find a formula connecting the number of diagonals and the number of sides. Write '$d =$ ……'.

14 In this sequence blue squares are surrounded by yellow squares.

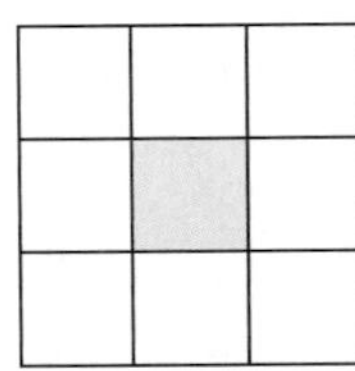

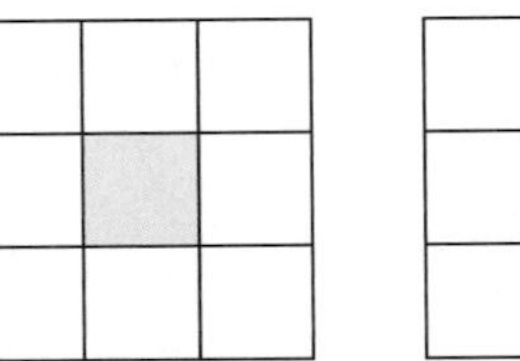

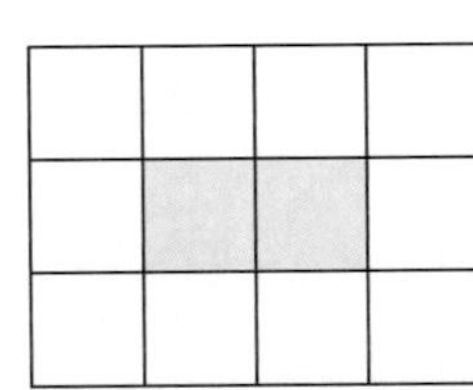

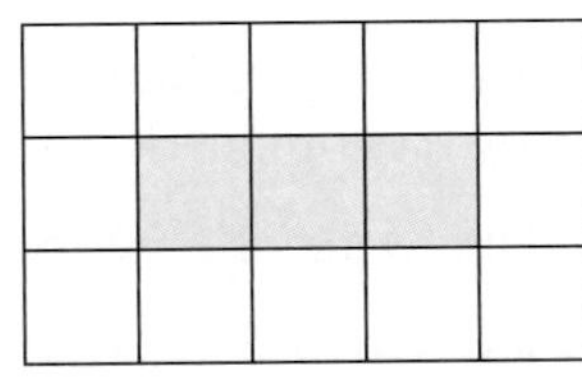

Blue squares:	$b = 1$	$b = 2$	$b = 3$
Yellow squares:	$y = 8$	$y = 10$	$y = 12$

(a) Draw the next diagram in the sequence and make a table.

blue squares, b	1	2	3	4
yellow squares, y	8	10	12	

(b) Work out the number of yellow squares in the diagram which has 20 blue squares.

(c) Write the formula, without words, for the number of yellow squares. Use b for the number of blue squares and y for the number of yellow squares. Write '$y =$ '.

Expressions

An expression does *not* have an equals sign. For example: $3x - 7$; $2a + b$; $5y - 10$. These are all expressions.

Below are three expressions involving *a*, *b*, *c* and *d*. Find the value of each expression given that $a = 3, b = 2, c = 5, d = -1$

(i) $5a + 7$
$= 5 \times 3 + 7$
$= 15 + 7$
$= 22$

(ii) $2b + d$
$= 2 \times 2 + (-1)$
$= 4 - 1$
$= 3$

(iii) $ab + 5c$
$= (3 \times 2) + (5 \times 5)$
$= 6 + 25$
$= 31$

Notice that the working goes *down* the page, not across. This helps to avoid errors.

Exercise 2M

In Questions **1** to **10** find the value of each expression

1 $2x + 1$ if $x = 4$

2 $3x - 1$ if $x = 2$

3 $5x - 2$ if $x = 3$

4 $4x + 3$ if $x = 3$

5 $10 + a$ if $a = 5$

6 $7 - a$ if $a = 4$

7 $12 - b$ if $b = 6$

8 $16 + b$ if $b = 3$

9 $4 + 3c$ if $c = 6$

10 $20 - 2c$ if $c = 7$

11 For each statement answer 'true' or 'false'

(a) $6 \times a = a \times 6$ (b) $n + n^2 = n^3$ (c) $2 \div n = n \div 2$

(d) $3t - t = 2t$ (e) $\frac{a + a}{a} = 2$ (f) $n + n + n = n^3$

(g) $\frac{a}{n} + \frac{b}{n} = \frac{a + b}{n}$ (h) $a - b = -b + a$ (i) $2(n + 2) = 2n + 4$

12 Find the value of these expressions when $n = 3$.

(a) $n^2 - 1$ (b) $2n^2$ (c) n^3

13 Find the value of these expressions when $a = 1.5$.

(a) $2a + 5$ (b) $6 - a$ (c) $3(a - 1)$

14 Find the value of these expressions when $x = 2$.

(a) $\frac{x + 2}{x}$ (b) $\frac{x + 4}{x - 1}$ (c) $\frac{1}{x} + 4$

15 Find the value of these expressions when $n = -2$.

(a) $n + 5$ (b) $3n$ (c) $n - 1$ (d) $5n$ (e) $n + 10$ (f) n^2

16 Which of the cards below have a value of 8 when $n = 2$?

$2n^2$	$\frac{18}{n}$	$(3 + n)^2$	$\frac{\left(\frac{4}{n} + n\right)^2}{n}$
$12 - n^2$	$(n + 1)^3$	$10 - 3n$	

Exercise 2E

In questions 1 to 10 find the value of the expressions given that $n = 3$, $p = -1$

1 $p + 1$

2 $2(n + 1)$

3 $3(n - 1)$

4 p^2

5 $n + p$

6 $3p$

7 $n^2 - 1$

8 $2(3n - 1)$

9 $\frac{n + 5}{n - 1}$

10 $\frac{p + 1}{p}$

In questions 11 to 34 find the value of the expressions given that $a = 5$, $b = 4$, $c = 1$, $d = -2$

11 $5a - c$

12 $2b + a$

13 $a + d$

14 $3c - b$

15 $4b + c$

16 $2d - a$

17 $5b + 10$

18 $a + b + c$

19 $b - c$

20 $7 - 2a$

21 $25 + 5b$

22 $3a - 4d$

23 $a^2 + b^2$

24 $ac + b$

25 $6 - 2c$

26 $d^2 + 4$

27 $ab + c$

28 $5d - 2c$

29 $b^2 + cd$

30 $5a + b + d$

31 $bd + c^2$

32 $2(a - c)$

33 $3(a + d)$

34 $a(c + b)$

35 Which five expressions below are the same for all values of n?

$2n + 2(n + 4)$	$4(n + 1) + \frac{4n}{n}$	$2^3 + n^3 + n$	$5(n - 1) - (n - 13)$
$4n + 8$	$\frac{10(4 + 2n)}{5}$	$(2n + 1)^2 - 4n^2$	

36 Given that $x = 3$ and $y = -4$, find the value of each of the following expressions.

(a) $4x + y$ (b) $x^2 + y^2$ (c) $3x - y$

(d) $y^2 - x$ (e) $xy + 12$ (f) $5(x - y)$

37 Given that $p = -2$ and $q = 5$, find the value of each of the following expressions.

(a) $2p + q$ (b) $p - q$ (c) $3(p + q)$

(d) $p^2 - 2q$ (e) $pq + 12$ (f) $p(2q + 1)$

38 Given that $m = 6$ and $n = -1$, find the value of each of the following expressions.

(a) $m^2 + n^2$ (b) $3mn + 20$ (c) $m(5 - n)$

(d) $m + n + 1$ (e) $n(m^2 - n^2)$ (f) $mn(5m + 2n)$

Race game

START ↓ →

$w - 3$	$1 - 3x$	x	$2(3 - x)$	$4 - p$	$a + 2$	$c + 1$	$4 - x$	$2y$
$2(a - 3)$								$5 - p$
$1 - y$								$b + 5$
↑ $3n - 9$								$3z$ ↓
$a - 2$								$11 - 3t$
$\frac{3x}{x}$								$2(a + 1)$
$5 - t$	$p + 3$	$3(2 - x)$	$(4 - x)^2$	$t + 1$	$2x - 7$	$6 - m$	$\frac{2n}{n}$	$-8 + c$

←

Players take turns to roll a dice.

The number rolled gives the value of the letter in the expression on each square

The value of the expression determines how many squares the player moves (forward for a positive number, backwards for a negative number).

For example, if you are on the square '$x - 3$' and you throw a 5 you move forward 2 places.

The winner is the first player to move around the circuit. [You can also play 'first player to make 3 circuits' or any other number.]

Teachers note: The diagram may be photocopied and enlarged to fill an A4 sheet. This makes the game easier to play.

CHECK YOURSELF ON SECTIONS 3.3 AND 3.4

1 Mental calculations

Work out, in your head

(a) 32×50 (b) 8×15 (c) $7 + 23 + 48$ (d) $64 + 39$

(e) double 89 (f) 7×31 (g) 45×101 (h) 28×50

(i) Write as a decimal $\frac{1}{4}$ plus $\frac{1}{100}$.

(j) Three angles in a quadrilateral are 45°, 65° and 100°.
What is the fourth angle?

(k) Divide £42 between four people. How much money does each person get?

2 Using formulas and expressions

(a) Using the formula $h = 55 - 3n$, find the value of h when

(i) $n = 10$ (ii) $n = \frac{2}{3}$ (iii) $n = -1$

(b) In the formulae below t is given in terms of n and a. Find the value of t in each case.

(i) $t = 3a - 10n$; $a = 5$, $n = 1$

(ii) $t = 20a + 7n - 4$; $a = 1$, $n = 2$

(iii) $t = an + 11$; $a = 4$, $n = 3$

(iv) $t = 5(3a - 8n)$; $a = 0$, $n = 1$

(c) Which of the cards below have a value of 4 when $n = 3$?

$n \times n - 6$ | $\frac{4n}{n}$ | $2n - 1 + n - 3$ | $\frac{12}{n}$ | $10^n - 996$

$(n^3 - 2n^2) \div 3$ | $\frac{(n+1)^2}{4}$ | $100n - 97n$

3.5 Construction and locus

In section 3.5 you will

- construct triangles with ruler, protractor and compasses
- learn to draw and describe the locus of a point
- learn to draw constructions with ruler and compasses only

Using a ruler, protractor and compasses you can construct the triangles below.

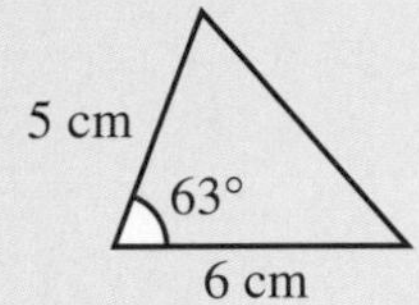

two sides and the included angle (SAS)

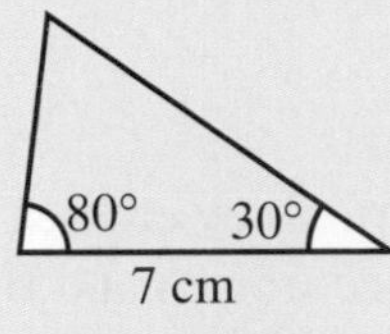

two angles and a side (ASA)

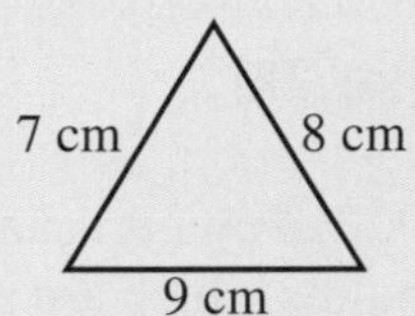

three sides (SSS)

Exercise 1M

Construct each shape and measure the side or angle x.

1 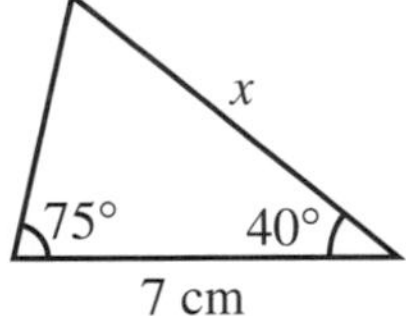

2 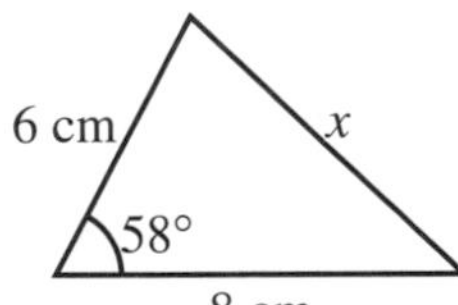

3 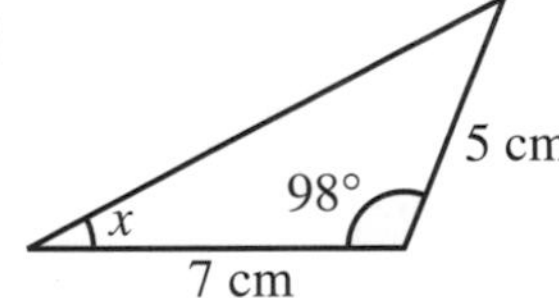

4 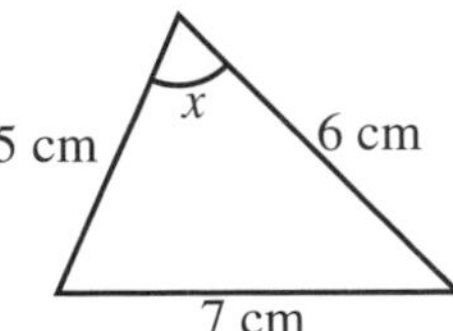

5 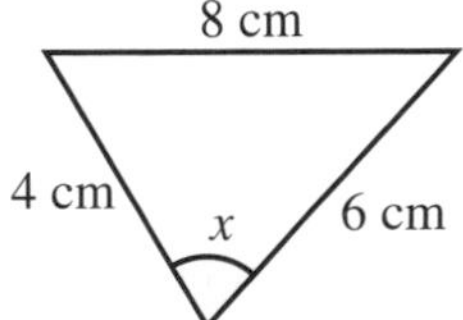

6 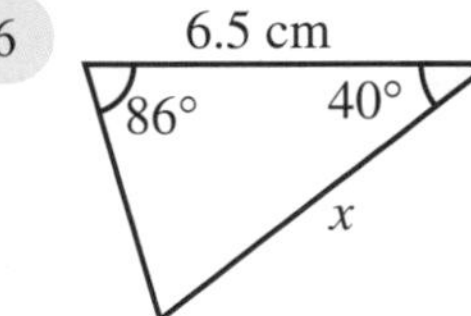

7 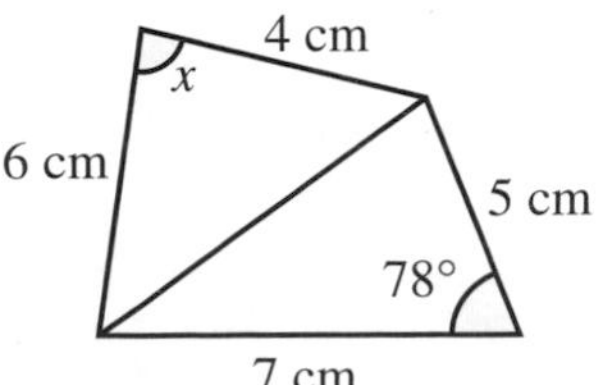

8 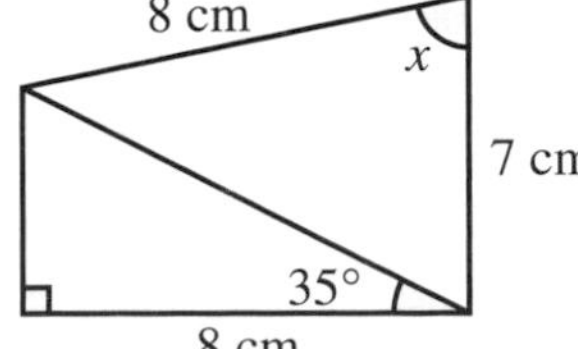

9 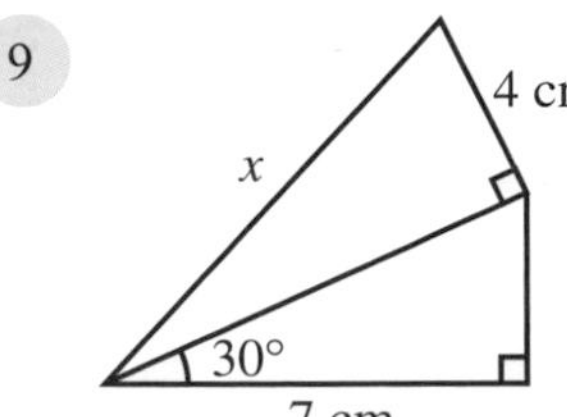

Locus

The *locus* of a point is the path traced out by the point as it moves.

(a) An athlete runs around a track.
The locus looks like this

(b) Alan throws a ball to Ben.

Exercise 2M

1 Mark two points A and B, 5 cm apart. Draw crosses at six points which are an equal distance from A and B. The crosses form the locus of points which are an equal distance [equidistant] from A and B.

2 Mark a point C with a dot. Draw crosses at ten points which are all 5 cm from C. The crosses form the locus of points which are 5 cm from C. Describe the locus.

3 With a dot, mark the bottom right corner of the page you are on. Draw crosses at six points which are the same distance from the two edges of the page.
Describe the locus of the crosses you have drawn.

4

(a) Describe the locus of the tip of the minute hand as the time goes from 10:10 to 11:10.

(b) Describe the locus of the tip of the *hour* hand as the time goes from 2 o'clock to 8 o'clock.

5 On a clock, the time goes from 9:00 to 9:05. Describe the locus of the tip of the *seconds* hand.

6 A bicycle moves forward on level ground in a straight line. Sketch the locus of the valve on one of the wheels.

Exercise 2E

1 Mark a point 0 with a dot. Imagine that a tiny insect can wander around on your page up to 2 cm from 0. Draw the locus of points where the insect could be.

2 

(a) Draw the locus of the shadow on a sun dial from 3 o'clock to 5 o' clock.

(b) At what time will the length of the shadow be shortest?

3 Here is a spiral shape. Write simple instructions describing how to draw the spiral so that another person would be able to draw it.

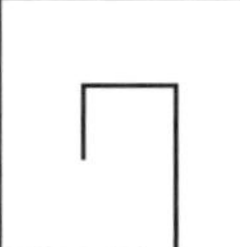

4 Work with a partner.

(a) Each person draws a fairly simple shape without showing it to their partner. Now write instructions so that your partner can draw the shape.

(b) Each person follows the written instructions to draw their partner's shape.

5 Draw x and y axes with values from –5 to +5.

Draw the locus of points which are an equal distance from the two axes.

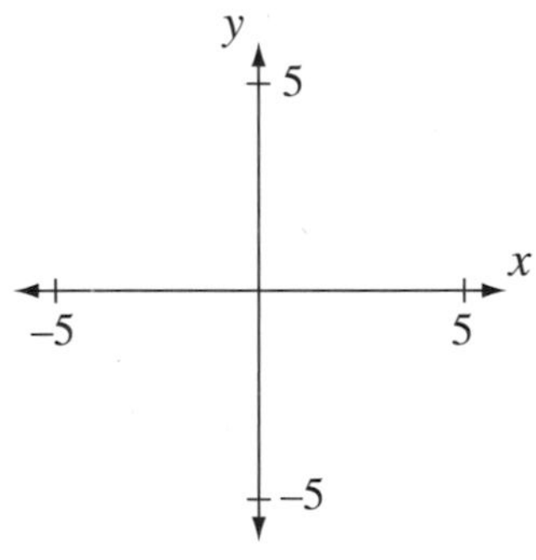

6 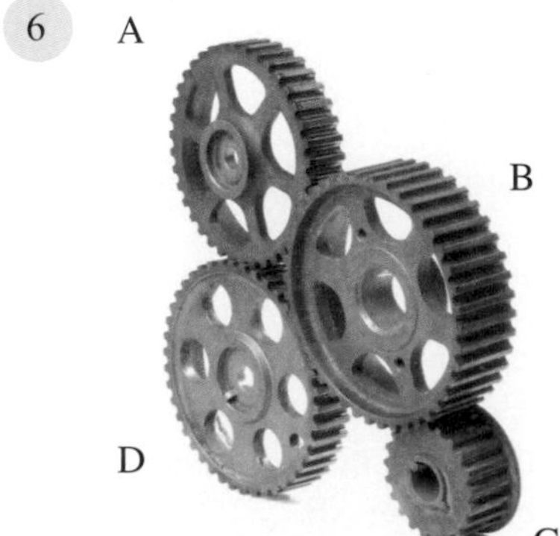

Four cogwheels are shown. Cogwheel C rotates in a clockwise direction. In what direction does

(a) cogwheel A rotate,

(b) cogwheel B rotate,

(c) cogwheel D rotate?

Standard constructions (using compasses)

Exercise 3M [use plain unlined paper]

You are given examples of standard constructions marked A, B, C, D.

You are then asked to draw your own constructions using *only* a pencil, a straight edge and a pair of compasses.

A Perpendicular bisector of a line segment AB.

With centres A and B draw two arcs.

The perpendicular bisector is shown as a broken line.

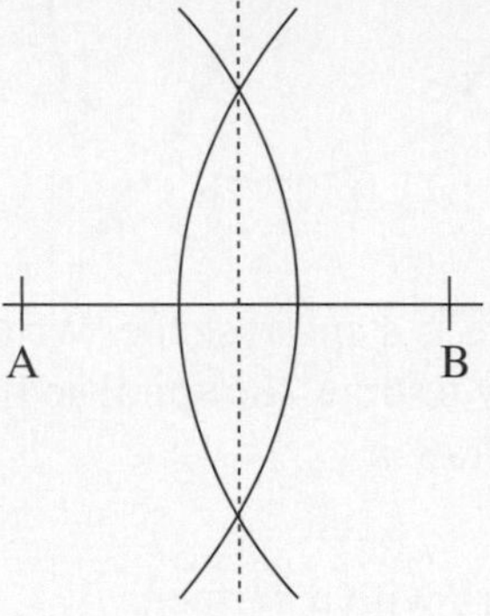

1 Draw a horizontal line AB of the length 6 cm. Construct the perpendicular bisector of AB.

2 Draw a vertical line CD of length 8 cm. Construct the perpendicular bisector of CD.

3 (a) Using a set square.
Draw a right-angled triangle ABC as shown.
For greater accuracy draw lines slightly longer than 8 cm and 6 cm and *then* mark the points A, B and C.

(b) *Construct* the perpendicular bisector of AB.

(c) Construct the perpendicular bisector of AC

(d) If done accurately, your two lines from (b) and (c) should cross exactly on the line BC.

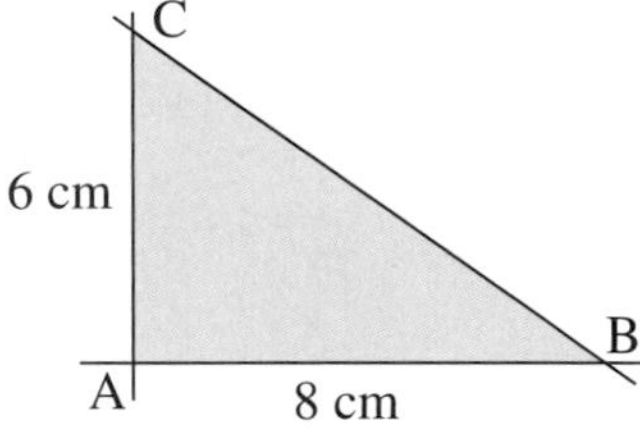

B Perpendicular from point P to a line

P
line

P
A
B

With centre P draw an arc to cut the line at A and B.

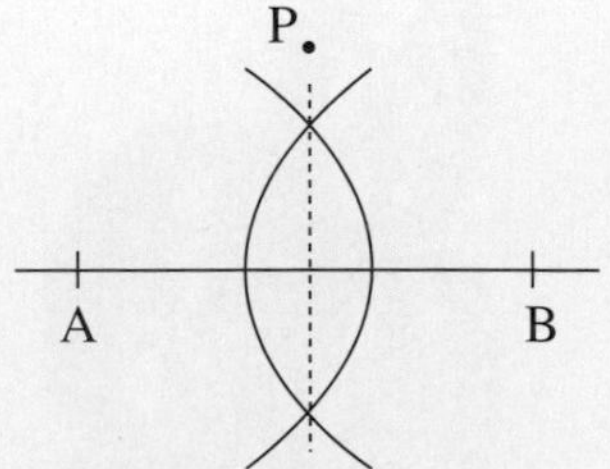

Construct the perpendicular bisector of AB.

4 Draw a line and a point P about 4 cm from the line. Construct the line which passes through P which is perpendicular to the line.

C Perpendicular from a point P on a line.

With centre P draw arcs to cut the line at A and B. Now bisect AB as above in (A).

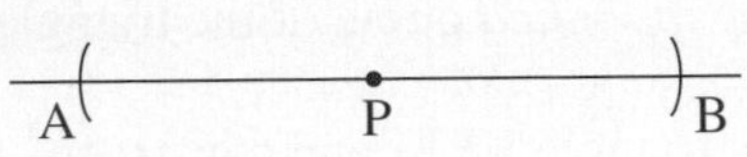

5 Draw a line and a point Q on the line. Construct the perpendicular from the point Q.

6

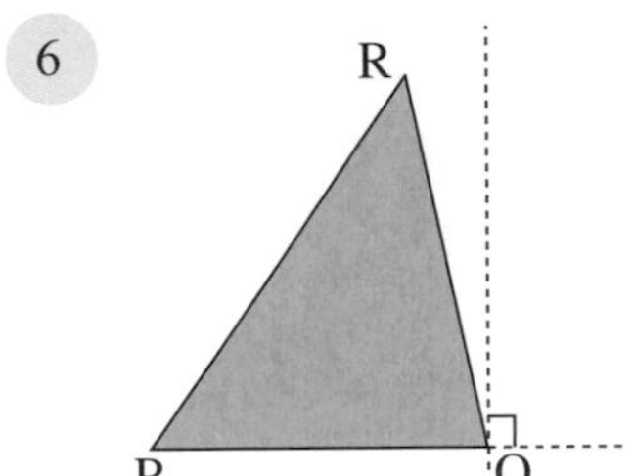

(a) Draw any triangle PQR. Construct a line through Q perpendicular to PQ

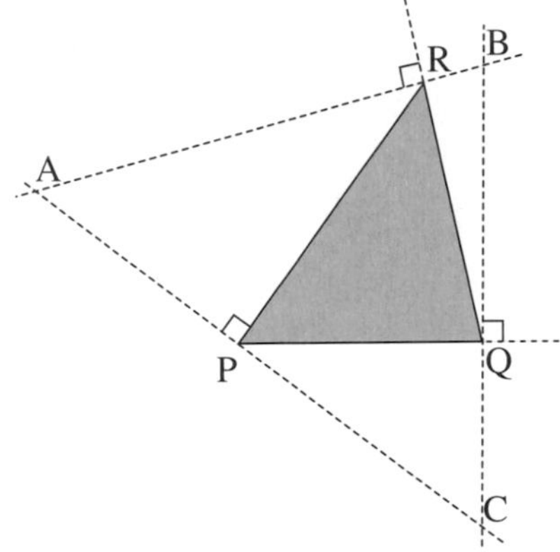

(b) Construct perpendiculars to PR and QR as shown to form triangle ABC.

Measure the angles of triangle ABC and compare them with the angles of triangle PQR. What do you notice?

Exercise 3E

D Bisector of an angle

With centre A draw arc PQ.
With centres at P and Q draw two more arcs.
The angle bisector is then drawn.

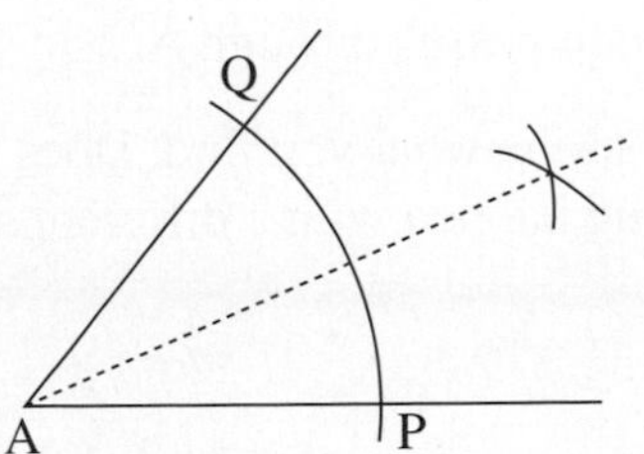

1 Draw an angle of about 70°. Construct the bisector of the angle.

2 Draw an angle of about 120°. Construct the bisector of the angle.

3 Draw any triangle ABC and construct the bisectors of angles B and C to meet at point Y.

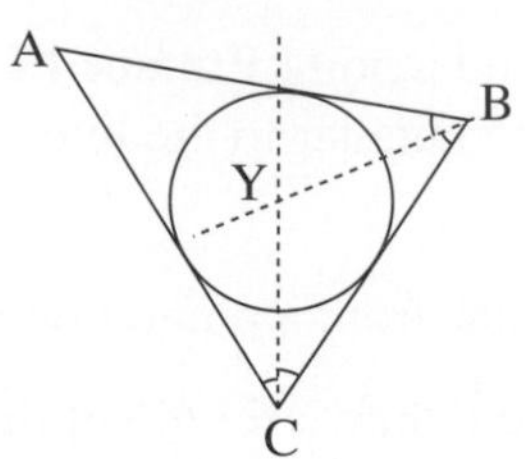

With centre at Y draw a circle which just touches the sides of the triangle.
This is the *inscribed* circle of the triangle.

4 Draw *any* triangle KLM and construct

(a) the perpendicular bisector of KM

(b) the perpendicular bisector of KL.

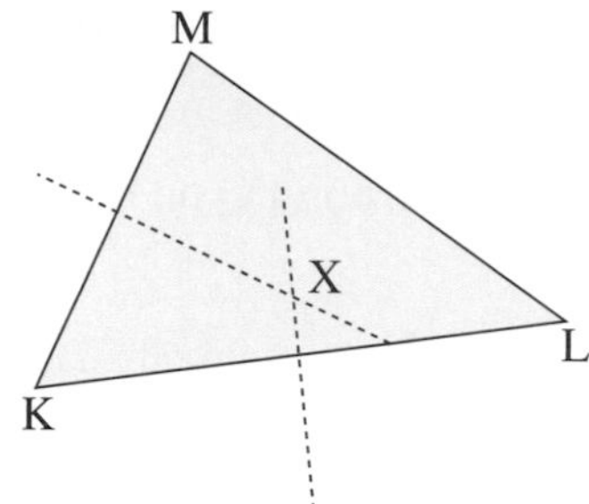

Mark the point of intersection X.

Take a pair of compasses and, with centre at X and radius KX, draw a circle through the points K, L and M.
This is the *circumcircle* of triangle KLM.

Repeat the construction for another triangle of different shape.

5 Using ruler and compasses only *construct* an angle of 30°.

6 Using ruler and compasses only construct an angle of

(a) 45°

(b) 75°

7 (a) Draw any triangle ABC.

(b) Construct a line perpendicular to AB which passes through C.

(c) Construct a line perpendicular to AC which passes through B.

(d) Construct a line perpendicular to BC which passes through A.

(e) Describe what you find. Does the same thing happen with a different shape triangle?

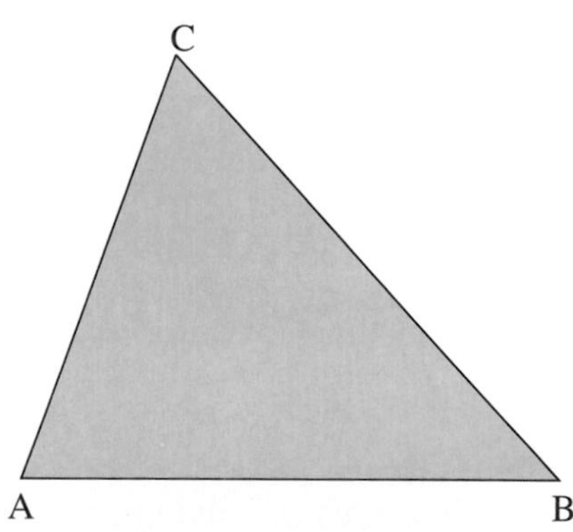

UNIT 3 MIXED REVIEW

Part one

1 Work out, without a calculator.

(a) 0.65×0.2 (b) 1% of 10^5 (c) $8 + 0.7 - 0.03$

(d) $2.48 \div 0.2$ (e) 13.2×0.4 (f) $2\,(4^3 \div 0.1)$

2 Copy each sequence and find the missing terms.

(a) ☐ 4 4.01 4.02 ☐

(b) ☐ ☐ 5.05 5.1 ☐ 5.2

3 Answer 'true' or 'false'

(a) $3 \times n = 3 + n$ (b) $a \times 5 = 5a$ (c) $a + b + a = 2a + b$

(d) $n + 2n = 3n$ (e) $n \div 3 = \frac{n}{3}$ (f) $n \times n = n^2$

4 (a) Find the change from 100p for six stamps at 10p each.

(b) Write an expression for the change from 100p for n stamps at 10p each

5

The velocity, v, of an accelerating snow mobile is given by the formula $v = u + at$.

Find v when $u = 0$, $a = 22.5$ and $t = 3$.

6 Write brackets to make the calculation correct.

(a) $19 + 16 \times 7 = 245$ (b) $13 - 4 \times 4 + 3 = 63$

(c) $7 \times 4.15 + 2.3 = 45.15$ (d) $19 \times 5 - 2 = 3 \times 14 + 17$

7 The frequency table shows the scores when a dice was rolled 20 times.

score	1	2	3	4	5	6
frequency	2	5	3	4	1	5

Calculate the mean score.

8 Work out in your head.

(a) $57 + 19$ (b) $68 - 29$ (c) $47 + 23 + 18$ (d) double 67

(e) 24×50 (f) 22×25 (g) double 136 (h) $74 + 29$

9 The total surface area A of the solid cuboid shown is given by the formula

$A = 2bc + 2ab + 2ac$

Find the value of A when $a = 2$, $b = 3$, $c = 4$.

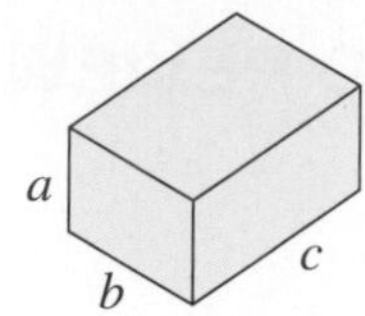

10 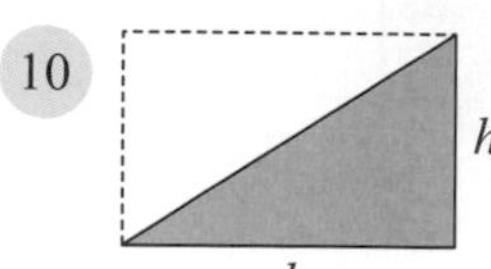

The diagram shows a rectangle with a diagonal drawn. The area of the shaded triangle is A.

Find a formula for A using b and h.

11 I am a 3 digit number. The product of my digits is 4. I am an odd number less than 200. What am I?

12 A micro engineering company developed a way of increasing the efficiency of insects. The insect shown works for 23 hours a day and is paid 1p an hour. Its food costs nothing.

How much does it cost a factory owner to pay his 5000 insect workers for a 365 day year?

(Insects have no concept of holidays.)

13 Look at the sequence of square numbers.

(a) Write a similar expression for 6^2.

(b) Write a similar expression for n^2.

Use brackets and do not simplify your answer.

$2^2 = 1^2 + 2 \times 1 + 1$
$3^2 = 2^2 + 2 \times 2 + 1$
$4^2 = 3^2 + 2 \times 3 + 1$
$5^2 = 4^2 + 2 \times 4 + 1$

14 (a) Copy the diagram.

(b) Reflect the L shape in the x axis.

(c) Reflect the L shape in the line $y = x$.

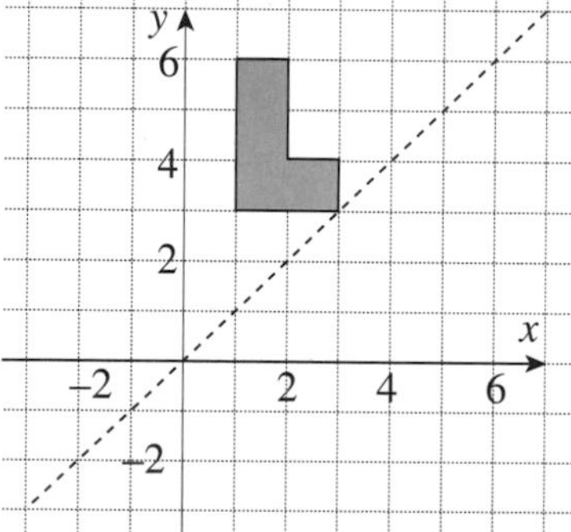

15 Work out 1 + [87654321 + 12345678].

16 I am a 3 digit number. The product of my digits is 2. I am an odd number, greater than 200. What number am I?

Part two

1 Draw axes with x and y from 0 to 6.

Plot A (1, 4) B (1, 1) C (3, 1)

Plot D (5, 4) E (5, 1) F (3, 1)

Write down the equation of the mirror line which reflects ΔABC onto ΔDEF.

2 (a) *Construct* the perpendicular bisector of AB.

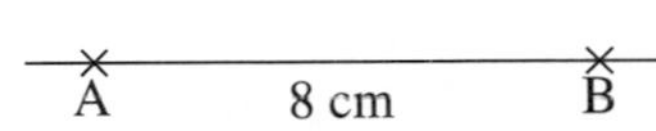

(b) *Construct* the bisector of the angle A.

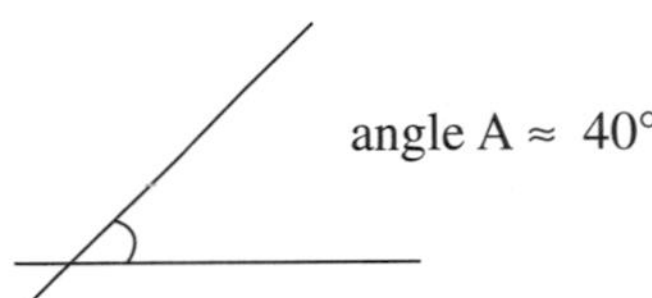

3 (a) Draw x and y axes with values from –5 to +5.

(b) Draw the locus of points which are equidistant from the points (3, 0) and (0, 3).

4 The maximum velocity v of a supermarket trolley depends on the mass m of the person flying behind the trolley and the saving s on a special offer.

$$v = \frac{s^2}{m - 10}$$

Find v when $s = 21$ and $m = 60$.

5 Find the value of these expressions when $n = 3$

(a) $n + 5$ (b) $4n$ (c) $n^2 \times 3n$ (d) $\frac{n+6}{n}$ (e) $\frac{5n}{n-2}$ (f) $n^2 + n$

6 Find the value of these expressions when $n = -2$

(a) $n + 8$ (b) $3n$ (c) $2n + 4$ (d) n^2 (e) $n - 10$ (f) $2(n + 2)$

7 

The coins in a box have the following values in pence.

5	1	2	10	50	20	5	5	1	1
100	2	10	5	5	2	2	2	200	50

For these coins find (a) the mean value
(b) the median value

8 Work out $10^5 - [1357 + 8642]$

9 I am a 4 digit number. The product of my digits is 4 and the sum of my digits is 6. I am an even number less than 1200. What am I?

10 The stem and leaf diagram shows the marks obtained in a test.

(a) What is the median mark?

(b) What is the range?

3	1 3
4	4 4 5 7 8
5	2 2 3 4 6 9
6	3 4 7 8
7	5 6

11 The total mass of five greyhounds is 76 kg. Calculate the mean mass of the dogs.

12 Some children collect 15.3 kg of sea shells.

The mean weight of the shells is 10.2 g.

How many shells were collected?

13 Find the value of c, using the formulae and values given.

(a) $c = mx + 9$; $m = -2, x = -3$

(b) $c = 13t - t^2$; $t = 3$

(c) $c = 3pq + p^2$; $p = 5, q = 0$

(d) $c = (2a + b)^2$; $a = 1, b = 3$

14 The diagrams show rods of different lengths. For example y is of length 7 units.

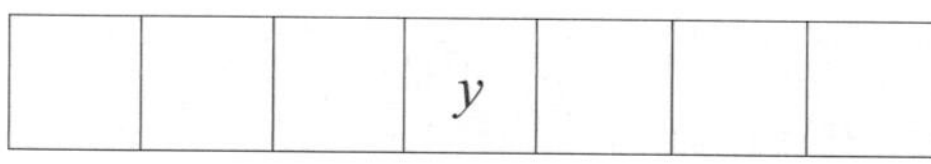

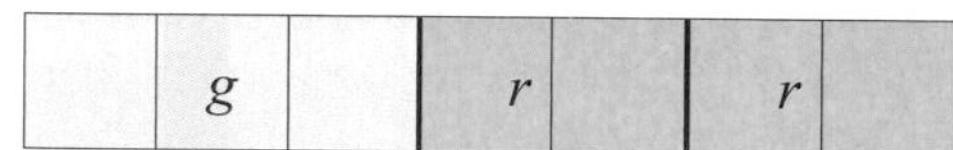

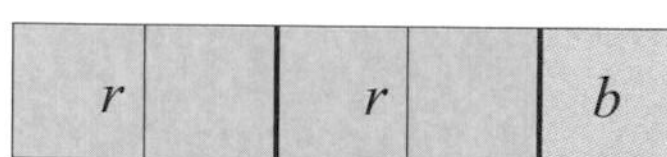

(a) Answer ‘true’ or ‘false’

(i) $g + r = 2r + b$ (ii) $y - r = r + g$ (iii) $g + 3b = y$ (iv) $y = 3r + b$

(b) Write the following using different letters.

(i) $y - 1$ (ii) $7b$ (iii) $4b + g$ (iv) $y - 2r$

15 The photo shows objects reflected in a mirror with the colours changed also.

(a) Draw a diagram of your own design with black sections and white sections.

(b) Draw a reflection of your design in a similar way to that shown in the photo.

16 Follow the instructions below to produce the outline of an egg.

(a) Draw line AB 10 cm long and mark the centre of the line.

(b) Draw a semi-circle of radius 5 cm below AB.

(c) Mark point C, 5 cm above the mid-point of AB.

(d) Draw lines AC and BC and extend them.

(e) Draw arc AD with radius 10 cm and centre B.

(f) Draw arc BE with radius 10 cm and centre A.

(g) Draw arc DE with radius CE and centre C.

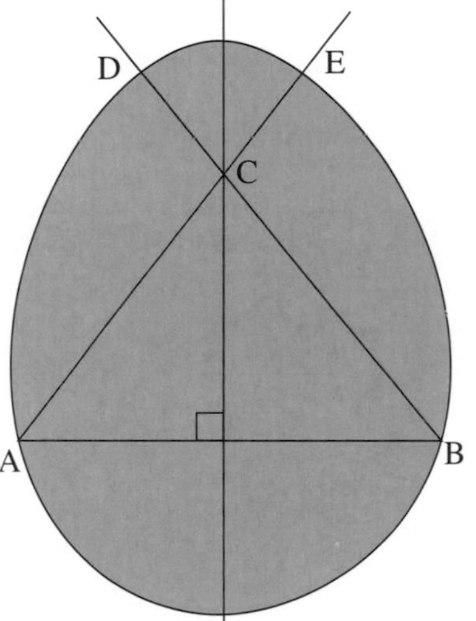

17 Imagine you are driving a car and the car behind you has an indicator flashing to show that it is about to pull out to overtake you. Draw a sketch to show what you would see in your rear view mirror.

18 In what country did Pythagoras live when he made his discovery about triangles? Write your answer in "mirror writing".

19 (a) Using a ruler and compasses only,

(i) construct triangle PQR

(ii) construct the perpendicular bisector of PR

(iii) construct the bisector of angle $P\hat{R}Q$

(iv) measure the length of RS

(b) Describe the locus of points which are 5 cm from point Q.

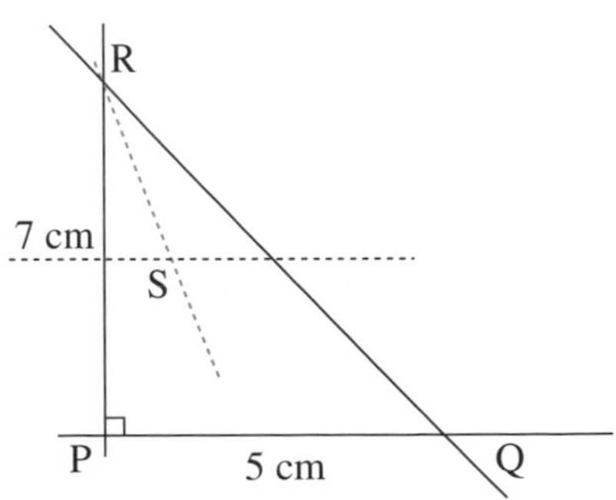

Puzzles and Problems 3

Hidden words (no calculators)

(a) Start in the top left box.

(b) Work out the answer to the calculation in the box.

(c) Find the answer in the top corner of another box.

(d) Write down the letter in that box.

(e) Repeat steps (b), (c) and (d) until you arrive back at the top left box.
What is the message?

1

<table>
<tr><td>$\frac{1}{2}$

25% of 84</td><td>613
S
$\frac{1}{2}$ of $\frac{3}{4}$</td><td>0.56
T
29.2 ÷ 8</td><td>0.01
G
0.5×10^3</td><td>6
E
10 000 ÷ 200</td></tr>
<tr><td>20
S
5.6 × 0.1</td><td>21
H
0.4 – 0.04</td><td>50
D
$\frac{2}{3}$ of 162</td><td>3.5
O
1234 + 4321</td><td>3.65
I
1% of 55</td></tr>
<tr><td>500
L
$\frac{7}{8} - \frac{1}{4}$</td><td>15
E
295 + 318</td><td>0
K
$\frac{5}{6} - \frac{1}{3}$</td><td>0.55
C
$2^4 - 4^2$</td><td>0.36
I
22.82 ÷ 7</td></tr>
<tr><td>3.26
S
$(0.1)^2$</td><td>$\frac{3}{8}$
N
7% of 50</td><td>5555
T
2 ÷ 0.1</td><td>$\frac{5}{8}$
U
5 + 5 ÷ 5</td><td>108
O
$2^4 - 1$</td></tr>
</table>

2

<table>
<tr><td>612

$\frac{6}{1.5} + \frac{9}{1.5}$</td><td>0.8
T
5% of 400</td><td>0.77
W
$\frac{5}{0.1} - 2$</td><td>0.2
V
15 × 23</td><td>0.62
T
20% of 65</td></tr>
<tr><td>32
C
50 000 ÷ 200</td><td>10
B
$\frac{2}{5}$ of 450</td><td>13
R
0.6 × 2.6</td><td>18
E
5 – (7 – 2)</td><td>250
U
$0.9^2 - 0.1^2$</td></tr>
<tr><td>1.56
E
$\frac{3}{8}$ of 48</td><td>0.6
R
$\frac{1}{4} - 0.1$</td><td>180
E
$(0.2)^2$</td><td>0.15
S
6.4 ÷ 0.2</td><td>0
S
18 × 34</td></tr>
<tr><td>0.04
A
10% of 2</td><td>0.27
O
$\frac{1}{10}(5.5 + 2.2)$</td><td>20
D
0.3 – 0.03</td><td>48
N
$\frac{3}{5} + 0.02$</td><td>345
E
$\frac{3}{4}$ of $\frac{4}{5}$</td></tr>
</table>

3

4 $(-6) \times 5$	-5 L $12 \div (-1)^3$	-19 N $\frac{1}{2} - 0.6$	-4 E $17 + (-25)$	0 S $24 \times (-3)$
30 N $(-5)^2 \times 10$	-30 S $8 - (-4)$	36 R $0.1 - 0.3$	-0.1 C $-3 + 10 - 4$	10 I $(-60) \times (-\frac{1}{2})$
-6 U $(-2 -6) \times (-2)$	-0.2 E $81 - 100$	3 H $(7 - 9)^2$	250 F $(-6) \times (-6)$	12 O $(-2)^2 + (-1)^2$
5 L $(-12) \div 3$	-8 I $-6 -7 + 8$	16 N $-7 + 17$	-12 I $3 - 8 + 5$	-72 S $-2\frac{1}{2} - 3\frac{1}{2}$

4

$-\frac{1}{2}$ $16 - 200$	19 H $(3 - 9)^2$	-2 C $[(-9) \times (-3)] + 20$	-80 A $15 + (-16)$	18 S $800 \div (-2)^3$
$4\frac{1}{2}$ M $27 - 270$	$2\frac{1}{2}$ E $(8 - 14) \times (-3)$	0.05 L $8 - (-4) - (+6)$	47 E $4 \times (-\frac{1}{8})$	$-4\frac{1}{2}$ Y $(-10)^3$
-1 T $0.4 \times (-\frac{1}{2})$	-100 O $(-0.1) \times (-0.1)$	-184 M $-8\frac{1}{2} + 4$	16 S $(-20) \div (-8)$	-243 I $(-8) \div (-2)^2$
-1000 C $-35 -45$	36 A $8 - 12 + 20$	6 Y $-1\frac{1}{2} + 6$	0.01 N $\frac{1}{4} - 0.2$	-0.2 C $17 + (-2) - (-4)$

Break the codes

1 The ten symbols below each stand for one of the digits 0, 1, 2, 3, 4, 5, 6, 7, 8, 9 but not in that order.

$\odot \quad \nabla \quad \square \quad * \quad \uparrow \quad ? \quad \ominus \quad \pi \quad \mp \quad \mathrm{I}$

Use the clues below to work out what number each symbol stands for.

(a) $* + * = ?$

(b) $\nabla \times \nabla = \ominus$

(c) $? + ? + ? = \odot$

(d) $\square - * = \odot$

(e) $\pi + \mathrm{I} = \ominus$

(f) $\pi \times \uparrow = \uparrow$

(g) $\mp - \mathrm{I} = \mathrm{I}$

2 The ten symbols used in part 1 are used again but with different values. The clues are more difficult to work out.

(a) $\ominus + \mp = \text{I}$

(b) $\nabla + \square = \text{I}$

(c) $\odot \times \square = \odot$

(d) $\odot \times ? = ?$

(e) $\pi \div \mp = \odot$

(f) $\square + \square + \square + \square = \odot$

(g) $\pi - \mp = \nabla$

(h) $* \times * = \uparrow$

3 Again the same ten symbols are used but with different values.

(a) $\nabla + \odot = \uparrow$

(b) $\mp - \pi = *$

(c) $\ominus \times \ominus \times \ominus = \square$

(d) $* \times \uparrow = \uparrow$

(e) $\square \div \nabla = \ominus$

(f) $\pi - \nabla = *$

(g) $? - \uparrow = \ominus$

(h) $\odot \times \odot = ?$

Mental Arithmetic Practice

Here is a set of mental arithmetic questions. Ideally a teacher will read out each question twice, with pupils books closed. The test of 30 questions should take about 20 minutes.

1 If I have 35 pence change from a ten pound note, how much have I spent?

2 My train leaves at 16.18. How many minutes do I have to wait if I arrive at the station at 15.55?

3 The area of a triangle is 20 cm^2. Its base measures 10 cm. What is the height of the triangle?

4 One eighth of the children in a class walk to school. What percentage of the class is this?

5 A man was born in 1939. How old was he in the year 2000?

6 A piece of string 54 cm long is cut into four equal parts. How long is each part?

7 True or false: Five miles is about the same as eight km.

8 The time in Miami is 5 hours earlier than the time in England. If I want to telephone Miami at 13.30 their time, what time will it be here?

9 I think of a number, multiply it by 2 and subtract 8. The result is 12. What number am I thinking of?

10 A plank of wood measures 2 metres by 50 cm. What is the area of the plank in square metres?

11 Which is largest: $\frac{1}{9}$ or 10%?

12 A bar of chocolate costs 18p. I buy as many as I can for 50p. How much change will I receive?

13 Add together 1, 2, 3, 4, 5, 6.

14 Write down ten million millimetres in kilometres.

15 By how much does a half of 130 exceed 49?

16 Work out two squared plus three squared.

17 Work out 5% of £40.

18 Two angles in a quadrilateral are each 80° and a third angle is 100°. What is the fourth angle?

19 Give an *estimate* for 291.4 × 0.486.

20 What number is a quarter of 140?

21 What is a half of a half of £60?

22 Rosie is going on a 2 week holiday. She leaves on the 5th of July. On what date will she return?

23 What is 2% as a simplified fraction?

24 What is the fraction exactly half way between $\frac{1}{4}$ and $\frac{1}{2}$?

For the last six questions you may write down the numbers in the question.

25 Work out 15% of £60.

26 I think of a number, subtract 8 and then divide by 2. The result is 1. What number am I thinking of?

27 My newspaper costs 45p per day from Monday to Friday and 50p on Saturday. How much do I spend on papers from Monday to Saturday?

28 The coordinates of the 4 corners of a rectangle are (1, 1), (5, 1), (5, 4) and (1, 4). What is the area of the rectangle in square units?

29 How many seconds are there in 1 hour?

30 A train journey of 480 miles took 4 hours. What was the average speed of the train?

A long time ago! 3

The Fibonacci sequence

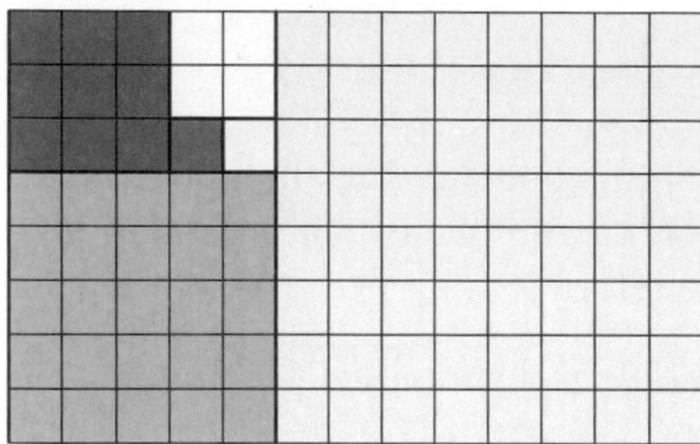

This rectangle is made from six squares drawn on centimetre squared paper. Write down the length of one side in each of the squares.

Can you arrange the numbers to make a pattern?

What would be the next number in your pattern?

Write down a rule for your pattern.

Fibonacci was born in Pisa, Italy. He lived in the 13th century.
He worked on the pattern

1, 1, 2, 3, 5, 8, …

Each number is found by adding the two terms immediately before it.

The next number is 13 from 5 + 8.

Fibonacci found that these numbers helped to explain things to do with spirals in flowers, shells, the breeding of rabbits, pine cones, the family tree of honeybees and many other cases.

Exercise

1 Write down the first twenty-two numbers in the Fibonacci sequence 1, 1, 2, 3, 5, 8, …

2 **Assembly Rules**

In Hatford High School, two boys are *not* allowed to sit next to each other in any single row of chairs in Assembly.

- If a row has 1 chair only, either a boy or a girl sits on the chair so there are 2 ways of filling the chair – B or G (B for Boy, G for Girl)
- If a row has 2 chairs only, there are 3 ways of filling the chairs – BG or GB or GG
- If a row has 3 chairs only, there are 5 ways of filling the chairs – BGG or BGB or GBG or GGB or GGG (remember: BB *not* allowed next to each other)

(a) Show all the different ways of filling the chairs if a row has 4 chairs only.

(b) How many different ways are there of filling the chairs if a row has 10 chairs only?

(c) How many different ways are there of filling the chairs if a row has 20 chairs only?

3 **RESEARCH:**

(a) Find out more about Fibonacci's life.

(b) List as many things as you can which are connected to Fibonacci numbers.

(c) Find a picture which shows how rabbits breeding give Fibonacci numbers.

UNIT 4

4.1 Bearings and scale drawing

In section 4.1 you will:

- learn about bearings
- make scale drawings to solve problems

Bearings are used by navigators on ships and aircraft and by people travelling in open country .

Bearings are measured from north in a *clockwise* direction. A bearing is always given as a three-figure number.

A bearing of 090° is due east. If you are going south-west, you are on a bearing 225°.

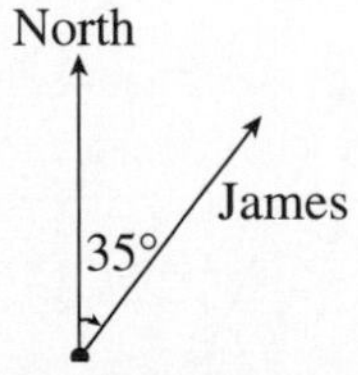

James is walking on a bearing of 035°.

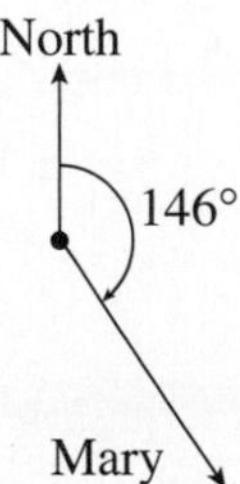

Mary is walking on a bearing of 146°.

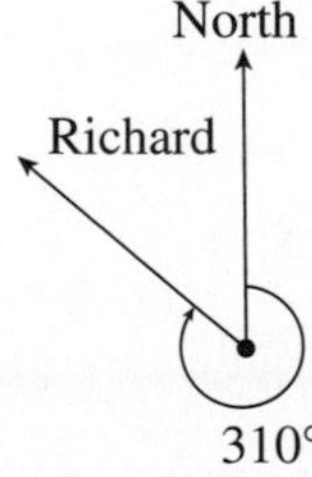

Richard is walking on a bearing of 310°.

Exercise 1M

1 Ten children on a treasure hunt start in the middle of a field and begin walking in the directions shown on the right. On what bearing is each child walking?

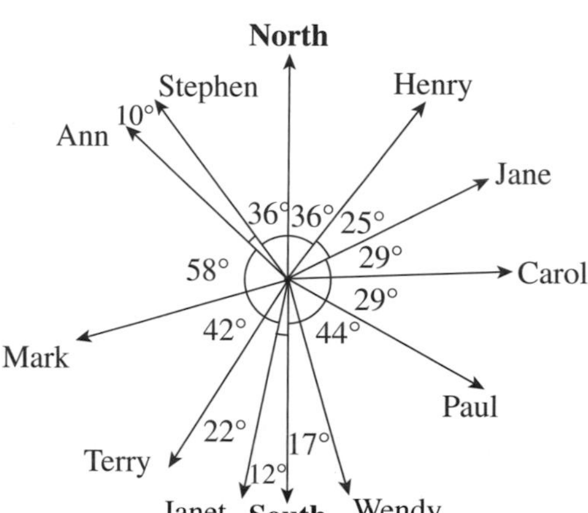

2 Ten pigeons are released and they fly in the directions shown below. On what bearing is each pigeon flying?

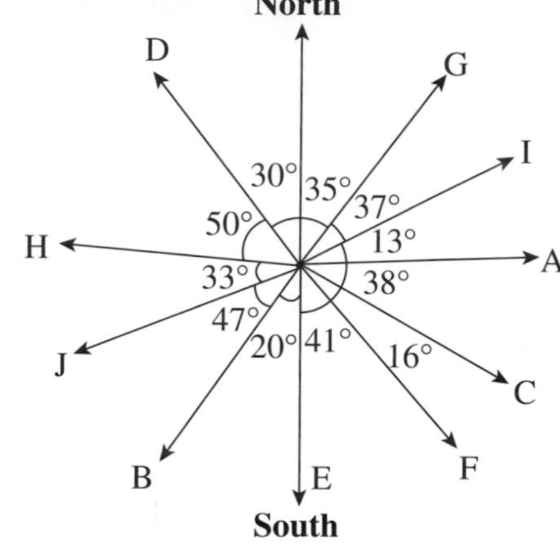

3 Measure the bearing on which each person is moving.

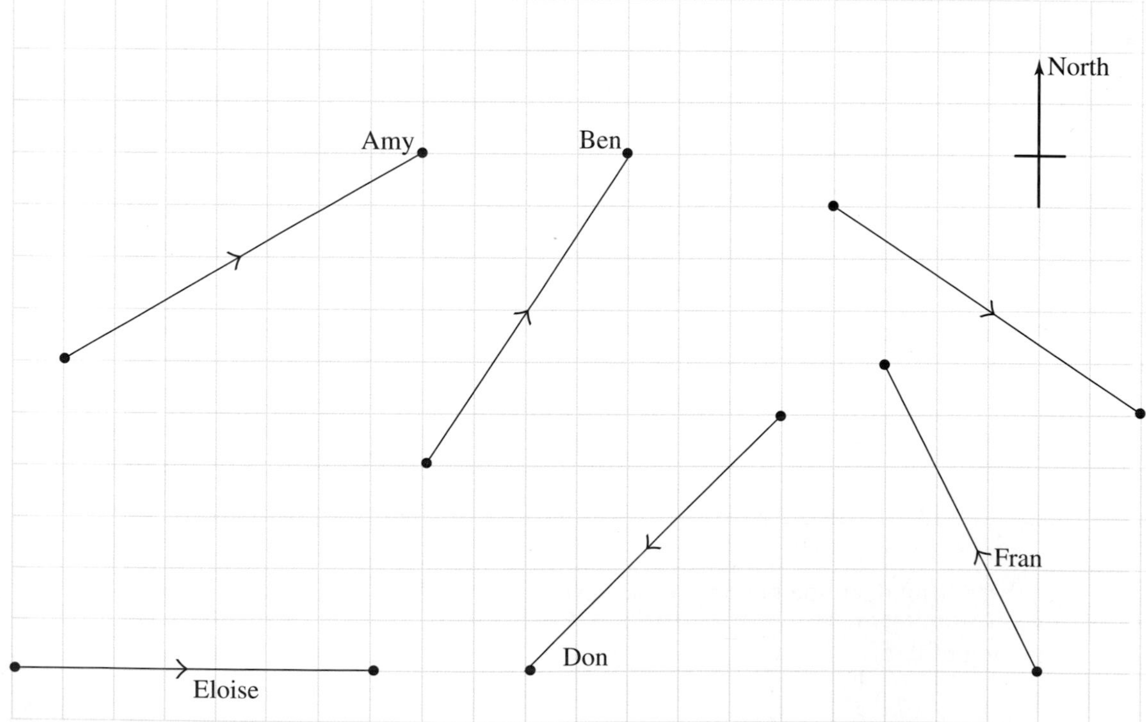

4 Measure the bearing of these journeys.

(a) A to B (b) B to C (c) A to C (d) A to D (e) C to D

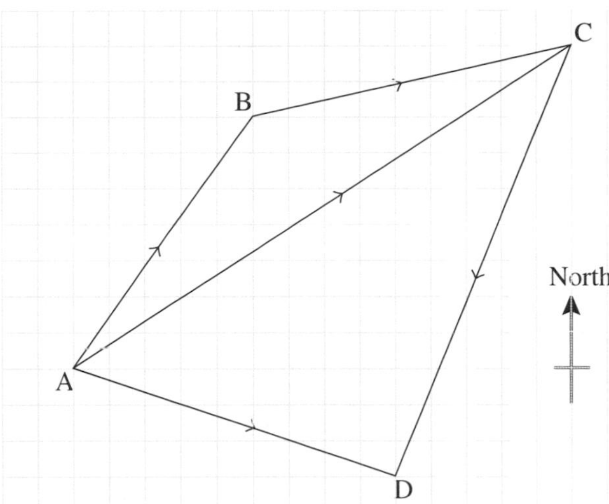

5 Draw lines on the following bearings.

(a) 040° (b) 075° (c) 120° (d) 200° (e) 300°

6 The map shows several features on and around an island. Axes are drawn to identify positions. [eg The coordinates of the cave are (9, 3).]

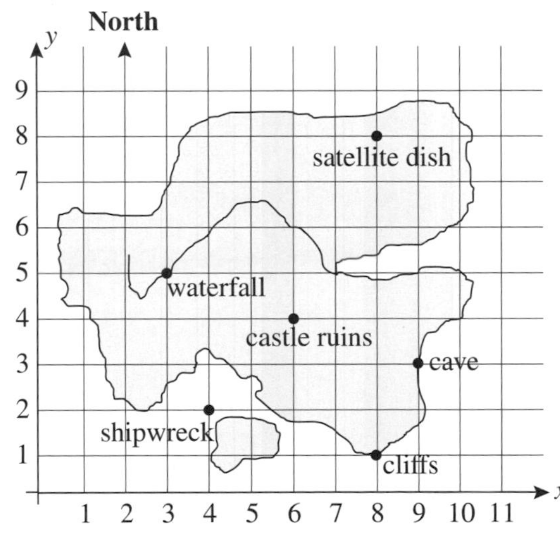

Four commandos, Piers, Quintin, Razak and Smudger, are in hiding on the island. Find the coordinates of the commandos, using the following information.

(a) The castle ruins are due south of Piers and the waterfall is due west of him.

(b) From Quintin, the bearing of the satellite dish is 045° and the shipwreck is due south of him.

(c) From Razak, the bearing of the waterfall is 315° and the bearing of the castle ruins is 045°.

(d) From Smudger, the bearing of the cave is 135° and the bearing of the waterfall is 225°.

(e) The leader of the commandos is hiding somewhere due north of the shipwreck in a hollow tree. From this tree, the castle ruins and the cliffs are both on the same bearing. Find the coordinates of this hollow tree.

7 For each diagram, write down the bearing of C from D.

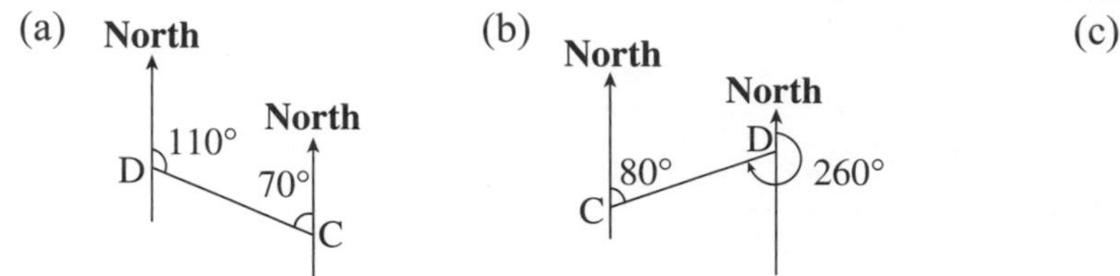

8 The bearing of point B from point A is 100°.
What is the bearing of point A from point B?

9 The bearing of point P from point Q is 200°.
What is the bearing of point Q from point P?

Scale drawing

Many problems involving lengths can be solved using a scale drawing. With questions about compass directions it is helpful to begin by drawing a small sketch to get an idea of where the lines will go. Choose as large a scale as possible for greater accuracy.

A ship sails 7 km north-east and then a further 10 km due south.
How far is the ship from its starting point?

We will use a scale of 1 cm to 1 km.

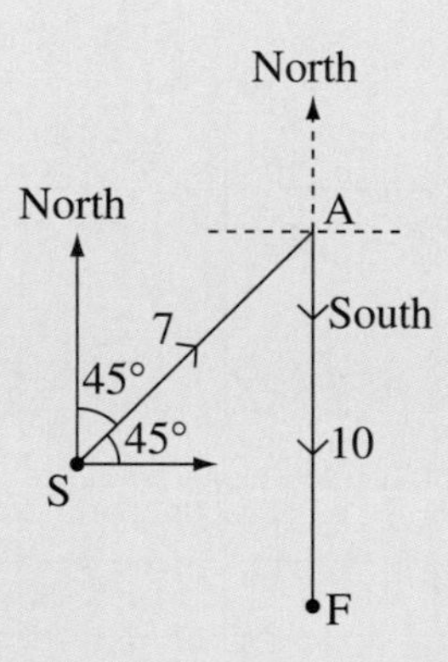

(a) Mark a starting point S and draw a line at 45° to the lines on the page.

(b) Mark a point A, 7 cm from S.

(c) Draw a line vertically through A and mark a point F, 10 cm from A

(d) Measure the distance SF.

Answer: The ship is 7.1 km from its starting point. (An answer between 7.0 km and 7.2 km would be acceptable.)

Exercise 1E

In questions 1 to 7 use a scale of 1 cm to represent 1 km.

1 A ship sails 7 km due east and then a further 5 km due south.
Find the distance of the ship from its starting point.

2 A ship sails 10 km due west and then a further 4 km due south-east.
Find the distance of the ship from its starting point.

3 A ship sails 8 km due north and then a further 7 km on a bearing 080°.
How far is the ship now from its starting point?

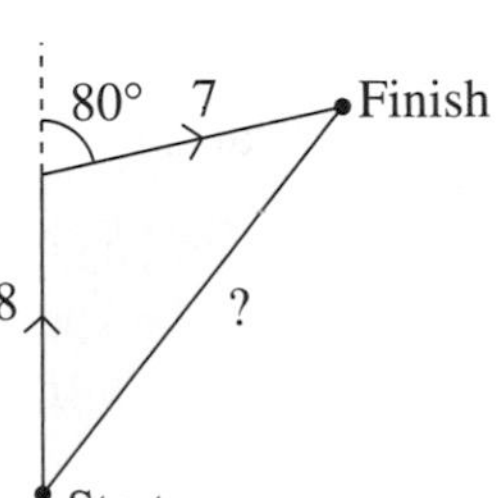

4 A ship sails 6 km on a bearing of 120° and then a further 4 km due south. How far is the ship from its starting point?

5 A ship sails 7 km on a bearing of 075° and then a further 5 km on a bearing of 130°.
How far is the ship from its starting point?

6 Point G is 9 km from F on a bearing of 130° from F.
Point H is 10 km from F on a bearing of 212° from F.
What is the bearing of G from H?

7 Point X is 7.2 km from Y on a bearing 215° from Y.
Point X is also 8.5 km from Z on a bearing 290° *from Z.*
How far is Y from Z?

8 Use a scale of 1 cm to represent 10 km. Mark the fixed points P and Q so that P is 70 km due north of Q.

(a) At noon ship A is on a bearing 230° from P and 300° from Q.
At 1500 ship A is on a bearing 162° from P and 096° from Q.

(b) Mark the position of ship A at noon and at 1500.

(c) On what bearing is ship A sailing?

(d) At what speed is ship A sailing?

9 Two explorers, Tina and Karen, have a tent at camp A. Tina leaves the tent and walks on a bearing 064° for 12 km to reach point B. A little later Karen leaves camp A and walks on a bearing 111° for 8 km, to arrive at point C. Karen hears strange noises and decides that she would be better off with Tina, who has a big gun.

Draw a scale diagram to show Tina's route to point B and Karen's route to point C.
How far, and on what bearing, must Karen walk to arrive at point B?

10 A boat left Dornoch to sail to the oil rig O. After two hours it was at a point A, on a bearing of 252° from O and 329° from Banff.

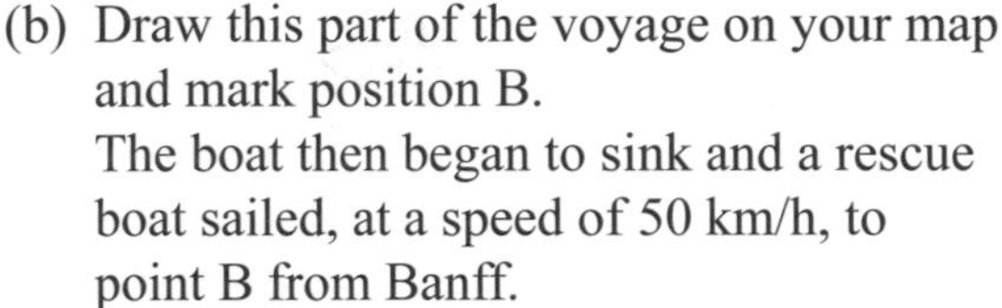

(a) Make a copy of the map on squared paper and find point A.
[Use the squared background to locate Dornoch, Banff, John o'Groats and point O.]
From A, the boat went on a bearing of 090° for 60 km to a new position B.

(b) Draw this part of the voyage on your map and mark position B.
The boat then began to sink and a rescue boat sailed, at a speed of 50 km/h, to point B from Banff.

(c) Measure the bearing to Banff from B.

11 One day at noon, on the radar screen of the Golden Hinde, Sir Francis Drake sees two ships.
One is a defenceless Spanish galleon, laden with treasure, and the other is a French pirate ship.

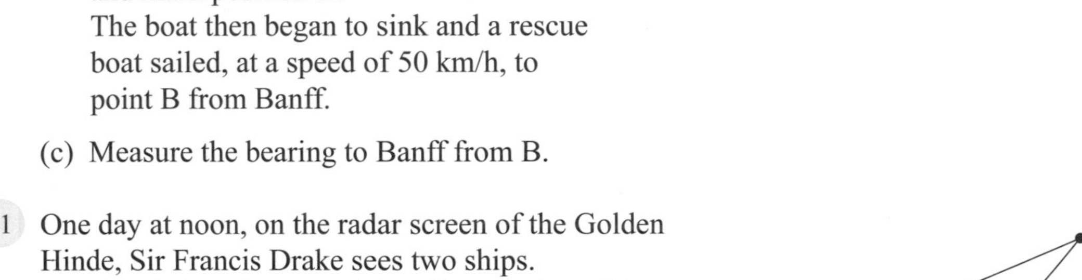

From the Golden Hinde, the Spanish galleon is 9 nautical miles away on a bearing 240° and the French pirate is 17 nautical miles away on a bearing 260°. The Spanish galleon sails due south at 8 knots. The French pirate sails south-east at 11 knots and Sir Francis sails at 14 knots on a bearing 211°.

At 1300 the captain of the Spanish galleon surrenders to the nearest ship.
Who gets the treasure?
[One knot is a speed of one nautical mile per hour].

12 At 0400 a customs patrol boat is 20 km due south of a suspect cargo ship. The cargo ship is sailing at a steady speed on a fixed bearing of 070°. The patrol boat sails on a fixed course at a speed of 26 km/h and intercepts the cargo ship at 0530.

(a) On what bearing did the patrol boat sail?

(b) At what speed was the cargo ship sailing?

[Use a scale of 1 cm to represent 2 km]

13 Here is a totally accurate transcript of an actual ratio conversation between a US naval vessel and the Canadian authorities off the coast of Newfoundland in October 1995. It was recently released by the chief of Naval Operations:

Americans: Please divert your course 15 degrees to the North to avoid a collision.

Canadians: recommend you divert YOUR course 15 degrees to the South to avoid a collision.

Americans: This is the Captain of a US Navy ship. I say again divert YOUR course.

Canadians: No, I say again, you divert YOUR course.

Americans: THIS IS THE AIRCRAFT CARRIER USS LINCOLN. THE SECOND LARGEST SHIP IN THE UNITED STATES OF ATLANTIC FLEET. WE ARE ACCOMPANIED BY THREE DESTROYERS. THREE CRUISERS AND NUMEROUS SUPPORT VESSELS. I DEMAND THAT YOU CHANGE YOUR COURSE 15 DEGREES NORTH. THAT'S ONE FIVE DEGREES NORTH, OR COUNTERMEASURES WILL BE

Canadians: This a lighthouse. Its your call....

Read the clip from a newspaper. Write a question about bearings using this incident or one of your own invention.

4.2 Using a spreadsheet on a computer

This section is written for use with Microsoft Excel. Other spreadsheet programs work in a similar way.

Select Microsoft Excel from the desk top.

A spreadsheet appears on your screen as a grid with rows numbered 1, 2, 3, 4,……..
and the columns lettered A, B, C, D, …….
The result should be a window like the one below.

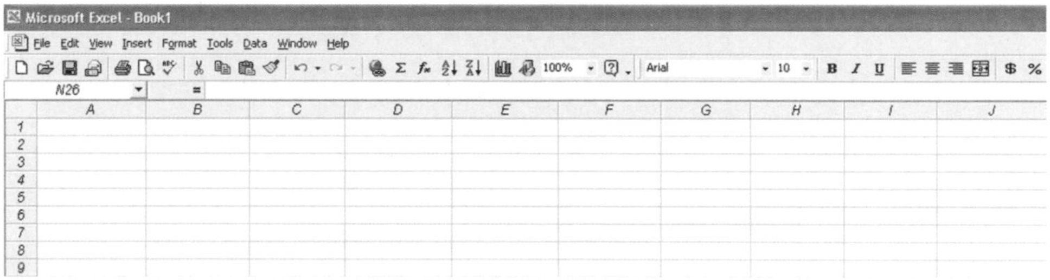

Cell The spaces on the spreadsheet are called cells. Individual cells are referred to as A1, B3, F9, like grid references. Cells may contain *labels*, *values* or *formulas*. The current cell has a black border.

Label Any words, headings or messages used to help the layout and organisation of the spreadsheet.

Value A number placed in a cell. It may be used as input to a calculation.

Tasks 1, 2 and 3 are written for you to become familiar with how the main functions of a spreadsheet program work. Afterwards there are sections on different topics where spreadsheets can be used.

Task 1. To generate the whole numbers from 1 to 10 in column A.

(a) In cell A1 type '1' and press *Return*. This will automatically take you to the cell below. (NOTE that you must use the *Return* button and not the arrow keys to move down the column.)

(b) In cell A2 type the formula ' = A1 + 1' and press *Return*. [NOTE that the = sign is needed before any formula.]

(c) We now want to copy the formula in A2 down column A as far as A10. Click on A2 again and put the arrow in the bottom right corner of cell A2 (a + sign will appear) and drag down to A10.

Task 2. To generate the odd numbers in column B.

(a) In B1 type '1' (press *Return*).

(b) In B2 type the formula ' = B1 + 2' (press *Return*).

(c) Click in B2 and copy the formula down column B as far as B10.

Task 3. To generate the first 15 square numbers.

(a) As before generate the numbers from 1 to 15 in cells A1 to A15.

(b) In B1 put the formula ' = A1 ∗ A1' and press *Return*.

(c) Click in B1 and copy the formula down as far as B15.

4.3 Handling data

In this section you will:

- draw and interpret scatter graphs
- answer questions with bar charts and pie charts
- learn how to produce charts with a computer

Scatter graphs

Sometimes it is important to discover if there is a connection or relationship between two sets of data.

Examples

- Are more umbrellas sold in wet countries?
- Do tall people weigh more than short people?
- Do tall parents have tall children?
- Do older people have higher pulse rates?

If there is a relationship, it will be easy to spot if your data is plotted on a scatter diagram – that is a graph in which one set of data is plotted on the horizontal axis and the other on the vertical axis

- Here is a scatter graph showing the test marks of some pupils in a maths test and a science test.
- We can see a connection: the pupils who got a high mark in science generally got a high mark in maths.

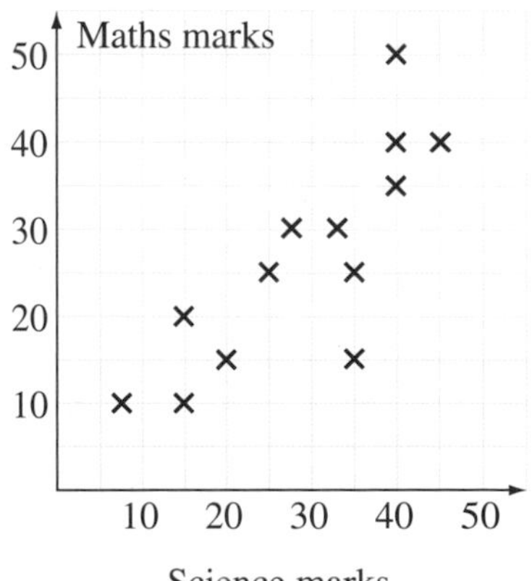

Exercise 1M

1 Here are the heights and masses of 9 people. Draw the axes shown and complete the scatter graph.

Name	Mass (kg)	Height (cm)
Alice	45	115
Fred	60	160
Jack	65	155
John	55	125
Percy	75	160
Hugh	75	170
Mabel	65	140
Diana	85	180
Cyril	52	146

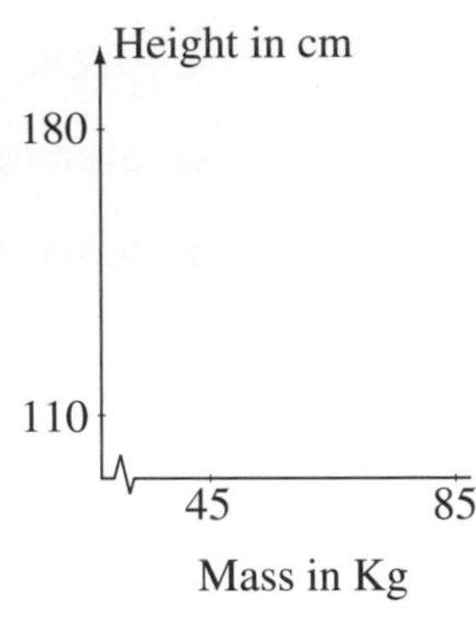

2 The scatter graph shows the number of hot drinks sold by a cafe and the outside temperature.

(a) On how many days was it less than 12°C?

(b) How many hot drinks were sold when it was 35°C?

(c) On how many days were 40 or more hot drinks sold?

(d) Fill the blank with either 'increases' or 'decreases': As temperature *increases* the number of drinks sold______.

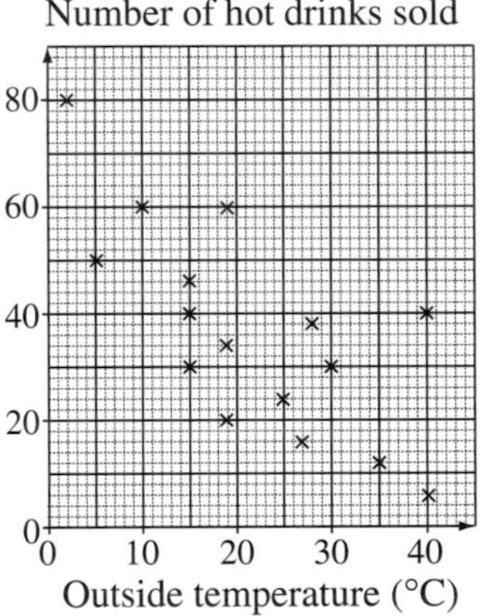

3 The graph shows the scores in a spelling test and the shoe sizes of 14 children.

(a) How many take size 6 or less?

(b) The pass mark is 4 or more. How many people failed?

(c) Is there a connection between a person's shoe size and test score?

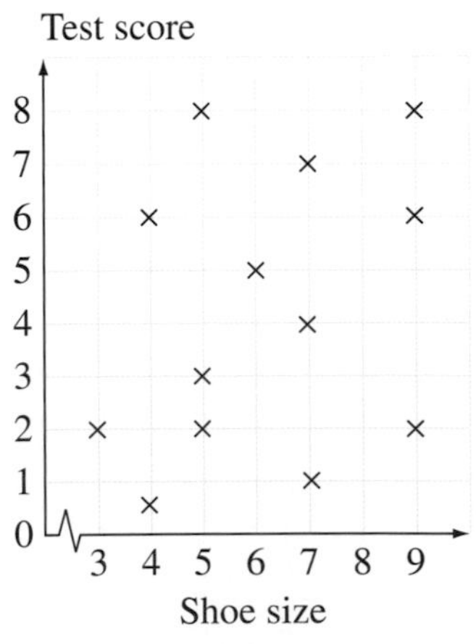

Correlation

The word correlation describes how things *co-relate*. There is correlation between two sets of data if there is a connection or relationship.

The correlation between two sets of data can be positive or negative and it can be strong or weak as indicated by the scatter graphs below.

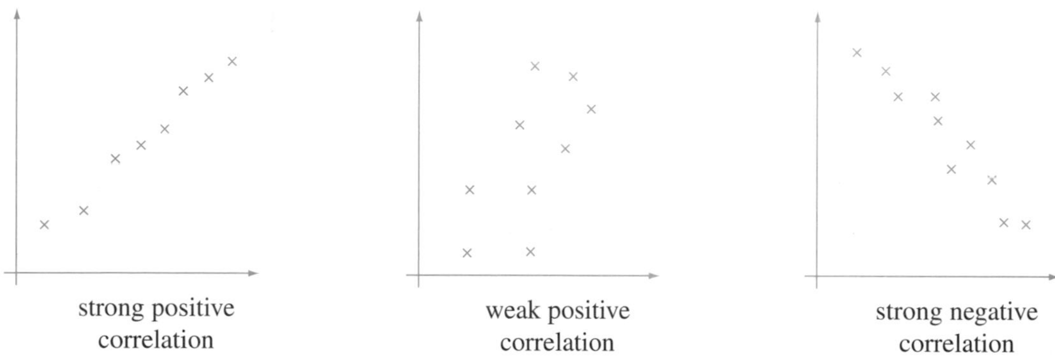

When the correlation is positive the points are around a line which slopes upwards to the right. When the correlation is negative the 'line' slopes downwards to the right.

When the correlation is strong the points are bunched close to a line through their midst. When the correlation is weak the points are more scattered.

It is important to realise that often there is *no* correlation between two sets of data.

If, for example, we take a group of students and plot their maths test results against their time to run 800 m, the graph might look like the one on the right. A common mistake in this topic is to 'see' a correlation on a scatter graph where none exists.

There is also *no* correlation in these two scatter graphs.

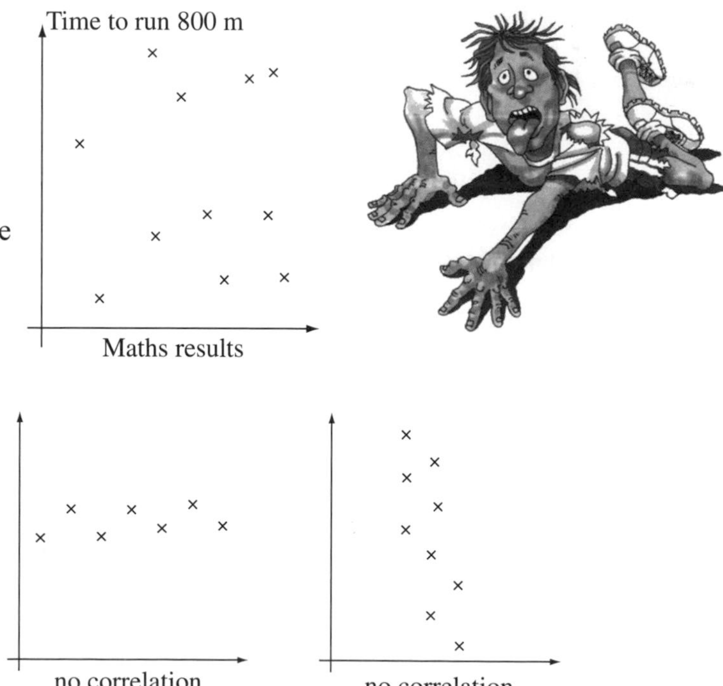

Exercise 2M

1 Make the following measurements for everyone in your class:

height	(nearest cm)
armspan	(nearest cm)
head circumference	(nearest cm)
hand span	(nearest cm)
pulse rate	(beats/minute)

For greater consistency of measuring, one person (or perhaps 2 people) should do all the measurements of one kind (except on themselves!)

Enter all the measurements in a table, either on the board or on a sheet of paper.

Name	Height	Armspan	Head
Roger	161	165	56 cm
Liz	150	148	49 cm
Gill			

(a) Draw the scatter graphs shown below

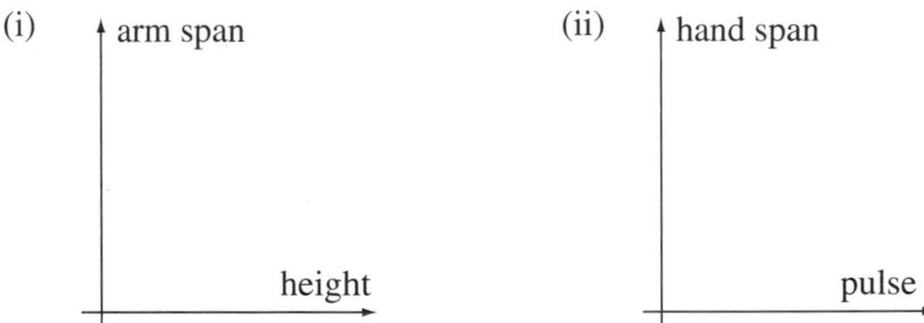

(b) Describe the correlation, if any, in the scatter graphs you drew in part (a).

(c) (i) Draw a scatter graph of two measurements where you think there might be a positive correlation?

(ii) Was there indeed a positive correlation?

2 Plot the points given on a scatter graph, with s across the page and p up the page. Draw axes with values from 0 to 20.

Describe the correlation, if any, between the values of s and p. [i.e. 'strong negative', 'weak positive' etc.]

(a)

s	7	16	4	12	18	6	20	4	10	13
p	8	15	6	12	17	9	18	7	10	14

(b)

s	3	8	12	15	16	5	6	17	9
p	4	2	10	17	5	10	17	11	15

(c)

s	11	1	16	7	2	19	8	4	13	18
p	5	12	7	14	17	1	11	8	11	5

(d)

s	18	6	8	4	12	16	2	20	10	13
p	6	12	12	15	10	8	16	4	10	8

3 Describe the correlation; if any, in these scatter graphs.

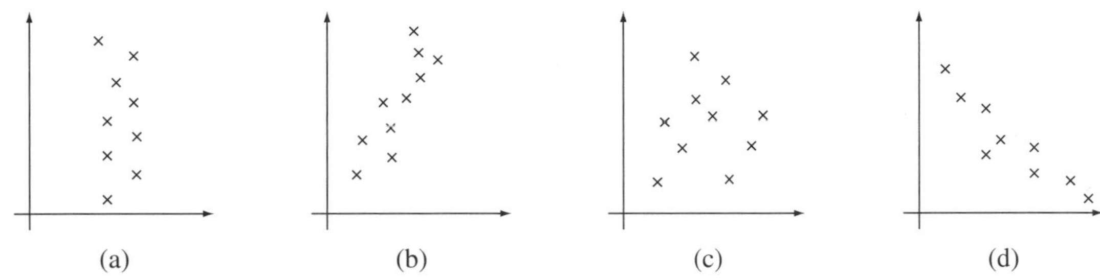

(a) (b) (c) (d)

4 What sort of scatter graph would you expect if you plotted 'footballers' wages' on one axis and 'that player's team position in the league' on the other axis?

Exercise 2E

1 The table shows the marks of 7 students in the two papers of a science examination.

Paper 1	35	10	60	17	43	55	49
Paper 2	26	15	40	15	30	34	35

(a) Plot the marks on a scatter diagram, using a scale of 1 cm to 5 marks.

(b) A student got a mark of 25 on paper 1 but missed paper 2. What would you expect her to get on paper 2?

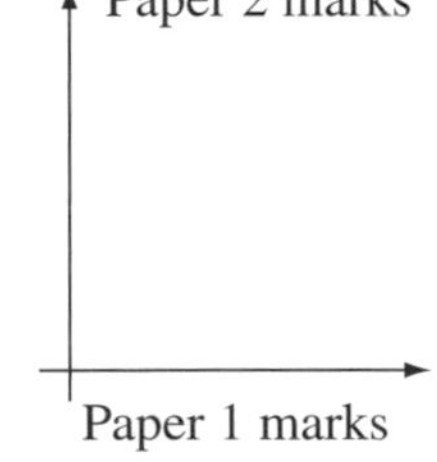

2 The table shows the mean weight of the apples from a certain apple tree together with the latitude of the farm where the tree was growing

Latitude (N)	37	50	32	45	36	30	44
Mean weight of apples (g)	100	70	115	75	110	120	80

(a) Draw a scatter graph, using a scale of 1 cm to 5 g across the page and 2 cm to 5° up the page.

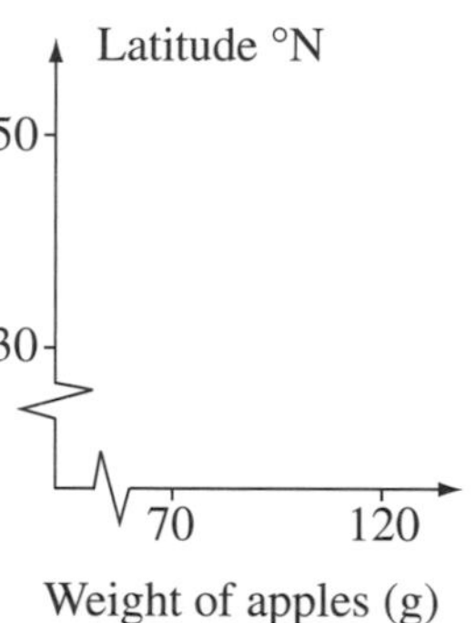

(b) What would you expect the mean weight of the apples to be on a farm at latitude 42N?

3 What sort of scatter graph would you expect if you plotted *number of daily flights* against *population of nearest city*?

4 Suppose scatter graphs were drawn, with the quantities below on the two axes. What sort of correlation, if any, would you expect to see in each case?

(a) height of a man; height of the man's father

(b) a person's pulse rate; a person's reaction time

(c) outside temperature; consumption of energy for heating a home

(d) value of a car; mileage of the car [far the same kind of car]

(e) price of goods in U.K; price of similar goods in Germany

(f) number of ice creams sold; outside temperature

(g) exposure to sun; degree of sunburn

(h) use of a calculator; ability to do mental arithmetic

(i) length of time sleeping; rate of growth of fingernails

5 The table below show details of the number of rooms and the number of occupants of 11 houses in a street.

Number of rooms	2	3	7	11	7	5	5	11	5	6	4
Number of occupants	2	8	5	2	6	2	7	7	4	0	1

(a) Draw a scatter graph

(b) Can you estimate the likely number of people living in a house with 9 rooms? If so, what is the number? Explain your answer.

6 

Predict what sort of scatter graph you would obtain if you drew a graph with the axes shown.

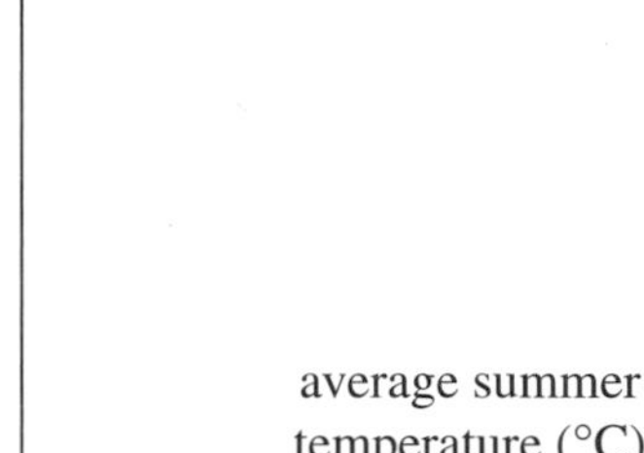

Bar charts and pie charts

Pie charts were invented by Florence Nightingale who was a distinguished mathematician as well as being the founder of modern nursing. She used pie charts to display medical statistics to government ministers in a form which was easy to understand.

Exercise 3M

1 In a survey almost 30 000 young people were questioned about smoking.

(a) What percentage of girls aged 13–14 said they 'don't smoke and never will'?

(b) Is there a connection between sections A and C?

(c) Estimate what percentage of boys aged 15–16 smoke and don't want to give up.

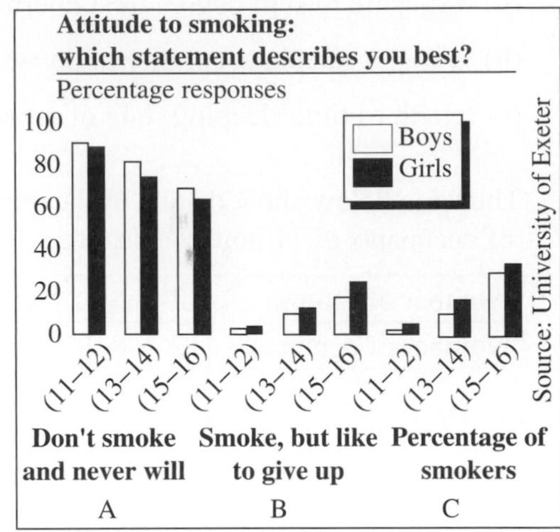

2

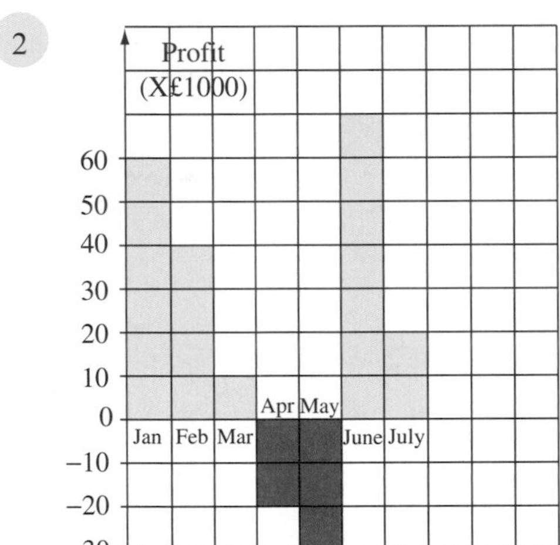

The bar chart shows the profit/loss figures for a shop.

(a) What was the profit in February?

(b) In how many months did the shop make a profit of more than £10 000?

(c) In which two consecutive months did the shop have its best performance?

(d) What was the overall profit for the first seven months after the losses were subtracted?

3 The bar chart shows the results of a survey in which 2000 people in each of 20 countries were asked if they had reported that their car had been stolen in the previous 12 months.

(a) In which country or countries was the reported rate of theft worst?

(b) Of the 2000 people questioned in the United States, how many had reported a car stolen?

(c) What does the chart show for Switzerland?

(d) Roughly how many times more likely were people in England and Wales to report a car theft compared to people in Germany?

(e) Why do you think Scotland's rate of theft is so much lower than that in England?

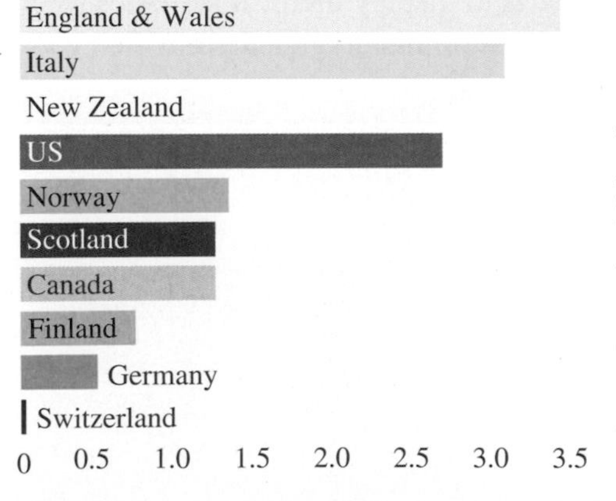

4 In an experiment two dice were thrown seventy times and the total score was recorded

5	7	2	8	6	6	7	5	3	9
2	3	5	4	8	6	4	7	5	10
7	8	7	6	12	11	8	11	7	6
6	5	7	7	8	6	7	3	6	7
12	3	10	4	3	7	2	11	8	5
7	10	7	5	7	5	10	11	7	10
4	8	6	4	6	11	6	12	11	5

Score	Tally marks	Frequency
2	||	
3	||||	
4		
:		

(a) Draw a tally chart to show the results.

(b) Draw a chart to illustrate the results.

5 The pie charts show how much money two shopkeepers get from selling different products.

Mr. Brown

Mrs. Evans

(a) Mr Brown gets £180 from selling ice cream. Estimate how much he gets from selling sweets.

(b) From all sales: Mr Brown gets a total of £800 and Mrs Evans gets a total of £1200. Estimate how much each shopkeeper gets from selling magazines.

6 The bar chart shows age groups on three different holidays.

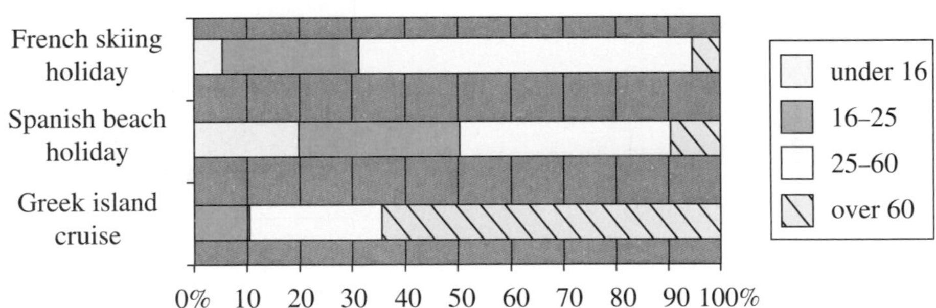

(a) What percentage of holiday makers are:

(i) between 25 and 60 on the Spanish beach holiday,

(ii) under 25 on the Greek island cruise,

(iii) over 25 on the French skiing holiday?

(b) Describe the main difference between the top and bottom charts. Why are they so different?

Exercise 3E

1 The bar chart shows the marks scored in a test.

(a) What mark was the mode?

(b) What was the median mark?

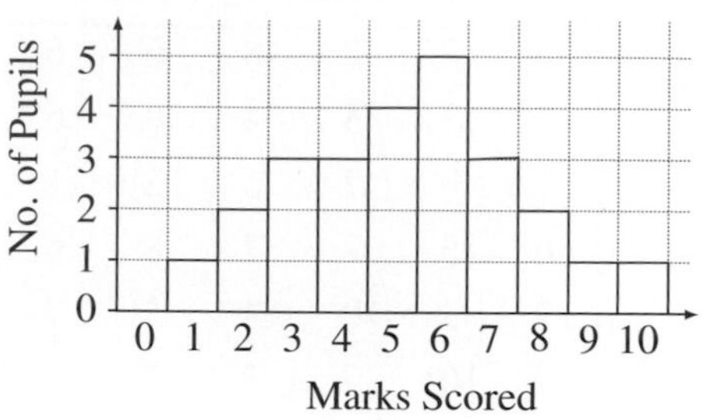

2 A firm employs 720 people in six departments as shown below.

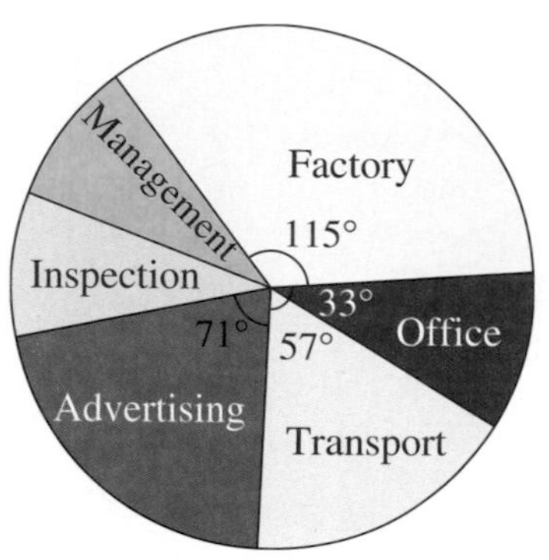

Copy and complete the table below.

Department	Angle on pie chart	Number employed
Factory	115°	
Office	33°	
Transport	57°	
Advertising	71°	
Inspection		140
Management		28

3 The table shows the number of periods for different subjects on a school timetable. Work out the angle for each sector and then draw a pie chart.

Subject	Frequency
Maths	5
English	5
Science	6
Humanities	4
Arts	4
Others	16

4 Eurostar did a survey of over a thousand passengers on one of their trains. Here are their nationalities:

British 30% French 20%

German 15% Dutch 35%

On a pie chart, the angle for British passengers is found by working out 30% of 360°. Find the angle on a pie chart representing

(a) French passengers (b) Dutch passengers.

5 The pie chart illustrates the sales of four brands of crisps.

(a) What percentage of total sales does Pringles have?

(b) If Walkers accounts for 35% of total sales, calculate the angles x and y.

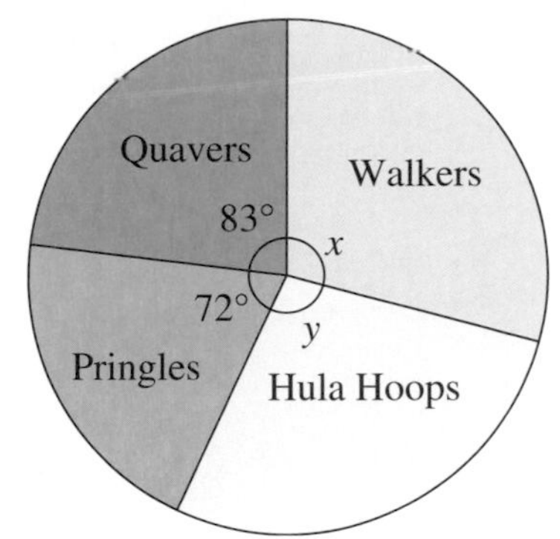

6 A car insurance company carried out some light-hearted but interesting research. They recorded the cost of accident repairs from hundreds of insurance claims and also recorded the driver's star sign. As an example suppose the average repair claim for all drivers is £500. Any average driver with star sign Sagittarius has a claim 19.3% higher than £500 [ie. £596.50]. In the questions below take the average repair claim to be £500.

(a) What is the average repair claim for drivers who are Taurus?

(b) Work out the average repair claim for drivers of your star sign.

(c) Does the chart provide data which reinforces your opinion of the car driving ability of your mother and/or father? (!)

Percentage difference from average repair claim

−30 −25 −20 −15 −10 −5 0 +5 +10 +15 +20

Star sign	Percentage difference
Sagittarius	19.3
Leo	13.5
Virgo	11.7
Capricorn	6.5
Cancer	4.5
Libra	2.3
Aquarius	0.73
Scorpio	0.04
Aries	5.87
Gemini	12.2
Pisces	14.0
Taurus	29.8

HIGH RISK

LOW RISK

7 A drug company claims that its new nutrient pill helps people to improve their memory.

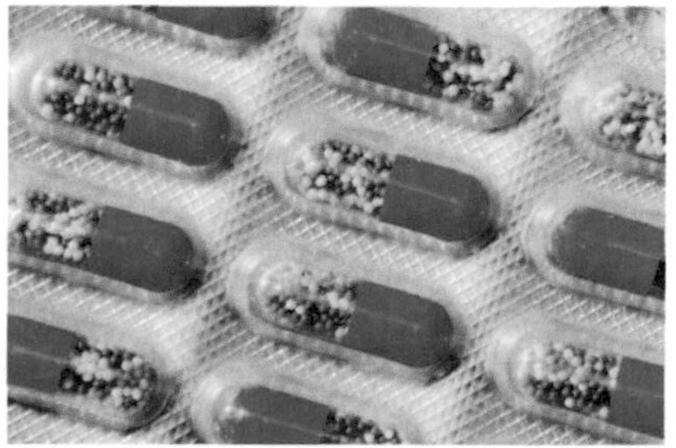

As an experiment two randomly selected groups of people were given the same memory test. Group A tool the new pills for a month while group B took no pills. Here are the results of the test: (A high score indicates a good memory).

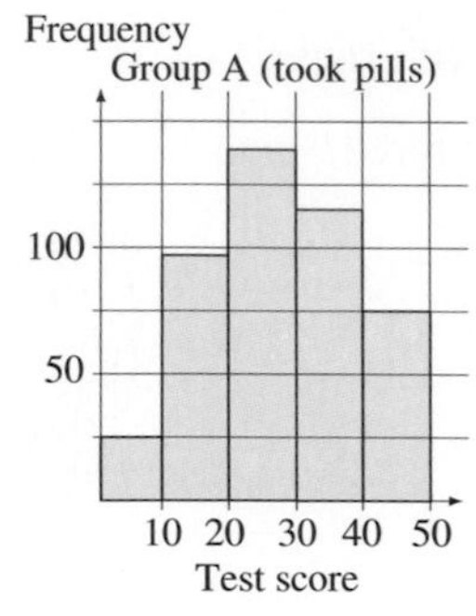

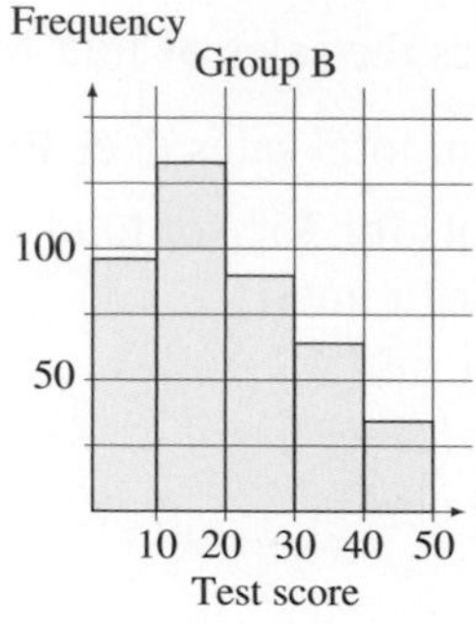

Does it appear that the new pills did in fact help to improve memory?

Pie charts and bar charts using a spreadsheet on a computer

Teacher's note: There is an introduction to using spreadsheets in section 4.2.

Example: Display the data about the activities in one day.

Enter the headings: Sleep in A1, School in B1 etc. [Use the *tab* key to move across the page.]

Enter the data: 8 in A2, 7 in B2 etc.

Microsoft Excel - Book1

File Edit View Insert Format Tools Data Window Help

A1 = Sleep

	A	B	C	D	E	F	G	H	I
1	Sleep	School	TV	Eating	Homework	Other			
2	8	7	1.5	1	1.5	5			
3									
4									
5									
6									
7									
8									
9									

Now highlight all the cells from A1 to F2. [Click on A1 and drag across to F2.]

Click on the ( ) Chart wizard on the tool bar.

Select 'pie' and then choose one of the examples displayed. Follow the on-screen prompts.

Alternatively, for a bar chart, select 'charts' after clicking on the chart wizard. Proceed as above.

You will be able to display your charts with various '3D' effects, possibly in colour. This approach is recommended when you are presenting data that you have collected as part of an investigation.

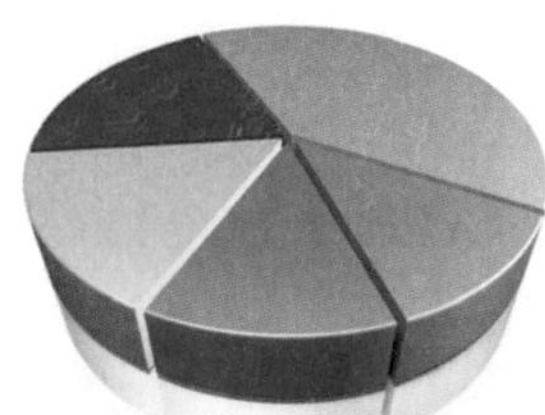

Task 1

Open the spreadsheet program on your computer (for example 'Excel') Enter the data from question 3 in the last exercise. Obtain a bar chart and a pie chart for the data and print your results.

Scatter graphs on a computer

Example: Plot a scatter graph showing the marks of 10 students in Maths and Science.

Enter the headings: *Maths* in A1, *Science* in B1
Enter the data as shown.

Now highlight all the cells from A2 to B11.
[Click on A1 and drag across and down to B11.]

Click on the Chart wizard on the toolbar.

Select XY (Scatter) and select the picture which looks like a scatter graph.

Follow the on-screen prompts.

On 'Titles' enter: Chart title: Maths/Sciencc results

Value (X) axis: Maths

Value (Y) axis: Science

Experiment with 'Axes', 'Gridlines,' 'Legend' and 'Data Labels'.

E9	A	B
1	Maths	Science
2	23	30
3	45	41
4	73	67
5	35	74
6	67	77
7	44	50
8	32	41
9	66	55
10	84	70
11	36	32

Task 1 Enter the data on a spreadsheet and print a scatter graph.
What does each scatter graph show?

(a)

Height	Armspan
162	160
155	151
158	157
142	144
146	148
165	163
171	167
148	150
150	147

(b)

Temperature	Sales
23	7
18	14
7	23
20	9
4	30
12	19
15	15
18	15
10	20

CHECK YOURSELF ON SECTIONS 4.1 AND 4.3

1 Bearings and scale drawing

(a)

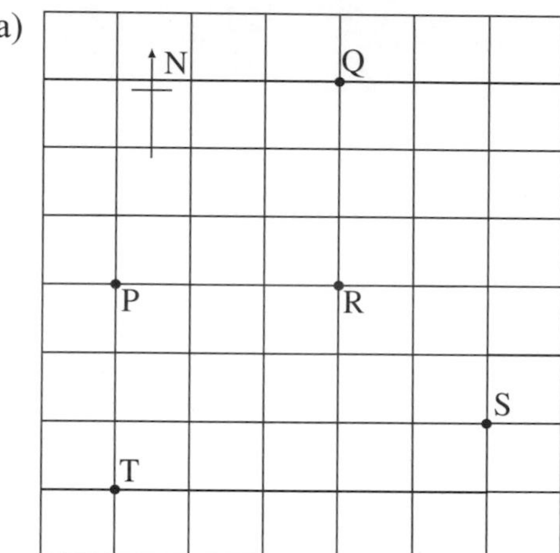

State the bearings of (a) Q from P
(b) R from P
(c) S from R
(d) R from Q
(e) T from R
(f) P from R

(b) Copy the diagram on squared paper. Mark a point P such that

(a) the bearing of P from A is 040°

(b) the bearing of P from B is 305°

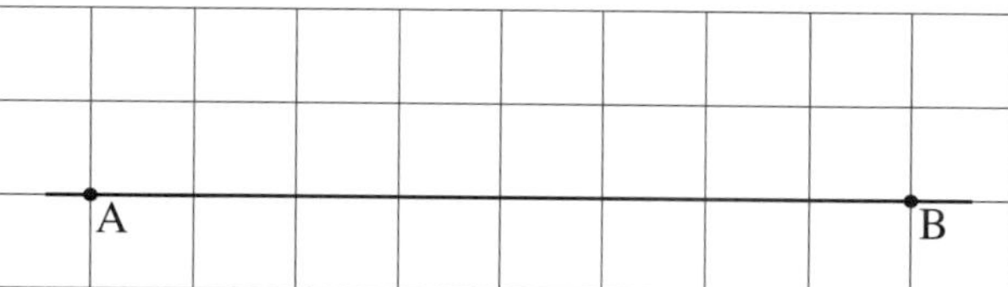

2 Handling data

(a) The table below shows the number of days absence for fifteen year 8 pupils and their maths test results.

Number of days absent	5	9	0	1	10	7	0	5	2	9	10	2	6	8	4
Test score	7	3	10	9	2	5	9	6	8	4	3	9	6	4	7

(i) Plot these points on a scatter graph.

(ii) Describe the correlation if any, in this scatter graph.

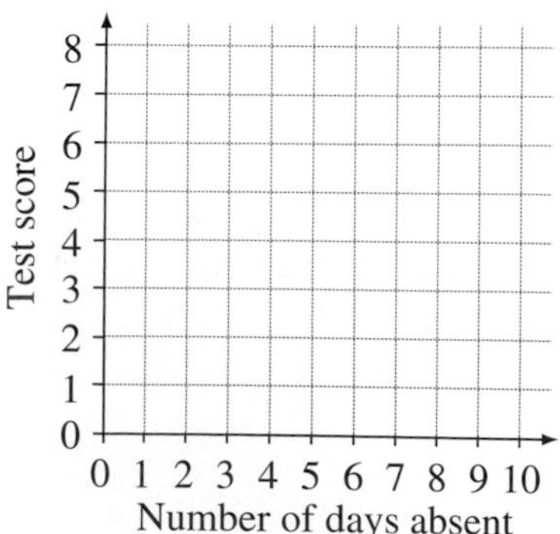

(b) Describe the correlation, if any, in these scatter graphs.

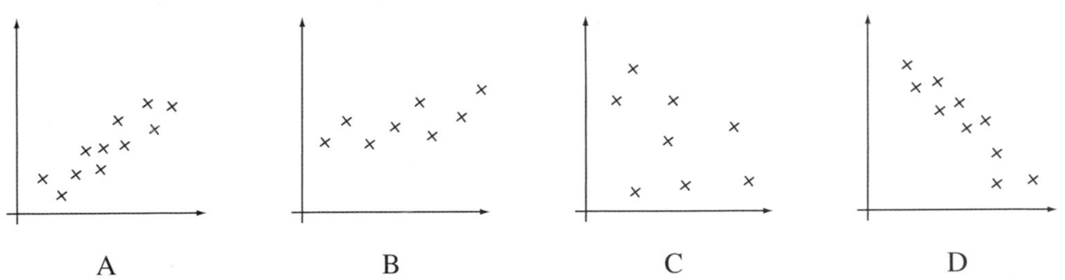

4.4 Fractions, decimals, percentages

In section 4.4 you will:

- write fractions, decimals and percentages in different forms
- learn about recurring decimals
- solve problems involving percentage increase or decrease

Changing fractions to decimals

(a) In book 7H we changed fractions to decimals using known equivalents.

Eg. $\frac{3}{12} = \frac{1}{4} = 0.25$ $\qquad \frac{11}{20} = \frac{55}{100} = 0.55$ $\qquad \frac{12}{25} = \frac{48}{100} = 0.48$

(b) We can think of the fraction $\frac{3}{5}$ as $3 \div 5$. When we perform the division, we obtain the decimal which is equivalent to $\frac{3}{5}$.

$5\overline{)3.{}^{3}0}$ with quotient 0.6 $\qquad$ Answer: $\frac{3}{5} = 0.6$

(c) $\frac{5}{8}$ can be thought of as $5 \div 8$.

$8\overline{)5.{}^{5}0{}^{2}0{}^{4}0}$ with quotient 0.625 $\qquad$ Answer: $\frac{5}{8} = 0.625$

Exercise 1M

Without using a calculator, change the following fractions to decimals. Afterwards use your calculator to check your answer.

1 $\frac{2}{5}$ $\qquad$ 2 $\frac{1}{4}$ $\qquad$ 3 $\frac{3}{8}$ $\qquad$ 4 $\frac{1}{5}$ $\qquad$ 5 $\frac{9}{10}$

6 $\frac{3}{4}$ $\qquad$ 7 $\frac{3}{5}$ $\qquad$ 8 $\frac{4}{8}$ $\qquad$ 9 $\frac{3}{10}$ $\qquad$ 10 $\frac{7}{8}$

Change these mixed numbers to decimals.

11 $1\frac{2}{5}$ **12** $4\frac{3}{4}$ **13** $3\frac{1}{2}$ **14** $1\frac{7}{8}$ **15** $5\frac{1}{100}$

Use a calculator, to convert the fractions to decimals. Write in order of size, smallest first.

16 $\frac{7}{8}$, 0.85, $\frac{9}{10}$ **17** $\frac{13}{20}$, 0.645, $\frac{31}{50}$

18 $\frac{3}{4}$, 0.715, $\frac{29}{40}$ **19** $\frac{3}{16}$, 0.18, $\frac{1}{5}$

20 What fraction of each shape is shaded?

(a)

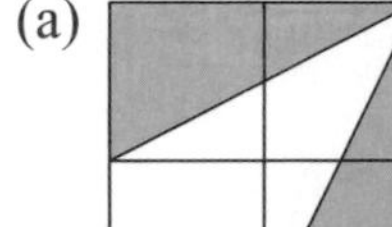

(b)

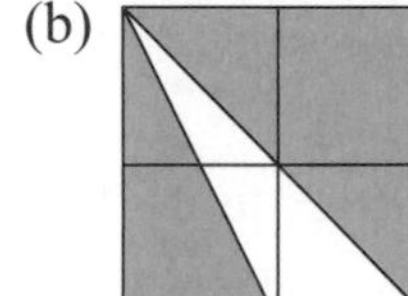

(c)

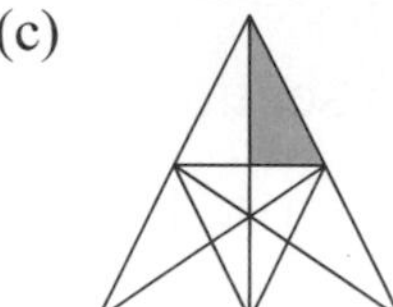

Recurring decimals

Some fractions give rise to decimals which repeat themselves forever.

We call these recurring decimals, and use the notation below to save us from writing out the number until our ink runs out.

(a) 0.555... We write $0.\dot{5}$

(b) 0.434343... We write $0.\dot{4}\dot{3}$

(c) 0.5265265... We write $0.\dot{5}2\dot{6}$

(a) Change $\frac{1}{3}$ to a decimal

$$3\,\overline{)\,1.{}^{1}0{}^{1}0{}^{1}0{}^{1}0{}^{1}0...}\quad = 0.\,3\,3\,3\,3\,3...$$

The calculation is never going to end.

We write $\frac{1}{3} = 0.\dot{3}$. We say 'nought point three recurring'.

(b) Change $\frac{3}{11}$ to a decimal.

$$11\,\overline{)\,3.{}^{3}0{}^{8}0{}^{3}0{}^{8}0{}^{3}0{}^{8}0...}\quad = 0.\,2\,7\,2\,7\,2\,2...$$

This time a *pair* of figures recurs.

We write $\frac{3}{11} = 0.\dot{2}\dot{7}$

(c) Change $\frac{1}{7}$ to a decimal.

$$7\,\overline{)\,1.{}^{1}0{}^{3}0{}^{2}0{}^{6}0{}^{4}0{}^{5}0{}^{1}0{}^{3}00...}\quad = 0.\,1\,4\,2\,8\,5\,7\,1\,42...$$

The sequence '142857' recurs.

We write $\frac{1}{7} = 0.\dot{1}4285\dot{7}$

Exercise 1E

Change the following fractions to decimals.

1 $\frac{2}{3}$ 2 $\frac{2}{9}$ 3 $\frac{7}{9}$ 4 $\frac{1}{6}$ 5 $\frac{2}{7}$

6 $\frac{3}{7}$ 7 $\frac{5}{6}$ 8 $\frac{6}{7}$ 9 $\frac{2}{11}$ 10 $\frac{5}{11}$

11 (a) Work out each of the following as a decimal: $\frac{1}{7}, \frac{2}{7}, \frac{3}{7}, \frac{4}{7}, \frac{5}{7}, \frac{6}{7}$.
(b) What do you notice about the answers?

12 (a) Write out the 13 times table up to and including 9×13.
(b) Use long division to change the following fraction to decimals.
(i) $\frac{1}{13}$ (ii) $\frac{4}{13}$ (iii) $\frac{9}{13}$.
(c) Write down what you notice about the answers.

Investigation: Recurrrrrrinngggġ decimals

1. Using a calculator, we obtain $\frac{1}{17} = 0.0588235$ (to 7 d.p.)

Similarly $\frac{2}{17} = 0.1\ \underbrace{17647}$

$\frac{3}{17} = 0.\overbrace{17647}05$

Notice the group of 5 digits '17647'

$\frac{4}{17} = 0.235\ \underbrace{2941}$

$\frac{5}{17} = 0.\overbrace{2941}\ 176$

Notice the group of 4 digits '2941'

Using a calculator,

(a) Work out the following as decimals: $\frac{6}{17}, \frac{7}{17}, \frac{8}{17}, \frac{9}{17}, \frac{10}{17}, \frac{11}{17}, \frac{12}{17}, \frac{13}{17}, \frac{14}{17}, \frac{15}{17}, \frac{16}{17}$.
Look out for the same sequence of digits occurring in different fractions.
In fact, $\frac{1}{17}$ is a recurring decimal with a group of 16 digits in the recurring interval.

(b) Use the sequences you observe in the figures above to write $\frac{1}{17}$ as a recurring decimal.

(c) As a final check you could perform the long division $1 \div 17$. It is easier if you begin by writing down the 17 times table up to 9×17.

2. Now consider $\frac{1}{19}$.

Use a calculator to work out $\frac{1}{19}, \frac{2}{19}, \frac{3}{19}, \frac{4}{19}$...... Do enough so that you can see sequences of digits in the answers.

$\frac{1}{19}$ is a recurring decimal with a group of 18 digits in the recurring interval. Use your answers above to write $\frac{1}{19}$ as a recurring decimal.

3. Look at other fractions which you think may be recurring decimals. Write down any observations that you make.

Changing decimals to fractions

- $0.8 = \frac{8}{10} = \frac{4}{5}$ $\qquad 0.21 = \frac{21}{100}$

  $0.35 = \frac{35}{100} = \frac{7}{20}$ $\qquad 0.08 = \frac{8}{100} = \frac{2}{25}$

Simplify the answer if possible

Exercise 2M

Change the following decimals to fractions in their most simple form.

1 0.4   2 0.7   3 0.03   4 0.05   5 0.007

6 0.006   7 0.08   8 0.12   9 0.38   10 0.015

11 0.25   12 0.45   13 0.37   14 0.025   15 0.125

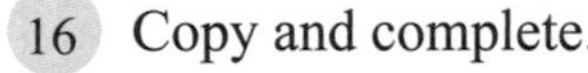

16 Copy and complete.

(a) $0.02 = \frac{\square}{\square}$ (b) $0.15 = \frac{\square}{\square}$ (c) $0.16 = \frac{\square}{\square}$

Changing to a percentage and vice versa

To change a fraction or a decimal to a percentage, multiply by 100

(a) To change $\frac{2}{5}$ to a percentage, multiply by 100.

$$\frac{2}{5} \times \frac{100}{1} = \frac{200}{5}$$
$$= 40\%$$

(b) To change $\frac{1}{8}$ to a percentage, multiply by 100.

$$\frac{1}{8} \times \frac{100}{1} = \frac{100}{8}$$
$$= 12\tfrac{1}{2}\%$$

(c) To change $\frac{3}{7}$ to a percentage, multiply by 100.

$$\frac{3}{7} \times \frac{100}{1} = \frac{300}{7}$$
$$= 42{\cdot}857\ldots\%$$
$$= 43\%, \text{ to the nearest whole number.}$$

(d) To change 0.37 to a percentage, multiply by 100.

$0.37 \times 100 = 37\%$

Exercise 3M

Change these fractions to percentages.

1 $\frac{1}{2}$ 2 $\frac{3}{4}$ 3 $\frac{2}{5}$ 4 $\frac{7}{10}$ 5 $\frac{13}{20}$

6 $\frac{1}{8}$ 7 $\frac{5}{8}$ 8 $\frac{1}{4}$ 9 $\frac{7}{20}$ 10 $\frac{71}{100}$

11 Here are some examination results. Change them to percentages.

(a) $\frac{14}{25}$ (b) $\frac{33}{40}$ (c) $\frac{42}{60}$ (d) $\frac{66}{120}$

12 Class 8P and class 8W were each set a maths test. The average mark for 8P was $\frac{25}{40}$ and the average mark for 8W was $\frac{15}{25}$. Which class had the higher average percentage result?

13 Change these decimals to percentages.

(a) 0.32 (b) 0.14 (c) 0.03 (d) 0.815 (e) 1.4

14 Change these fractions to percentages, rounding to the nearest whole number.

(a) $\frac{5}{6}$ (b) $\frac{7}{12}$ (c) $\frac{4}{9}$ (d) $\frac{6}{11}$ (e) $\frac{2}{3}$

15 The chart opposite shows the way that 40 people travel to work.
What percentage travel

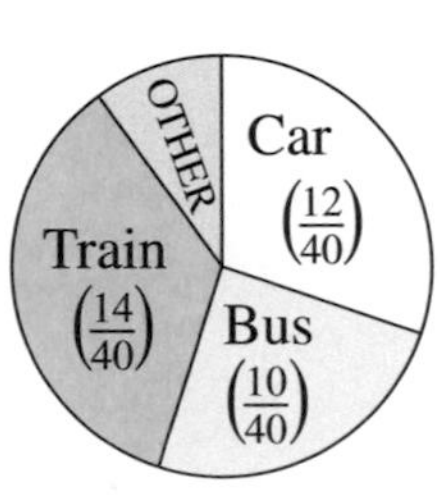

(a) By car

(b) By train

(c) By bus

(d) By some other method?

16 Write in order of size, smallest first.

(a) 66%, 0.6, $\frac{5}{8}$ (b) $\frac{5}{9}$, 0.056, 55%

(c) $\frac{3}{7}$, $45\frac{1}{2}$%, $\frac{5}{11}$ (d) $\frac{1}{1000}$, 0.2%, 0.0005

Exercise 3E

1 24% of the grid below is shaded (Of the 100 squares on the grid exactly 24 are shaded).

Draw a grid like this one and draw a number of your own choice. For example if you chose '16' make sure you shade in 16 out of the 100 squares. Try to make both figures the same size!

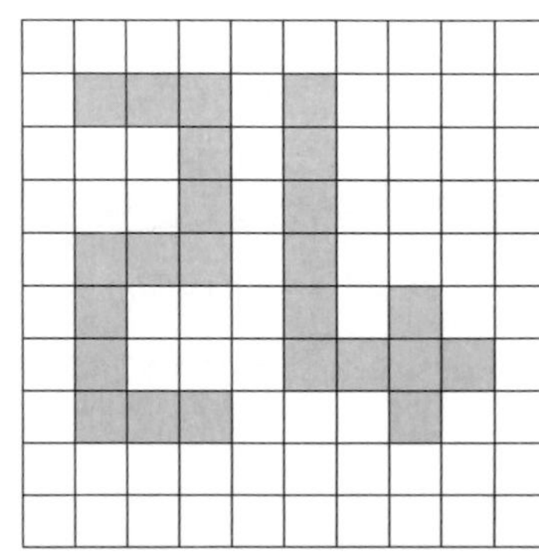

2 The letters shown on the right are each given a number as either a fraction, a decimal or a percentage.

In (a), (b), (c) below the numbers 1, 2, 3, …. give the positions of the letters in a sentence. So 1 is the first letter, 2 is the second letter and so on.

Find the letter whose value is the same as the number given, and write it in the correct position.

A	24%	N	0.9
E	0.05	O	0.625
F	0.32	R	0.6
G	$\frac{3}{20}$	S	$\frac{7}{20}$
H	0.36	T	0.02
I	3%	U	$\frac{3}{25}$
L	0.49	V	0.1%
M	$\frac{3}{4}$	Y	99%

For example in part (a) number 1 is $\frac{3}{5}$. Since $\frac{3}{5} = 0.6$, letter R goes in the first box.
Find the sentence in each part.

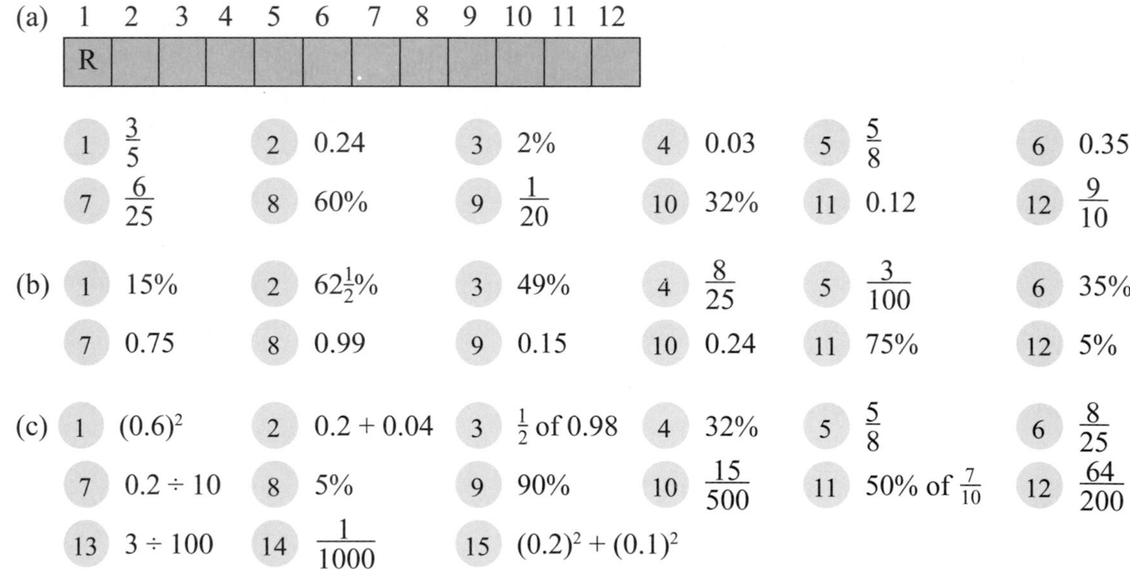

(a) 1 2 3 4 5 6 7 8 9 10 11 12

R											

1 $\frac{3}{5}$ 2 0.24 3 2% 4 0.03 5 $\frac{5}{8}$ 6 0.35
7 $\frac{6}{25}$ 8 60% 9 $\frac{1}{20}$ 10 32% 11 0.12 12 $\frac{9}{10}$

(b) 1 15% 2 $62\frac{1}{2}\%$ 3 49% 4 $\frac{8}{25}$ 5 $\frac{3}{100}$ 6 35%
7 0.75 8 0.99 9 0.15 10 0.24 11 75% 12 5%

(c) 1 $(0.6)^2$ 2 $0.2 + 0.04$ 3 $\frac{1}{2}$ of 0.98 4 32% 5 $\frac{5}{8}$ 6 $\frac{8}{25}$
7 $0.2 \div 10$ 8 5% 9 90% 10 $\frac{15}{500}$ 11 50% of $\frac{7}{10}$ 12 $\frac{64}{200}$
13 $3 \div 100$ 14 $\frac{1}{1000}$ 15 $(0.2)^2 + (0.1)^2$

3 Make up a sentence of your own using the letters given in question 2 .
Write clues and try it out on a friend.

4 Work out the following correct to 2 decimal places.

(a) $\frac{7}{12} - 0.22$ (b) $0.\dot{4}5\dot{2} + \frac{2}{9}$ (c) $\frac{3}{5}$ of 0.713 (d) ($\frac{3}{4}$ of 0.8) – (15% of $\frac{4}{5}$)

(e) $0.\dot{4}$ – (22% of $0.5\dot{1}$) (f) $(\frac{1}{12} + \frac{1}{7} - \frac{1}{13}) \times 0.73$ (g) 85% of ($0.8\dot{1}\dot{2} - \frac{4}{5}$)

5 (a) Graham claims that 35% of £40 is the same as 40% of £35. Is he correct?

(b) Graham also claims that 35% of £40 is the same as $\frac{35}{40}$ of £100. Is he correct this time?

Using percentages

(a) Work out 16% of £15.

16% of £15

$= \frac{16}{100} \times \frac{15}{1}$

= £2.40

(b) Work out 14% of £260.
(Quick way)

14% = 0.14 as a decimal

So 14% of £260 = 0.14 × 260

= £36.40

(c) Work out, to the nearest penny:

8% of £11.99

$= \frac{8}{100} \times \frac{11.99}{1}$

= 0.9592

= £0.96, to the nearest penny

(d) Work out, to the nearest penny:
(Quick way)

21% of £6.92

= 0.21 × 6.92

= 1.4532

= £1.45, to the nearest penny

Exercise 4M

Work out.

1. 12% of £600
2. 6% of £250
3. 81% of £9
4. 8% of £450
5. 7% of £440
6. 43% of £185
7. 5% of £22
8. 4% of £660
9. 8% of £2555
10. 85% of £400
11. 6.5% of £200
12. 7% of £6
13. 29% of £2000
14. 4.5% of £400
15. 17% of £175
16. At six months old a cow weighed 84 kg.
    In the next month its weight increased by 15%.

    How much did its weight increase?

17 In a restaurant a service charge of 10% is added to the price of a meal. What is the service charge on a meal costing £28.50?

In questions 18 to 32 give the answer correct to the nearest penny.

18 13% of £2.13

19 27% of £5.85

20 15.1% of £7.87

21 11% of £6.27

22 13% of £6.17

23 16% of £0.87

24 37% of £5.20

25 15% of £11.23

26 4% of £0.65

27 6.2% of £8.55

28 31% of £35.04

29 78% of £3.17

30 8.9% of £17.10

31 6.8% of £16.10

32 23% of £18.05

Percentage increase or decrease

In 2009 the cost of taxing a car increased from £220 by 70%. What is the new cost?

70% of £220

$$= \frac{70}{100} \times \frac{220}{1} = £154$$

New cost of taxing car = £220 + £154

= £374

Exercise 4E

1 The price of a phone was £90 but it is increased by 5%. What is the new price?

2 In a closing-down sale, a shop reduces all its prices by 20%. Find the sale price of a jacket which previously cost £60.

3 The petrol consumption of a car is 35 miles per gallon. After a service the car does 6% more miles per gallon. What is the new consumption?

4 A dog normally weighs 28 kg. After being put on a diet for three months its weight is reduced by 35%. How much does it weigh now?

5 The length of a new washing line is 21 m. After being used it stretches by 3%. Find the new length.

6 A shop increases all its prices by 4%. What are the new prices of the items below?

£20 £90 £65

7 A marathon runner weighs 55 kg at the start of a race. During the race his weight is reduced by 4%. How much does he weigh at the end of the race?

8 A hen weighs 2.7 kg. After laying an egg her weight is reduced by 1%. How much does she weigh now?

9 A mouse weighs 630 g. While escaping from a cat it loses its tail and its weight is reduced by 4%. How much does it weigh now?

10 In ten years the population of a town is increased by 7% from its original number of 55 400. What is the new population?

(a) Work out 16% of £440.

Either 16% of £440

$= \frac{16}{100} \times \frac{440}{1}$

= £70.40

Or 16% of £440

= 0.16 × £440

= £70.40

(b) A cooker cost £700. Find the new price after a 22% increase.

New price = 122% of £700

= 1.22 × 700

= £854

Exercise 5E

1 Copy and complete.

(a) 25% of 620 = 0.25 × 620 = ▢

(b) 37% of 2400 = ▢ × 2400 = ▢

(c) ▢ % of 48 = 0.12 × 48 = ▢

2 Work out

(a) 11% of 240 kg (b) 7% of £330 (c) 84% of $2400

(d) 3% of £55 000 (e) 150% of 22 m

3 A holiday costs £620. After a 12% increase the new price is 112% of £620. The 'quick' way to work this out is as follows:

New price = 112% of £620

= 1.12×620

= £694.40

Use this quick method to find the new price of a boat costing £560, when the price is increased by 8%.

4 Copy and complete:

(a) To increase £400 by 6%, work out 1.☐☐ × 400.

(b) To reduce £720 by 15%, work out 0.85 × ☐.

5 Increase a price of £80 by 4%

6 Increase a price of £250 by 4%

7 Increase a price of £400 by 8%

8 Increase a price of £16 by 1%

9 Reduce a price of £3000 by 7%

10 Increase a price of £90 by 23%

11 Increase a price of £85 by 20%

12 Reduce a price of £8000 by 2.5%

13 Increase a price of £6500 by 2%

14 Reduce a price of £23 by 5.7%

15 

The cost of a 'billionaires space cruise' is reduced from the normal price of $25 million by 11.2%
Work out the reduced cost.

16 A price of £650 is increased by 11% and then, a week later, it is increased by a further 8%. Find the final price.

17 The price of a villa is £65 000. The price is reduced by 5% but it is still not sold. The price is reduced by a further 9%. Find the final price.

4.5 Interpreting and sketching real life graphs

In section 4.5 you will:

- interpret a range of graphs
- sketch graphs from a real life context.

Exercise 1M

1 Which of the graphs **A** to **D** best fits each of the following statements?

(a) 'The price of petrol was steady for several years but has fallen recently.'

(b) 'The cost of air flights was falling slowly until 2009, but is now rising.'

(c) 'The birthrate in Italy has fallen steadily over the last decade.'

(d) 'The weight of the bird increased steadily after hatching.'

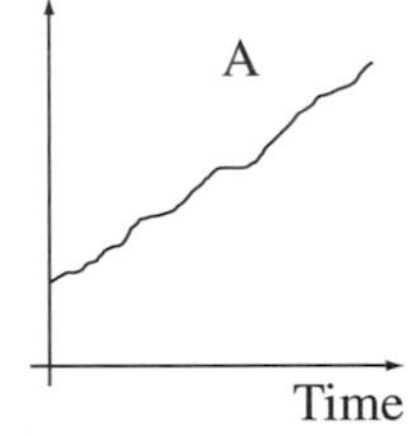

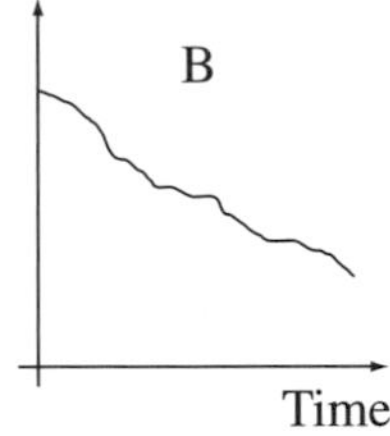

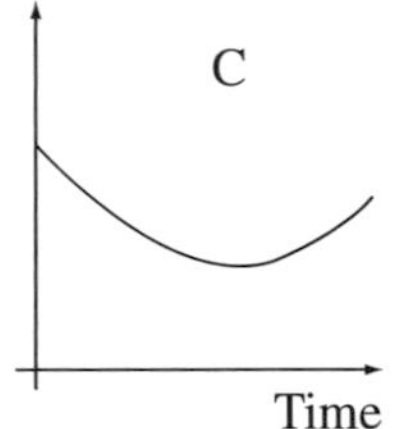

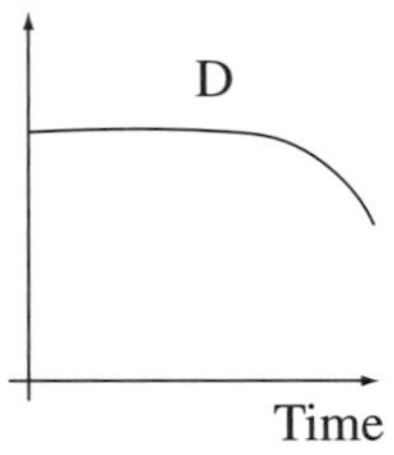

2 

A graph is drawn to show the value of a car over a period of 4 years. The car was bought for £9000. At the end of the fourth year the car was in an accident.
Sketch a graph to show how you think the value of the car might change over the years.

3 Water is poured at a constant rate into each of the containers A, B and C. The graphs X, Y and Z shows how the water level rises.

Decide which graph fits each container. State your reasons.

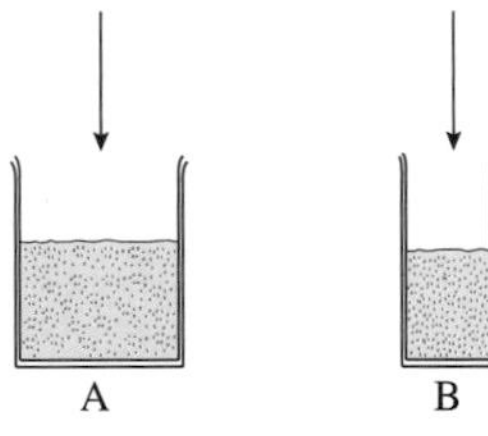

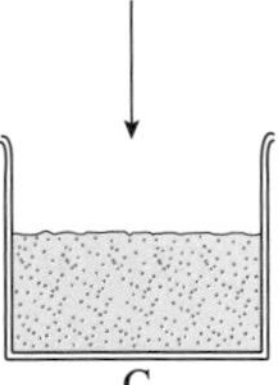

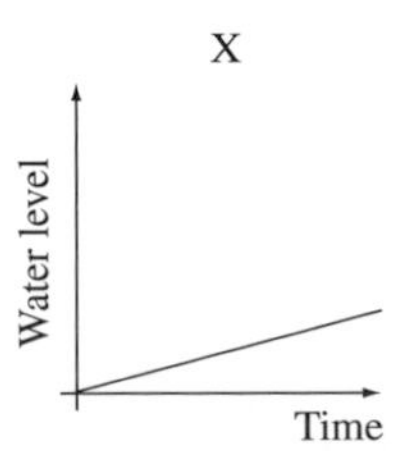

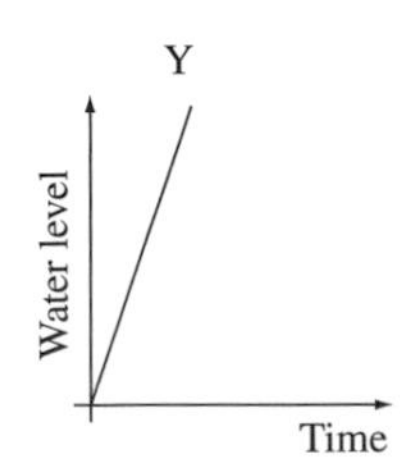

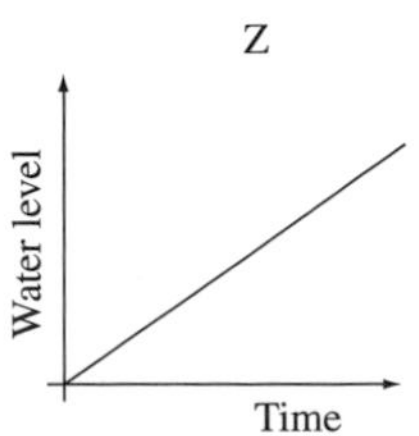

4 Water is poured at a constant rate into each of the container P and Q. Sketch graphs to show how the water level rises in each container.

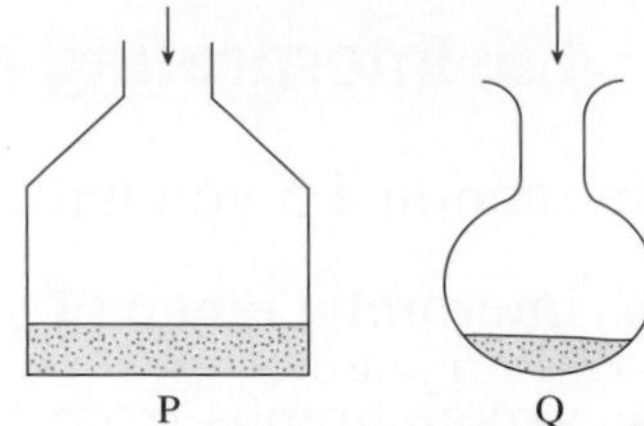

5 The graph shows the mass of crisps in a packet during the time after opening the packet.

(a) Were all the crisps eaten?
(b) What is the mass of a full packet or crisps?
(c) Explain the shape of the graph. Why are some vertical lines on the graph longer than others?

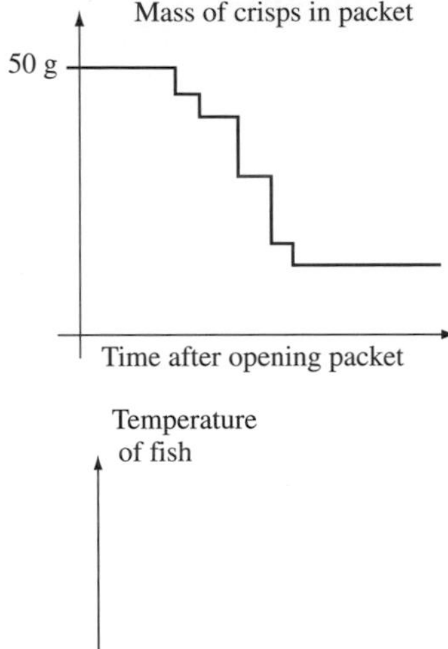

6 A packet of frozen fish is taken out of a freezer and left on a kitchen table for 4 hours. The fish is then heated in a frying pan. Sketch a graph to show the temperature of the fish after it is taken from the freezer.

7 Many houses are fitted with water meters to measure how much water is consumed. Draw one sketch graph and label it to show the likely water consumption of:

A. A house with one retired person.
B. A house with a family of five people.
C. An empty house with a leaking tap.

8 The graph shows the amount of petrol in the tank of a car. Explain briefly what you think is happening in each section of the graph: AB, BC, CD, DE, EF, FG.

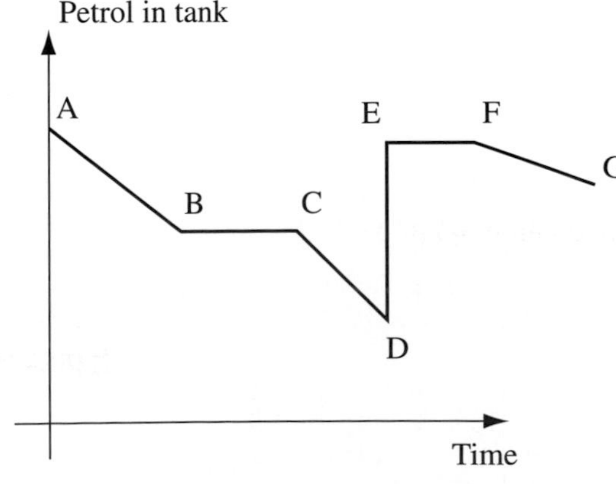

Exercise 1E

1 The graph shows a return journey from A.

(a) When is the car halfway between A and C on the outward journey?
(b) Between what times does the car stop at B?
(c) When is the car halfway between C and B on the return journey?
(d) Find the speed of the car

(i) From A to C
(ii) From C back to B
(iii) From B back to A

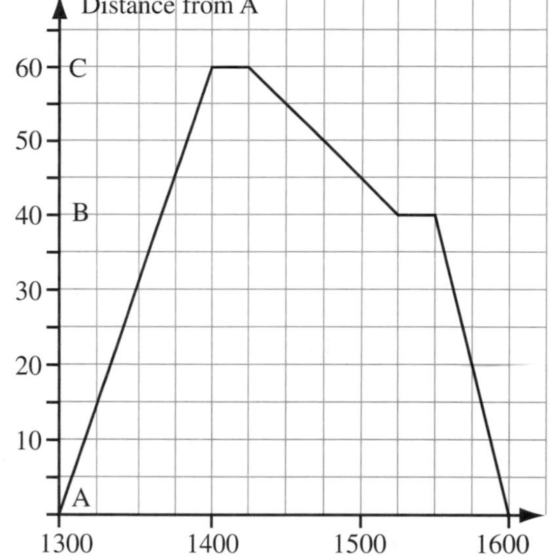

2 (a) Draw axes like those in question 1 but go up to 70 km on the vertical axis and up to 4 hours on the horizontal axis.
(b) Draw the graph for the following journey:

part 1. Car leaves home at 13:00 and travels at 40 km/h for 30 minutes.
part 2. Car stops for 45 minutes.
part 3. Car travels away from home at 50 km/h for one hour.
part 4. Car stops for 30 minutes.
part 5. Car returns home at 70 km/h.

(c) Answer the following questions:
(i) How far from home is the car at 14:45?
(ii) At what time does the car return home?

3 The graph shows the energy generated by one of the turbines on a wind farm.
Describe what you think may have happened.

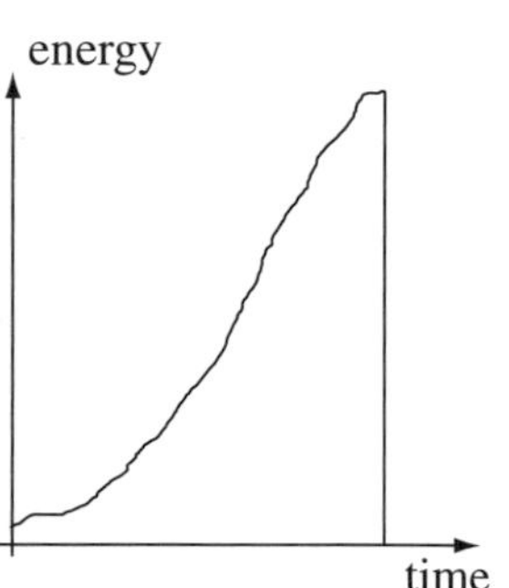

4

N

Lake Knox

S

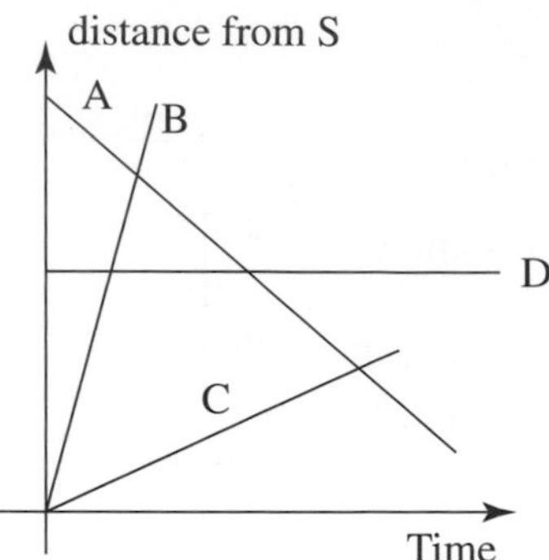

Points S and N are on the banks of Lake Knox. A, B, C, D are travel graphs for different people/objects. Decide which graph fits with each description.

(a) A man swimming from S to N.
(b) A motor boat travelling from S to N.
(c) A marker buoy on the lake.
(d) A rowing boat going from N to S.

5 Sketch a graph to show how a man's height changes from birth until the age of 30 years.

6 The petrol consumption of a car depends on the speed, as shown on the graph.

(a) What is the petrol consumption at a speed of
  (i) 30 km per hour
  (ii) 100 km per hour
  (iii) 180 km per hour?

(b) At what speed is the petrol consumption
  (i) 8 km per litre
  (ii) 12 km per litre
  (iii) 9 km per litre?

(c) At what speed should the car be driven in order to use the least amount of petrol?

(d) A car is driven at 160 km per hour. How far can it travel on 20 litres of petrol?

(e) A car has 60 litres of petrol. Estimate the greatest distance the car can travel before it runs out of petrol.

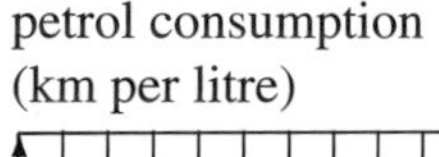

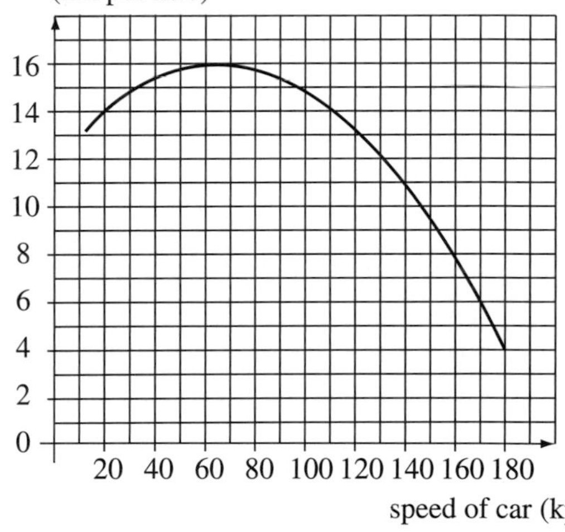

7 A young child is ill and stays in bed with her teddy bear for several days. Draw two graphs: one to show the teddy bear's temperature and the other to show the child's temperature over a seven day period as she is ill and then recovers.

CHECK YOURSELF ON SECTIONS 4.4 AND 4.5

1 Fractions, decimals and percentages

(a) (i) write $\frac{2}{5}$ as a percentage

(ii) write 2% as a decimal

(iii) write $\frac{2}{9}$ as a recurring decimal

(iv) write $\frac{2}{3}$ of 0.93 as a percentage.

(b) Work out 3.8% of £560.

(c) Decrease the price of the objects shown by 5%.

€4.40

€129.40

2 Interpreting real life graphs

The graph shows the water level when Simon has a bath.

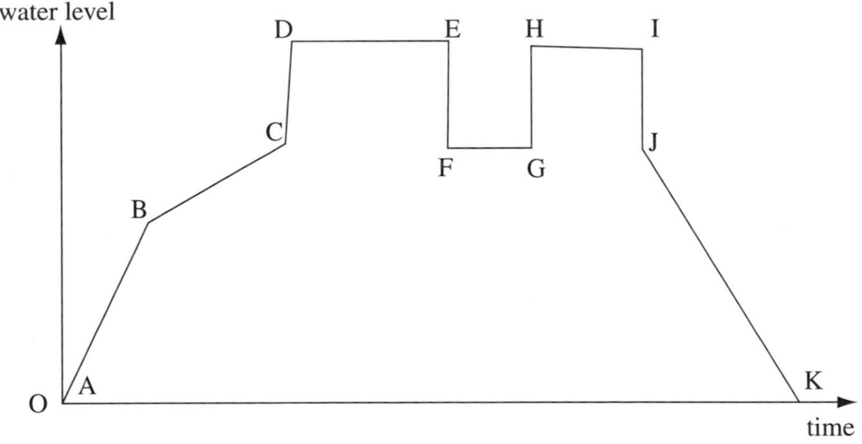

Use the letters to describe what you think was happening in each section of the graph. Here are some possibilities.

Simon gets out of bath. One tap is on. Bath is emptied.

Simon gets into bath. Simon lies in bath memorising maths formulas.

Two taps are on. Simon is out of bath looking for shampoo.

4.6 Rotation and combined transformations

In section 4.6 you will learn about:

- rotating shapes
- finding the centre of a rotation
- combined transformations

Rotate the triangle through 90° anticlockwise about the point O.

The diagram on the right shows how tracing paper may be used.

Notice that we need three things to describe fully a rotation:

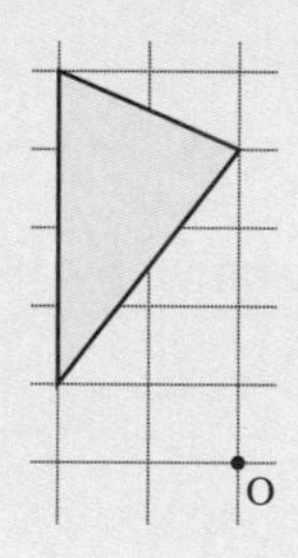

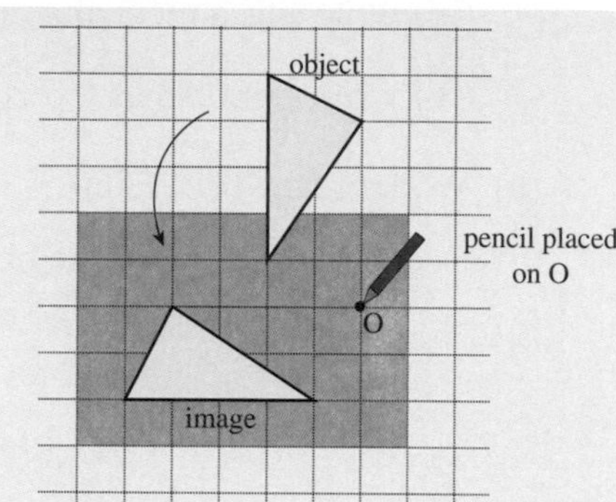

(a) the angle,
(b) the direction, (clockwise or anticlockwise)
(c) the centre of rotation.

Exercise 1M

In questions 1 to 6 draw the object and its image under the rotation given. Take O as the centre of rotation in each case.

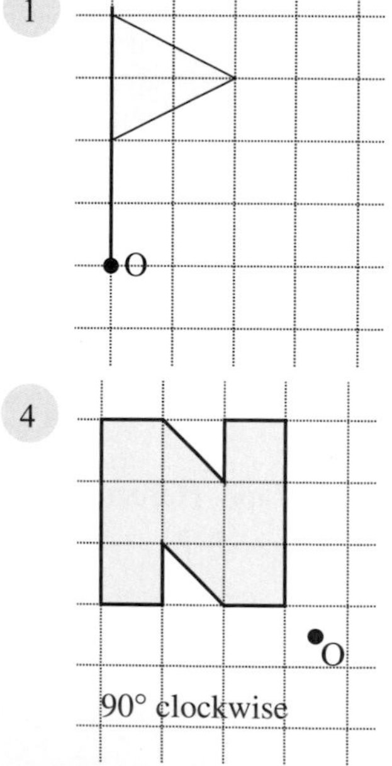

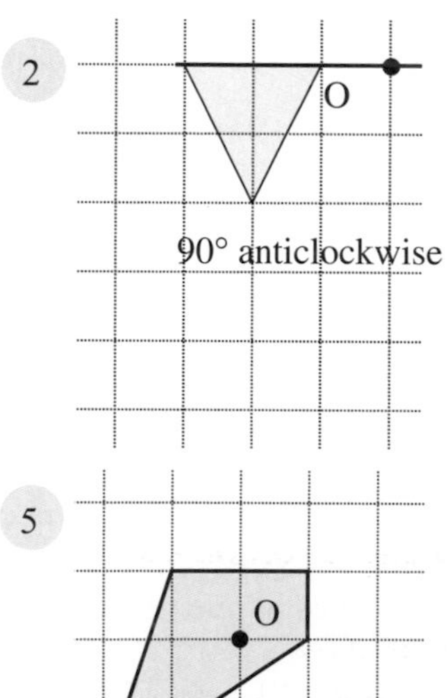

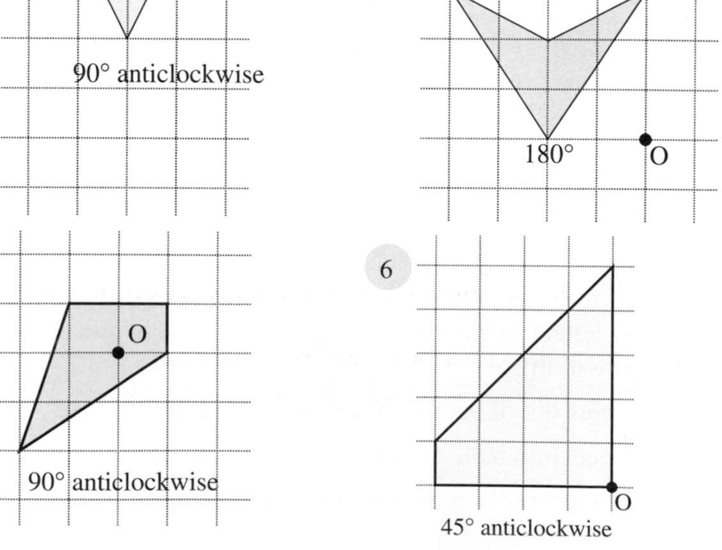

7 Describe the rotation which

(a) moves the red piece onto the yellow piece,
(b) moves the green piece onto the yellow piece.

Exercise 1E

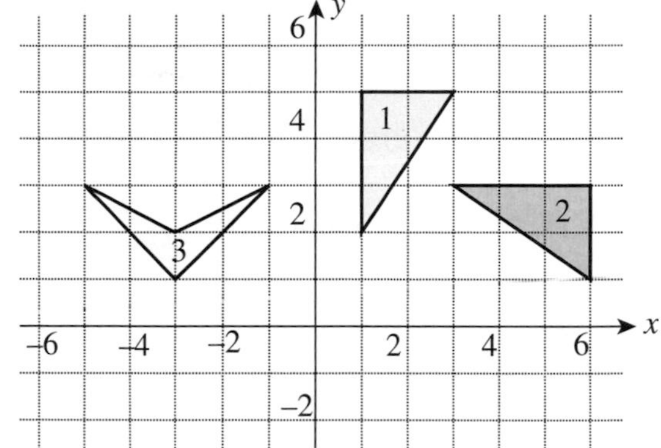

1 Copy the diagram shown, using axes from –6 to 6.

(a) Rotate Δ1 90° clockwise about (0, 0) onto ΔA.
(b) Rotate Δ2 180° about (0, 0) onto ΔB.
(c) Rotate shape 3 90° anticlockwise about (2, 2) onto shape C.

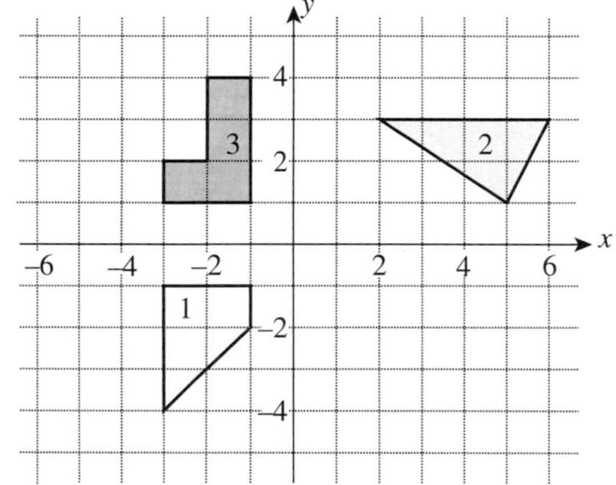

2 Copy the diagram shown.

(a) Rotate shape 1 90° anticlockwise about (–3, –4) onto shape A.
(b) Rotate Δ2 90° clockwise about (1, 0) onto ΔB.
(c) Rotate shape 3 90° clockwise about (2, 1) onto shape C.
(d) Rotate shape 3 180° about (–2, 3) onto shape D.

3 (a) Draw axes with values from –6 to 6 and draw Δ1 with vertices at (2, 6) (6, 6) (6, 4).
(b) Rotate Δ1 90° clockwise about (2, 6) onto Δ2.
(c) Rotate Δ2 180° about (2, 0) onto Δ3.
(d) Rotate Δ3 90° clockwise about (1, 0) onto Δ4.
(e) Rotate Δ4 90° anticlockwise about (–1, 4) onto Δ5.
(f) If Δ5 is in the correct position you can now easily rotate Δ5 onto Δ1. Give the angle, direction and centre for this rotation.

4 (a) Draw axes with values from –6 to 6 and draw Δ1 with vertices at (–5, 2), (–5, 6), (–3, 5).
(b) Rotate Δ1 90° clockwise about (–4, –2) onto Δ2.
(c) Rotate Δ2 90° clockwise about (6, 0) onto Δ3.
(d) Rotate Δ3 180° about (1, 1) onto Δ4.
(e) Rotate Δ4 90° anticlockwise about (–5, 1) onto Δ5.
(f) Describe fully the rotation which moves Δ5 onto Δ1.

5 Assume that the pencils in the photo are spaced out evenly.

Describe the rotation which moves
(a) pencil A onto pencil B
(b) pencil A onto pencil C.

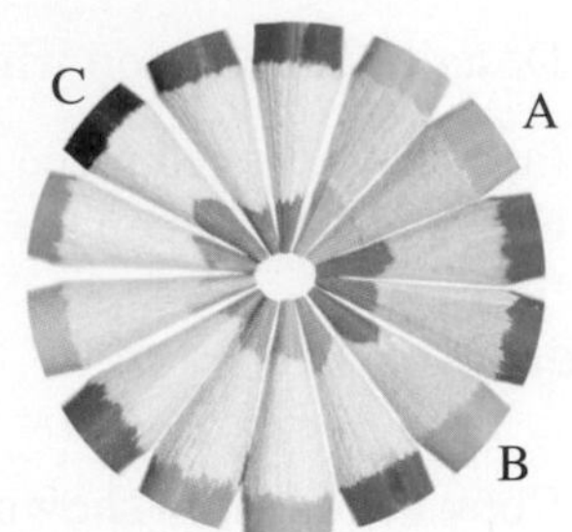

Finding the centre of a rotation

Exercise 2M

In questions 1 to 4 copy each diagram. Draw the shaded shape on tracing paper. Place the tip of a pencil on different points until the shape can be rotated onto the other shape. Mark the centre of rotation with a dot.

1

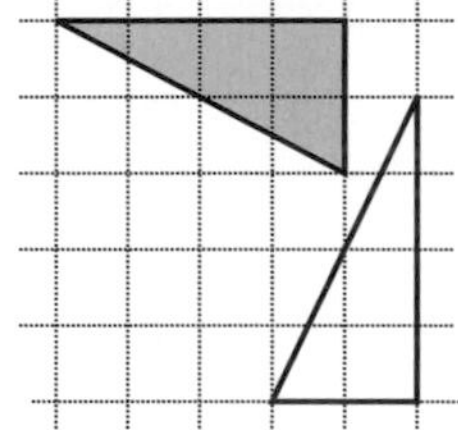

2

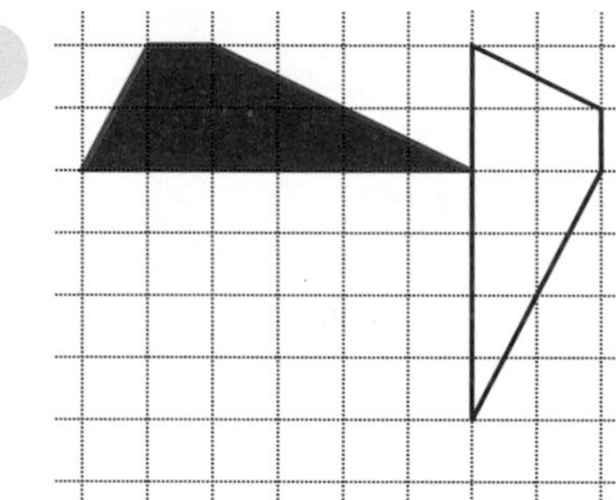

3

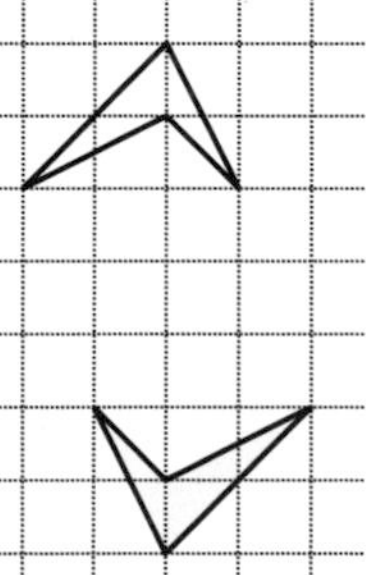

4

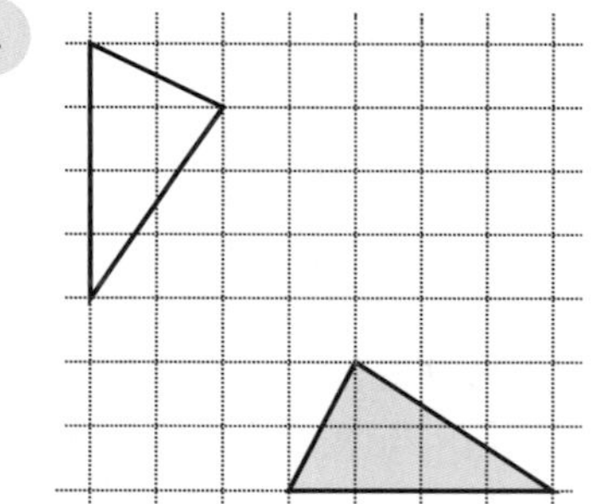

5 Find the coordinates of the centres of the following rotation:

(a) $\Delta 1 \rightarrow \Delta 2$

(b) $\Delta 1 \rightarrow \Delta 3$

(c) $\Delta 1 \rightarrow \Delta 4$

(d) $\Delta 3 \rightarrow \Delta 5$

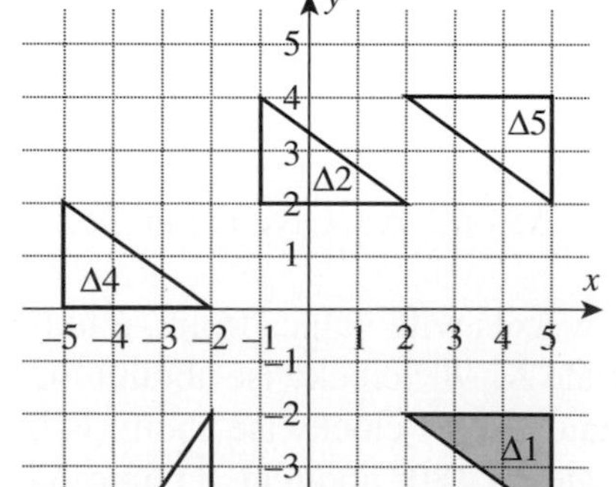

Exercise 2E

1 Copy the two squares carefully. It is possible to rotate the pink square onto the unshaded square using three different centres of rotation. Find and mark these three points.

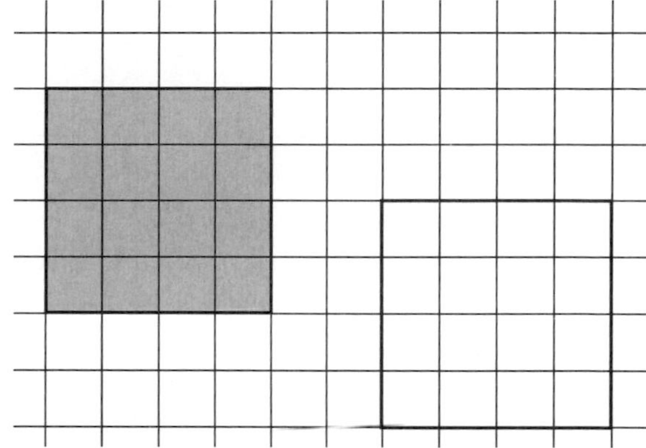

Questions 2 and 3 involve both rotations and reflections.

2 Draw axes with values from –7 to +7 and draw triangles with the following vertices:

Δ1 :	(–6, –6)	(–2, –6)	(–2, –4)
Δ2 :	(–6, –6)	(–6, –2)	(–4, –2)
Δ3 :	(6, 2)	(2, 2)	(2, 0)
Δ4 :	(–6, 2)	(–2, 2)	(–2, 0)
Δ5 :	(6, 3)	(6, 7)	(4, 7)

Describe fully the following rotations or reflections. For rotations give the angle, direction and centre. For reflections, give the equation of the mirror line.

(a) Δ1 → Δ2 (b) Δ1 → Δ3
(c) Δ1 → Δ4 (d) Δ1 → Δ5

3 Draw axes with values from –7 to +7 and draw triangles with the following vertices:

Δ1 :	(3, 1)	(7, 1)	(7, 3)
Δ2 :	(1, 3)	(1, 7)	(3, 7)
Δ3 :	(7, –1)	(3, –1)	(3, –3)
Δ4 :	(–1, –7)	(–3, –7)	(–3, –3)
Δ5 :	(–2, 2)	(–6, 2)	(–6, 0)
Δ6 :	(3, –4)	(3, –6)	(7, –6)

Describe fully the following rotations or reflections:
(a) Δ1 → Δ2 (b) Δ1 → Δ3
(c) Δ1 → Δ4 (d) Δ1 → Δ5
(e) Δ3 → Δ6

4 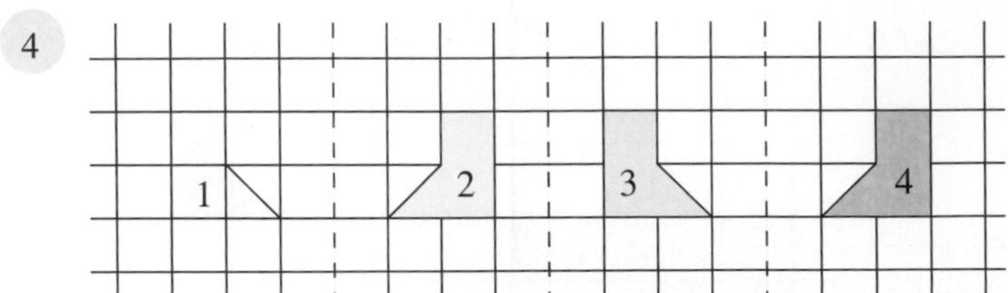

Copy and complete these statements.

(a) Successive reflections in two parallel lines is the same as a ☐.

(b) Successive reflections in three parallel lines in the same as a ☐.

(c) Successive reflections in two *perpendicular* lines is the same as a ☐.

Combinations of two transformations

Reflection, rotation, translation and enlargement are all transformations. Sometimes we need a combination of transformations to move a shape where we want to.

Exercise 3M

1 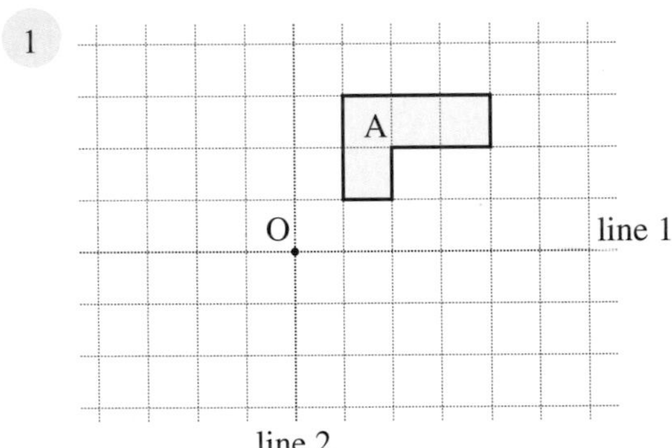

(a) Reflect shape A in line 1 onto shape B.
(b) Reflect shape B in line 2 onto shape C.
(c) What single transformation will move shape A onto shape C?

2 (a) Rotate ΔD 90° clockwise about (0, 0). Label the image ΔE.
(b) Rotate ΔE 90° clockwise about (0, 0). Label the image ΔF.
(c) What single transformation will move ΔD onto ΔF?

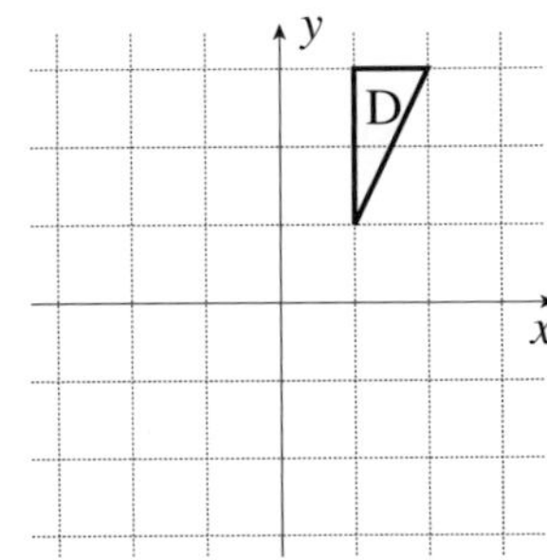

3 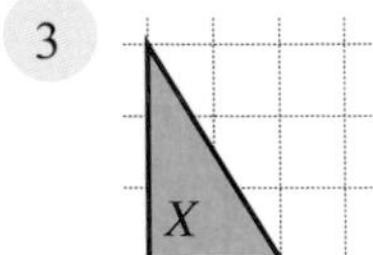

(a) Draw ΔX.
(b) Translate ΔX 4 unit right onto ΔY.
(c) Translate ΔY 1 unit right and 2 units up onto ΔZ.
(d) What single translation will move ΔX onto ΔZ?

4 Describe the transformations below. Mark any points and lines necessary to write the answers.
(a) $\Delta A \rightarrow \Delta B$ in one move.
(b) $\Delta B \rightarrow \Delta C$ in one move.
(c) $\Delta D \rightarrow \Delta C$ in one move.
(d) $\Delta A \rightarrow \Delta C$ in two moves.

5 Describe fully the following transformations
(a) $\Delta A \rightarrow \Delta B$
(b) $\Delta B \rightarrow \Delta C$
(c) $\Delta A \rightarrow \Delta D$
(d) $\Delta C \rightarrow \Delta E$
(e) $\Delta A \rightarrow \Delta C$ (in two transformations)
(f) $\Delta A \rightarrow \Delta E$ (in two or three transformations).

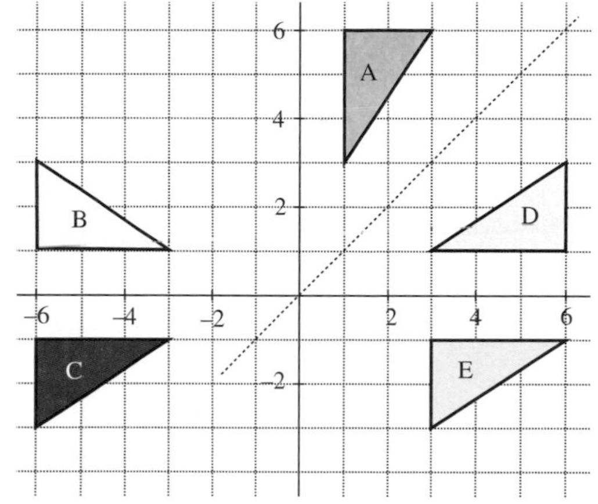

6 Make three copies of the diagram below, but leave out the dotted lines.

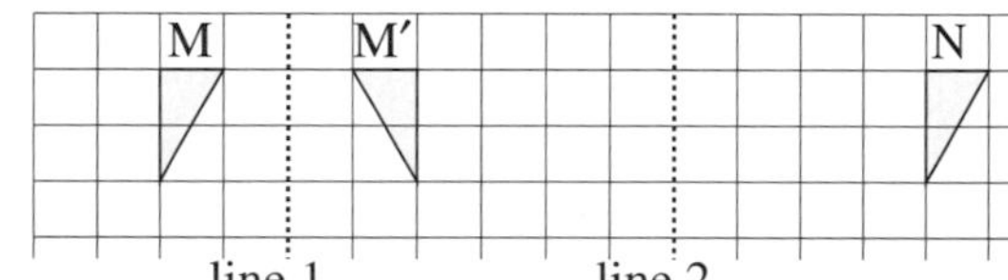

Triangle M is reflected in line 1 onto triangle M′.
Then triangle M′ is reflected in line 2 onto triangle N.
(a) Show that M can be reflected onto N using two different mirror lines. Do this three times.
(b) What do you notice each time? (How far apart are your two lines?)
(c) Do you obtain the same connection if one of the mirror lines is to the left of triangle M?

7 Show that ΔB can be transformed onto ΔA by a combination of a translation and a reflection Describe the translation and the reflection. Find another way of doing this.

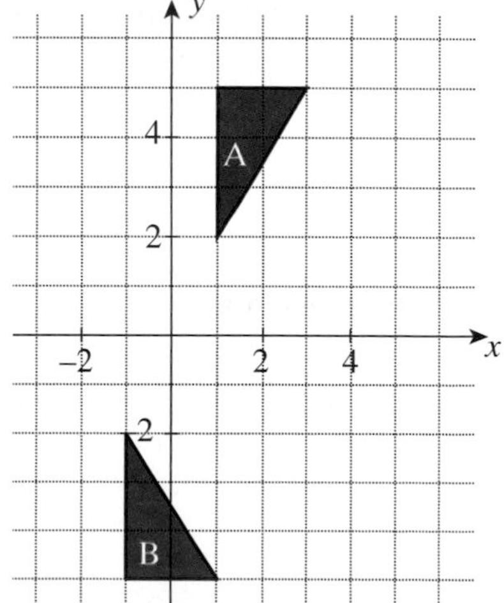

Exercise 3E

1 The pink triangle can be moved onto triangles 1 to 6 by a combination of a rotation and a reflection (in either order).

Describe the rotation and reflection for each triangle.

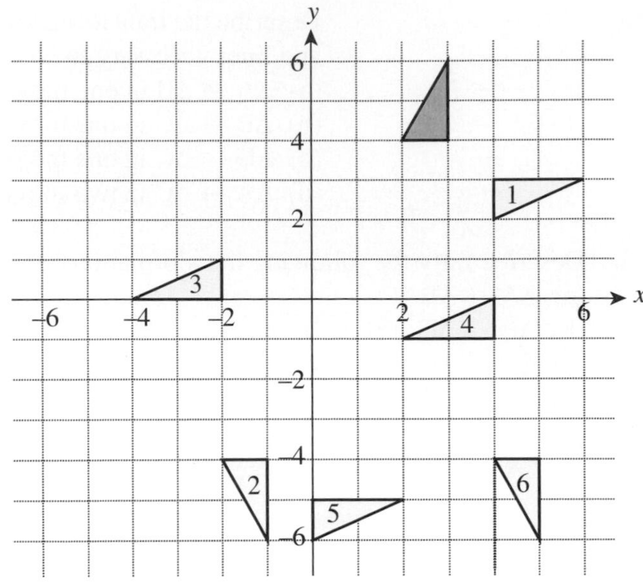

2 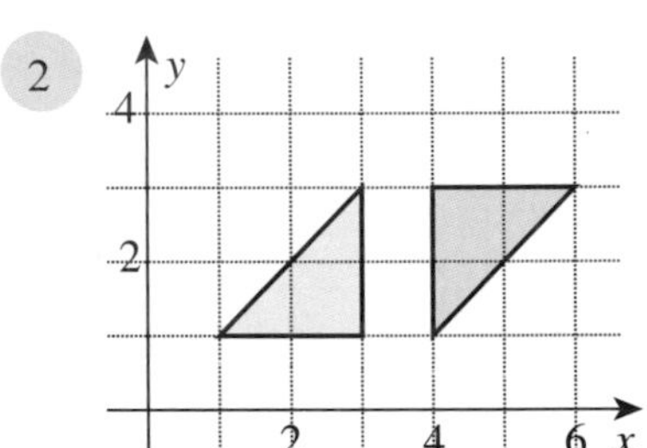

Map the green triangle onto the blue triangle by:

(a) a rotation followed by a translation
(b) a translation followed by a rotation
(c) a rotation followed by a reflection
(d) a reflection followed by a rotation

In questions 3 to 6 the transformations used are:

A: reflection in $y = 1$
B: rotation 90° clockwise, centre (0, 2)
C: translation $\begin{pmatrix} -4 \\ 2 \end{pmatrix}$
[4 units left and 2 units up]
E: reflection in $y = x$
F: translation $\begin{pmatrix} 3 \\ -3 \end{pmatrix}$
[3 units right and 3 units down]

For each question draw a set of axes for x and y from –8 to +8

3 Plot and label L (–2, –2) M(–2, –4) , N (–1, –4).

Draw and label the image ΔLMN after the transformations:

(a) **E** followed by **A**
(b) **B** followed by **F**
(c) **A** followed by **F**
(d) **F** followed by **C**

Write down the coordinates of the image of the point L in each case.

4 Plot and label X(–4, 0), Y(–4, –4), Z(–2, –4).
Draw the label the image of ΔXYZ after:
(a) **B** followed by **F**
(b) **A** followed by **C**
(c) **B** followed by **F** followed by **E.**
Write down the coordinates of the image of point X in each case.

5 (a) Plot and label L(1, 5), M(1, 1), N(3, 1).
(b) Draw and label the image of ΔLMN after:
 (i) **B** followed by **C**
 (ii) **F** followed by **B**
(c) Describe the equivalent *single* transformation in each case.

6 (a) Plot and label P(0, 4), Q(–2, 0), R(0, 0).
(b) Draw and label the image of ΔPQR after:
 (i) **E** followed by **A**
 (ii) **C** followed by **B**
 (iii) **E** followed by **F**
(c) Describe the equivalent single transformation in each part.

4.7 Brackets and equations

In this section you will:

- multiply out brackets and simplify expressions
- solve linear equations
- solve problems by forming equations

Multiplying out brackets

The area of the whole rectangle shown can be found by multiplying its length by its width.

Area $= 4(x + 2)$

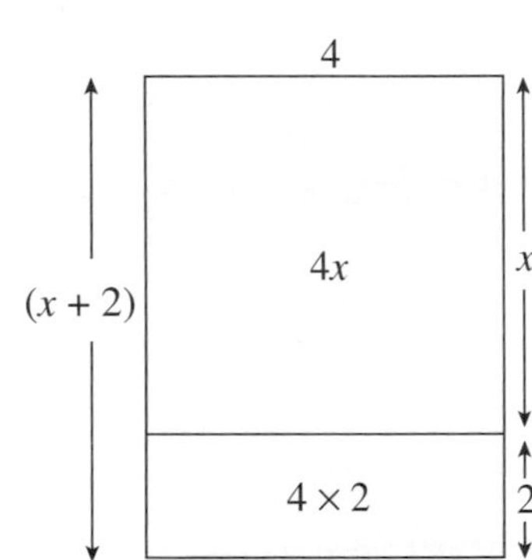

Alternatively the area can be found by adding together the areas of the two smaller rectangles.

Area $= 4x + 4 \times 2$

We see that $4(x + 2) = 4x + 4 \times 2$

In general a number or symbol outside a pair of brackets multiplies each of the numbers or symbols inside the brackets.

$5(x + 2) = 5x + 10$ $\quad$ $3(x - 2) = 3x - 6$

$4(2x + 1) = 8x + 4$ $\quad$ $2(1 + 3x) = 2 + 6x$

$a(x + b) = ax + ab$ $\quad$ $n(a + b + c) = na + nb + nc$

Remove the brackets and simplify.

(a) $3(x+2)+2(x+1)$
$= 3x+6+2x+2$
$= 5x+8$

(b) $4(x+1)+2(2x+3)$
$= 4x+4+4x+6$
$= 8x+10$

Note the method: First, remove the brackets.
Second, add the x terms and the number terms separately

(c) Find expressions for the area and the perimeter of the photo

Area $= 7(x+5)$
$= 7x+35$

Perimeter $= x+5+x+5+7+7$
$= 2x+24$

Exercise 1M

In questions 1 to 15 remove the brackets.

1 $3(x+4)$ 2 $5(x+3)$ 3 $4(x-2)$ 4 $6(x-2)$

5 $2(2x+1)$ 6 $3(2x+3)$ 7 $4(3x+1)$ 8 $3(4x+5)$

9 $9(2-x)$ 10 $2(4x-5)$ 11 $7(3x-1)$ 12 $10(2x+5)$

13 $5(3x-5)$ 14 $2(3-2x)$ 15 $3(x+y)$

16 Copy and complete.

(a) $3(2x+\square) = 6x+21$ (b) $\square(4-\square) = 12-9x$

(c) $5(\square+\square) = 10x+30$ (d) $\square(\square-7) = 8a-28$

In questions 17 to 26 remove the brackets and simplify.

17 $2(x+1)+3(x+3)$ 18 $3(x+4)+2(x+1)$ 19 $4(x+2)+2(x+2)$

20 $5(x+1)+3(x+2)$ 21 $2(4x+3)+4(3x+4)$ 22 $3(4x+5)+2(x+5)$

23 $5(x+1)+3(x-2)$ 24 $6(2x+1)+3(1+2x)$ 25 $4(3x+1)+(2x-1)$

26 $2(4+x)+(5x-2)$

27

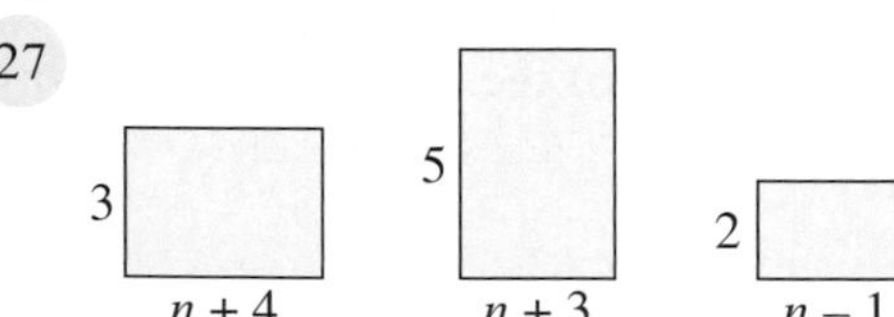

Find an expression for the total area of the three rectangles.
Simplify your answer.

In questions 28 to 37 remove the brackets and simplify.

28 $3(2x + 4) + 2(x + 1)$

29 $5(3 + 2x) + 10x$

30 $7(2x - 1) - 4x$

31 $4x + 5(2x + 1) - 7x + 4$

32 $6x + 3(2x + 3)$

33 $9 + 3(3x - 1) + 2(4 - x)$

34 $5(3x - 1) + 6(2x + 1)$

35 $8(1 + 2x) - 5 + 3(x + 2)$

36 $x + 6(3x + 2)$

37 $4(3x - 2) - 10x + 5(x + 2)$

38 (a) Write an expression for the area of the picture.

(b) Write an expression for the perimeter of the picture.

7

$x + 3$

Remove the brackets and simplify. Be careful with negative numbers.

(a) $3(n + 3) - 2(n + 1)$
$= 3n + 9 - 2n - 2$
$= n + 7$

(b) $3(a + b) - 2(a + 2b)$
$= 3a + 3b - 2a - 4b$
$= a - b$

(c) $2(a + 1) - (a - 2)$
↑
[put a '1' here]
$= 2(a + 1) - 1(a - 2)$
$= 2a + 2 - a + 2$
$= a + 4$

(d) $5(a + b) - (2a + b)$
$= 5(a + b) - 1(2a + b)$
$= 5a + 5b - 2a - b$
$= 3a + 4b$

Exercise 1E

Remove the brackets and simplify

1 $3(n + 2) + (n - 2)$

2 $4(n + 3) - 2(n + 1)$

3 $8(a + 1) - 3(a + 2)$

4 $7(a + 3) - 2(a - 1)$

5 $5(m + 2) - (m + 3)$

6 $6(m + 1) - (m - 2)$

7 $3(a + b) + 5(2a + b)$

8 $3(3a + b) - 2(a + b)$

9 $4(2a + b) - 2(a - b)$

10 $5(a + 3b) - (2a + b)$

11 $5(a - b) - 3(a - 2b)$

12 $4(2a + b) - (3a - b)$

13 Copy and complete.

(a) $3(n-2) + \square(n+1) = 5n + \square$

(b) $5(n+3) - \square(n + \square) = 2n + 9$

(c) $\square(2n-1) + 3(\square + \square) = 7n + 10$ (This is harder.)

Write in a more simple form.

14 $a^2 + a^2$

15 $2n^2 - n^2$

16 $m^3 + 2m^3$

17 $a^2 + 2a + a^2$

18 $n + 2n^2 + 5n$

19 $2a^2 - a - a^2$

20 $n \times n^2$

21 $n \times n \times n \times n$

22 $n^3 \div n$

23 $n(n+1) - 2n$

24 $n \div n$

25 $3(n+2) - (n-1)$

26 $5 - (n+5)$

27 $2(n-3) - (n-4)$

28 $n \div n^2$

29 In number walls each brick is made by adding the two bricks underneath it.

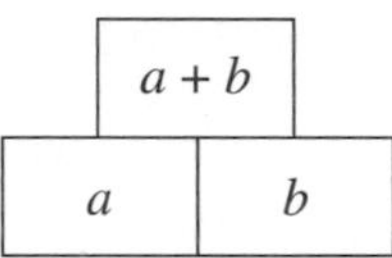

Draw the walls below and fill in the missing expressions.

(a)

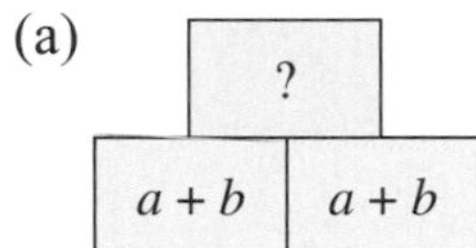

(b)

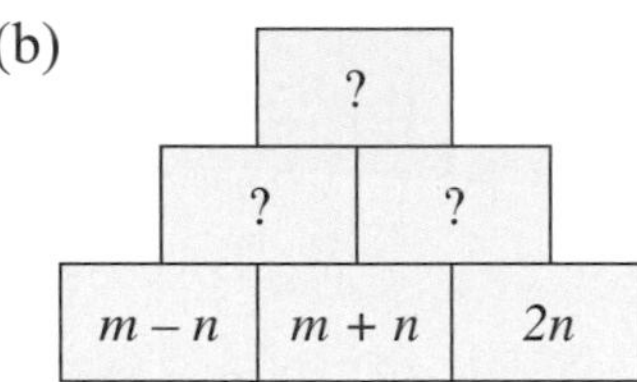

(c)

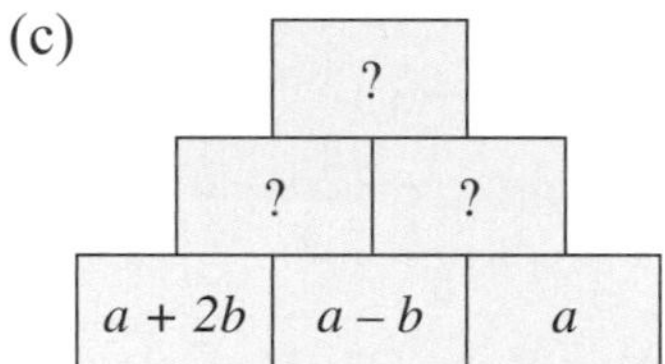

30 Draw the walls and fill in the missing expressions.

(a)

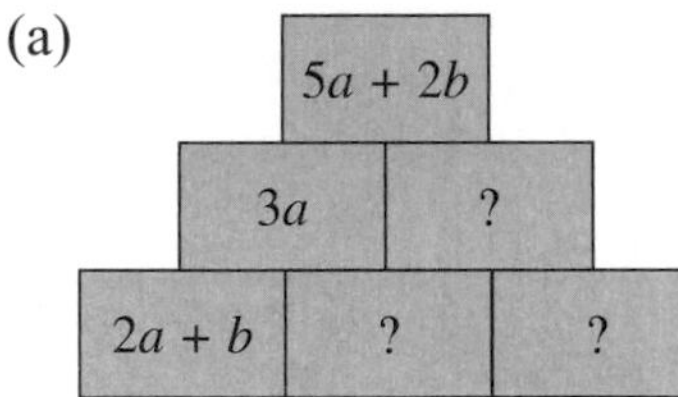

(b)

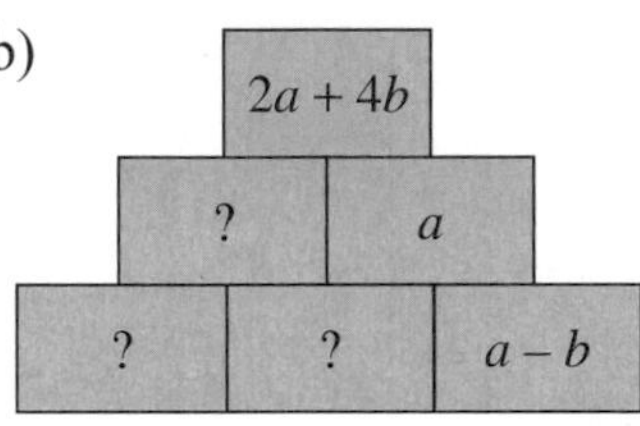

(c)

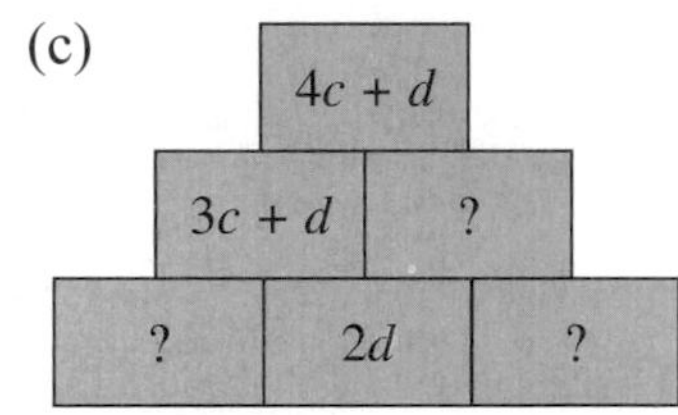

(d)

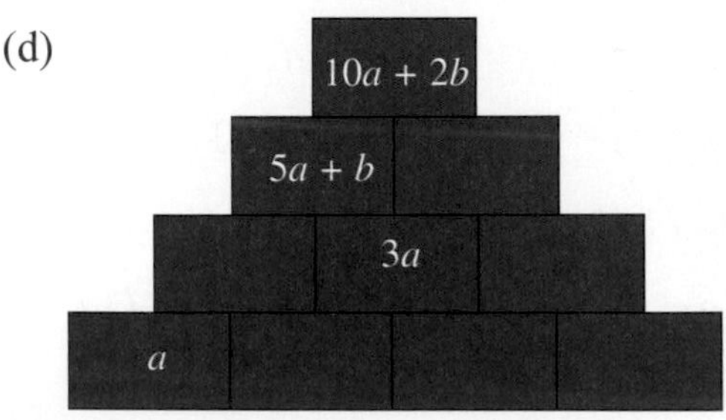

(e)

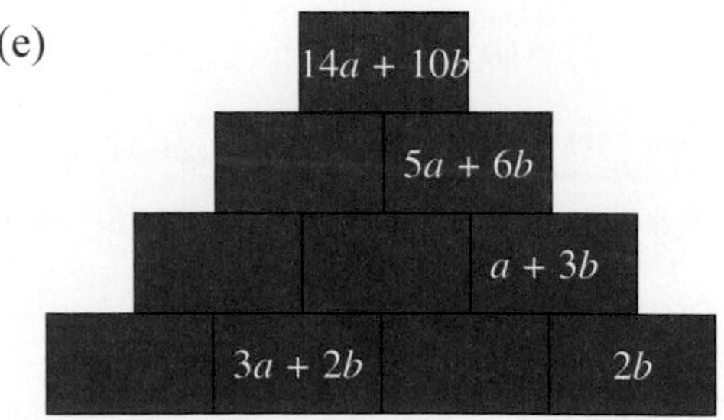

Rules for solving equations

Equations are solved in the same way as we solve the weighing scale problems.

The main rule when solving equations is

'Do the same thing to both sides'

You may *add* the same thing to both sides.

You may *subtract* the same thing from both sides.

You may *multiply* both sides by the same thing.

You may *divide* both sides by the same thing.

Solve the equations. The operations circled are performed on both sides.

(a) $n + 5 = 12$

(−5) (−5)

$n = 7$

(b) $n - 7 = 11$

(+7) (+7)

$n = 18$

(c) $2n + 3 = 15$

(−3) (−3)

$2n = 12$

(÷2) (÷2)

$n = 6$

(d) $3n - 5 = 16$

(+5) (+5)

$3n = 21$

(÷3) (÷3)

$n = 7$

Exercise 2M

Solve the equations.

1 $n + 7 = 11$

2 $n + 3 = 15$

3 $n - 7 = 7$

4 $n - 5 = 25$

5 $6 + n = 100$

6 $8 + n = 28$

7 $11 = n + 2$

8 $7 = n - 52$

9 $0 = n - 3$

10 $6 + n = 6$

11 $n - 11 = 11$

12 $14 = 5 + n$

Questions 13 to 24 involve different operations.

13 $3a = 18$

14 $2a = 60$

15 $5a = 40$

16 $8 = 2a$

17 $6 = 2a$

18 $2a = 1$

19 $2a + 1 = 7$

20 $3a + 2 = 14$

21 $4a + 7 = 19$

22 $3a + 2 = 17$

23 $4a + 6 = 50$

24 $6a + 5 = 41$

Questions 25 to 36 are more difficult

25 $5x - 3 = 7$

26 $3x - 4 = 11$

27 $7x + 3 = 24$

28 $6x + 5 = 6$

29 $9x + 1 = 100$

30 $3x - 5 = 10$

31 $3 + 2x = 15$

32 $5 + 3x = 11$

33 $8 + 4x = 8$

34 $14 = 3x - 1$

35 $31 = 7x + 3$

36 $100 = 5x - 5$

Equations involving brackets

(a) $3(2x + 1) = 15$

$6x + 3 = 15$

(−3) (−3)

$6x = 12$

(÷6) (÷6)

$x = 2$

(b) $4(3x - 1) = 8$

$12x - 4 = 8$

(+4) (+4)

$12x = 12$

(÷12) (÷12)

$x = 1$

Notice that in both examples we began by *removing the brackets*.

Exercise 2E

Solve the equations for x.

1 $2(x + 1) = 10$

2 $2(x + 3) = 12$

3 $3(x + 4) = 21$

4 $3(x - 2) = 12$

5 $3(2x + 1) = 9$

6 $4(x - 2) = 8$

7 $5(x + 1) = 5$

8 $2(3x - 1) = 10$

9 $2(3x + 2) = 10$

10 $2(x + 3) = 7$

11 $4(x + 1) = 5$

12 $6(x + 2) = 13$

Questions 13 to 24 involve different unknowns.

13 $5(a + 1) = 20$

14 $3(t - 1) = 18$

15 $4(b + 3) = 20$

16 $3(2y + 3) = 10$

17 $14 = 2(3a + 1)$

18 $16 = 4(n - 2)$

19 $18 = 2(2m + 3)$

20 $5(2x + 2) = 10$

21 $3(2n - 7) = 3$

22 $8(2 + x) = 24$

23 $10(3 + x) = 100$

24 $5(1 + 2x) = 20$

Using equations to solve problems

Mike is thinking of a number. He tells us that when he doubles it and adds 5, the answer is 12. What number is Mike thinking of?

Suppose that Mike is thinking of the number x.

He tells us that	$2x + 5 = 12$
Subtract 5 from both sides	$2x = 7$
Divide both sides by 2	$x = \frac{7}{2}$
	$x = 3\frac{1}{2}$

So Mike is thinking of the number $3\frac{1}{2}$

Exercise 3M

In each question I am thinking of a number. Use the information to form an equation and then solve it to find the number.

1. If we multiply the number by 3 and then add l, the answer is 25.
2. If we multiply the number by 10 and then subtract 3, the answer is 19.
3. If we multiply the number by 5 and then add 8, the answer is 11.
4. If we multiply the number by 4 and then subtract 3, the answer is 297.
5. If we double the number and add 7, the answer is 20.
6. If we treble the number and subtract 7, the answer is 0.
7. If we double the number and subtract 20, the answer is 9.

In questions 8 to 13 form an equation with brackets

8. If we add 3 to number and then double the result, the answer is 140.
9. If we subtract 5 from the number and then treble the result, the answer is 15.
10. If we add 7 to the number and then multiply the result by 3, the answer is 22.
11. If we subtract 4 from the number and then multiply the result by 5, the answer is 15.
12. If we double the number, add 3 and then multiply the result by 4, the answer is 16.
13. If we double the number, subtract 5 and then multiply the result by 7, the answer is 7.

Equations with the unknown on both sides

(a) $2n + 3 = n + 7$

$(-n)$ $(-n)$

$n + 3 = 7$

(-3) (-3)

$n = 4$

(b) $5n - 3 = 2n + 9$

$(-2n)$ $(-2n)$

$3n - 3 = 9$

$(+3)$ $(+3)$

$3n = 12$

$n = 4$

Exercise 3E

Solve the equations.

1 $5n = 3n + 10$

2 $7n = n + 12$

3 $3n = n + 2$

4 $4n = n + 30$

5 $4n = n + 15$

6 $12n = n + 66$

7 $13n = 7n + 24$

8 $10n = 3n + 21$

9 $5n = 8 + n$

10 $2n = 7 + n$

11 $4n + 3 = n + 9$

12 $7n + 1 = 6n + 8$

13 $3n + 7 = n + 15$

14 $6n - 1 = 3n + 8$

15 $5n - 4 = 2n + 5$

16 $1 + 3n = n + 2$

17 $4n - 11 = 2n + 11$

18 $1 + 5n = 3n + 13$

19 $6n = 3n + 24$

20 $5n - 4 = n$

Questions 21 to 30 involve brackets.

21 $3(x + 2) = 2(x + 5)$

22 $4(x + 1) = 3(x + 3)$

23 $2(x + 5) = x + 13$

24 $6x - 10 = 2(x + 7)$

25 $3(x - 1) = 2(x + 6)$

26 $5(x - 2) = 3(x + 2)$

27 $6(2x + 1) = 10x + 4$

28 $2(2x - 3) = 3(x + 7)$

29 $7(2x - 1) = 7$

30 $5(5x + 2) = 2(3x + 5)$

Exercise 4E

Solve the equations for x.

1 $3(x - 1) = 2x - 2$

2 $4(x + 2) = 3x + 10$

3 $2(2x - 1) = x + 4$

4 $3(x - 1) = 2(x + 1) - 2$

5 $4(2x - 1) = 3(x + 1) - 2$

6 $5 + 2(x + 1) = 5(x - 1)$

7 $6 + 3(x + 2) = 2(x + 5) + 4$

8 $5(x + 1) = 2x + 3 + x$

9 $4(2x - 2) = 5x - 17$

10 $x + 2(x + 4) = -4$

11 $3x + 2(x + 1) = 3x + 12$

12 $4x - 2(x + 4) = x + 1$

Questions 13 to 18 involve different unknowns.

13 $5(2a + 1) - 5 = 3(a + 1)$

14 $3(4a - 1) - 3 = a + 1$

15 $2(a - 10) = 4 - 3a$

16 $7(n - 3) = 10 - n$

17 $3(n + 1) = 2(n + 3) - 6$

18 $5(2n - 1) = 9(n + 1) - 8$

Exercise 5M

Solve each problem after forming and then solving an equation.

1 When a number is doubled and then added to 15, the result is 28. Find the number.

2 When a number is added to 9 and the result is multiplied by 7, the answer is 147. Find the number.

3 The length of a photo is twice its width. The perimeter is 30 cm. Find the width.

4 The length of a rectangle is three times its width. If the perimeter is 32 cm, find its width. [Hint : Let the width be x.]

5 The length of a rectangle is five times its width. If the perimeter is 60 cm, find its width.

6 Form equations to find x.

(a)

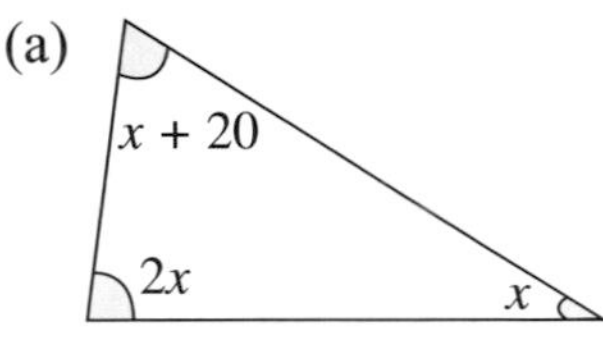

(b)

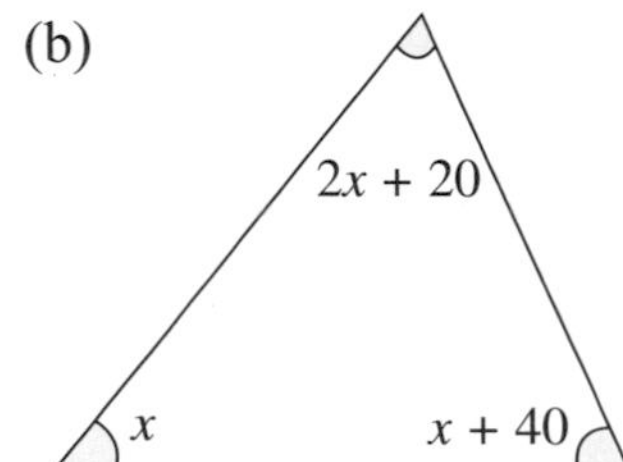

7 If I treble a number, take away 6 and then multiply the result by 2, the answer is 18. Find the number.

8 The sum of three consecutive numbers is 63. Let the first number be n and write down the other two numbers in terms of n. Find the three numbers.

9 The sum of the three consecutive numbers is 165. Find the three numbers.

10 $2x + 1$, 3

The rectangle has an area of 27 square units.

Form an equation and solve it to find x.

11 In the triangle, BC is twice as long as AB. AC is 9 cm long.

If the perimeter is 24 cm, form an equation and solve it to find x.

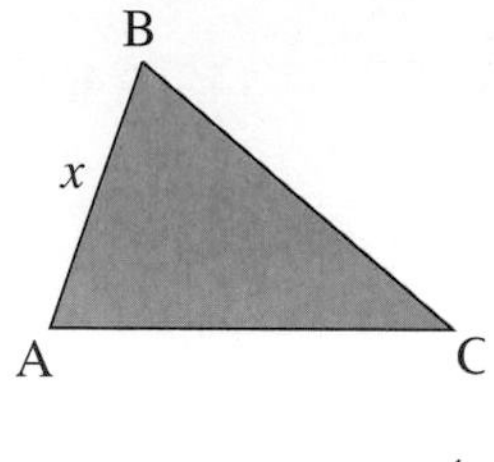

Exercise 5E

1 If AB is a straight line, form an equation involving x and solve it to find x.

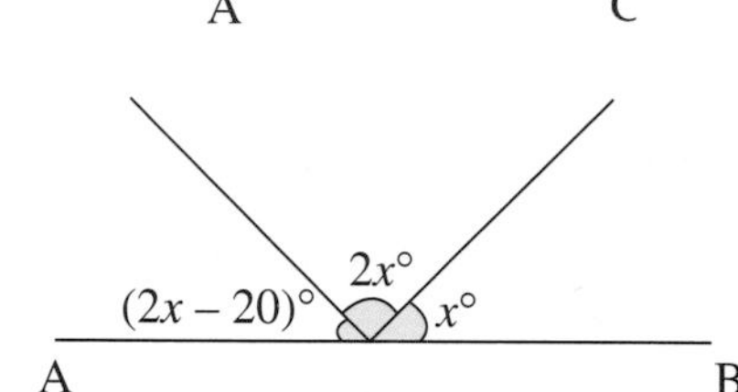

2 The angles in a triangle are $x°$, $(2x - 10)°$ and 70°. Find the angles in the triangle.

3 $x + 1$, $3x - 1$

The perimeter of this rectangle is 40 cm. Find x and hence find the area of the rectangle.

4 The total mass of three stones A, B and C is 60 kg.
Stone B is twice as heavy as stone A.
Stone C is 30 kg heavier than stone A.
Find the mass of stone A. [Call it x kg.]

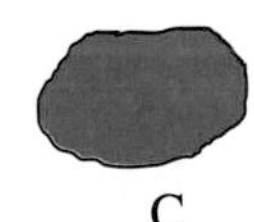

5 An equilateral triangle has sides of length $3x + 1$, $2x + 3$ and $2x + 3$. Find x.

6 The perimeter, P, of a rectangle is given by the formula $P = 2(a + b)$.

If $P = 19$ and $b = 7$, find the value of a.

7 The volume of a cuboid is given by the formula $V = \ell\, b\, h$.

If $V = 30$, $\ell = 2$ and $b = 6$, find the value of h.

8 In an arithmagon, the number in a square is the sum of the numbers in the two circles either side of it.

(a) Explain why the number in circle B is $20 - x$.
(b) Explain why the number in circle C is $15 - x$.
(c) Form an equation across the lowest side of the triangle. Solve the equation to find x.

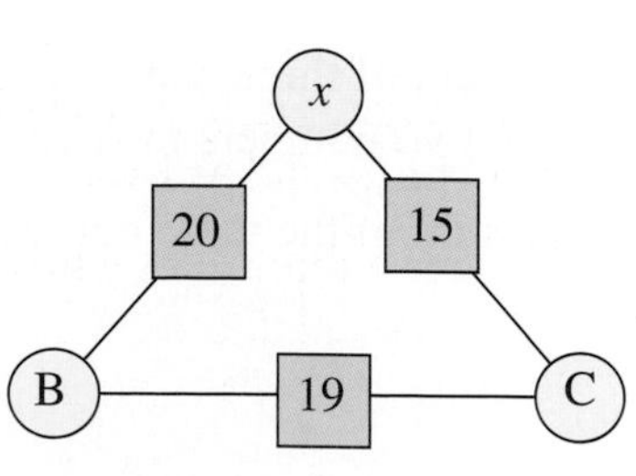

9 Use the method above to find x in these arithmagons.

(a)

x
26
18
22

(b)

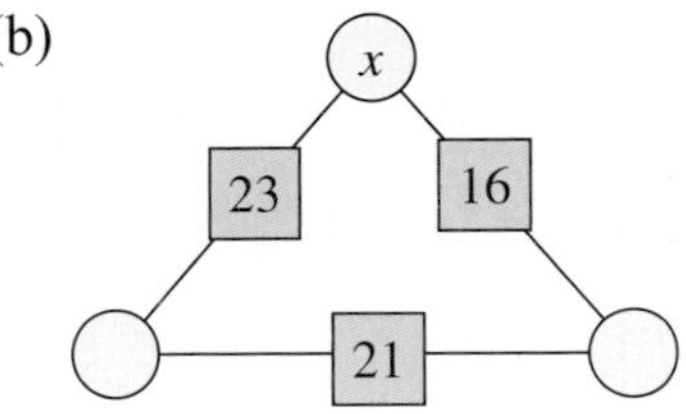

(c)

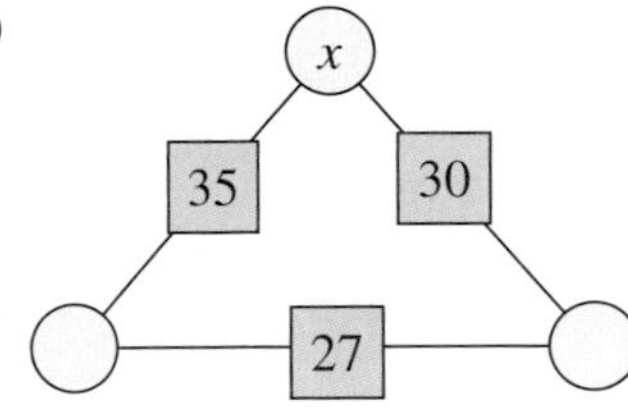

10 The diagram shows a road from A to E.

A to B is 5 km more than D to E.

C to D is twice the distance from A to B.

C is midway between B and D.

If the total distance from A to E is 91 km, find the distance from D to E.

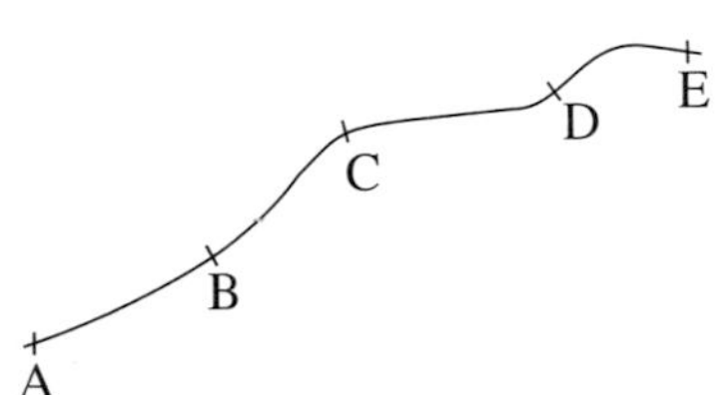

11 The sum of four consecutive whole numbers is 98. Let the first number be x and write down the other three numbers in terms of x. Find the four numbers.

12 The sum of four consecutive *odd* numbers is 216. Find the numbers.

13 The triangle and the rectangle have the same area. Find x.

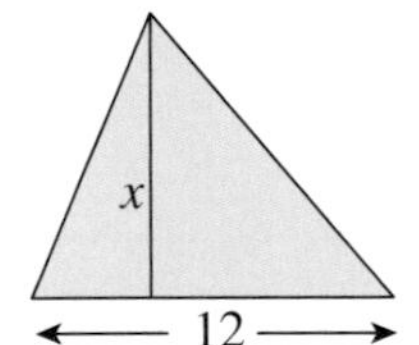

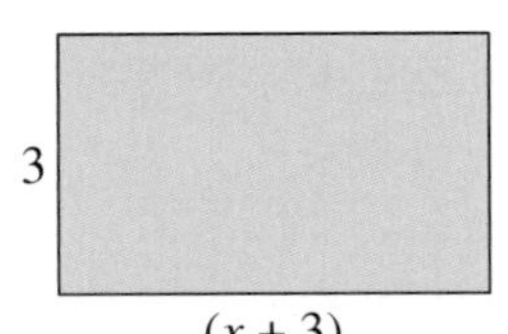

14 (a) The area of rectangle P is five times the area of rectangle Q. Find x.

(b) The value of x is changed and the areas of the unshaded rectangles become equal. Find the new value of x.

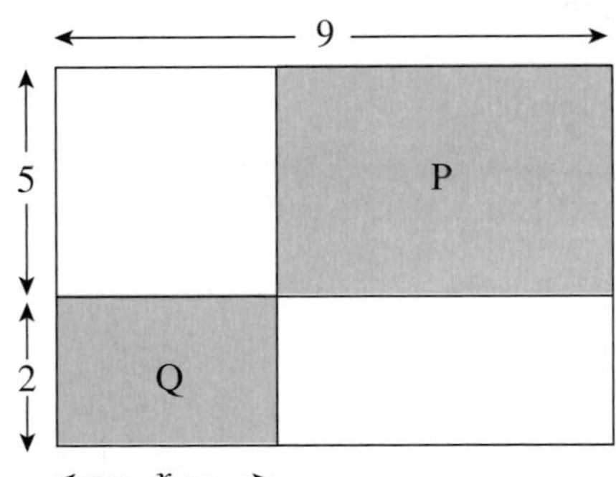

15 My daughter asked how old I am. I answered 'In 20 years, I'll be twice as old as I was 12 years ago.' How old am I?

16 You have three consecutive even numbers so that the sum of twice the smallest number plus three times the middle number is four times the largest number.
Find the three numbers.

'L' puzzles

(a) This is an 'L' puzzle.

$3 + 9 = 12$

$3 + 1 = 4$

3	9	12
1		
4		

(b) Here is another.

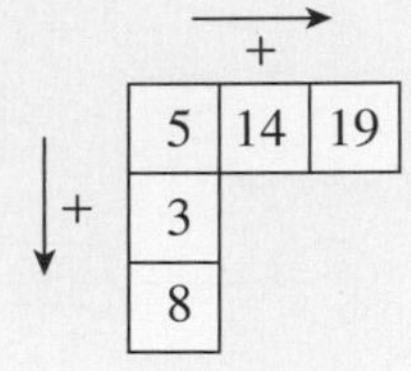

(c) Find all the numbers in this puzzle given that the number in box B is twice the number in box A.

	A	12
B		
17		

Let the number in box A be x.
Then the number in box B is $2x$.
Write? for the corner number.

?	x	12
$2x$		
17		

Across the top row: $? + x = 12$

so $? = 12 - x$

Using this value in the left hand column,

$12 - x + 2x = 17$

$x = 5$

The puzzle can now be completed:

7	5	12
10		
17		

Exercise 6E

1 Copy and complete the following puzzles. You do not need an equation.

(a)

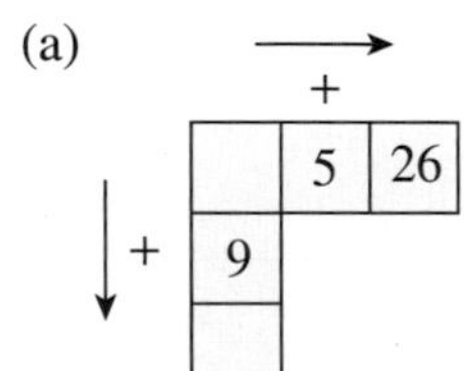

(b)

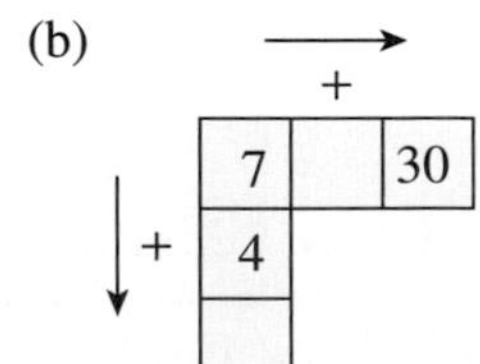

(c)

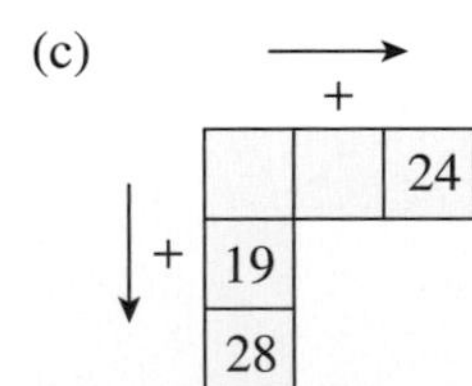

In question 2 onwards use the method shown in the above example to form an equation and then solve it to find the missing numbers.

2 The number in box B is twice the number in box A. Start by letting x be the number in box A.

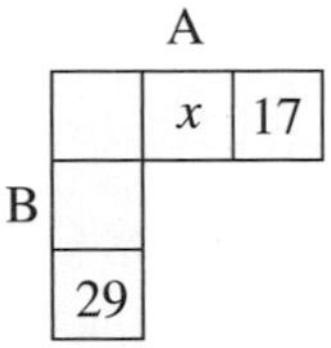

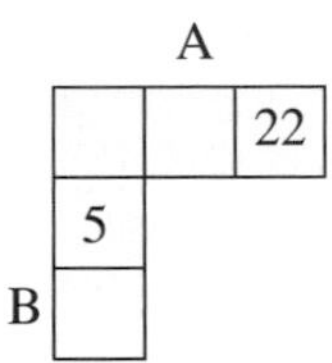

3 The number in box B is four times the number in box A.

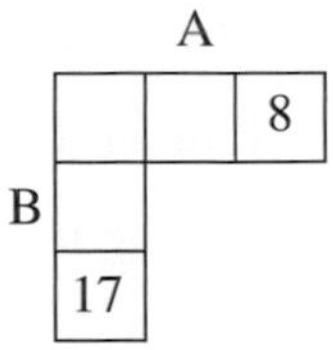

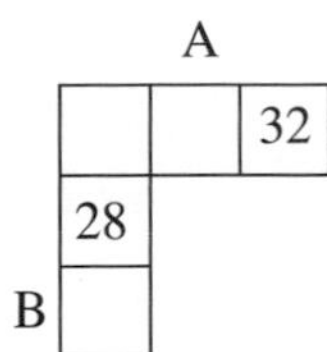

4 The number in box B is twice the number in box A. [Notice that box B is different to Qu. 3].

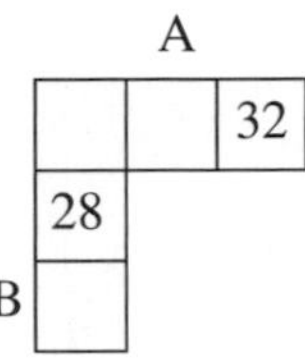

5 The number in box B is three times the number in box A.

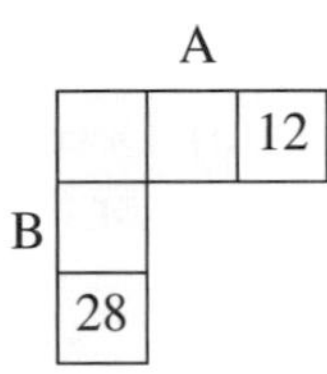

6 The number in box B is four times the number in box A.

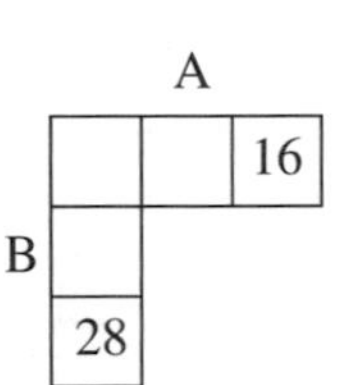

7 The numbers in boxes A and B add up to 20. Let the number in box A be x.

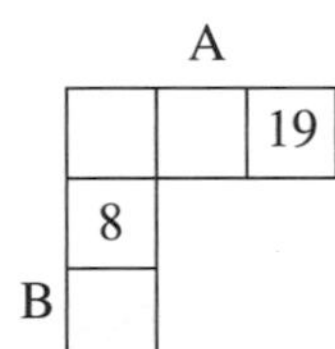

8 The numbers in boxes A and B add up to 20.

9 The number in box B is 5 *less* than the number in box A.

10 The diagram has changed here but the principle is similar to the above.

$9 + 5 = 14$; $9 + 7 = 16$; $14 + 4 = 18$; $16 + 2 = 18$.

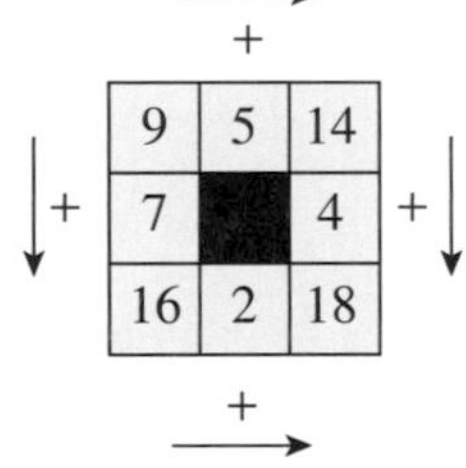

Find all the missing numbers given that:

(a) the number in box B is four times the number in box A.

(b) the number in box C is nine times the number in box A.

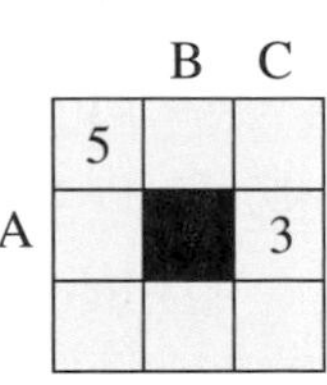

11 Find all the missing numbers given that:

(a) the number in box B is one less than the number in box A.

(b) the number in box C is one third of the number in box A.

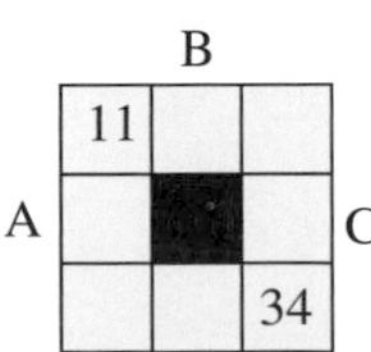

12 This one is more difficult.

Find all the missing numbers given that:

(a) the number in box A is three times the number in box C.

(b) the number in box B is two more than the number in box A.

(c) the number in box D is one more than twice the number in box B.

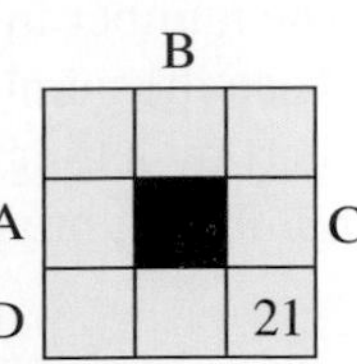

CHECK YOURSELF ON SECTIONS 4.6 AND 4.7

1 Rotation and combined transformations.

(a) Describe fully the single transformations for the following.

(i) $\Delta 1 \rightarrow \Delta 3$ (ii) $\Delta 1 \rightarrow \Delta 4$

(iii) $\Delta 2 \rightarrow \Delta 3$ (iv) $\Delta 3 \rightarrow \Delta 5$

(v) $\Delta 5 \rightarrow \Delta 2$

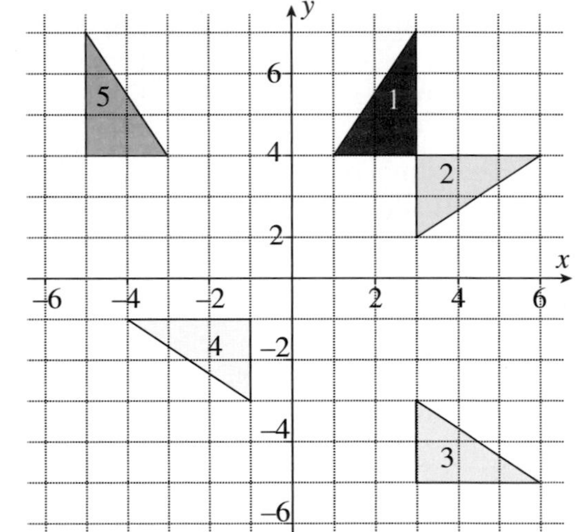

(b) Describe a rotation followed by a reflection which moves $\Delta 4$ onto $\Delta 2$.

2 Brackets and equations.

(a) Remove the brackets and simplify.

(i) $4(n - 3)$ (ii) $3(n + 1) + 2(2n - 1)$ (iii) $3(2n - 4) - 5(n - 2)$

(b) Solve the equation for x.

(i) $3(x - 1) = 15$ (ii) $6x = x + 7$ (iii) $2(2x - 1) = x + 7$

(c) A square has sides of length $4x - 1$ and $3x + 2$. Form an equation and solve it to find the sides of the square.

UNIT 4 MIXED REVIEW

Part one

1 Copy the diagram on squared paper.

(a) Measure the bearing of B from A.

(b) Measure the bearing of A from B.

(c) Mark the point C which is on a bearing 225° from B and on a bearing 090° from A.

N

B

A

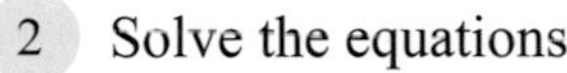

2 Solve the equations

(a) $3x - 3 = 2x + 5$ (b) $5(x - 1) = 2(3 - x)$

3 The length of the rectangle is three times its width. The perimeter of the rectangle is 60 cm.

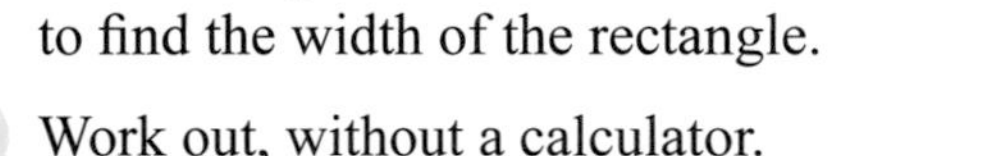

Form an equation and solve it to find the width of the rectangle.

4 Work out, without a calculator.

(a) 8×0.01 (b) $15 \div 0.1$ (c) 10% of 10^4

(d) 0.02×0.03 (e) $18 \div 5$ (f) $\frac{1}{4}$ of 5% of 20000

5 A school teacher thinks there is a connection between her pupils' test results and the average number of hours of television they watch per week. She thinks that those who watch the most television will do least well in the tests.

Here are scatter graphs for her classes in year 8 and year 9.

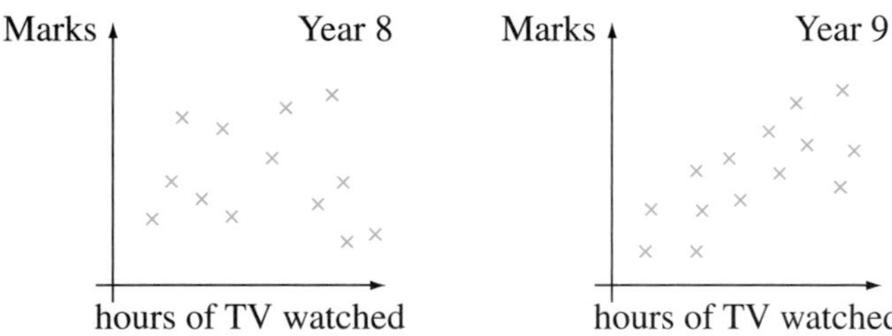

Was the teacher's theory correct for

(a) Year 8 (b) Year 9?

In both cases state briefly what the graphs show.

6 The number of children having school dinners is 640. When chips are not on the menu the number goes down by 5%. How many fewer children have school dinners?

7 At a garage 140 cars were given a safety test and 65% of the cars passed the test.

(a) How many passed the test?
(b) How many failed the test?

8 Of the 980 children at a school, 45% cycle to school, 15% go by bus and the rest walk.

(a) How many cycle to school?
(b) How many walk to school?

9 This pentagon has been drawn in a 3 × 3 grid.

Use 3 × 3 grids on squared or dotty paper. Make as many different polygons with more than three sides as you can. Show pairs of parallel and perpendicular lines as in the example.

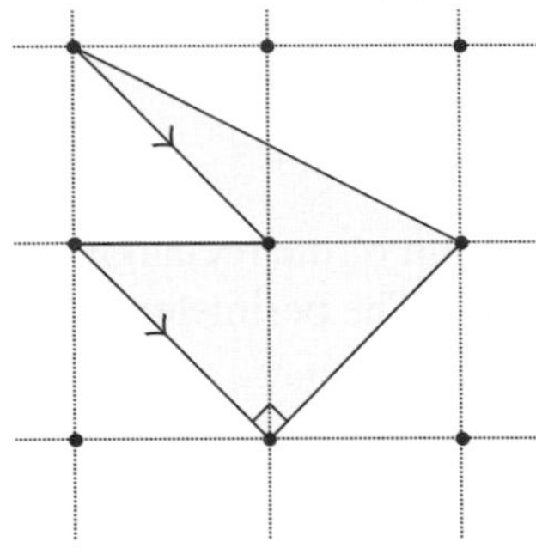

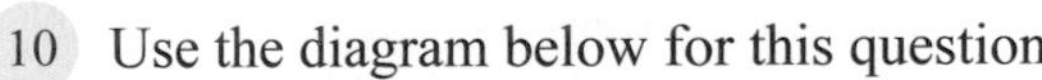

10 Use the diagram below for this question

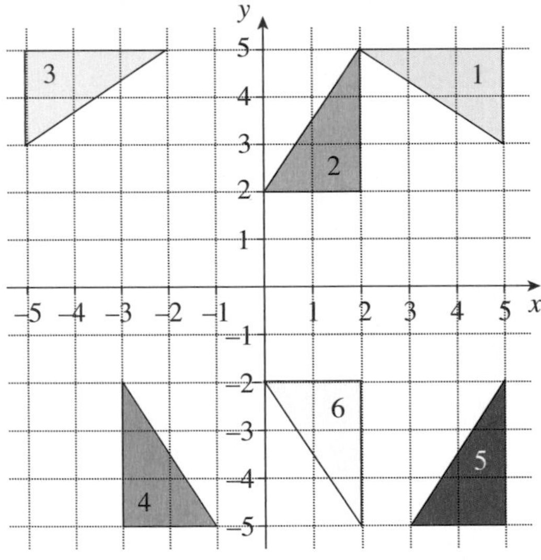

(a) Which triangle is the image of $\Delta 3$ after reflection in the y axis?

(b) What is the centre of the rotation from $\Delta 1$ onto $\Delta 5$?

(c) In what line is $\Delta 4$ the image of $\Delta 5$ after reflection?

(d) Which triangle is the image of $\Delta 3$ after 90° rotation about (–5, –2)?

11 The pie charts show how land is used on two farms.

(a) How many acres of land on Oak Farm are used for:

(i) growing maize (ii) grazing sheep?

(b) How many acres of land on Ash Farm are used for:

(i) grazing cattle (ii) growing barley?

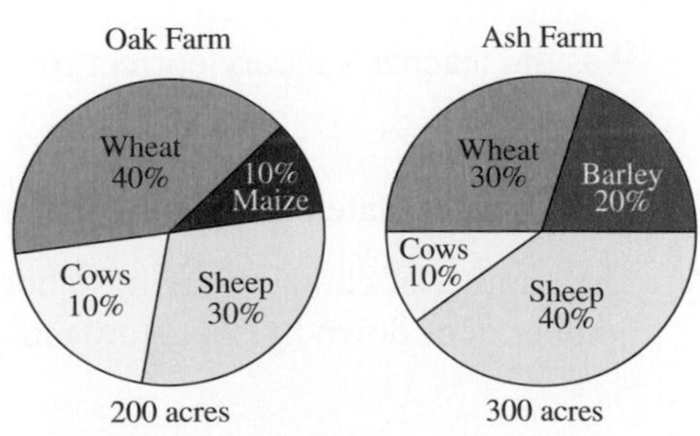

(c) Gina says

More land is used on Oak Farm than on Ash Farm for growing wheat.

Use both charts to explain why this is not correct.

Part B

1 A ship sails 7 km due south and then a further 8 km on a bearing of 240°. It then sinks. How far is the wreck from its starting point?

2 The test results of eight pupils are recorded in the table below.

Pupil	A	B	C	D	E	F	G	H	I
Maths	25	10	35	45	20	10	40	15	?
Geography	10	15	15	25	30	35	45	50	38
History	10	15	20	22	27	30	36	40	?

50 Maths

0 50 Geography

50 History

0 50 Geography

Draw scatter graphs for

(a) the Maths and Geography marks.
(b) the History and Geography marks.
(c) What correlation, if any, is there in the results?
(d) Pupil I got 38 marks in Geography. Estimate, if possible, her marks in Maths and History.

3

Swansea council staff were designing a bilingual road sign barring heavy goods vehicles from a street in the city and had consulted an in-house translation service.

As the translator was not available, an automatic e-mail response was triggered in Welsh which read:"I am not in the office at the moment. Please send any work to be translated."

Staff mistakenly thought that it was the correct translation and had it printed on the sign beneath the message in English, which read:"No entry for heavy goods vehicles. Residental site only."

No entry for heavy
goods vehicles.
Residental site only

Nid wyf yn y swyddfa
ar hyn o bryd. Anfonwch
unrhyw waith i'w gyfieithu.

Write the last line of the Welsh statement and then draw a reflection of the letters in a horizontal mirror line.

4 (a) At what point will the line $y = 2x + 3$ cut the y axis?

(b) At what point will the line $y = x$ cut the line $y = -2$?

5 The diagram shows the lengths of the sides of a rectangle in cm.

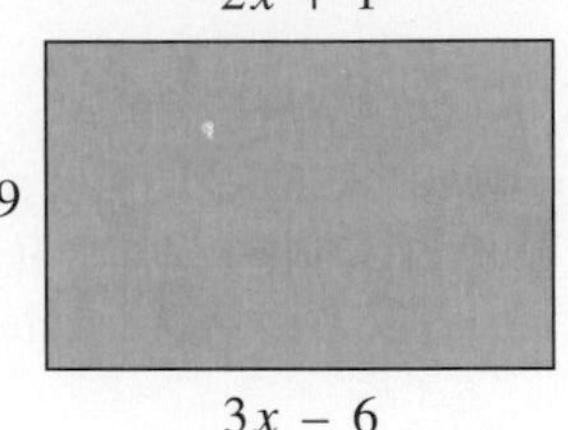

(a) Form an equation involving x.

(b) Solve your equation and hence find the *area* of the rectangle.

6 (a) Draw a graph for converting litres to gallons. Use scales of 1 cm to 5 litres across the page and 1 cm to 1 gallon up the page.

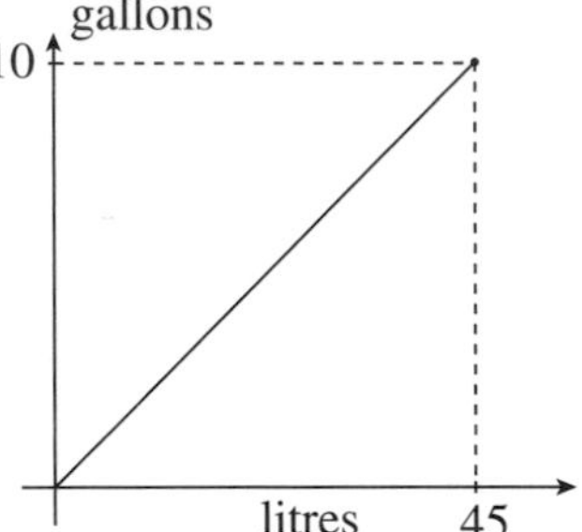

(b) Convert the following to the nearest tenth of a gallon:

(i) 18 litres (ii) 26 litres (iii) 10 litres

(c) Steve drives 140 miles and uses 36 litres of petrol. How many miles is he travelling for every gallon of petrol?

7 (a) In five years the number of pupils at a school increased by 5% from the original number of 780. How many pupils were then at the school?

(b) Increase a price of £8500 by 4%

(c) Reduce a mass of 780 kg by 18%

8

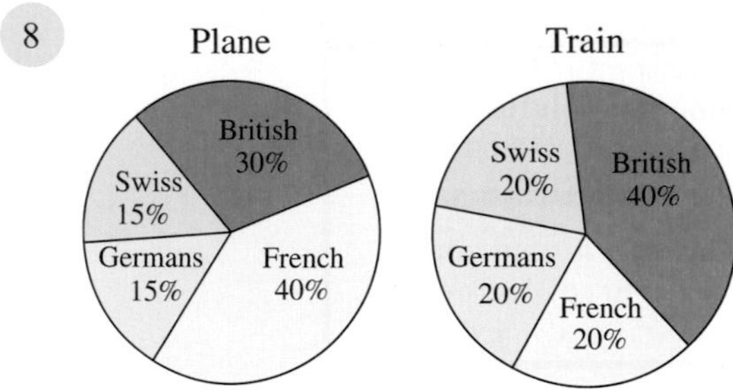

The pie charts show how 570 people travelled from London to Paris, either by air or by rail.

33 people from Switzerland went by plane.

(a) How many more British people went by train than plane?

(b) How many more French people went by plane than train?

9 Conrad is thinking of a number. When he doubles the number and then adds 7 he gets the same answer as when he adds 10 to the number. What number is he thinking of?

10 Two of the angles of an isosceles triangle are $x°$ and $(x + 9)°$. Form equations to find the *two* possible values of x.

11 Describe the single transformation equivalent to reflection in the line $y = x$ followed by reflection in the line $x = 4$.

Puzzles and Problems 4

1 The totals for the rows and columns are given. Find the values of the letters.

(a)

B	C	A	A	37
C	C	C	C	44
D	A	D	A	
A	B	B	A	37
35	40	35	32	

(b)

T	S	T	R	T	27
P	Q	S	R	T	36
T	R	T	R	T	26
S	P	R	R	P	47
T	T	S	R	R	35
25	36	36	50	24	

2 Show how the cross can be cut along the broken lines and the pieces rearranged to make a square.

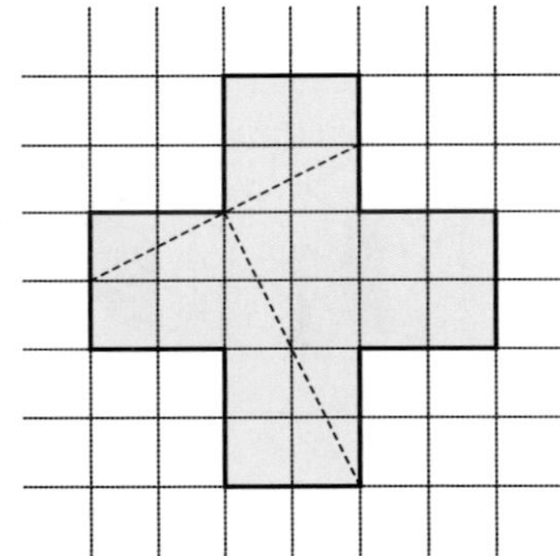

3 For this multiplying box, there are five *outside* numbers [5, 7, 11, 2, 9] and six *inside* numbers [10, 14, 22, 45, 63, 99].

	5	7	11
2	10	14	22
9	45	63	99

Draw a 4 × 3 box and position the seven outside numbers [26, 45, 11, 15, 9, 33, 22] and the twelve inside numbers [495, 99, 572, 135, 286, 990, 390, 495, 675, 363, 198, 726] so that the box works like the one above.

4 Fill in the space in words so that it is correct:
'This sentence has ______ letters.'

5 Replace the question marks with three mathematical symbols (+, –, ×, ÷) so that the calculation is correct.
(105 ? 7) ? 3 ? 7 = 38

6 A lottery prize of £5555 was shared equally between a number of people so that each person received a whole number of pounds. There were between 20 and 100 people. How many people shared the prize and how much did each person receive?

7 A double-decker bus has just 10 seats. There are 5 seats in a line upstairs and 5 downstairs.

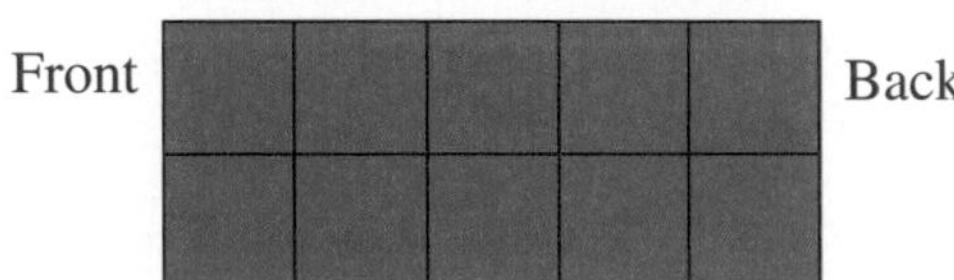

Dave is sitting directly below Karen and in front of eight people. Philip is sitting right at the back, directly above Neha. Lisa is directly in front of Greg and directly above Richard. Chris is just behind Jim and directly below Bob. Who is directly behind Karen?

8 The diagram on the right is the net of a cube made from cardboard. Which of the six cubes below could not be made from this net?

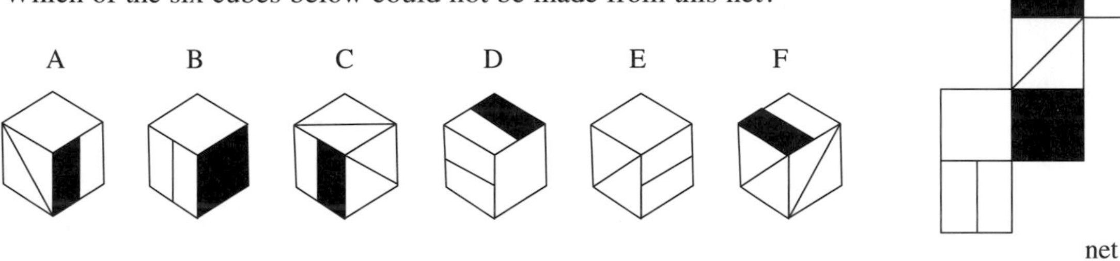

Finding areas by counting dots

- Shapes can be drawn on dotty paper, with vertices on dots.

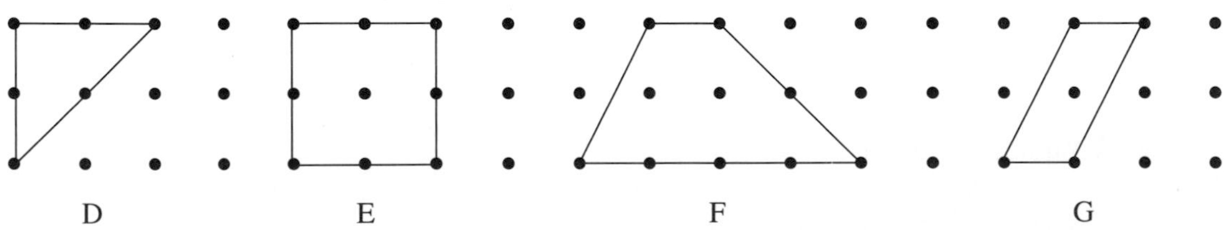

Triangle D has 6 dots on its perimeter. For short, we will write $p = 6$.

Square E has 8 dots on its perimeter and 1 dot inside. We will write $p = 8$, $i = 1$.

Write down the values of p and i for shapes F and G.

- Is there a connection between the values for p, i and the *area* A for each shape?

  Here are some of the areas:

  For shape D: $p = 6$, $i = 0$, A = 2. (area is in square units)

  For shape E: $p = 8$, $i = 1$, A = 4.

  For shape F: $p = 8$, $i = 2$, A = 5.

  For shape G: $p = 4$, $i = 1$, A = 2.

  It is certainly not easy to see a connection or a formula that works for all the shapes.

- Make the problem simpler.

  When you have a complicated problem it is often helpful to make it simpler.

  We will start by drawing shapes with no dots inside [$i = 0$].

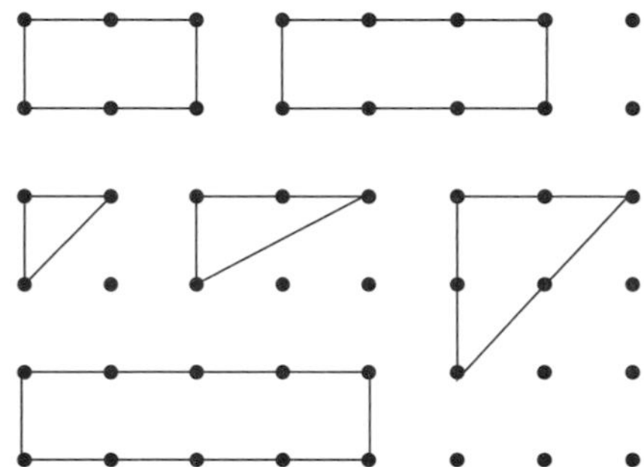

Record the values for p and A in a table:

p	A
6	2
8	3
10	
3	
5	

Try to find a connection between p and A. Write it in the form 'A = ...'

- Now draw shapes with one or more dots inside. Record the values for p, i and A in a new table. Try to find a connection between p, i and A.

  Write it in the form 'A = . . .'.

p	i	A
8	1	4
10	2	6
4	1	
5	3	

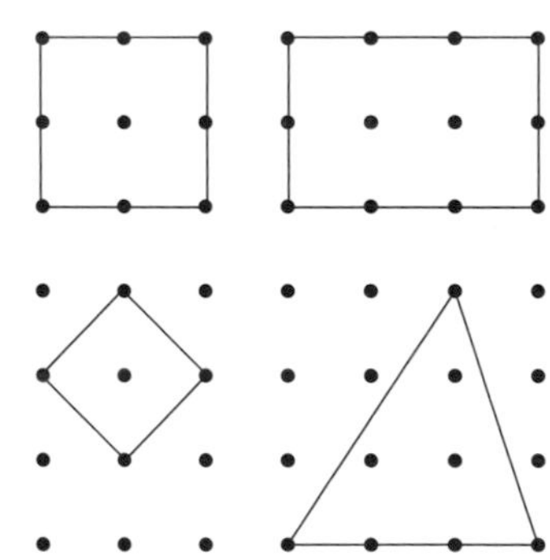

- Predictions

  If you think you have a formula for A, in terms of p and i, use it to predict the area of each of the shapes below.

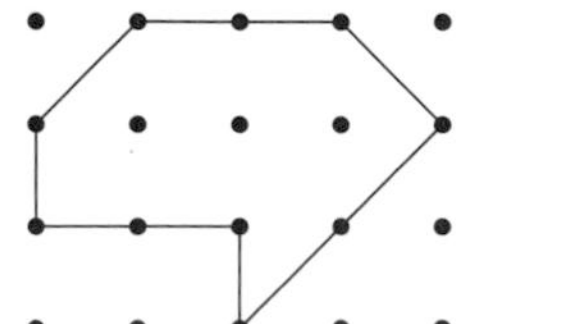

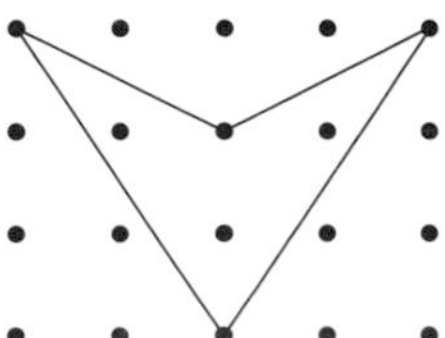

Check by calculating the areas by 'traditional' methods.

Mental Arithmetic Practice

Here is a set of mental arithmetic questions. Ideally a teacher will read out each question twice, with pupils books closed. The test of 30 questions should take about 20 minutes.

1. How many 20 pence coins are needed to make £8?
2. What number is mid-way between 0.1 and 0.2?
3. Work out 5% of £320.
4. True or false: one yard is approximately one metre.
5. Work out 2.2 divided by 10.
6. One sector of a pie chart represents 10% of the whole chart. What is the angle of the sector?
7. Find the approximate area of a circle of diameter 6 cm.
8. I pay for a pen costing £3.40 with a £20 note. What change do I receive?
9. Who is taller: Jan who is 5 feet tall or Sam who is 1 metre 10 tall?
10. A jar contains 1000 5p coins. Find the total value of the coins.
11. A rectangle measures 2.4 m by 10 cm. What is its perimeter in cm?
12. A rope of length 1 foot 4 inches is cut in half. How long is each piece?
13. A film started at 7.10 and finished at 10.55. How long was the film in hours and minutes?
14. Which has the longer perimeter: a square of side 10 cm or a circle of diameter 10 cm?
15. What fraction is equivalent to 40%?
16. Find the cost of 4 litres of wine at £1.25 per litre.
17. How many 24p stamps can be bought for £3?
18. Add together 34 and 164.
19. How long will it take to travel 60 miles at a speed of 30 m.p.h?
20. Work out $3 \times 30 \times 30$.
21. What is the angle between the hands of a clock at 4 o'clock?
22. Find the cost of buying a newspaper for 40 days if each paper costs 20p.
23. Work out two fifths of £40.
24. How many prime numbers are there between 10 and 20?
25. I am thinking of a number. If I double it, add one and then square the result the answer is 25. What number am I thinking of?
26. Work out $\frac{1}{4}$ plus $\frac{1}{2}$ and give the answer as a decimal.
27. Divide one million by 100.
28. A rectangle has area 12 cm^2. What is the area of a rectangle whose sides are twice as long as those of this rectangle?
29. In a quiz, David got 15 out of 20. What percentage is that?
30. Increase a price of £300 by 10%.

A long time ago! 4

Perfect numbers

496	What a perfect number!

The factor pairs of 496 are 1, 496
2, 248
4, 124
8, 62
16, 31

Ignore the number **496** itself. Add up all the other factors.

$1 + 2 + 4 + 8 + 16 + 31 + 62 + 124 + 248 = \mathbf{496}$

A number is perfect if it is equal to the sum of its factors (excluding itself).

The ancient Greeks looked very closely at perfect numbers to help them although there are not many perfect numbers which have been found.

Exercise

1 Find all the factors of 6 then show that 6 is a perfect number.

2 Find out if any of the numbers 24, 25, 26, 27, 28 or 29 are perfect by finding factors and adding them up.

Your answer to this question should be the number of days between full moons. Hundreds of years ago people felt that the *perfection* of the universe was shown by this period for the moon.

3 Find out if any of the numbers between 10 and 20 are perfect.

4 **RESEARCH:**

(a) The number 33550336 is a perfect number. Find at least two more perfect numbers.

(b) Find out what is meant by 'abundant' and 'deficient' numbers.

(c) The formula $2^{n-1}(2^n - 1)$ will give perfect numbers. Research this formula. How does it work and what must be true about $2^n - 1$?

UNIT 5

5.1 Enlargement

In this unit you will learn how to

- recognise enlargements and their properties
- draw enlargements of shapes
- use the centre of enlargement
- solve problems with fractional scale factors

- The original picture here has been enlarged by a scale factor of 2

Notice that both the height *and* the width have been doubled.

- For an enlargement the original and the enlargement must be exactly the same shape. All angles in both shapes are preserved.

Length of A = 2 × length of B

Width of A = 2 × width of B

∴ A *is* an enlargement of B

Exercise 1M

Look at each pair of diagrams and decide whether or not one diagram is an enlargement of the other. For each question write the scale factor of the enlargement or write 'not an enlargement'.

1 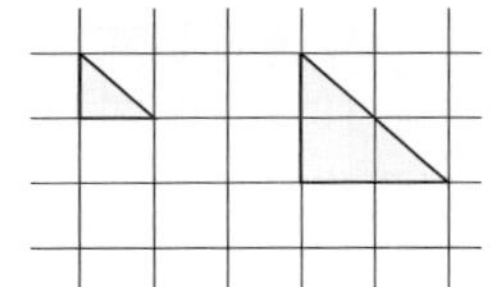

2 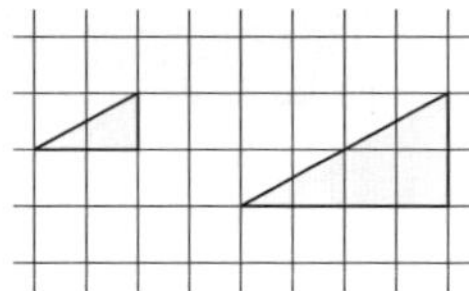

3 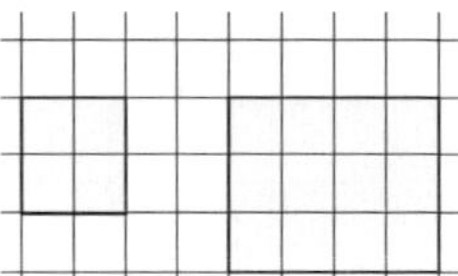

4 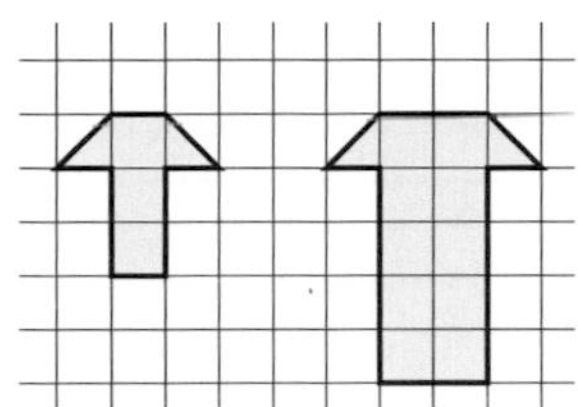

5 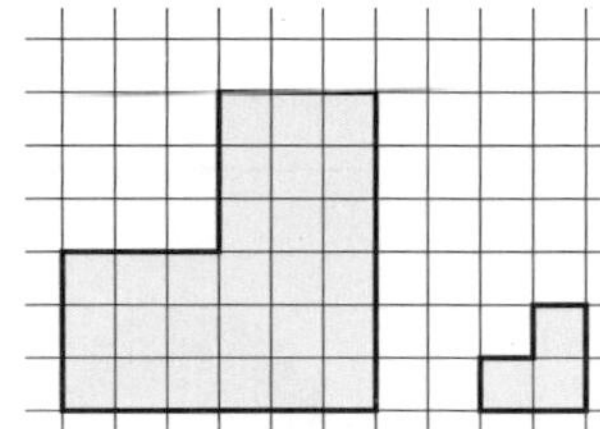

6 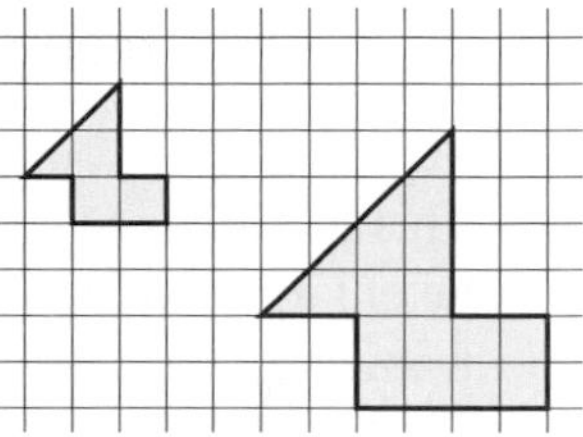

Exercise 1E

Enlarge the following shapes by the scale factor given. Make sure you leave room on your page for the enlargement!

1 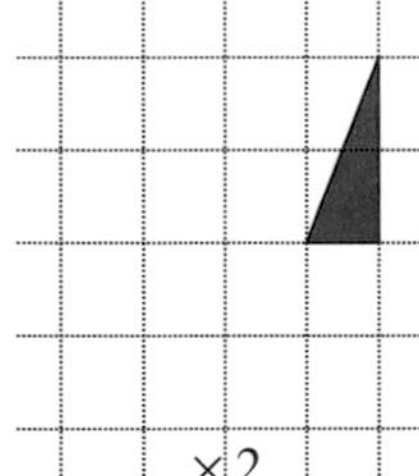

2 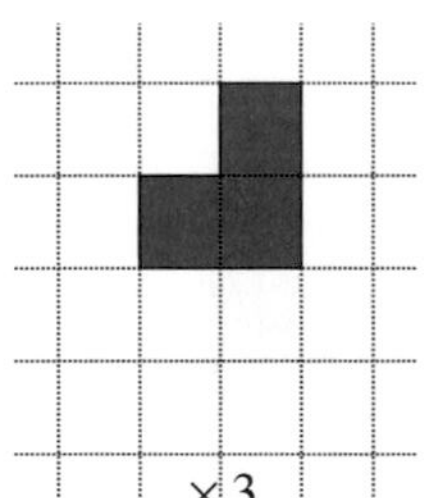

3 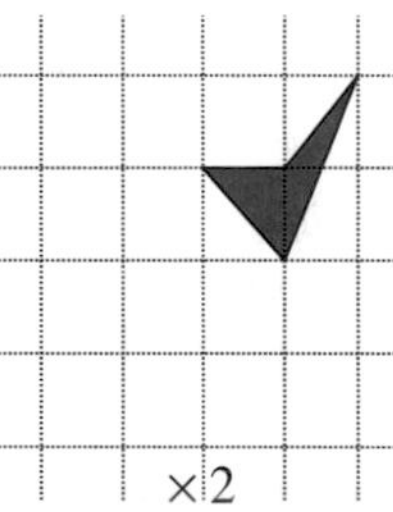

4 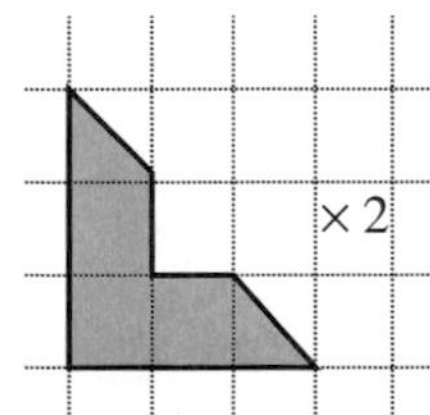

5 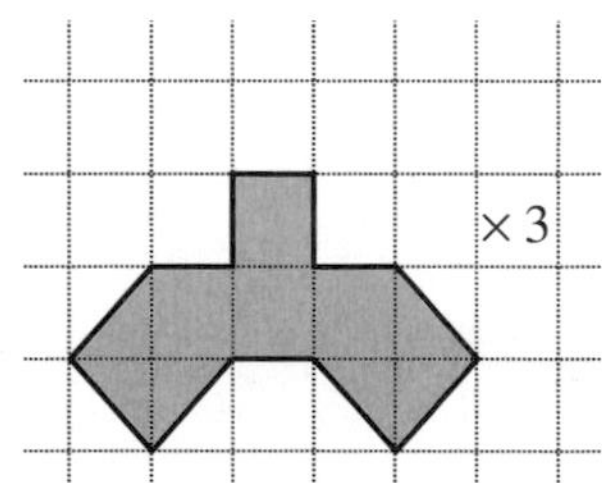

6 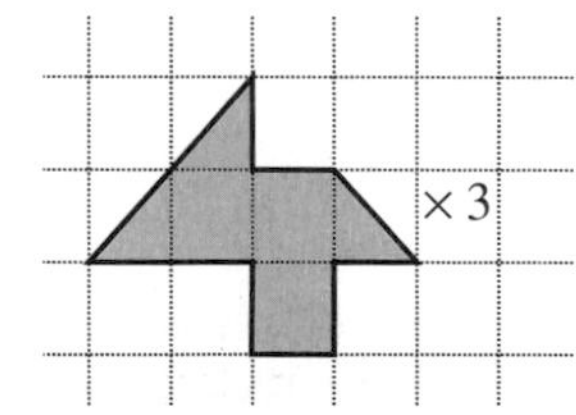

7 Here are some letters of the alphabet.

(a) Enlarge them by a scale factor of 2.

(b) Draw your own initials and enlarge them by a scale factor of 2.

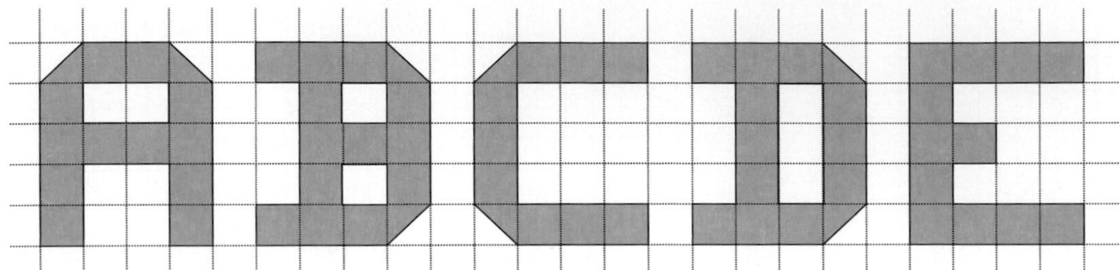

8 This picture is to be enlarged to fit the frame.
Find the height of the frame.

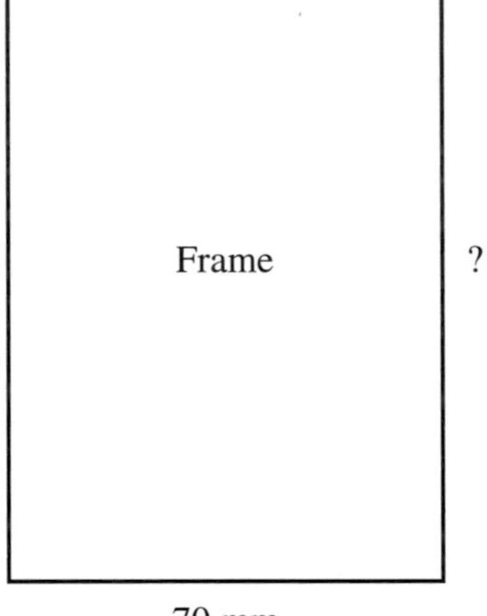

60 mm

35 mm

Frame

?

70 mm

9 A photograph measuring 5 cm by 3.5 cm is enlarged so that it fits exactly into a frame measuring 20 cm by x cm.
Calculate the value of x.

3.5 cm

5 cm

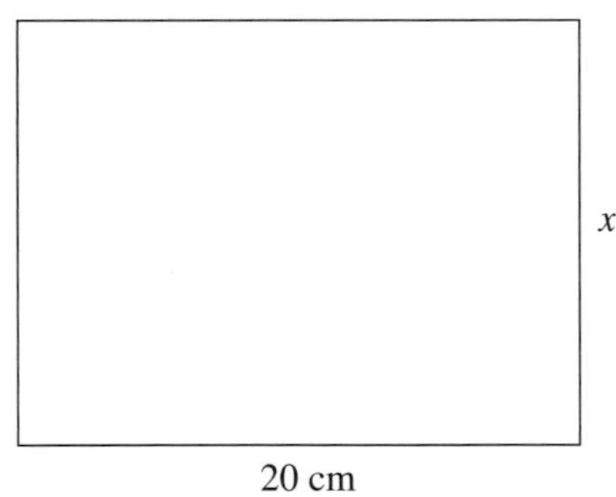

x

20 cm

10 The large rectangle is reduced so that the new height is 0.8 cm.
Work out the base of the new rectangle.

Large

2.4 cm

5.1 cm

New

0.8 cm

?

11 A photograph measuring 6 cm by 4 cm is reduced to fit frame A and another copy of the photograph is enlarged to fit frame B.

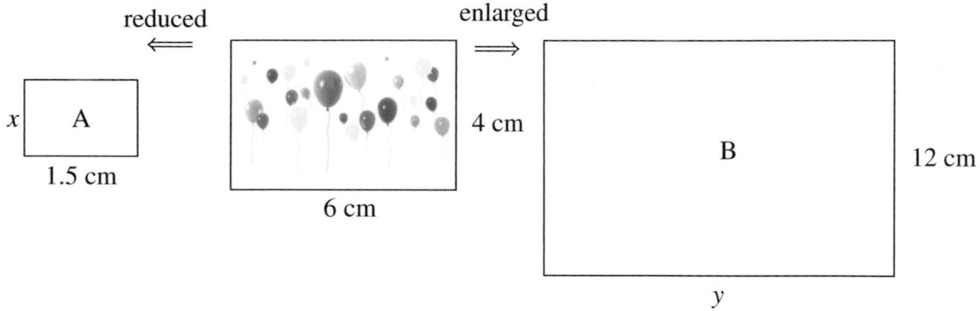

Calculate the value of x and the value of y.

Centre of enlargement

A mathematical enlargement always has a *centre of enlargement* as well as a scale factor. The center of enlargement is found by drawing lines through corresponding points on the object and image and finding where they intersect. For greater accuracy it is better to count squares between points because it is difficult to draw construction lines accurately over a long distance.

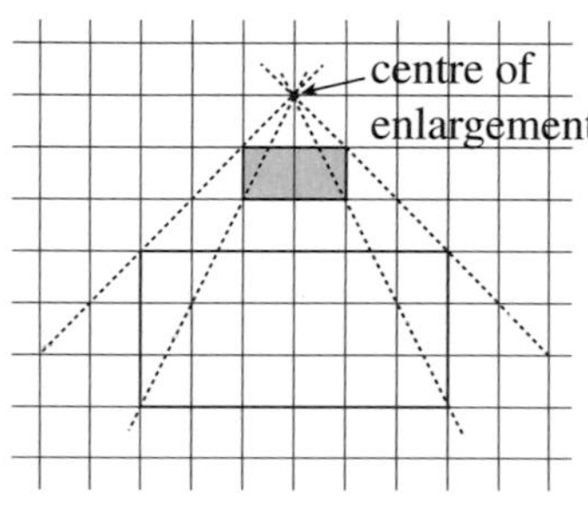

In the second diagram. $A'B'C'$ is an enlargement of ABC with scale factor 2 and centre O.

Observe that $OA' = 2 \times OA$

$OB' = 2 \times OB$

$OC' = 2 \times OC$

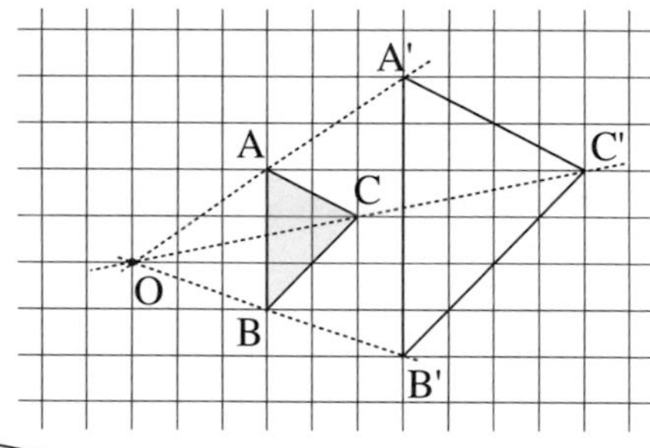

Always measure distances from the centre of enlargement.

Exercise 2M

Draw the shapes and then draw lines through corresponding points to find the centre of enlargement. Don't draw the shapes too near the edge of the page!

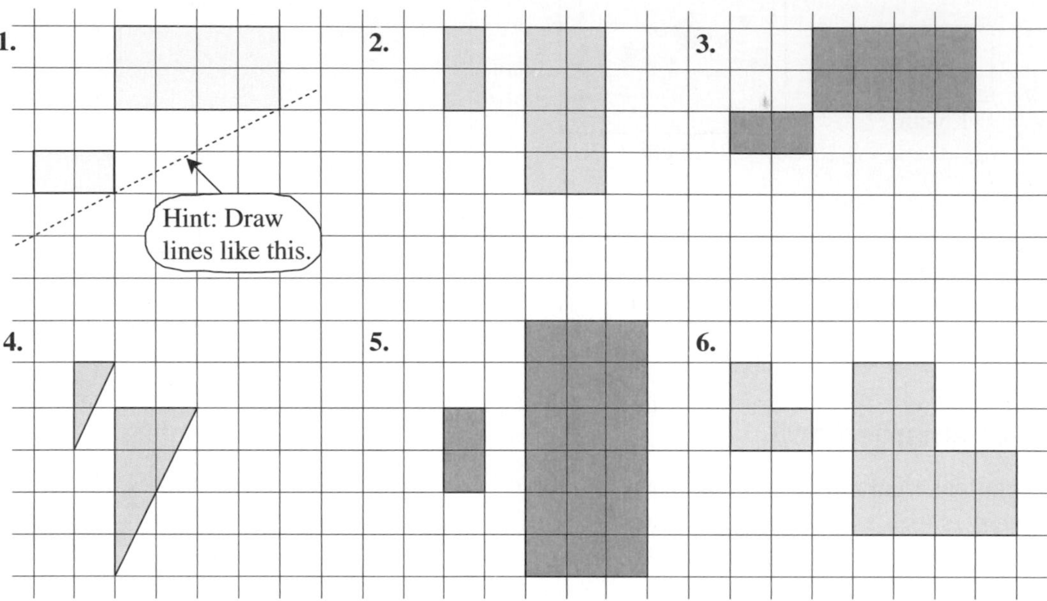

To fully describe an enlargement we need two things: the scale factor and the centre of enlargement.

(a) Draw an enlargement of Δ1 with scale factor 3 and centre O.

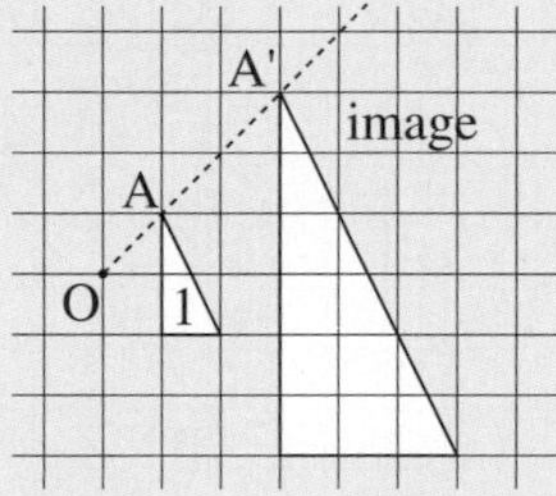

Notice that OA′ = 3 × OA.

(b) Draw an enlargement of shape P with scale factor 2 and centre O.

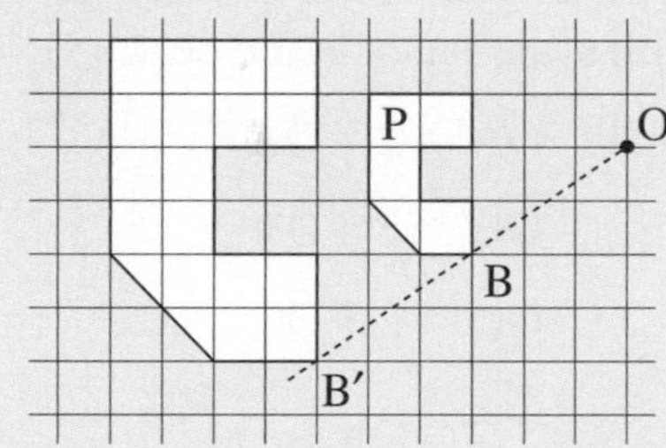

Notice that OB′ = 2 × OB.

In both diagrams, just one point on the image has been found by using a construction line or by counting squares. When one point is known the rest of the diagram can easily be drawn, since the size and shape of the image is known.

Exercise 2E

In questions 1 to 6 copy the diagram and then draw an enlargement using the scale factor and centre of enlargement given.

Leave room for the enlargement!

1 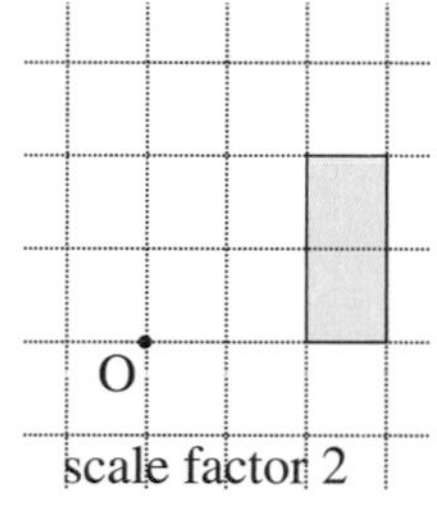

2 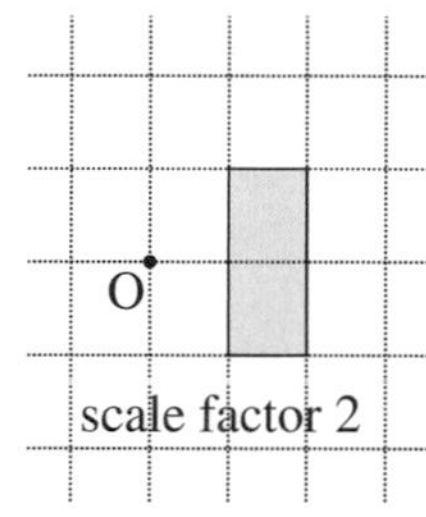

3 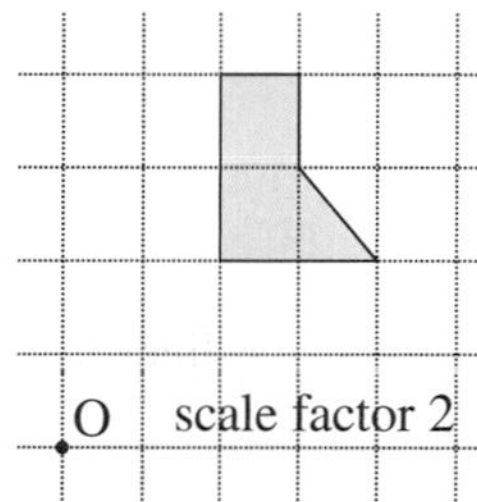

4 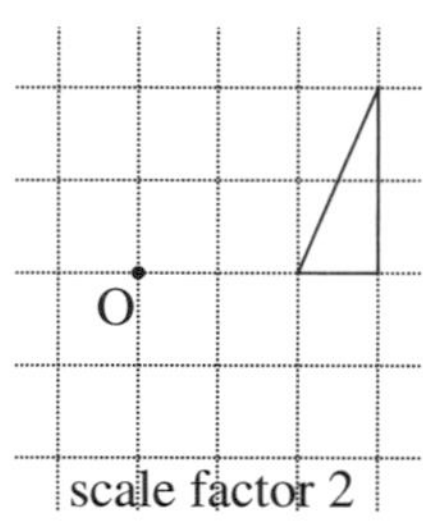

5 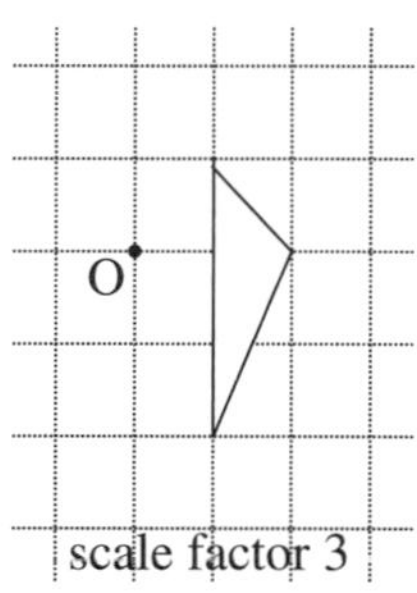

6 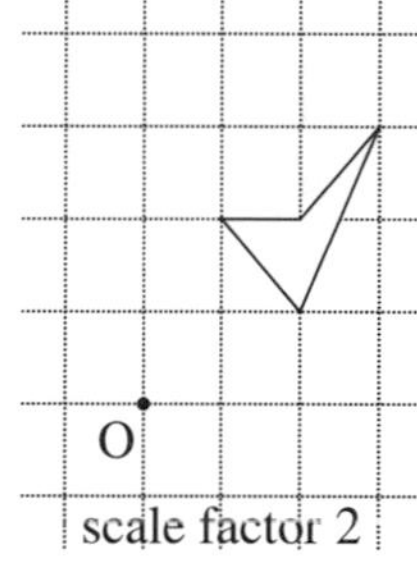

7 Copy the diagram. Draw an enlargement of the triangle with scale factor 2 and centre of enlargement (0, 0).

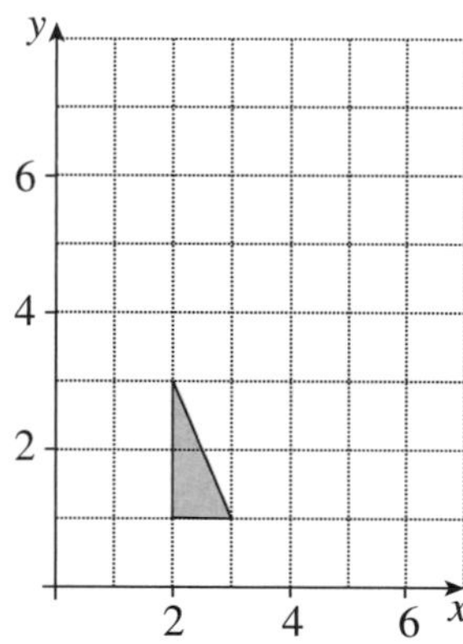

8 For (a), (b) and (c) draw a grid similar to the one in question 7. Draw an enlargement of each shape.

Shape	Centre of enlargement	Scale factor
(a) (1, 1) (2, 1) (2, 2) (1, 2)	(0, 0)	3
(b) (2, 1) (4, 2) (2, 2)	(0, 0)	2
(c) (4, 5) (6, 5) (6, 6) (4, 6)	(8, 8)	2

9 (a) Draw axes with values from 0 to 12 and draw $\Delta 1$ with vertices at (5, 4), (3, 4), (3, 6).

(b) Draw $\Delta 2$, the image of $\Delta 1$ under enlargement with scale factor 2, centre (5, 2).

(c) Draw $\Delta 3$, the image of $\Delta 1$ under enlargement with scale factor 3, centre (2, 3).

(d) Draw $\Delta 4$, the image of $\Delta 3$ (not $\Delta 1$!) under enlargement with scale factor $\frac{1}{2}$, centre (11, 0).

(e) Draw $\Delta 5$, the image of $\Delta 3$ under enlargement with scale factor $\frac{1}{6}$, centre (11, 12).

(f) Write down the coordinates of the right angled vertex in $\Delta 2$, $\Delta 3$, $\Delta 4$ and $\Delta 5$.

10 Copy the diagram.
(You will need it because you have to draw several construction lines).
Find the scale factor and centre for each of the following enlargements:

(a) $\Delta A \rightarrow \Delta F$

(b) $\Delta B \rightarrow \Delta C$

(c) $\Delta D \rightarrow \Delta C$

(d) $\Delta B \rightarrow \Delta E$

(e) $\Delta B \rightarrow \Delta D$.

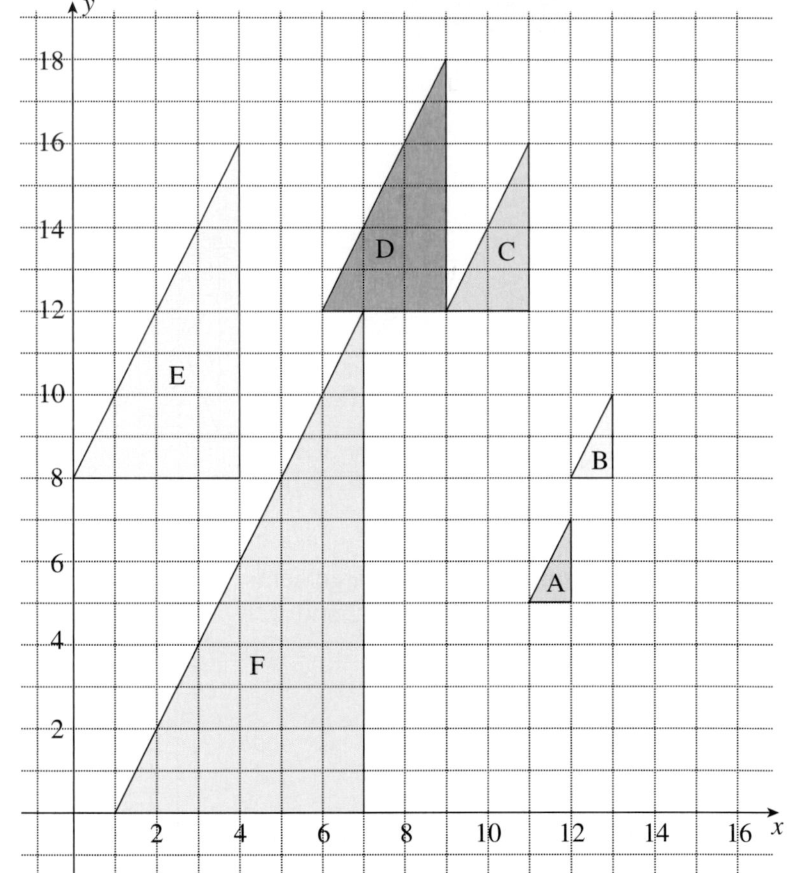

11 Draw axes with values from 0 to 14.
Draw quadrilateral ABCD at A(2, 12), B(4, 10), C(2, 8), D(3, 10).

(a) A′B′C′D′ is an enlargement of ABCD with A′ at (4, 14) and C′ at (4, 6). Complete the quadrilateral A′B′C′D′.

(b) A*B*C*D* is an enlargement of ABCD with A* at (8, 12) and B* at (14, 6). Complete the quadrilateral A*B*C*D*.

(c) Draw A°B°C°D° which is an enlargement of A*B*C*D* with scale factor $\frac{1}{6}$ and centre of enlargement (2, 6).

(d) Write down the coordinates of A°.

12 Copy the diagram. Describe fully each of the following enlargements

(a) square 1 → square 3

(b) square 2 → square 5

(c) square 2 → square 7

(d) square 3 → square 5

(e) square 7 → square 5

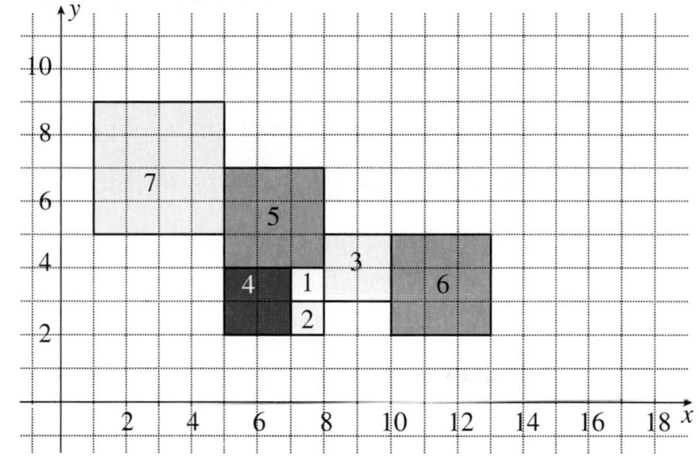

13 Copy shape A inside the rectange shown. Shape A is enlarged so that it just fits inside the rectangle.

Draw the enlargement of shape A and mark the centre of enlargement.

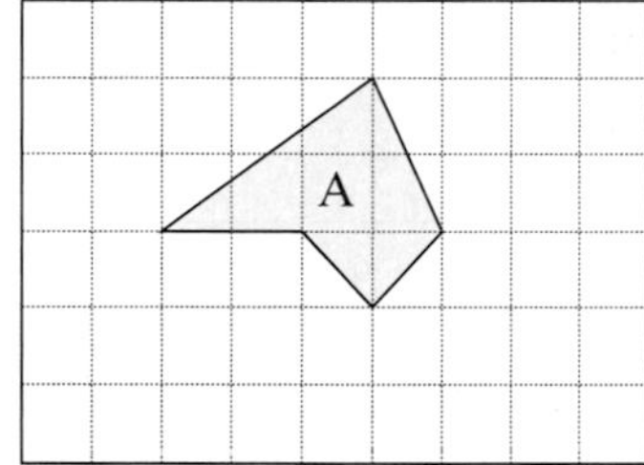

14 (a) Draw axes with values from 0 to 14.

(b) Draw the following shapes:

(i) Rectangle A at (9, 11), (11, 11), (11, 12), (9, 12)

(ii) Triangle B at (2, 10), (2, 12), (1, 12)

(iii) Square C at (3, 6), (4, 6), (4, 7), (3, 7)

(c) Enlarge A onto A′ with scale factor 2, centre (10, 14)

(d) Enlarge B onto B′ with scale factor 3, centre (0, 11)

(e) Enlarge C onto C′ with scale factor 4, centre (3, 8)

(f) Write down the areas of shapes A, A′, B, B′, C, C′.

(g) Work out the ratios: $\left(\frac{\text{area of A}'}{\text{area of A}}\right)$; $\left(\frac{\text{area of B}'}{\text{area of B}}\right)$; $\left(\frac{\text{area of C}'}{\text{area of C}}\right)$.

(h) Write down any connection you observe between the ratios above and the scale factor for each enlargement.

5.2 Sequences and formulas

In this unit you will:

- learn about the *n*th term in a sequence
- use mapping diagrams to find the *n*th term
- solve a range of problems involving the *n*th term of a sequence.

Sequences, the *n*th term

Here are numbers written in a 'wave' pattern. The top numbers are shown by arrows.

1st top number ↓ (above 5), 2nd top number ↓ (above 9), 3rd top number ↓ (above 13)

<table>
<tr><td></td><td></td><td>5</td><td></td><td></td><td></td><td>9</td><td></td><td></td><td></td><td>13</td><td></td><td></td><td></td><td>17</td></tr>
<tr><td></td><td>4</td><td></td><td>6</td><td></td><td>8</td><td></td><td>10</td><td></td><td>12</td><td></td><td>14</td><td></td><td>16</td><td></td></tr>
<tr><td>3</td><td></td><td></td><td></td><td>7</td><td></td><td></td><td></td><td>11</td><td></td><td></td><td></td><td>15</td><td></td><td></td></tr>
</table>

(a) What is the 10th top number?

(b) What is the *n*th top number? [*n* stands for any whole number]. 'In other words,' Is there a formula so that we can easily find the 50th or the 1000th top number?'

The top numbers form the sequence 5, 9, 13, 17,……

The 10th term in the sequence is $(4 \times 10) + 1 = 41$

The 50th term in the sequence is $(4 \times 50) + 1 = 201$

The 1000th term in the sequence is $(4 \times 1000) + 1 = 4001$

The *n*th term (the *n*th top number) is $(4 \times n) + 1 = 4n + 1$

Mapping diagrams

(a) For the sequence 4, 8, 12, 16, 20,….. the rule is 'add 4'.

Here is the *mapping diagram* for the sequence.

Term number (n)		Term
1	⟶	4
2	⟶	8
3	⟶	12
4	⟶	16
⋮		⋮
10	⟶	40
⋮		⋮
n	⟶	$4n$

The terms are found by multiplying the term number by 4. So the 10th number is 40, the 20th term is 80.

A *general* term in the sequence is the *n*th term, where *n* stands for any number.

The *n*th term of this sequence is $4n$.

(b) Here is a more difficult sequence: 4, 7, 10, 13,……..

The rule is 'add 3' so, in the mapping diagram, we have written a column for 3 times the term number [i.e. $3n$].

Term number (n)		$3n$		Term
1	⟶	3	⟶	4
2	⟶	6	⟶	7
3	⟶	9	⟶	10
4	⟶	12	⟶	13

We see that each term is 1 more than $3n$.

So, the 10th term is $(3 \times 10) + 1 = 31$

the 15th term is $(3 \times 15) + 1 = 46$

the nth term is $(3 \times n) + 1 = 3n + 1$

(c) Look at these two mapping diagrams. Decide what the missing numbers would be.

Term number (n)		$2n$		Term
1	⟶	2		3
2	⟶	4		5
3	⟶	6		7
4	⟶	8		9
⋮		⋮		⋮
10	⟶	□	⟶	□
⋮				
n	⟶	$2n$	⟶	□

Term number (n)		$5n$		Term
1	⟶	5	⟶	7
2	⟶	10	⟶	12
3	⟶	15	⟶	17
4	⟶	20	⟶	22
⋮		⋮		⋮
20	⟶	□	⟶	□
⋮		⋮		⋮
n	⟶	□	⟶	□

Exercise 1M

1 Copy and complete these mapping diagrams.

(a)

Term number (n)		Term
1	⟶	6
2	⟶	12
3	⟶	18
4	⟶	24
⋮		⋮
12	⟶	□
⋮		⋮
n	⟶	□

(b)

Term number (n)		Term
1	⟶	8
2	⟶	16
3	⟶	24
4	⟶	32
⋮		⋮
8	⟶	□
⋮		⋮
n	⟶	□

(c)

Term number (n)		Term
1	⟶	10
2	⟶	20
3	⟶	30
⋮		⋮
15	⟶	□
⋮		⋮
n	⟶	□

2 Copy and complete these mapping diagrams: Notice that an extra column has been written.

(a)

Term number (n)		$4n$		Term
1	→	4	→	5
2	→	8	→	9
3	→	12	→	13
4	→	16	→	17
⋮		⋮		⋮
20	→	□	→	□
⋮		⋮		⋮
n	→	□	→	□

(b)

Term number (n)		$5n$		Term
1	→	5	→	4
2	→	10	→	9
3	→	15	→	14
4	→	20	→	19
⋮		⋮		⋮
12	→	□	→	□
⋮		⋮		⋮
n	→	□	→	□

3 Write down each sequence and select the correct expression for the nth term from the list given.

(a) 3, 6, 9, 12, ...
(b) 5, 10, 15, 20, …
(c) $1^2, 2^2, 3^2, 4^2$, …
(d) 7, 14, 21, 28, …
(e) 2, 3, 4, 5, 6, …
(f) $1^3, 2^3, 3^3, 4^3$, ...
(g) 1, 3, 5, 7, 9, …

n^3 | $n+1$ | $3n$ | $7n$ | $2n-1$ | n^2 | $5n$

4 Here you are given the nth term. Copy and complete the diagrams.

(a)

Term number (n)		$7n$		Term
1	→	7	→	8
2	→	□	→	□
3	→	□	→	□
4	→	□	→	□
⋮		⋮		⋮
n	→	$7n$	→	$7n+1$

(b)

Term number (n)		$3n$		Term
1	→	3	→	1
2	→	□	→	□
3	→	□	→	□
4	→	□	→	□
⋮		⋮		⋮
n	→	$3n$	→	$3n-2$

(c)

Term number (n)		$5n$		Term
1	→	5	→	□
2	→	□	→	□
3	→	□	→	□
8	→	□	→	□
⋮				
n	→	$5n$	→	$5n+1$

(d)

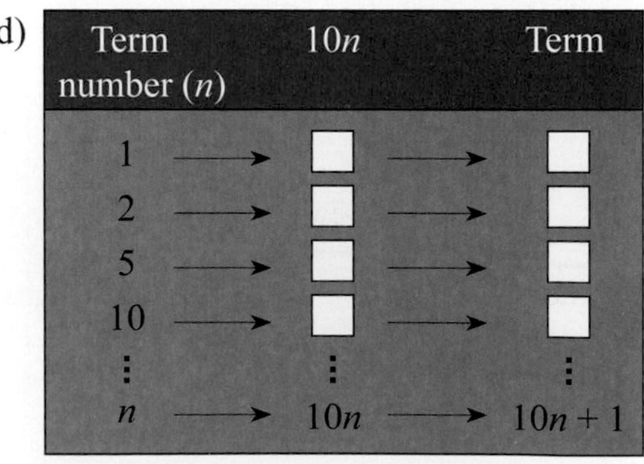

Term number (n)		$10n$		Term
1	→	□	→	□
2	→	□	→	□
5	→	□	→	□
10	→	□	→	□
⋮		⋮		⋮
n	→	$10n$	→	$10n+1$

- It is convenient to use the notation: T(1) for the first term,
  T(2) for the second term,
  T(3) for the third term and so on.

  The nth term of a sequence is written as T(n).

- The nth term of a sequence is $3n + 1$.
  So we have T(n) = $3n + 1$.

The first term, T(1) = $3 \times 1 + 1 = 4$

The second term, T(2) = $3 \times 2 + 1 = 7$

The seventh term, T(7) = $3 \times 7 + 1 = 22$

Remember:
For the first term, put $n = 1$
For the second term, put $n = 2$.

Exercise 1E

Remember:
T(1) means 'the first term'
T(2) means 'the second term'
... and so on.

1 For the sequence 3, 5, 7, 9, 11, 13,… write down

(a) T(1) (b) T(2) (c) T(5)

2 For the sequence 2, 4, 6, 8, 10,… write down

(a) T(1) (b) T(4) (c) T(6)

3 The nth term of a sequence is T(n) and T(n) = $2n + 1$.
Copy and complete the following

(a) T(1) = $2 \times 1 + 1 = \square$

(b) T(2) = $2 \times \square + 1 = \square$

(c) T(3) = $2 \times \square + 1 = \square$

(d) T(10) = $2 \times \square + 1 = \square$

4 The nth term of a sequence is T(n) and T(n) = $4n$.

Find (a) T(1) (b) T(2) (c) T(20)

5 For a sequence, T(n) = $5n + 1$.

Find (a) T(1) (b) T(3) (c) T(10)

6 For a sequence, T(n) = $20 - n$.

Find (a) T(2) (b) T(5) (c) T(11)

7 The nth term of a sequence is $3n - 1$.

Find (a) T(1) (b) T(100)

8 Write the first five terms of the sequence whose nth term,

$T(n) = 2n + 3$.

9 Write the first five terms of the sequence where $T(n)$ is:

(a) $n + 2$ (b) $5n$ (c) $10n - 1$ (d) $n - 2$ (e) $\frac{1}{n}$ (f) n^2

10 Here is a 'wave pattern'.

1st top number ↓ 2nd top number ↓ 3rd top number ↓

		3						9						15				
	2		4				8		10				14		16			
1				5		7				11		13				17		19
					6						12						18	

(a) The top numbers form the sequence 3, 9, 15, 21, ...

Which of the following is the correct expression for $T(n)$:

$6(n + 3)$ $3 + 6n$ $6n - 3$ $n - 3$

(b) The bottom numbers (yellow) form the sequence 6, 12, 18, ...

Write down the expression for $T(n)$ of this sequence.

Finding the *n*th term

- In an *arithmetic* sequence the difference between successive terms is always the same number.

  Here are some arithmetic sequences:
  A 5, 7, 9, 11, 13
  B 12, 32, 52, 72, 92,
  C 20, 17, 14, 11, 8,

- The expression for the nth term of an arithmetic sequence is always of the form $an + b$

  The *difference* between successive terms is equal to the number a.

  The number b can be found by looking at the terms.

  Look at sequences A, B and C above.

  For sequence A, the nth term $= 2n + b$ [the terms go up by 2]

  For sequence B, the nth term $= 20n + b$ [the terms go up by 20]

  For sequence C, the nth term $= -3n + b$ [the terms go up by -3]

  Look at each sequence and find the value of b in each case.

Find the nth term of the sequence 5, 7, 9, 11, 13, ………..

This is an arithmetic sequence, so the nth term is of the form $an + b$.
The difference between terms is 2, so $a = 2$.

Put the sequence in a table and write a column for $2n$.

We can see that the term is always 3 more than $2n$, so $b = 3$.

The nth term is $2n + 3$.

n	$2n$	term
1	2	5
2	4	7
3	6	9
4	8	11

Exercise 2M

1 Look at the sequence 5, 9, 13, 17, …

The difference between terms is 4.
Copy the table, which has a column for $4n$.
Copy and complete:
'The nth term of the sequence is $4n + \square$'.

n	$4n$	term
1	4	5
2	8	9
3	12	13
4	16	17

2 Look at the sequence and the table underneath. Find the nth term in each case.

(a) Sequence 7, 10, 13, 16, ………

n	$3n$	term
1	3	7
2	6	10
3	9	13
4	12	16

nth term = $\square$

(b) Sequence 4, 9, 14, 19, ………

n	$5n$	term
1	5	4
2	10	9
3	15	14
4	20	19

nth term = $\square$

3 In the sequence 6, 10, 14, 18, …
the difference between terms is 4.
Copy and complete the table and
write an expression for the nth term
of the sequence.

n	$\square$	term
1	$\square$	6
2	$\square$	10
3	$\square$	14
4	$\square$	18

4 Look at the sequence 5, 8, 11, 14, …
Write down the difference between terms.
Make a table like the one in question 3 and use it to find an expression for the nth term.

5 Write down each sequence in a table and then find the nth term.

(a) 8, 10, 12, 14, 16, ...

(b) 3, 7, 11, 15, ...

(c) 8, 13, 18, 23, ...

6 Make a table for each sequence and write the nth term.

(a) 11, 19, 27, 35, ...

(b) $2\frac{1}{2}, 4\frac{1}{2}, 6\frac{1}{2}, 8\frac{1}{2}, \ldots$

(c) –7, –4, –1, 2, 5, ...

7 Here is a sequence of shapes made from sticks

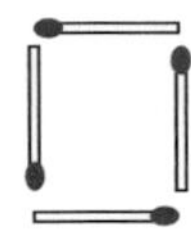

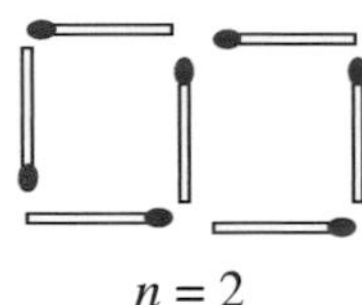

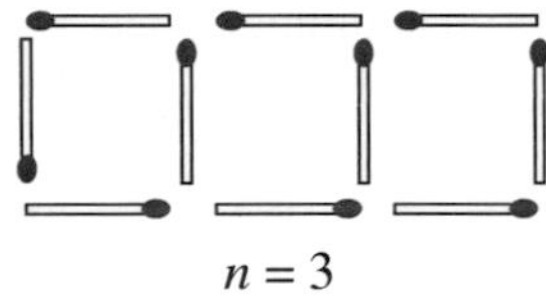

Shape number:	$n = 1$	$n = 2$	$n = 3$
Number of sticks:	4	7	10

The number of sticks makes the sequence 4, 7, 10, 13, ...
Make a table for the sequence and find the nth term.

8 Here is a sequence of triangles made from dots. Draw the next diagram in the sequence. How many dots are in nth diagram in the sequence?

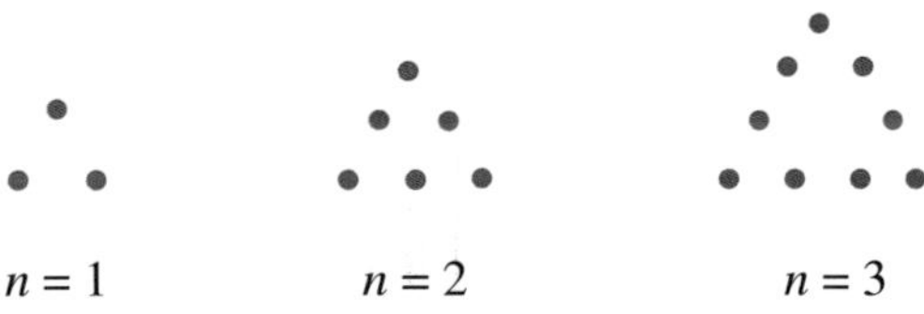

Shape number:	$n = 1$	$n = 2$	$n = 3$
Number of dots:	3	6	9

9 Here is a sequence of 'steps' made from sticks. Draw the next diagram in the sequence and make a table. How many sticks are in the nth term?

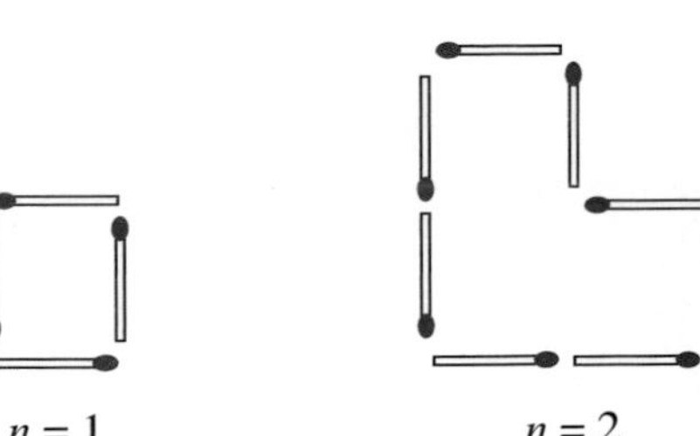

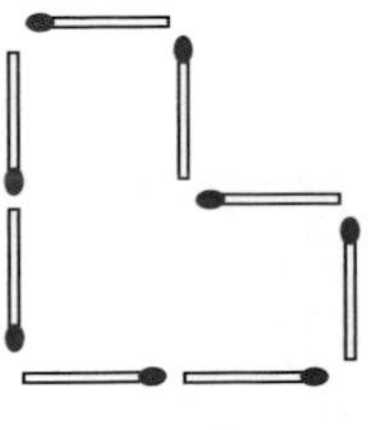

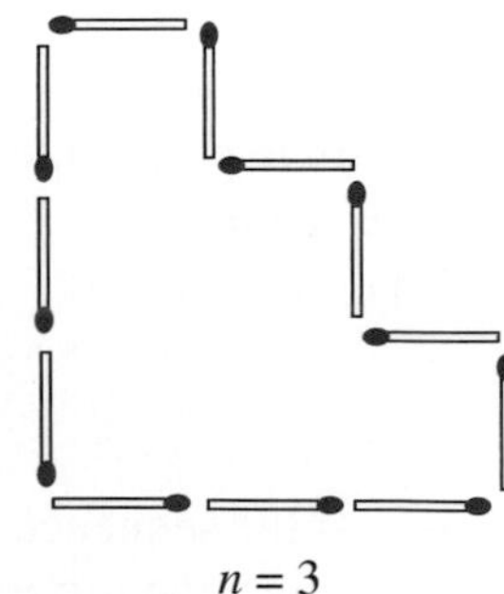

Shape number:	$n = 1$	$n = 2$	$n = 3$
Number of sticks:	4	8	12

Exercise 2E

1 Louise makes a pattern of triangles from sticks.

Shape number:	$n = 1$	$n = 2$	$n = 3$
Number of sticks:	3	5	7

Draw shape number 4 and shape number 5 and make a table.
How many sticks are in the nth diagram in the sequence?

2 Here is a sequence of houses made from sticks

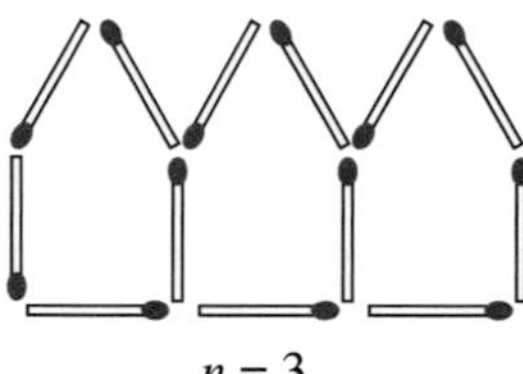

Shape number:	$n = 1$	$n = 2$	$n = 3$
Number of sticks:	5	9	13

Draw shape number 4 and make a table. How many sticks are in the nth diagram in the sequence?

3 Paul makes a pattern of squares from dots.

Shape number:	$n = 1$	$n = 2$	$n = 3$
Number of dots:	4	6	8

Draw shape number 4 and shape number 5 and make a table.
How many dots are in the nth term?

4 Here is another sequence made from dots.

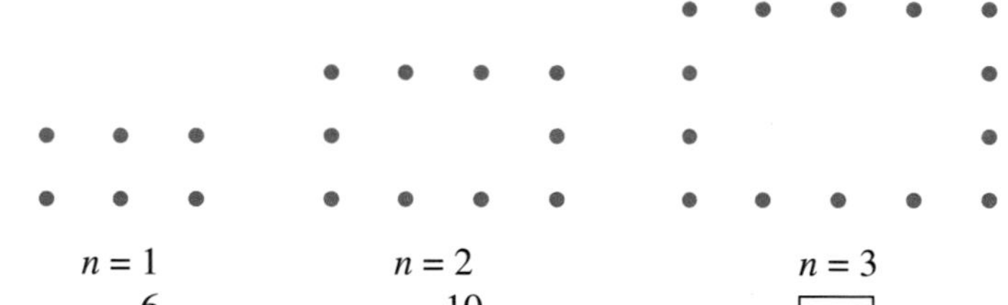

Shape number:	$n = 1$	$n = 2$	$n = 3$
Number of dots:	6	10	☐

Draw shape numbers 4 and 5 and make a table. How many dots are in the nth shape?

In questions 5 to 9 find the number of white squares, dots or sticks in the nth term of the sequence.

5 In these diagrams pink squares are surrounded on three sides by white squares.

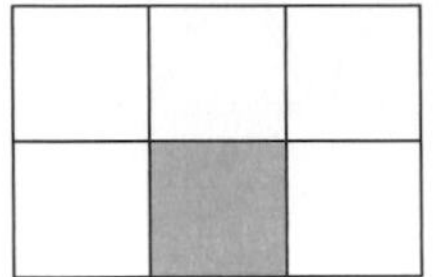
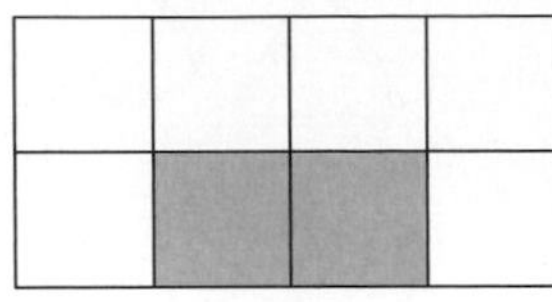
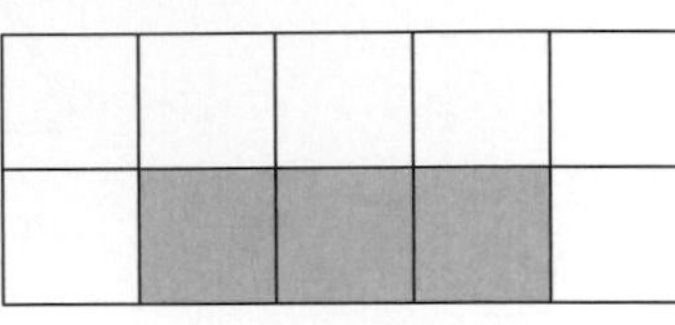

Diagram number:	$n = 1$	$n = 2$	$n = 3$
White squares:	$w = 5$	$w = 6$	$w = 7$

6 In this sequence blue squares are surrounded by white squares.

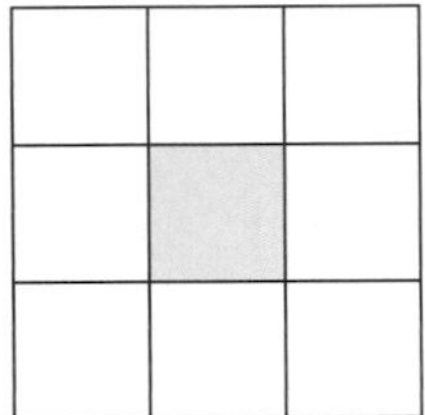
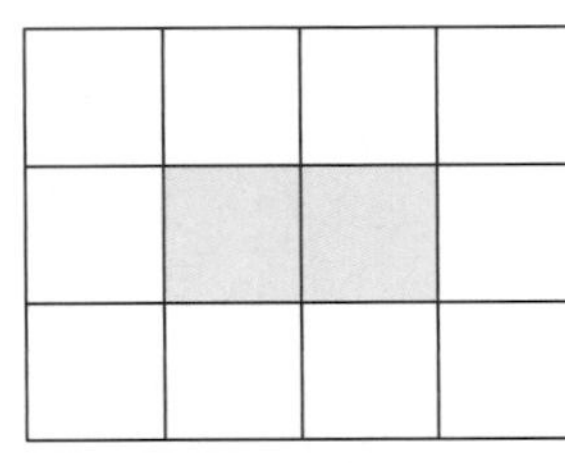
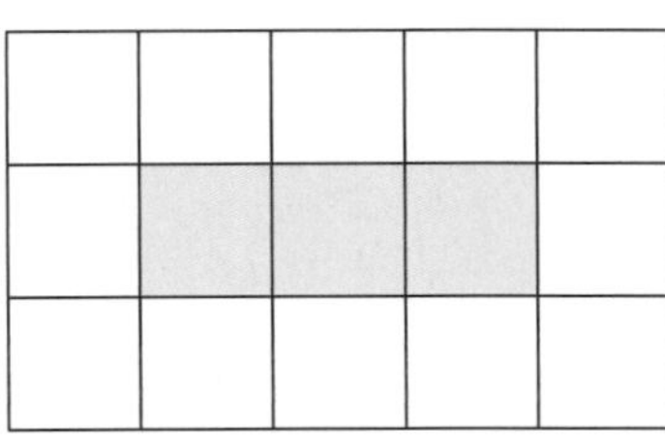

Diagram number:	$n = 1$	$n = 2$	$n = 3$
White squares:	$w = 8$	$w = 10$	$w = 12$

7 In the diagrams below rectangles are joined together and dots are drawn around the outside with 2 dots on a long side and one dot on a short side.

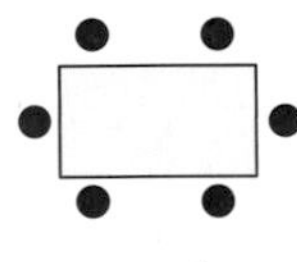
$n = 1$

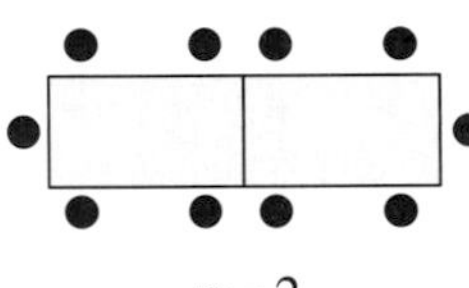
$n = 2$

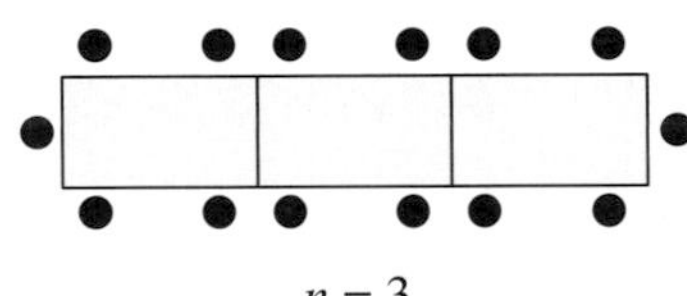
$n = 3$

8 Now the rectangles are joined along their longer sides.

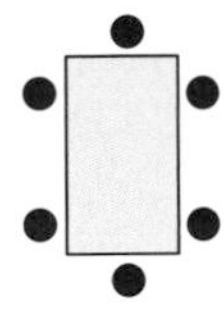
$n = 1$

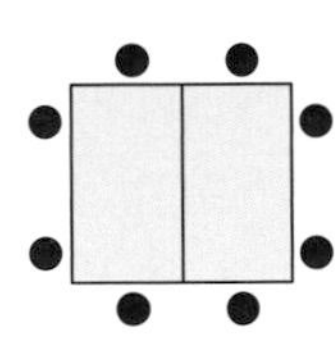
$n = 2$

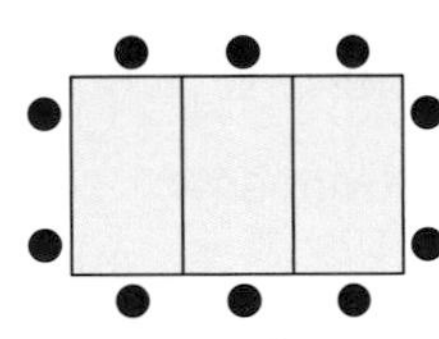
$n = 3$

9

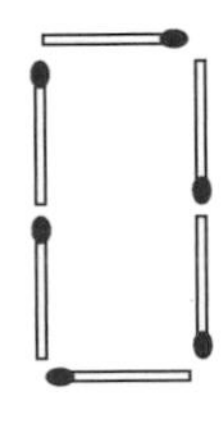
$n = 1$

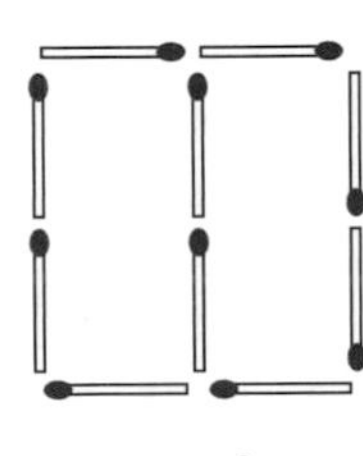
$n = 2$

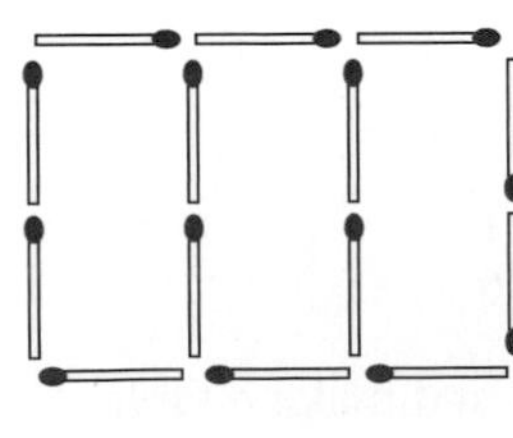
$n = 3$

10 Design your own sequence of shapes using sticks or squares.
Find an expression for the nth term of the sequence.

11 In these diagrams a shaded letter 'L' is surrounded by white squares.

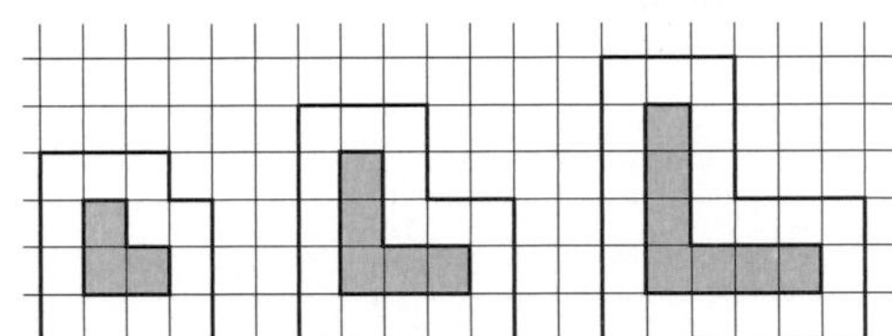

Find a formula connecting the number of pink squares (p) and the number of white squares (w). Write '$w =$ '.

Vending machine problem

- You have lots of 10p coins and 20p coins to put into a vending machine.
  In how many different ways can you put 40p in the machine?
- This is not difficult. Make a systematic list:

  10, 10, 10, 10 — 1 way
  20, 20 — 1 way
  20, 10, 10
  10, 20, 10 } 3 ways. These count as different because the order of the coins is different.
  10, 10, 20

  So there are 5 ways of putting in 40p.
- How many ways are there of putting in 120p?
  This is much harder because there are so many ways of doing it. If you start to make a list you soon realize how difficult it will be. In many investigations it is a good idea to attempt an easier problem:
- (a) Find the number of ways you can put in 10p,
  20p,
  30p,
  40p etc.

  Put the results in a table and look for a *sequence*.

Amount put in	Number of ways
10p	1
20p	2
etc	etc

  (b) Find the number of ways for 50p. Can you see a sequence in your results? If so use the sequence to *predict* the number of ways of putting in 60p. Now check your prediction by *listing* the ways of putting in 60p.
- Hopefully you now have some confidence in your sequence. Use the sequence to predict the number of ways of putting in 120p.

TEST YOURSELF ON SECTIONS 5.1 AND 5.2

1 Enlargement

(a) Copy the diagram on squared paper.

(b) Draw the enlargement of the pink triangle with centre of enlargement A and scale factor 2.

(c) Draw the enlargement of the pink triangle with centre of enlargement B and scale factor 3.

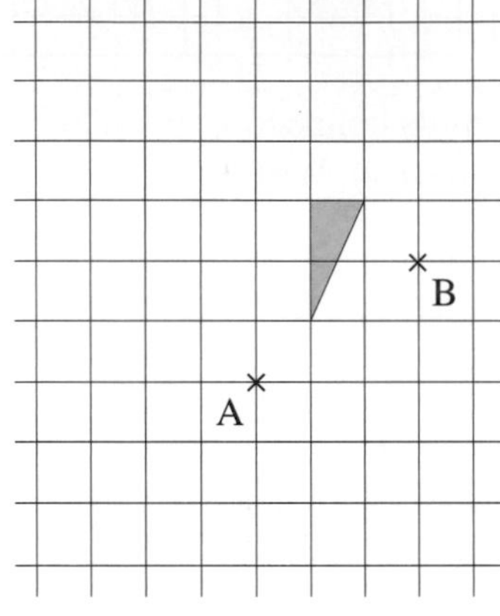

2 The *n*th term of a sequence

(a) Write down each sequence and select the correct expression for the *n*th term from the list given.

(i) 4, 8, 12, 16, ……………..

(ii) 3, 5, 7, 9,………………..

(iii) 3, 4, 5, 6, 7,…………

(iv) $\frac{1}{2}, \frac{2}{3}, \frac{3}{4}, \frac{4}{5}, \ldots$

$\frac{n}{n+1}$ $2n+1$ $4n$ $n+2$ $\frac{n}{n-1}$ $3n+1$

(b) The *n*th term of a sequence is $n^2 + 1$.

Write down (i) the 5th term

(ii) the 100th term.

(c) Find the *n*th term of each sequence.

(i) 2, 5, 8, 11, 14, ...

(ii) 10, 17, 24, 33, 40, ...

(iii) 3, 7, 11, 15, ...

5.3 Applying mathematics in a range of contexts 2

In section 5.3 you will:

- solve problems in a wide range of contexts

Exercise 1M

1 (a) Copy the pattern below and continue it to the line for 10^2.

$2^2 = 1^2 + 1 + 2 = 4$
$3^2 = 2^2 + 2 + 3 = 9$
$4^2 = 3^2 + 3 + 4 = 16$

(b) Without a calculator, use the pattern to work out:
(i) 31^2 (ii) 71^2 (iii) 101^2 (iv) 19^2

2 An orange drink costs 60p. A cola costs 70p. Some children buy orange and cola drinks for exactly £10. How many orange drinks are bought and how many colas? Find both possible solutions.

3 Asif is working on the top floor of a very tall office building. He walks up 826 steps from the ground floor to his office. Each step is 24 cm.

(a) How high does he climb in cm?

(b) Change the height into km, correct to one decimal place.

4 Three babies, Petra, Quentin and Rusty, are all weighed on April 1st. After that, Petra is weighed every second day, Quentin every third day and Rusty every fifth day. So, for example, Petra is next weighed on April 3, Quentin is next weighed on April 4 and Rusty is next weighed on April 6. What is the next date when all three babies will be weighed on the same day?

5 A 375 g packet of Greek currants costs £1.14. Calculate the cost of a 500 g packet, if both packets represent the same value for money.

6 A floor measuring 4.2 m by 3.4 m is covered with square tiles of side 20 cm. The tiles cost £3.30 for a pack of 10. How much will it cost to tile the floor?

7 The rule for the sequences is '*double and subtract 3*'. Write down each sequence and find the missing numbers.

(a) 4 → 5 → ☐ → ☐

(b) ☐ → 19 → ☐ → ☐

(c) 1 → ☐ → ☐ → ☐

8 A tin has a mass of 170 g when empty. When it is full of currants the total mass is 510 g. What is its mass when it is a quarter full?

9 Maggie has the same number of 20p and 50p coins. The total value of the coins is £7. How many of each coin does she have?

10 Work out (a) $\frac{1}{2} + \frac{1}{4} + \frac{1}{8} + \frac{1}{16} + \frac{1}{32}$

(b) $\frac{1}{2} \times \frac{2}{3} \times \frac{3}{4} \times ..... \times \frac{15}{16} \times \frac{16}{17}$.

Exercise 2M

1 Martian creatures are either tripods or octopods. Tripods have three legs. Octopods have eight legs. The Martians, on an exploratory visit to Earth, have 60 legs between them. How many are tripods and how many are octopods? Find both possible solutions.

2 Here are two numbers written as the sum of four or fewer square numbers:

$21 = 16 + 4 + 1$ $\qquad$ $19 = 16 + 1 + 1 + 1$

Make the following numbers from four or fewer square numbers.

(a) 24 (b) 62 (c) 438 (d) 2436

(e) 6190 (f) 9909

3 A car begins a journey at 11.35 and ends it at 13.05.

(a) How long, in hours, did the journey take?

(b) The car travelled at an average speed of 100 km/h. How far did the car travel?

4 The cooks at McDonalds use 3400 ml of oil in 4 days. How many days will a 200 litre tank of oil last?

5 Write down the most appropriate *metric* unit for measuring:
(a) the capacity of a car's fuel tank,
(b) the height of the London Eye,
(c) the mass of a Jumbo Jet,
(d) the area of a small farm.

6 At a players' meeting at Arsenal football club all the players can speak French or English or both. If 72% can speak English and 45% can speak French, what percentage of the players can speak both languages?

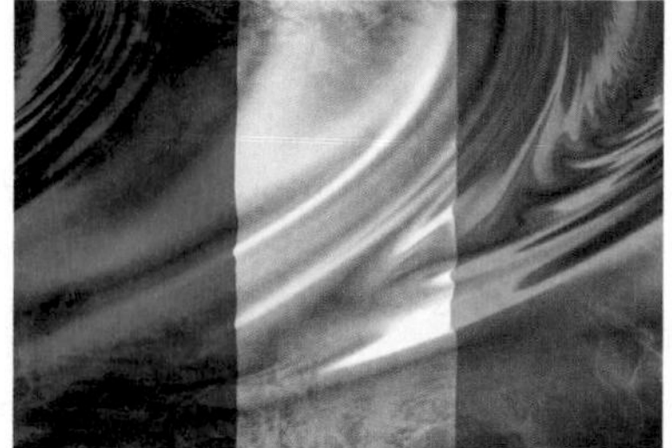

7 Work out: (a) A fifth of 400 000
(b) 5% of £680
(c) A half of 999

8 Find the number I am thinking of.

A multiple of 9
A 3-digit number below 200
The product of its digits is 16

9 One sector of a pie chart has an angle of 44°. What percentage of the whole chart does this sector represent? Give your answer correct to one decimal place.

10 Find three numbers which add up to 10 and multiply to give 30.

$\square + \square + \square = 10 \qquad \square \times \square \times \square = 30$

Exercise 3M

1

Mouse that roared

Fort summer: A mouse that had been thrown on a pile of burning leaves ran back into the house in New Mexico from which it had been ejected, setting it alight. Luciano Mares, 81, said that the mouse caught fire and ran back beneath a window, from where flames spread throughout the house. (*AP*)

Read this news item which appeared in a newspaper.

(a) Remember not to throw mice onto a pile of burning leaves.

(b) Express Luciano's age as the sum of three square numbers.

2 A sky diver opens his parachute 750 m above ground level. He has already fallen seven ninths of the distance to the ground. How high was the plane from which he jumped?

3 Amy is 8 years older than Ben. In 5 years time she will be twice Ben's age. How old is Amy now?

4 Consider the numbers from 1 to 2000 inclusive. In how many of these numbers is the sum of the digits 2?

5 A 336 g packet of Almonds costs £2.75. How much per 100 g of Almonds is this? Give your answer correct to the nearest penny.

6 The floor of a room was covered with black and white square tiles of side 30 cm. The rectangular room measured 27 m by 42 m. How many tiles were there on the floor?

7 Canada has an area of 9 980 000 km^2 and a population of 28 200 000. Hong Kong has an area of 1030 km^2 and a population of 7 300 000. How many times is Hong Kong more densely populated than Canada?

8 H T U

The number 898 can be made on an abacus using 25 beads. How many different 3-digit numbers can be made on an abacus using:

(a) 25 beads

(b) 24 beads?

9 The Day Return train fare from Stevenage to London is £16.60 and an annual season ticket costs £3350. What is the smallest possible number of return journeys a person needs to make in a year so that it is cheaper to buy the season ticket?

10 The diagram shows the areas of three faces of a cuboid.

Work out the dimensions of the cuboid.

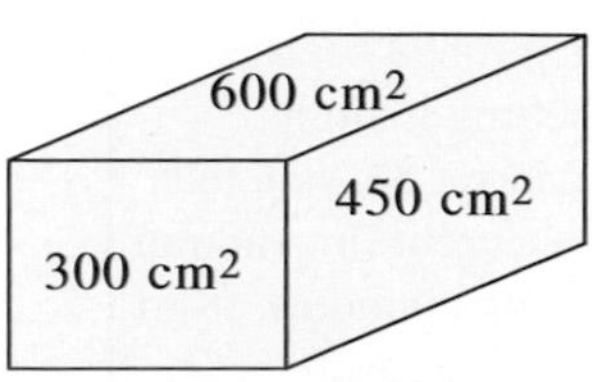

Exercise 4M

1 Postage stamps are printed on large sheets 38 cm across by 60 cm down. How many stamps are there on each sheet?

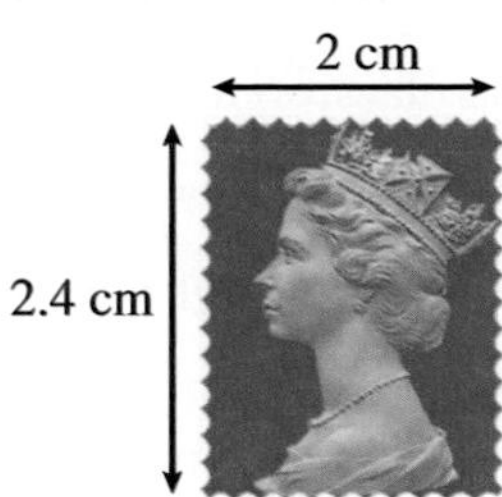

2 What is the largest 2-digit number that can be multiplied by itself to give a 3-digit number?

3 Find two numbers between 30 and 40 with a product of:

(a) 1254

(b) 1224

4 **Garden monster**

Fang, with 27,000 teeth and weighing in at 27.1 g and 5 in long, beat 30 contenders for the heavyweight title of the slug world. The event at a Bristol garden centre raised several hundred pounds for charity. Fang, a common black slug, was entered by Betty Baptiste, 60.

Read this article from a newspaper.

(a) How long was Fang, to the nearest cm?

(b) Fang actually had 27550 teeth. Is this number rounded off to the nearest thousand correctly?

(c) Suggest a suitable prize for Fang.

5 (a) Draw the diagram shown, on squared paper.

(b) Give the coordinates of the point to which you would move

(i) A to make a square,
(ii) B to make a rectangle.

(c) What type of quadrilateral do you make if you move:

(i) D to (5, 4)
(ii) C to (9, 8)
(iii) D to (10, 5)
(iv) A to (2, 9)?

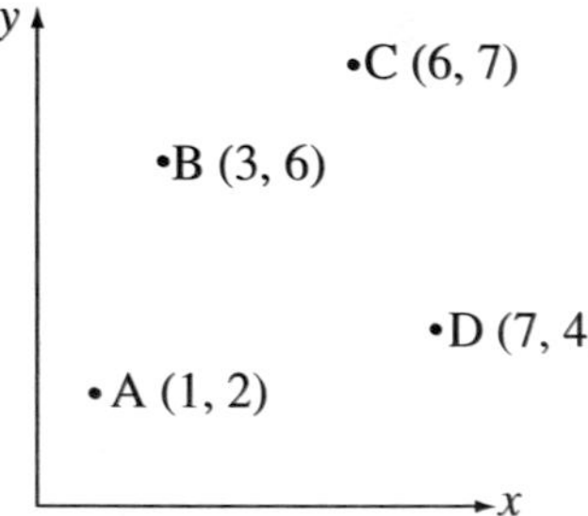

6 Put the correct sign, < or = or >, into each number sentence.

(a) $10 \times 0.1 \square \frac{1}{2}$ (b) $20 - 4 \square 20 - 5$ (c) $8 - 11 \square -2$

(d) $\frac{1}{2} + \frac{1}{3} \square \frac{2}{5}$ (e) $\frac{3}{4} \times \frac{2}{5} \square 0.3$ (f) $\frac{2}{3} \div \frac{1}{3} \square \frac{2}{9}$

7 Write each sentence with the number you think is most likely.

(a) The door to the classroom is ☐ high. [80 cm, 2 m, 3 feet]

(b) A large bottle of coke contains ☐ of drink. [20 ml, 2 litres, 5 gallons]

(c) A large chicken's egg weighs about ☐ [6 g, 60 g, 600 g]

8 For his prize-winning three dimensional puzzle of planet earth the inventor received £10 000 plus 2.4% of the profits made by the distributor. In ten years the distributor's profit was £8 795 400. How much did the inventor receive altogether?

9 Avram's age is a multiple of 9. Next year it will be a multiple of 8. How old is Avram?

10 Copy and complete by finding the missing numbers.

(a) 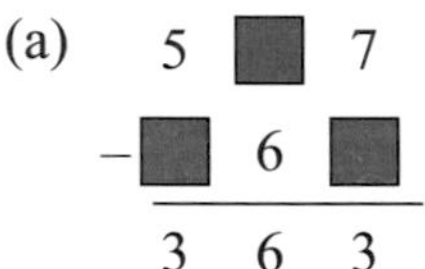

(b) 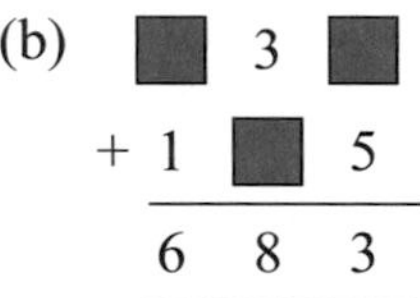

(c) 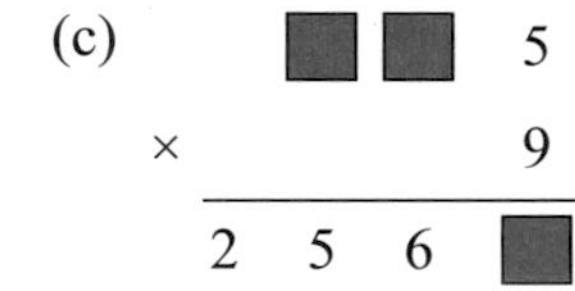

Exercise 5M

Some questions in this exercise require a use of the formulas for the circumference and area of a circle.

1 As part of an advertising campaign, the message '*Exercise is good for you*' is taped individually right around 500 000 tennis balls, each of diameter 6.5 cm. Find the total cost of the tape for the campaign, given that a 33 m roll of tape costs 96p.

2 'Wimbledon' grass seed is sown at a rate of 40 grams per square metre and a 2 kg box of seed costs £6.25. Mrs James wishes to sow a circular lawn and she has up to £50 to spend on seed. Find the radius of the largest circular lawn she can sow.

3 Packets of the same kind of flour are sold in two sizes. A 2 pound bag costs 69 p and a 1500 g bag costs £1.05. Given that 1 kg = 2.205 pounds, work out which bag represents the better value for money.

4 Janice needed a spectacular hair style for a magazine photo shoot. The hairdresser charged her \$85 plus 10% of the fee that Janice received from the magazine.

The photo was very popular and Janice received fees of \$17800 in the U.S.A. plus €12400 in Europe.

How much was the hairdresser paid altogether in dollars?

[£1 = €1.25 and £1 = \$1.95]

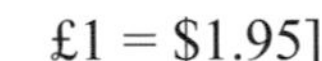

5 a and b are positive whole numbers and $a^2 + 15 = b^3$.
Which of the following is a possible value of a?

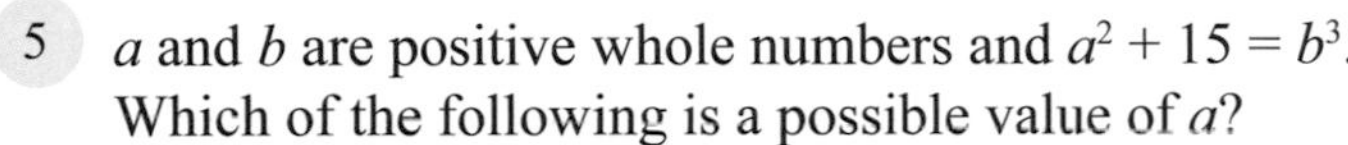

A 5 B 6 C 7 D 8

6 Write a number in the box to make the statement correct.

(a) $1000 - 275 = 5 \times \square$ (b) $220 \div 11 = 4^2 + \square$ (c) $5(25 + 36) = \square \times 6.1$

(d) $5 \times 2^3 = 18000 \div \square$ (e) $2^2 + 3^3 + 4^4 = 10^3 - \square$ (f) $5000 \div 50 = 500 \div \square$

7 At a steady speed of 70 m.p.h. a car travels 21 miles per gallon of petrol. If petrol costs £5.50 per gallon, work out the cost per minute of driving the car.

8 On Mark's watch, the tip of the seconds hand is 13 mm from the centre of the watch.

(a) How far does the tip of the seconds hand move in 1 hour?

(b) Find the speed at which the tip of the seconds hand moves, in mm/s.

(c) The minutes hand is the same length as the seconds hand. At what speed, in mm/s, does the tip of the minutes hand move?

9 For one unit of electricity, which costs 12p, you can either watch 18 episodes of 'EastEnders' or heat water for 36 cups of tea.

How much will it cost in electricity for Mr and Mrs Jamel to watch 54 episodes of EastEnders and each drink a cup of tea while doing so?

10 Find all the possible whole number solutions of

$1\square\square - 1\square\square = 96$

5.4 Pythagoras' theorem

In section 5.4 you will:

- calculate the length of a side in a right angled triangle
- solve problems using Pythagoras' theorem

Pythagoras' theorem

Below are two dissections which demonstrate a result called Pythagoras' theorem. Pythagoras was a famous Greek mathematician who proved the result in about 550 B.C.
The first dissection works only for isosceles right angled triangles.

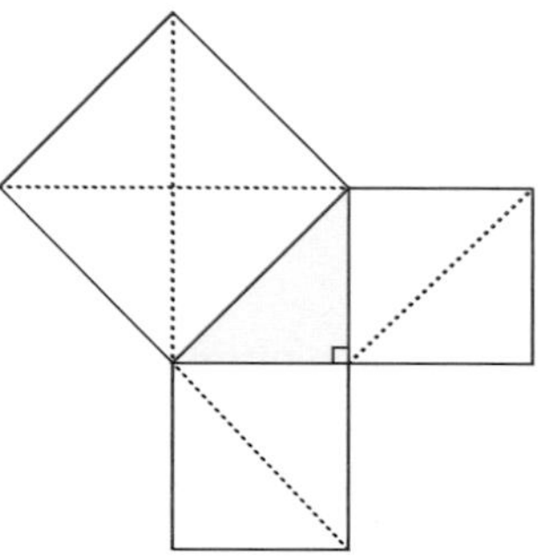

The second dissection, which is Perigal's dissection, is more impressive. It has been left for you to complete as a demonstration of Pythagoras' Theorem.

- Copy triangle ABC on dotted paper.
- Find the point X which is the centre of square (1)
- Draw PQ parallel to AB and draw RS perpendicular to PQ.
- Cut out square (2) and the four pieces of square (1).
- Rearrange these five pieces to fit exactly into square (3)

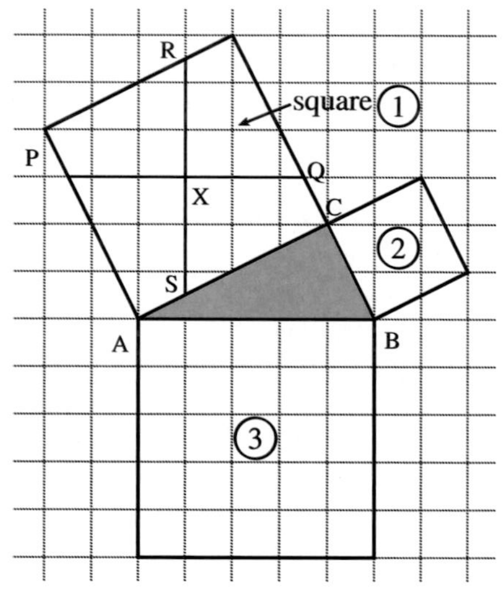

Both of these dissections demonstrate Pythagoras' theorem…

'In a right angled triangle, the square on the hypotenuse is equal to sum of the squares on the other two sides.'

The 'hypotenuse' is the longest side in a right angled triangle.

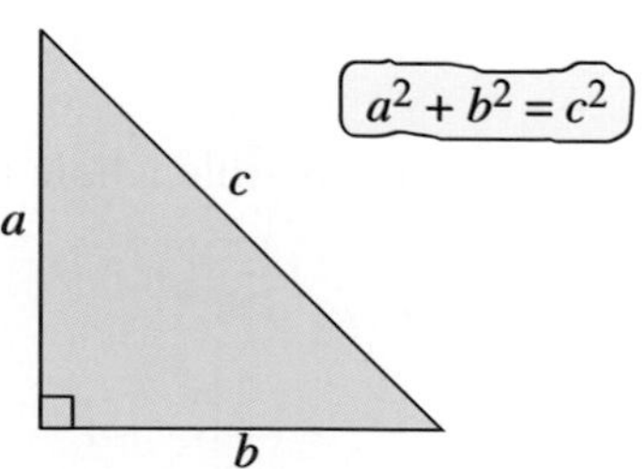

$$a^2 + b^2 = c^2$$

The theorem can be used to calculate the third side of a right angled triangle when two sides are known.

Find the length x

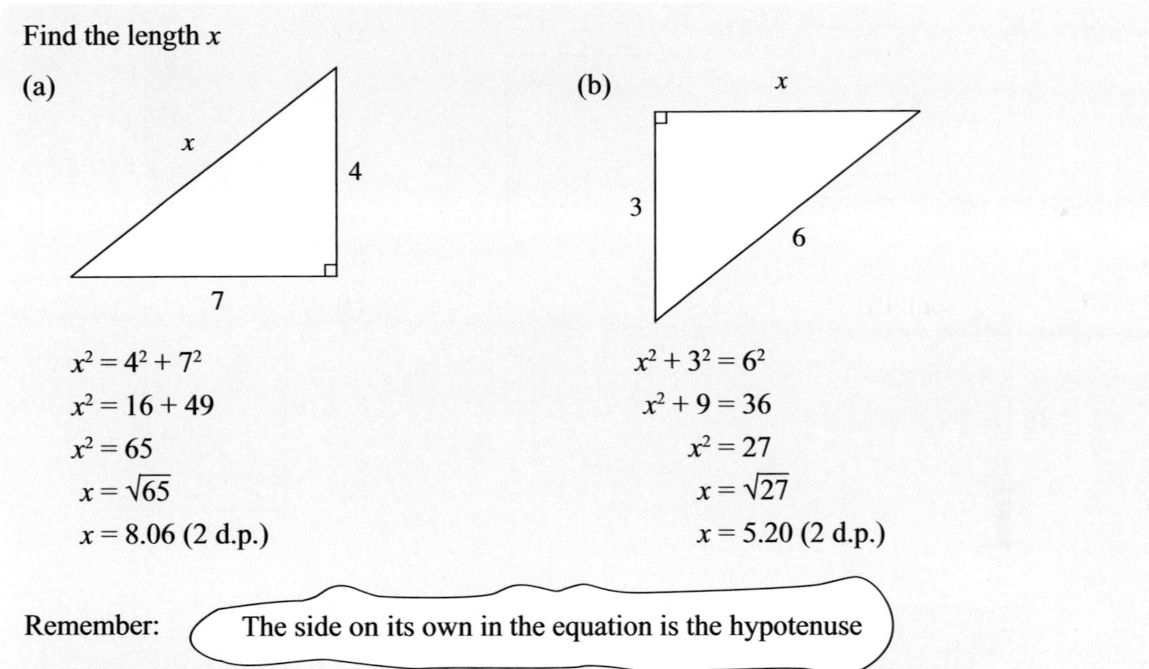

(a)

$x^2 = 4^2 + 7^2$

$x^2 = 16 + 49$

$x^2 = 65$

$x = \sqrt{65}$

$x = 8.06$ (2 d.p.)

(b)

$x^2 + 3^2 = 6^2$

$x^2 + 9 = 36$

$x^2 = 27$

$x = \sqrt{27}$

$x = 5.20$ (2 d.p.)

Remember: The side on its own in the equation is the hypotenuse

Exercise 1M

Give your answers correct to 2 d.p. where necessary. The units are cm unless you are told otherwise.

1 Find x.

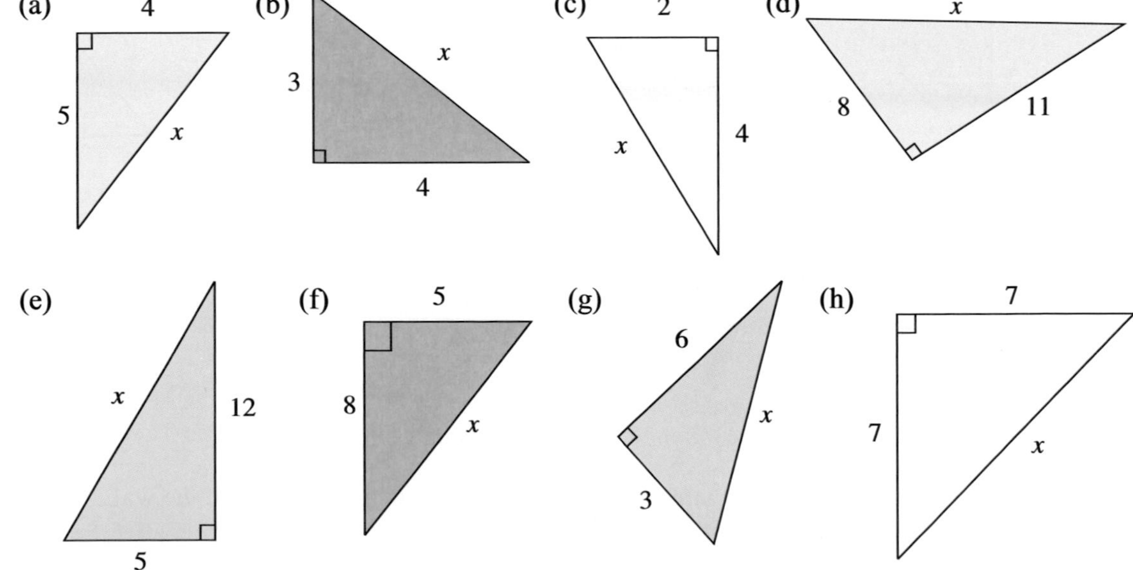

2 Find y.

Hint: In part (a) write $y^2 + 4^2 = 8^2$

(a)

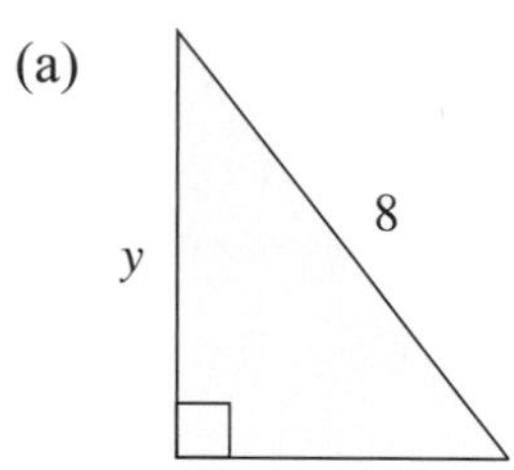

(b)

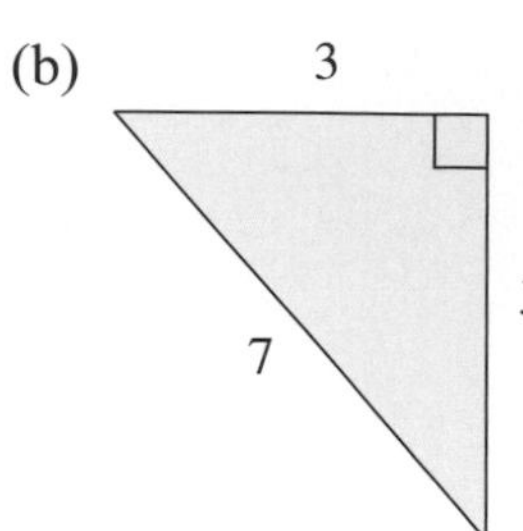

(c)

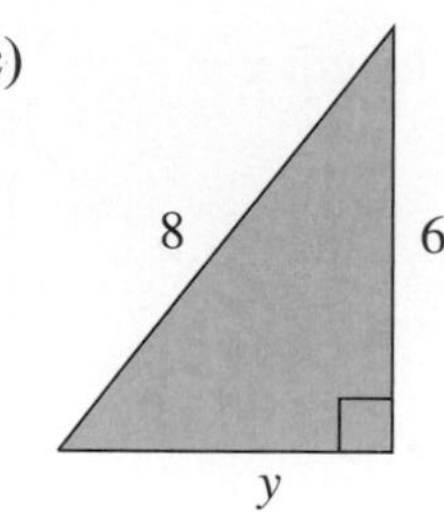

(d)

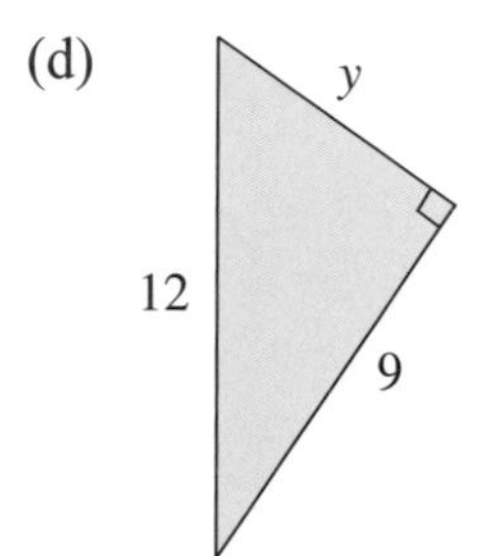

(e)

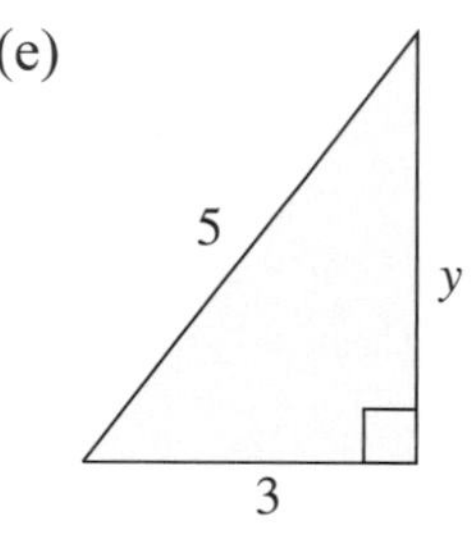

(f)

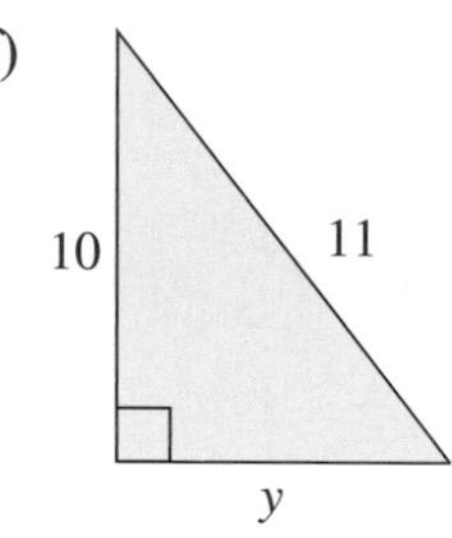

(g)

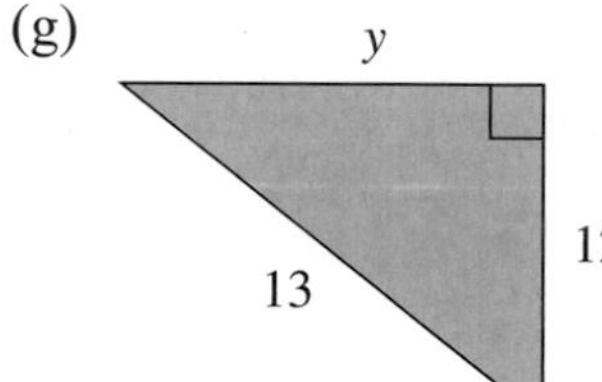

(h)

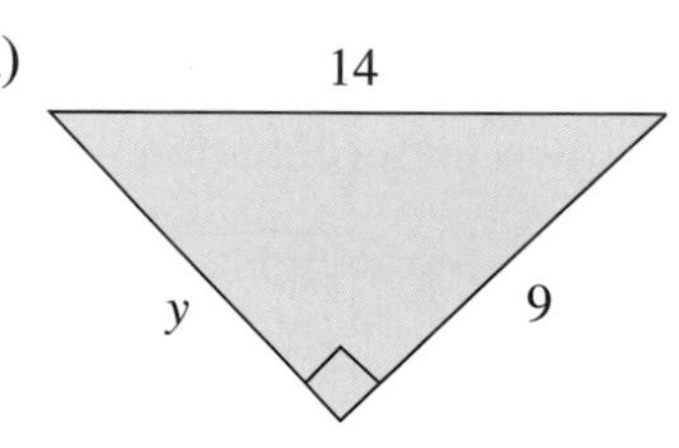

3 Find the side marked with a letter. It may be the hypotenuse or one of the other sides.

(a)

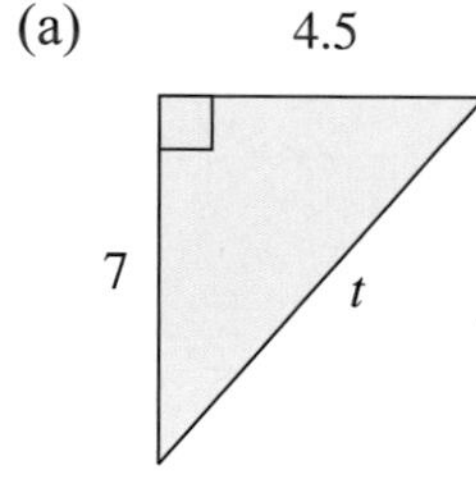

(b)

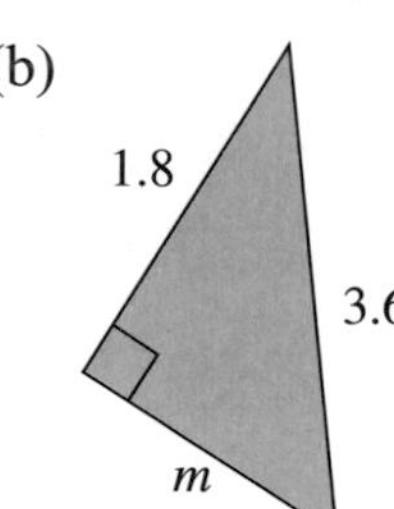

(c)

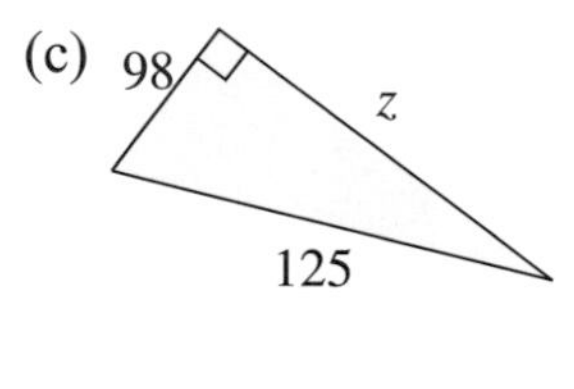

(d)

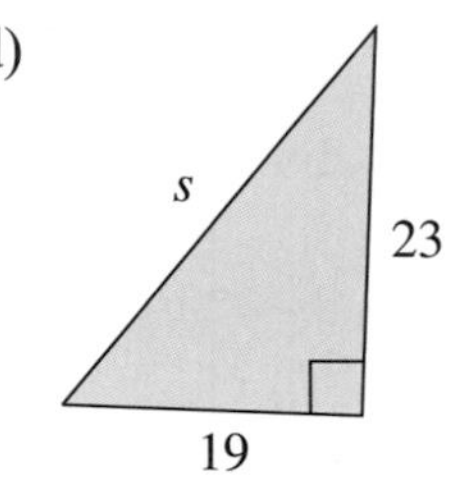

(e)

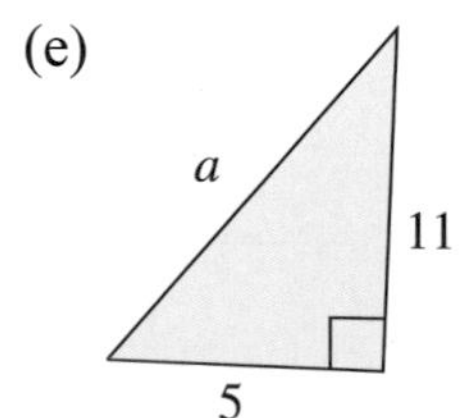

(f)

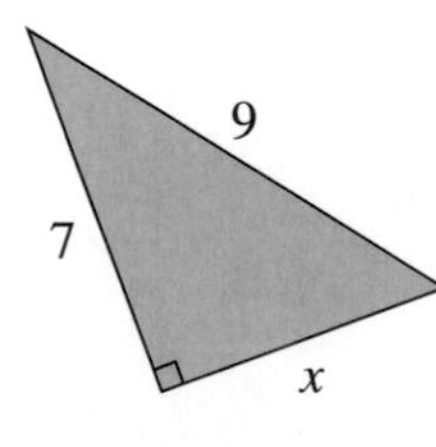

(g)

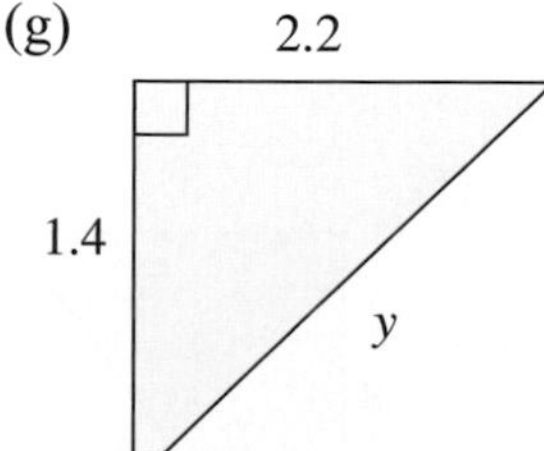

(h)

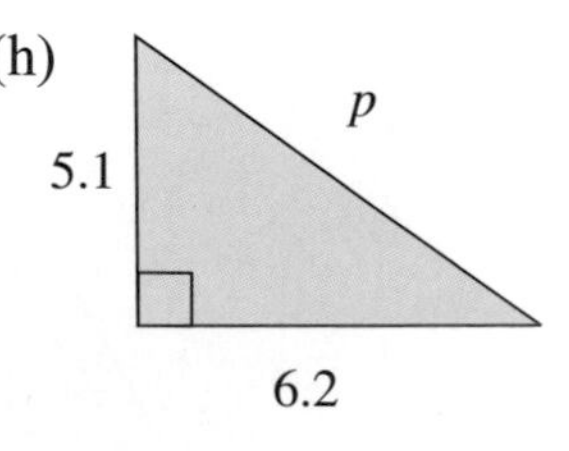

4 A ladder of length 5 m rests against a vertical wall, with its foot 2 m from the wall. How far up the wall does the ladder reach?

5 A ladder of length 4 m reaches 32 m up a vertical wall. How far is the foot of the ladder from the wall?

6 A boat sails from the harbour to the lighthouse. The lighthouse is 11 km to the south and 8 km to the east of the harbour.
Calculate the distance between the harbour and the light house.

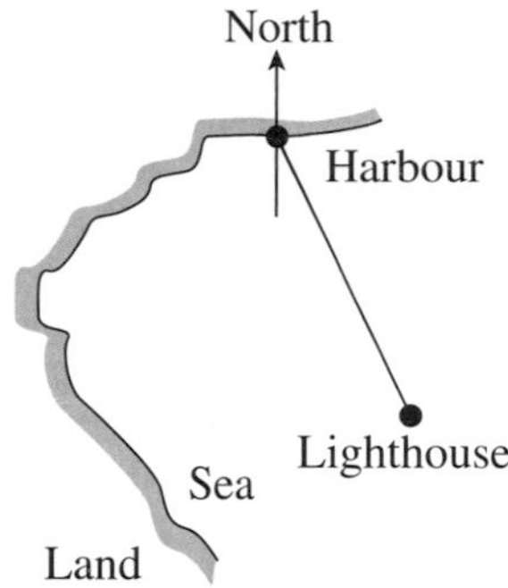

7 

Each of the small squares on a chess board has an area of 16 cm^2.

Calculate the length of a diagonal drawn across the whole board.

8 The square and the rectangle have the same perimeter. Which has the longer diagonal and by how much?

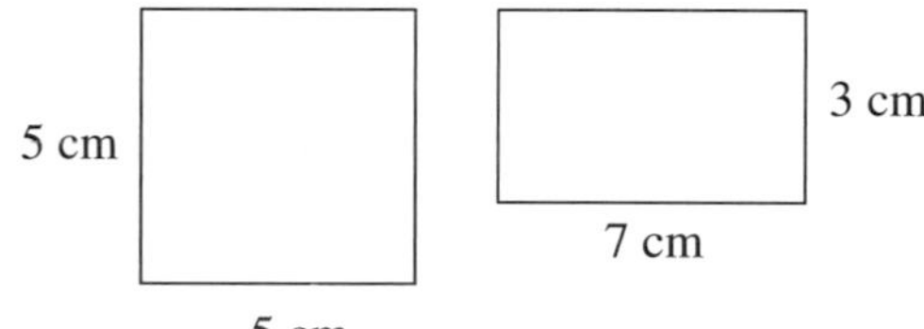

Exercise 1E

Give answers correct to 2 d.p. where necessary. The units are cm unless you are told otherwise.

1 Find the side marked with a letter

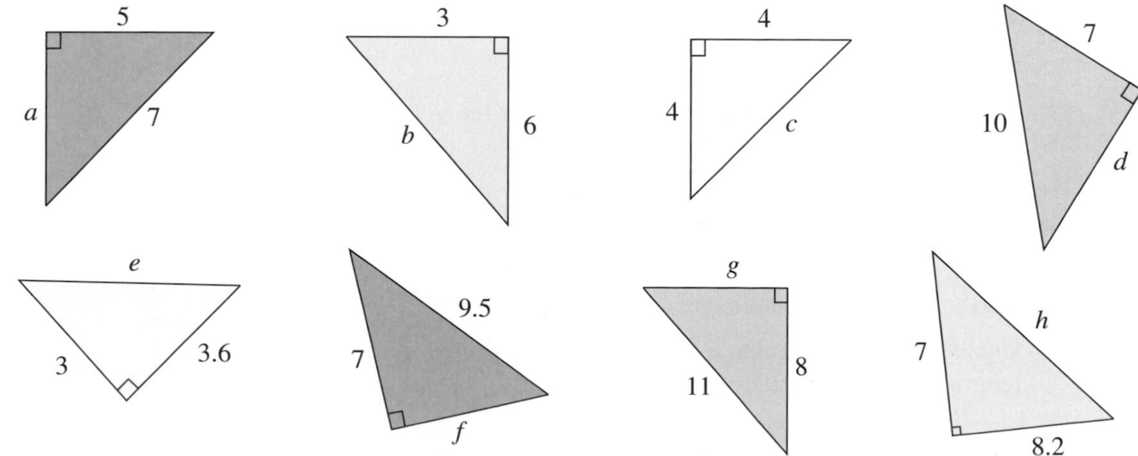

2 A ship sails 40 km due south and then a further 65 km due east. How far is the ship from its starting point?

3 A square has diagonals of length 24 cm. Find the length of a side of the square to the nearest cm.

4 What is the longest shot you could have to play on a snooker table measuring 12 feet by 6 feet?

5 Calculate the height of the isosceles triangle shown.

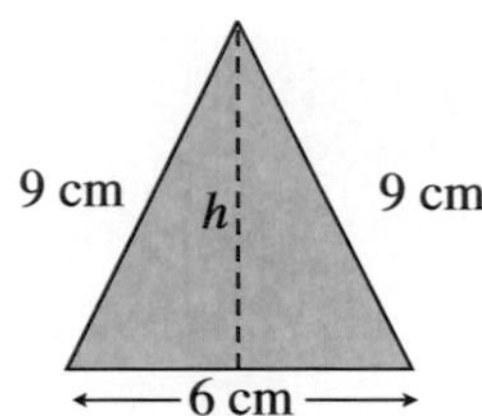

6 Calculate the vertical height and hence the area of an equilateral triangle of side 14 cm.

7 Calculate the length of a side of the largest square which can be drawn inside a circle of radius 10 cm.

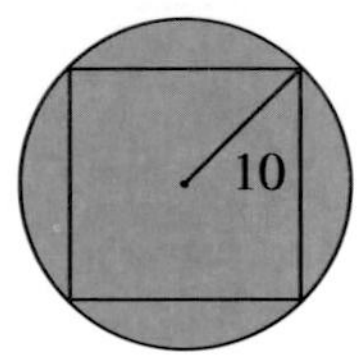

8 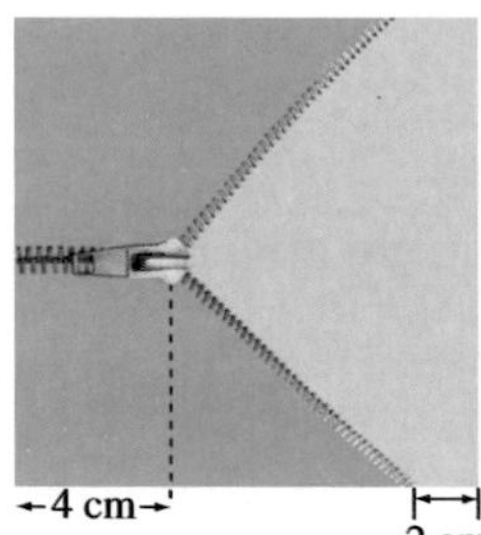

A zip is shown inside a square of side 11 cm. Calculate the length of sloping parts of the zip.

9 (a) Calculate the length of the hypotenuse AC of the triangle ABC.

(b) Calculate the area of the triangle.

A line BX is drawn perpendicular to AC.

(c) Use the area of the triangle and your value for the length of AC to calculate the length of BX.

Exercise 2E

1 A square field has an area of 4 hectares.
Calculate the length of the diagonals of the field.

2 Find the length x. All lengths are in cm.

(a)

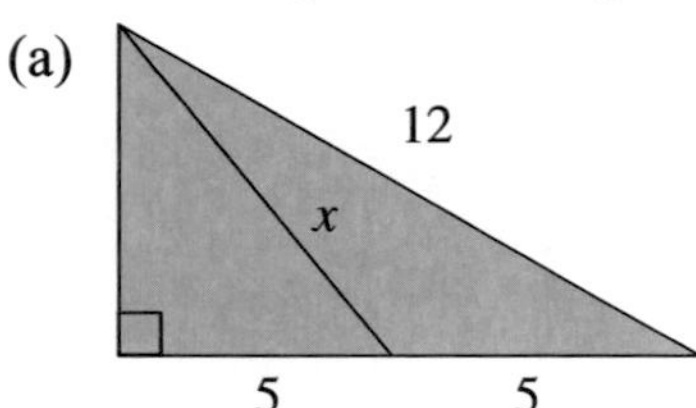

(b)

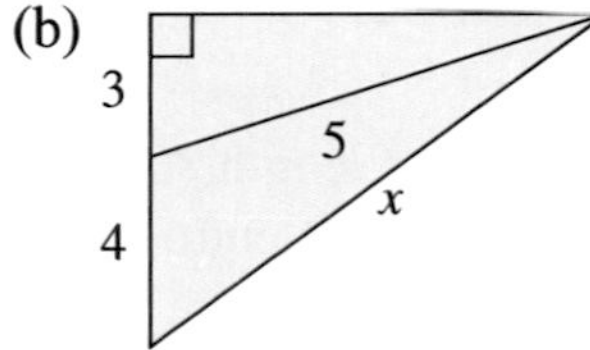

(c)

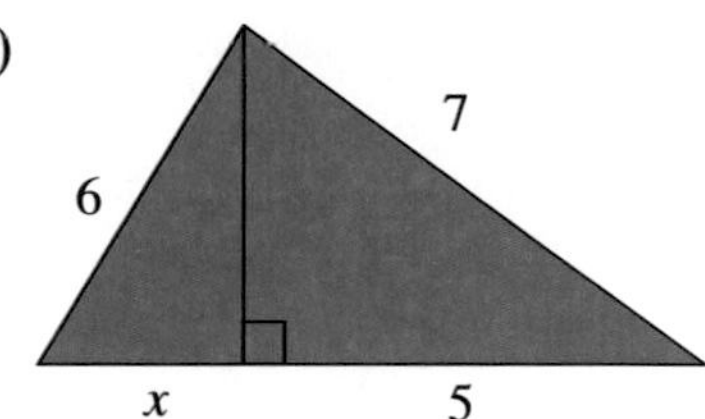

(d)

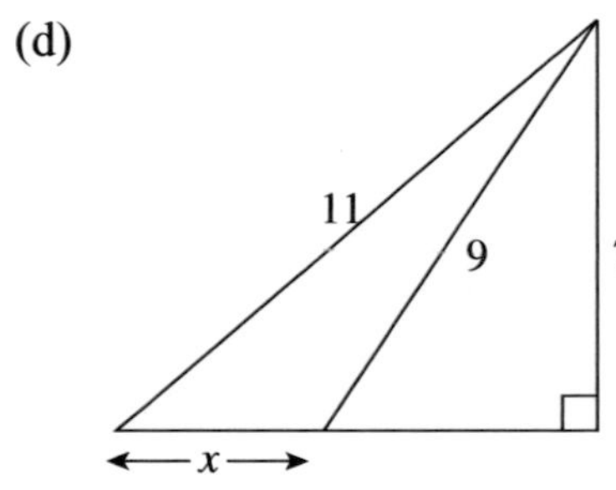

(e)

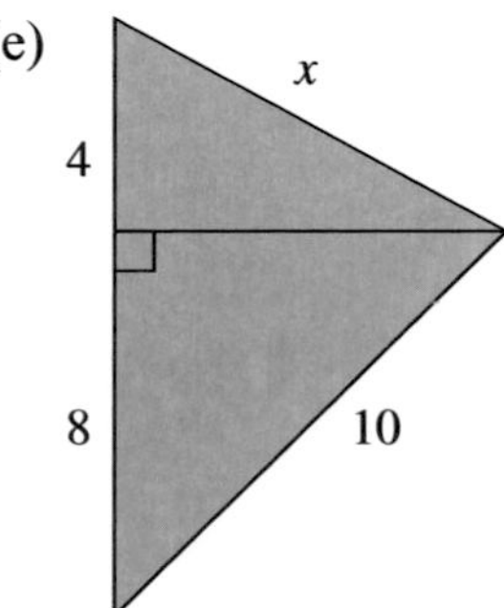

(f)

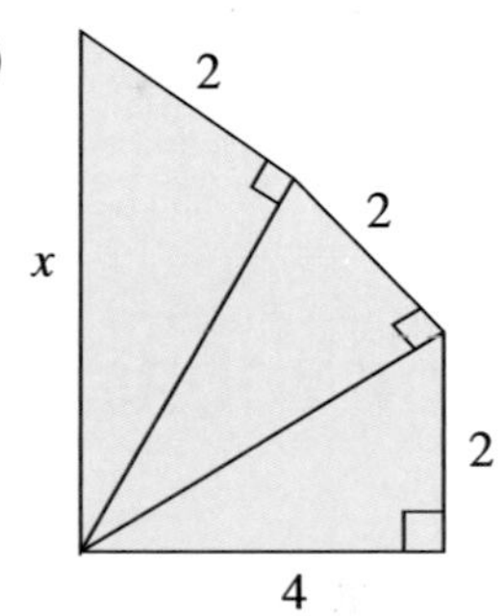

3 The diagonal of a square has length 5 cm. What is the area of the square (in cm^2)?

4 The diagram shows a rectangular box (a cuboid).

Calculate the length of

(a) AB

(b) AC

(c) AD. [Draw triangle ACD].

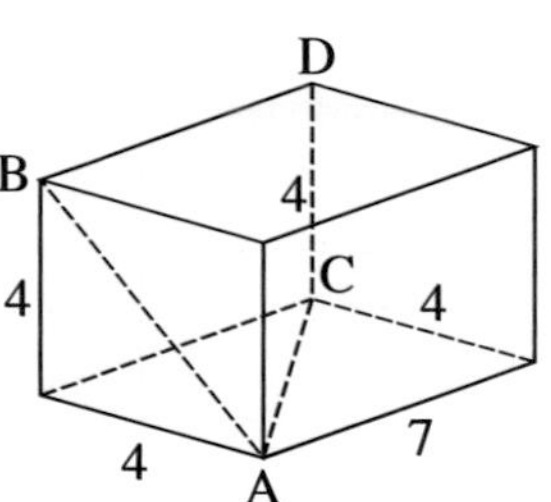

5 Calculate the length of the longest diagonal of a cube of side 10 cm.

6 The inside dimensions of a removal lorry are 2.5 m by 3 m by 4 m.
A pole vaulter's pole is 5.7 m long. Will it fit inside the lorry?

7 The diagram shows water lying in a semi-circular channel. Calculate the maximum depth d of water in the channel.

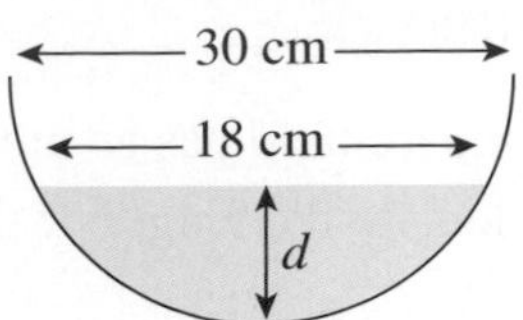

8 Calculate x and y.

(a)

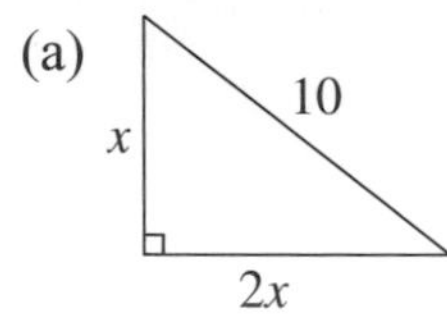

(b)

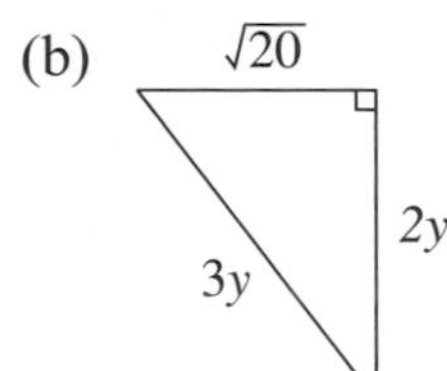

9 A pyramid in Egypt has a square base of length 80 m. The apex of the pyramid is 90 m above the centre of the base.

Calculate the length of a sloping edge of the pyramid.

CHECK YOURSELF ON SECTION 5.4

1 Calculating the length of a side of a triangle

Find the length of the sides marked with letters. All lengths are in cm.

(a)

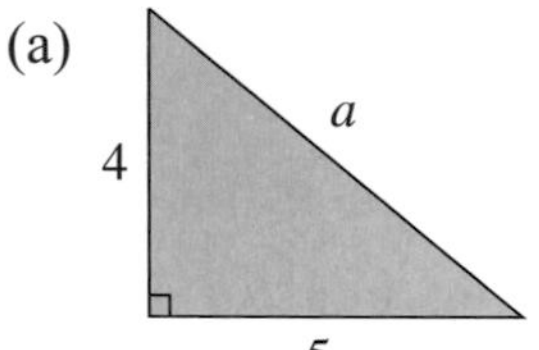

(b)

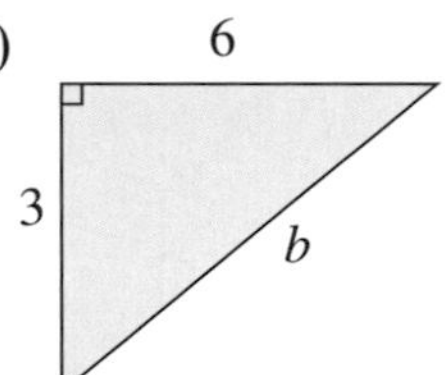

(c)

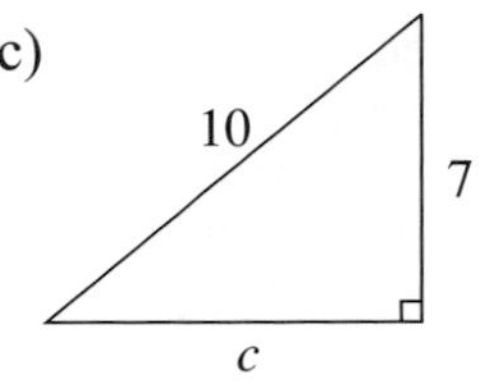

(d)

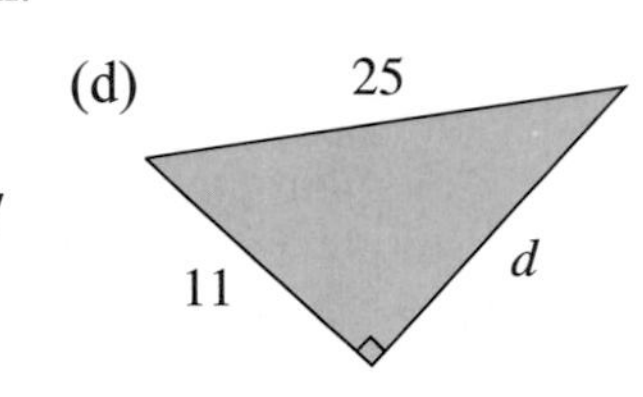

2 Solving problems using Pythagoras' theorem

(a) An isosceles triangle has sides of length 8 cm, 8 cm and 10 cm. Find the area of the triangle.

(b) A square has diagonals of length 10.4 cm. Find the length of the sides of the square.

5.5 Drawing and using graphs

In this section you will:

- draw straight line graphs
- draw graphs using a computer or graphical calculator
- find the equation of a straight line
- draw curved graphs
- use graphs in a real life context

Straight line graphs

(a) We have seen that when a calculation [like $5 + 7 \times 3$] is performed, the order of operations follows 'BIDMAS'.

The same rules apply for the expressions involved in graphs.

Brackets
Indices
Divide
Multiply
Add
Subtract

(b) Consider the graph $y = 3x - 1$. Two operations are performed: 'multiply by 3', 'subtract 1'.
Multiply is done before subtract and a *flow chart* can be drawn

$x \rightarrow \boxed{\times 3} \rightarrow \boxed{-1} \rightarrow y$

So when $x = 2$, $y = 2 \times 3 - 1 = 5$. On the graph plot (2, 5)
when $x = 4$, $y = 4 \times 3 - 1 = 11$. On the graph plot (4, 11)
when $x = 7$, $y = 7 \times 3 - 1 = 20$. On the graph plot (7, 20)

(c) Consider the graph $y = 2(x + 1)$. The operation in brackets is done first.
The flow chart is:

$x \rightarrow \boxed{+1} \rightarrow \boxed{\times 2} \rightarrow y$

When $x = 2$, $y = (2 + 1) \times 2 = 6$. Plot (2, 6)
$x = 3$, $y = (3 + 1) \times 2 = 8$. Plot (3, 8)
$x = 5$, $y = (5 + 1) \times 2 = 12$. Plot (5, 12)

Using the flow diagram, complete the table below.

Hence draw the graph of $y = 2x + 4$ for x from 0 to 5

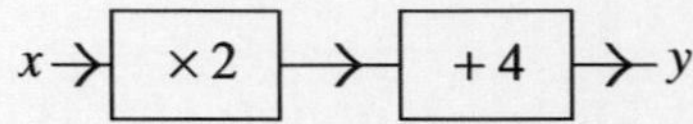

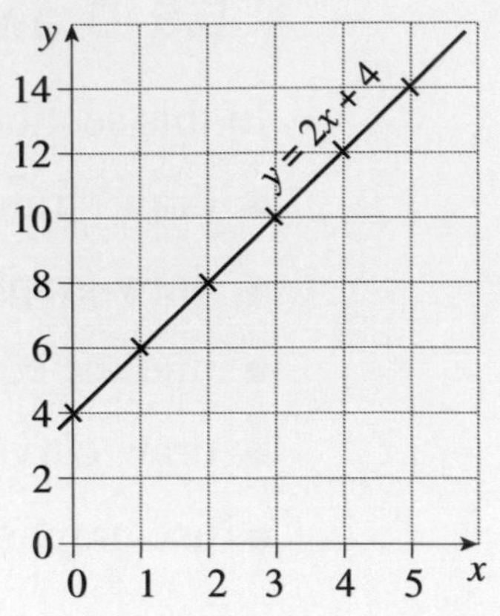

x	0	1	2	3	4	5
y	4	6	8	10	12	14
Coordinates	(0, 4)	(1, 6)	(2, 8)	(3, 10)	(4, 12)	(5, 14)

Exercise 1M

For each question copy and complete the table using the flow diagram. Then draw the graph using the scales given.

1 $y = 2x + 1$ for x: 0 to 6 $\begin{pmatrix} x\text{: 1 cm} = \text{1 unit} \\ y\text{: 1 cm} = \text{1 unit} \end{pmatrix}$

$x \rightarrow$ [×2] $\rightarrow$ [+1] $\rightarrow y$

x	0	1	2	3	4	5	6
y					9		
coordinates					(4, 9)		

2 $y = x + 4$ for x: 0 to 7 $\begin{pmatrix} x\text{: 1 cm} = \text{1 unit} \\ y\text{: 1 cm} = \text{1 unit} \end{pmatrix}$

$x \rightarrow$ [+4] $\rightarrow y$

x	0	1	2	3	4	5	6	7
y			6					
coordinates			(2, 6)					

3 $y = 3x - 2$ for x: 0 to 5 $\begin{pmatrix} x\text{: 1 cm} = \text{1 unit} \\ y\text{: 1 cm} = \text{2 units} \end{pmatrix}$

$x \rightarrow$ [×3] $\rightarrow$ [−2] $\rightarrow y$

x	0	1	2	3	4	5
y	−2	1				
coordinates		(1, 1)				

4 $y = \frac{x}{2}$ for x: 0 to 7 (Set up your own table)

$x \rightarrow$ [÷ 2] $\rightarrow y$ (x: 1 cm = 1 unit; y: 2 cm = 1 unit)

5 $y = 6 - x$ for x: 0 to 6 (Set up your own table)

$x \rightarrow$ [subtract from 6] $\rightarrow y$ (x: 1 cm = 1 unit; y: 1 cm = 1 unit)

6 $y = 12 - 2x$ for x: 0 to 6 (x: 1 cm = 1 unit; y: 1 cm = 1 unit)

$x \rightarrow$ [× 2] $\rightarrow$ [subtract from 12] $\rightarrow y$

7 $y = 3(x + 1)$ for x: 0 to 5 (x: 1 cm = 1 unit; y: 1 cm = 2 units)

$x \rightarrow$ [+ 1] $\rightarrow$ [× 3] $\rightarrow y$

8 $y = 3(6 - x)$ for x: 0 to 6 (x: 1 cm = 1 unit; y: 1 cm = 2 units)

$x \rightarrow$ [subtract from 6] $\rightarrow$ [× 3] $\rightarrow y$

9 $y = 2x + 4$ for x: 0 to 8 (x: 1 cm = 1 unit; y: 1 cm = 2 units)

$x \rightarrow$ [× 2] $\rightarrow$ [+ 4] $\rightarrow y$

10 $y = \frac{1}{2}x + 3$ for x: 0 to 8 (x: 1 cm = 1 unit; y: 2 cm = 1 unit)

$x \rightarrow$ [÷ 2] $\rightarrow$ [+ 3] $\rightarrow y$

Exercise 1E

In questions 1 to 5 make a table and draw the graph. The values of x include negative values

1 $y = 2x + 2$ for x: –2 to +4 (x: 1 cm = 1 unit; y: 1 cm = 2 units) $x \rightarrow$ [× 2] $\rightarrow$ [+ 2] $\rightarrow y$

2 $y = 3x - 2$ for x: –2 to +3 (x: 1 cm = 1 unit; y: 1 cm = 2 units) $x \rightarrow$ [× 3] $\rightarrow$ [– 2] $\rightarrow y$

3 $y = 4x - 1$ for x: -2 to $+3$ $\begin{pmatrix} x\text{: 1 cm} = 1 \text{ unit} \\ y\text{: 1 cm} = 2 \text{ units} \end{pmatrix}$ $x \to$ $\boxed{\times 4}$ $\to$ $\boxed{-1}$ $\to y$

4 $y = 2 - 2x$ for x: -2 to 3 $\begin{pmatrix} x\text{: 1 cm} = 1 \text{ unit} \\ y\text{: 1 cm} = 5 \text{ units} \end{pmatrix}$

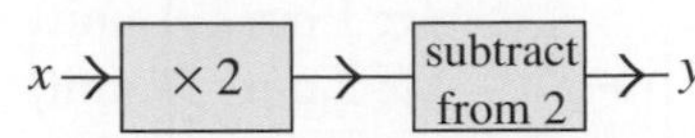

5 $y = 5 - 3x$ for x: -2 to $+3$ $\begin{pmatrix} x\text{: 1 cm} = 1 \text{ unit} \\ y\text{: 1 cm} = 5 \text{ units} \end{pmatrix}$

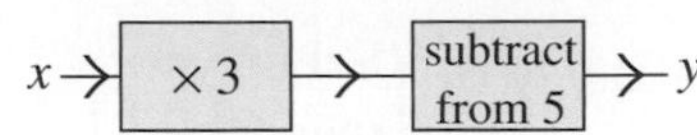

6 (a) Copy the graph of $y = 2x - 1$

(b) Using the same axes, draw the graph of $y = x + 2$. Take x from -2 to $+3$.

(c) Write down the coordinates of the point where the lines meet.

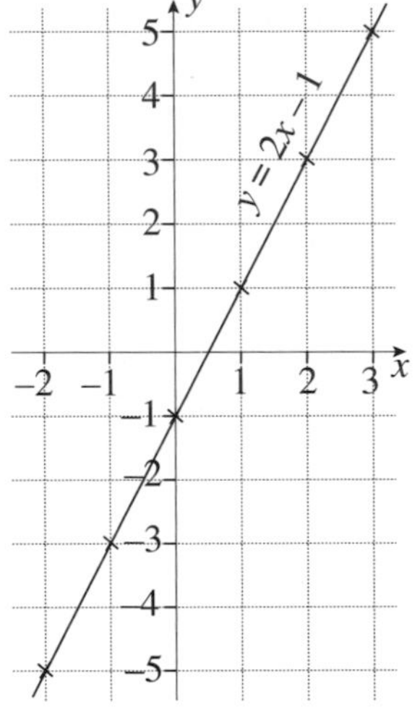

7 Draw $x + y = 5$; take x from 0 to 6.

8 Draw $2x + y = 10$; take x from 0 to 6.

9 Using the same axes draw the graphs of $y = x + 1$ and $x + y = 7$. Take values of x from 0 to 6. Write down the coordinates of the point where the lines meet.

10 On the same graph, draw the lines $y = 2x - 3$,

$y = \frac{1}{2}x$,

$x + y = 9$.

Take values of x from 0 to 8.

Write down the coordinates of the three vertices of the triangle formed.

11 On the same graph, draw the lines $x + y = 8$,

$y = 2x + 2$,

$y = 2$.

Take values of x from 0 to 8.

Find the area of the triangle formed.

Exercise 2M

Use a *graphical calculator* or a *graph plotter* on a *computer*.

1 Draw the graphs of $y = x + 5$, $y = x + 3$, $y = x - 1$, $y = x - 4$

Write down what you notice. [Look at the point where the lines cut the y axis.]

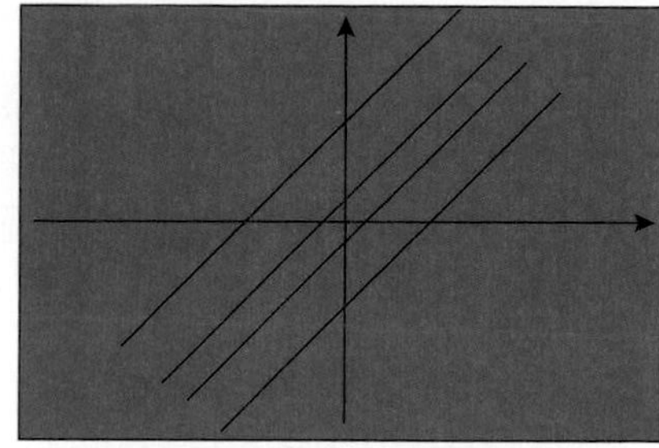

2 Draw the graphs of $y = 2x + 1$, $y = 2x - 3$, $y = 2x + 5$.
Write down what you notice.

3 Draw the graphs of $y = 3x$, $y = 3x - 5$, $y = 3x + 6$
What do you notice?

4 (a) Where do you expect $y = 4x + 7$ to cut the y axis?
(b) Where do you expect $y = 4x - 3$ to cut the y axis?

5 Write down the equations of any line parallel to $y = 6x + 3$.

6 Draw the graphs of $y = x^2$, $y = 12 \div x$, $y = x^2 - 5$

7 State which of the following represent straight line graphs

$y = 3x + 2$ $\quad$ $y = 10 \div x$ $\quad$ $y = 5x - 1$ $\quad$ $y = x^3$

8 Experiment with different equations until you can obtain three lines which form a triangle like the one shown.

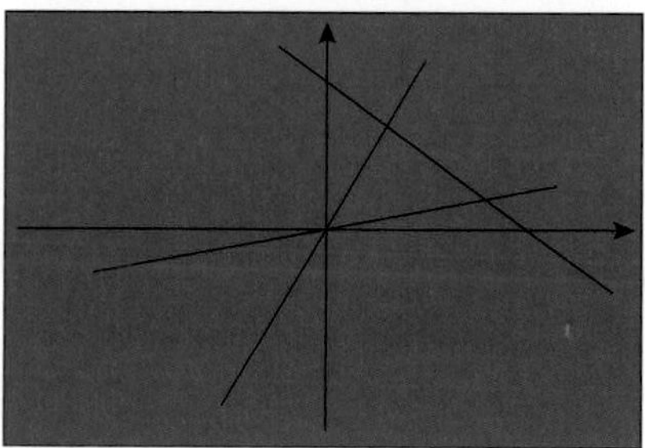

9 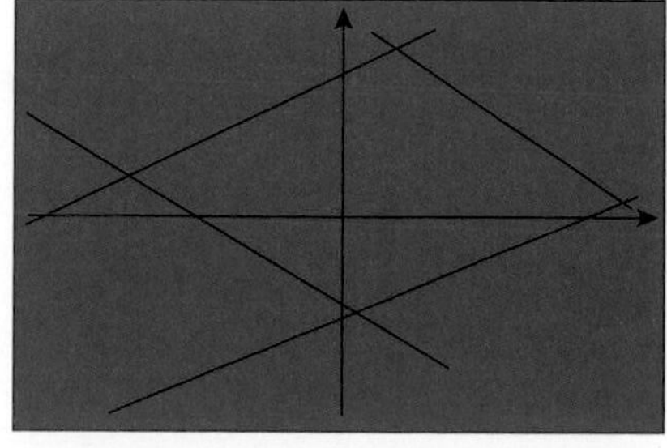

Experiment with different graphs until you obtain a parallelogram like the one shown here.

Find the equation

(a) The line of crosses goes through the points (–1, 1), (0, 2), (1, 3)…(5, 7).

For each point, the y coordinate is 2 more than the x coordinate.

The equation of the line is $y = x + 2$.

(b) The line of dots goes through the points (0, 7), (1, 6), (2, 5)….(7, 0).

For each point, the sum of the two coordinates is 7.

The equation of the line is $x + y = 7$.

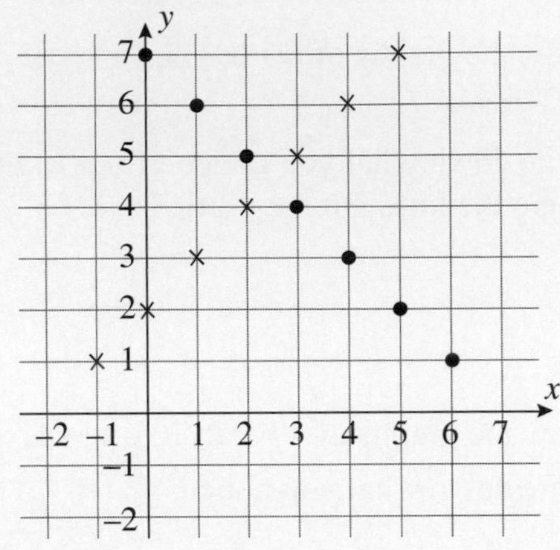

Exercise 2E

In questions 1 to 6, the points given lie on a straight line. Copy and complete the box.

1

(1, 4)
(3, 6)
(4, 7)
(6,)
equation is
$y =$

2

(1, –1)
(4, 2)
(8, 6)
(12,)
equation is
$y =$

3

(1, 3)
(4, 12)
(5, 15)
(7,)
equation is
$y =$

4

(1, 3)
(3, 7)
(4, 9)
(5, 11)
(–1,)
equation is
$y =$

5

(1, 4)
(3, 14)
(4, 19)
(6, 29)
(10,)
equation is
$y =$

6

(1, 4)
(2, 3)
(3, 2)
(6, –1)
(10,)
equation is

7 Draw axes with x and y from 0 to 14. Plot all the points below.
(0, 0) (0, 2) (0, 13) (1, 4) (1, 8) (2, 1) (2, 8) (3, 6) (3, 10)
(10, 5) (10, 8) (11, 2) (11, 14) (12, 1) (12, 6) (12, 8) (14, 7)
(14, 8) (4, 2) (4, 7) (4, 8) (4, 9) (6, 0) (7, 6) (7, 8) (7, 10) (8, 4)
(8, 11) (11, 5)

(a) There are four lines on the graph, each with at least 6 points on the line. Find the equation of each line.

(b) There are two further lines, each with 4 points. Write down the equation of these two lines.

In questions 8 and 9, find the equation for the line of dots and the equation for the line of crosses.

8

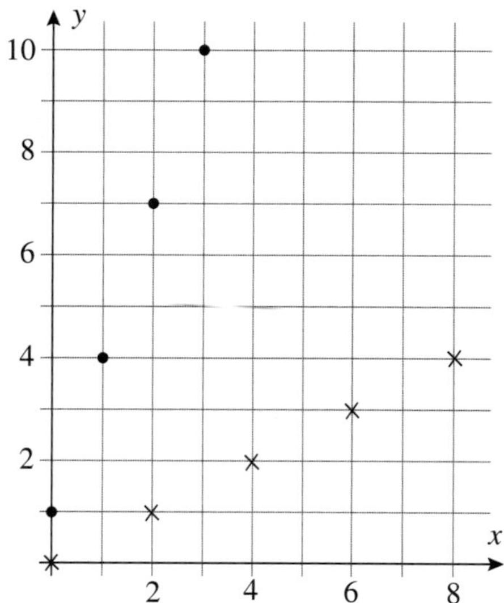

9

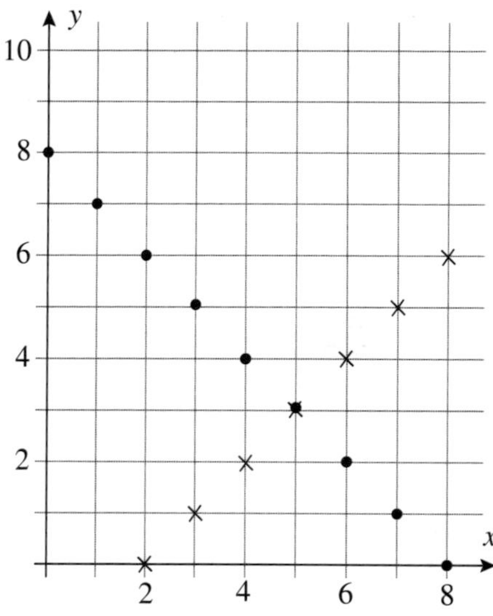

10 Find the equations of the lines which pass through:

(a) A and B (b) B and G (c) A and D (d) H and C

(e) F and E (f) C and E

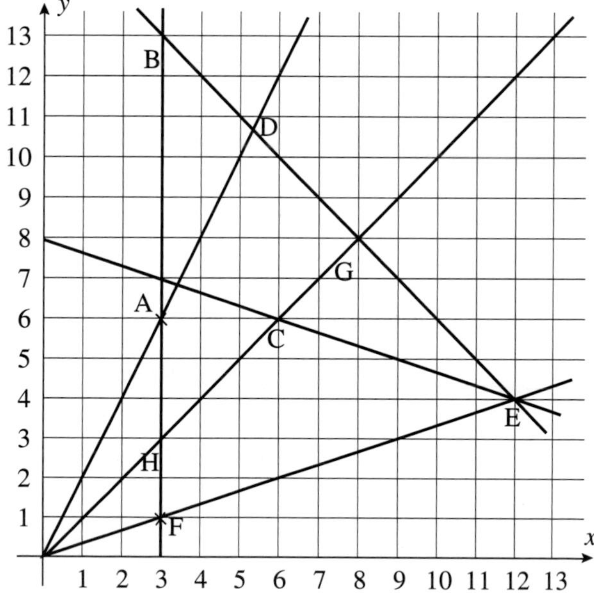

Curved graphs

Draw the graph of $y = x^2 - 3$ for values of x from –3 to +3

$x = -3$, $y = (-3)^2 - 3 = 6$

$x = -2$, $y = (-2)^2 - 3 = 1$

$x = -1$, $y = (-1)^2 - 3 = -2$

$x = 0$, $y = 0^2 - 3 = -3$

$x = 1$, $y = 1^2 - 3 = -2$

$x = 2$, $y = 2^2 - 3 = 1$

$x = 3$, $y = 3^2 - 3 = 6$

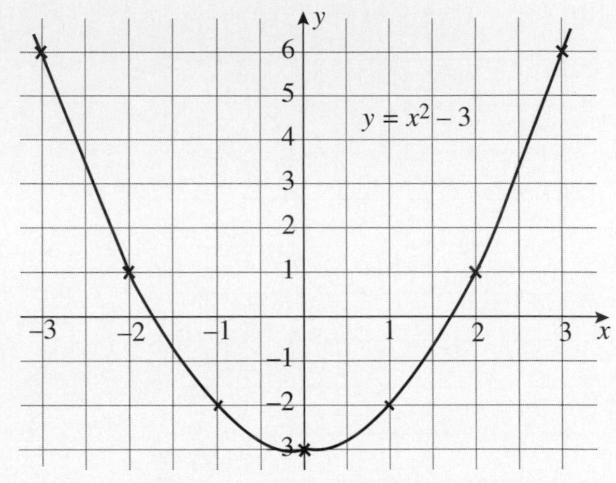

Draw a *smooth* curve through the points.
It helps to turn the page upside down so that your hand can be 'inside' the curve. Try not to look at the tip of your pencil. Instead look at next point through which you are drawing the curve.

Exercise 3E

Draw the graph, using a scale of 2 cm to 1 unit on the x axis and 1 cm to 1 unit on the y axis (as in the above example).

1 $y = x^2$; take x from –3 to +3.

2 $y = x^2 + 2$; take x from –3 to +3.

3 $y = (x + 1)^2$; take x from –3 to +3.

4 $y = (x - 2)^2$; take x from –1 to +5.

5 $y = x^2 + x$; take x from –3 to +3.

6 $y = x^2 + x + 2$; take x from –3 to +3.

7 Draw the graph of $y = x^2 - 3x$ for values of x from –3 to +3.
 (a) What is the lowest value of y?
 (b) For what value of x does the lowest value occur?

8 Using the same axes, draw the graphs of $y = x^2 - 6x + 16$ and $y = 6x - x^2$ for values of x from 0 to 6.
 Write down the equation of the line which can be drawn through the two points of intersection.

9 Draw the graphs of $y = 2x^2 + x - 6$ and $y = 2x + 3$ for values of x from –3 to +3.
 Write down the x coordinates, correct to 1 d.p., of the two points where the line cuts the curve.

Using graphs

Exercise 4M

1 A car hire firm charges an initial fee plus a charge depending on the number of miles driven, as shown.

(a) Find the total cost for driving 140 miles.

(b) Find the total cost for driving 600 miles.

(c) Find how many miles 1 can drive for a cost of £45.

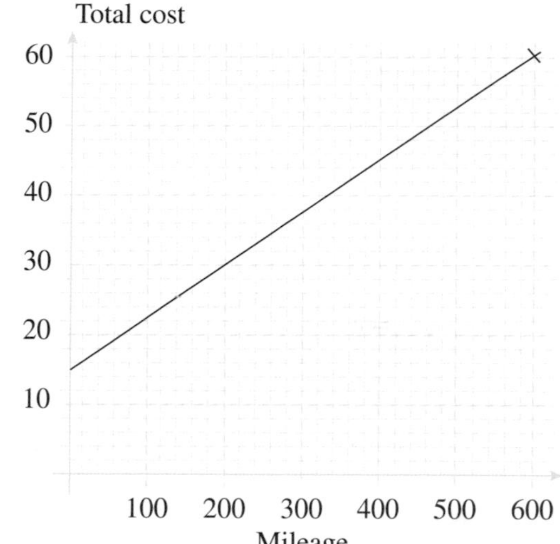

2 A teacher has marked a test out of 80 and wishes to convert the marks into percentages. Draw axes as shown and draw a straight line through the points (0, 0) and (80, 100).

(a) Use your graph to convert

(i) 63 marks into a percentage

(ii) 24 marks into a percentage

(b) The pass mark was 60%. How many marks out of 80 were needed for a pass?

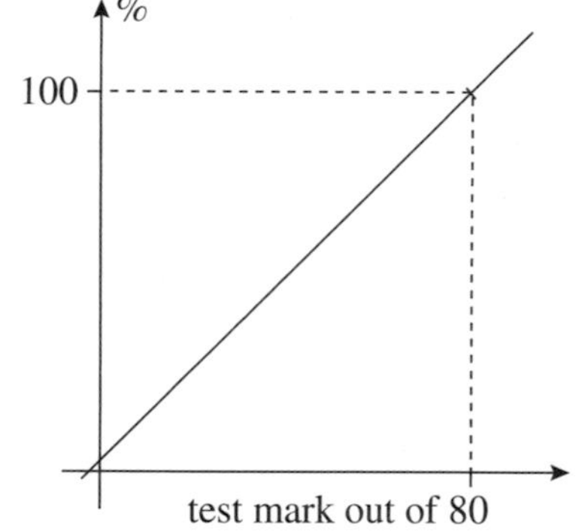

3 The graph converts pounds into euros in 2004 and 2009.

(a) Convert into euros in 2004

(i) £2 (ii) £2.70

(b) Convert into pounds in 2009

(i) €6 (ii) €4.50

(c) A painting is priced at €30000. How much would it cost in pounds

(i) in 2004 (ii) in 2009?

(d) A few years ago the exchange rate was about 1.6 euros to the pound. Is it cheaper or more expensive nowadays as a British tourist in Europe?

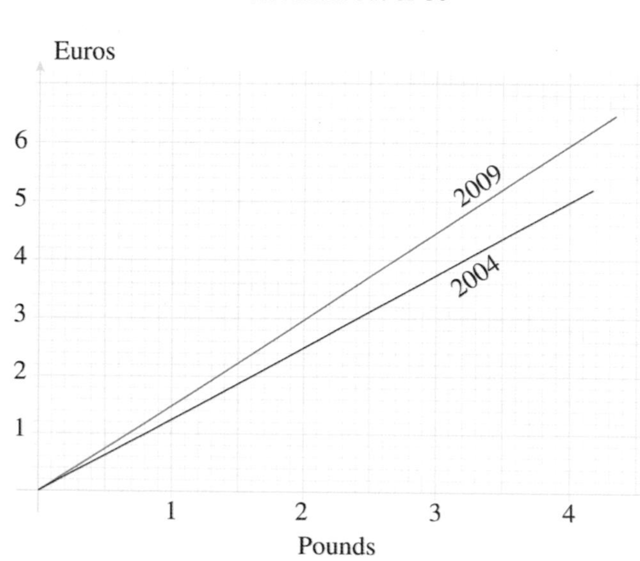

4 (a) Draw axes, as shown, with a scale of 1 cm to 5°. Two equivalent temperatures are 32°F = 0°C and 86°F = 30°C.

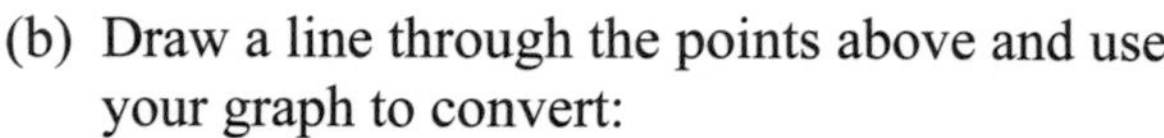

(b) Draw a line through the points above and use your graph to convert:

(i) 20°C into °F

(ii) –10°C into °F

(iii) 50°F into °C

(c) The normal body temperature of a healthy person is 98°F. Susie's temperature is 39°C. Should she stay at home today, or go to school as usual?

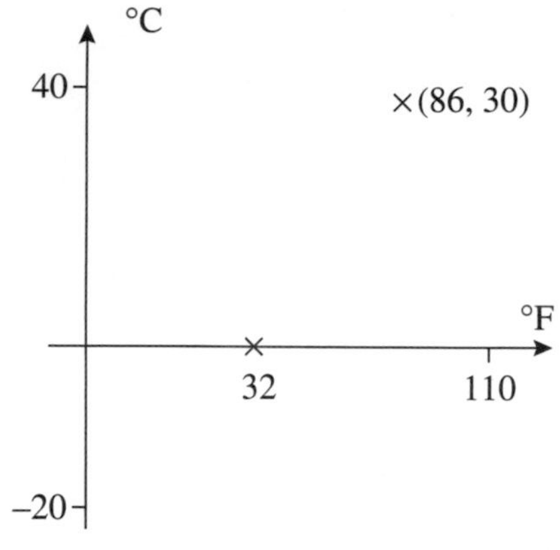

5 In the U.K., petrol consumption for cars is usually quoted in 'miles per gallon'. In other countries the metric equivalent is 'km per litre'.

(a) Convert 7 m.p.g. into km per litre.

(b) Convert 5 km per litre into m.p.g.

(c) A car travels 9 km on one litre of petrol. Convert this consumption into miles per gallon. Work out how many gallons of petrol the car will use, if it is driven a distance of 100 miles.

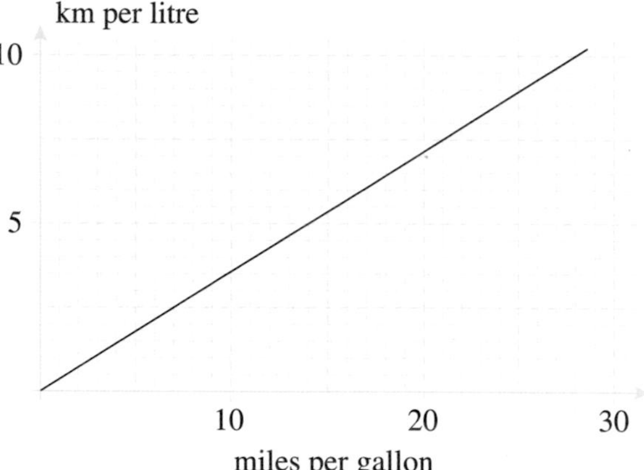

6 Maggie and Tania make different charges for people wanting pages typed professionally.

Maggie	Tania
£20 fixed charge plus £1 per page	£1.50 per page

(a) How much would Maggie charge to type 30 pages?

(b) How much would Tania charge to type 10 pages?

(c) Draw axes for the number of pages typed and the total cost, using the scales given.

(d) On the same diagram, draw a graph for each typist to show their charges for up to 60 pages.

(e) Use your graphs to decide for what number of pages Maggie is the cheaper typist to choose.

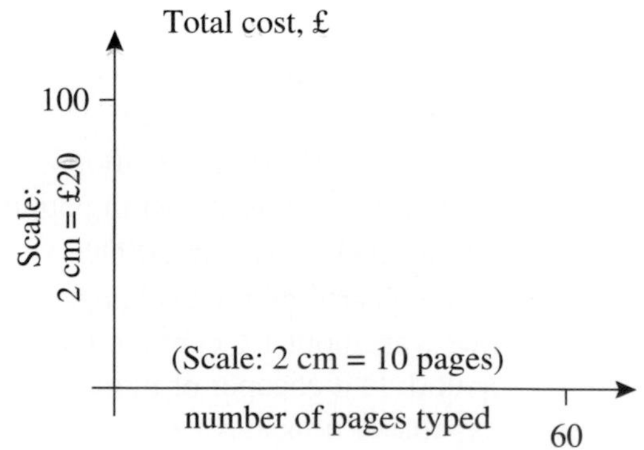

5.6 Using ratios

In this unit you will:

- use and simplify simple ratios
- share quantities in a given ratio
- use ratio in a range of contexts
- solve problems using map scales.

Ratio

- Here are seven balls. The ratio of red balls to yellow balls is 5:2

- In a mixed class of 30 children, 13 are girls. Since there are 30 children altogether, there are 17 boys. The ratio girls: boys is 13:17
- Ratios can sometimes be written in a simpler form:
  The ratios 4:10 and 2:5 are the same. [divide by 2]
  The ratios 10:20:25 and 2:4:5 are the same. [divide by 5]

Exercise 1M

In questions 1 to 5, make sure that your answers are in their simplest form.

1. In a hall there are 36 chairs and 9 tables.
   Find the ratio of chairs to tables.
2. In a room there are 14 women and 12 men.
   Find the ratio of women to men.
3. In a mixed class of 20 children, 8 are boys.
   Write down the ratio boys : girls.
4. In an office there are twice as many men as women. Write down the ratio men : women.
5. From the diagram write down the ratio:
   (a) ticks : crosses
   (b) green shapes : pink shapes
   (c) triangles : squares

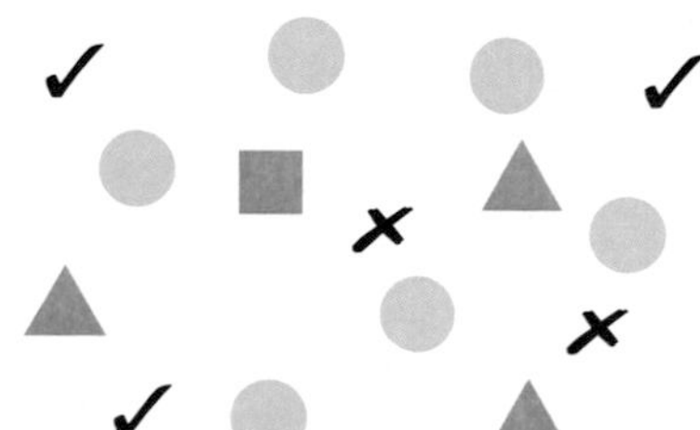

6 Write these ratios in a more simple form.

(a) 9:6 (b) 15:25 (c) 10:40 (d) 48:44 (e) 18:24 (f) 40:25

7 In a box, the ratio of rulers to pencils is 1:3. If there are 5 rulers, how many pencils are there?

8 In a classroom the ratio of girls to boys is 3:2. If there are 14 boys, how many girls are there?

9 In a greengrocer's shop, the ratio of apples to pears is 5:2. If there are 200 pears, how many apples are there?

10 Look at this diagram. Write down the ratio grey cubes : non-grey cubes.

11 Write these ratios in a more simple form.

(a) 9:6:12 (b) 40:5:15 (c) 12:10:8

(d) 18:12:18 (e) 70:10:50 (f) 14:7:35

12 In a box, the ratio of apples to peaches to bananas is 3:1:2. If there are 24 apples, how many peaches are there and how many bananas are there?

13 On a Saturday the football results gave a ratio of home wins to away wins to draws of 6:2:1. If there were 10 away wins, how many home wins were there and how many draws were there?

14 On a farm, the ratio of cows to sheep to pigs is 3:4:5. If there are 35 pigs, how many sheep are there and how many cows are there?

15 Find the ratio (shaded area):(unshaded area) for each diagram.

(a)

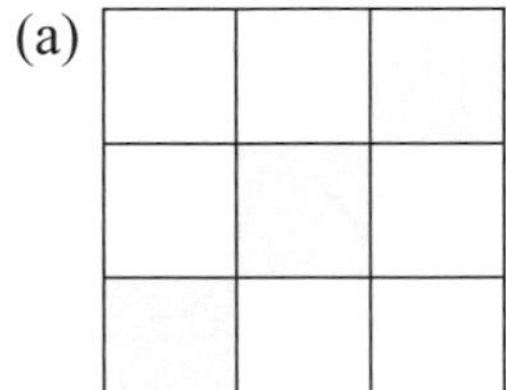

(b)

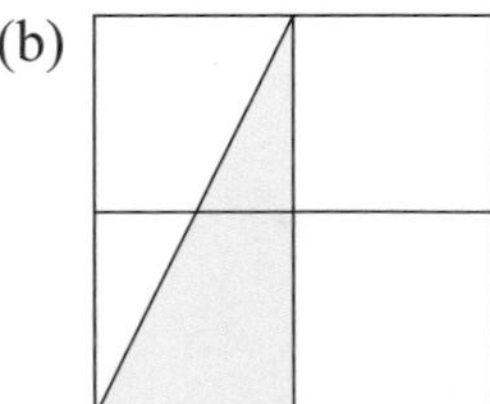

(c)

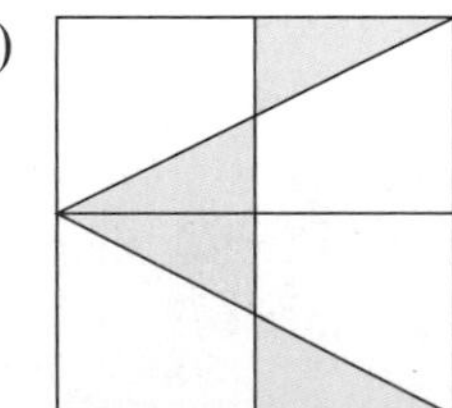

16 If $\frac{2}{5}$ of the children in a school are girls, what is the ratio of girls to boys?

17 The ratio of men to women in a cinema is 3:4. What fraction of the people are men?

Ratio and sharing

- Share 30 apples between Ken and Denise in the ratio 2:3

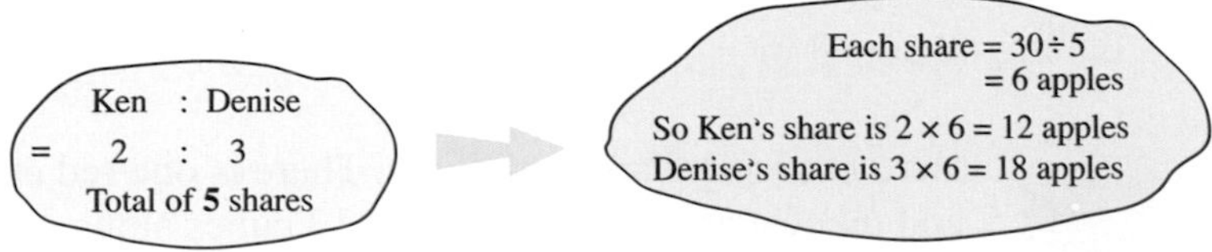

[Check: 12 + 18 = 30 ✓]

- Share a prize of £63 between Ann, Ben and Carol in the ratio 2:3:4.

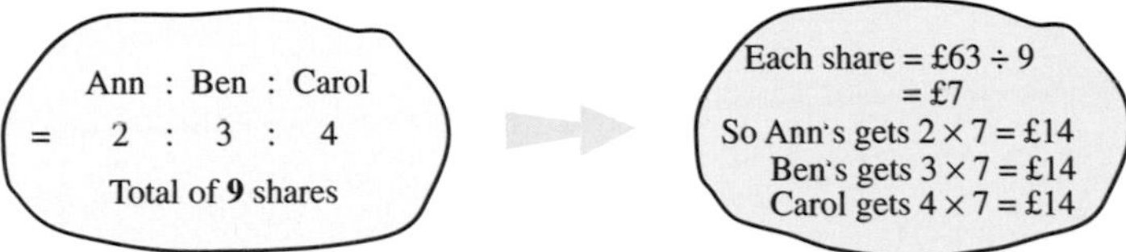

[Check: 14 + 21 + 28 = 63 ✓]

Exercise 1E

1. Saffon and Sam share a bag of 30 sweets in the ratio 3:2.
   How many sweets does each person get?
2. A mother and her son share a prize of £60 in the ratio 3:1.
   How much does each person receive?
3. Share each quantity in the ratio given.
   (a) 54 cm, 4:5 (b) £99, 4:7 (c) 132 km, 6:5
   (d) £36, 2:3:4 (e) 200 kg, 5:2:3 (f) £2000, 1:9
4. Three starving dogs share a meal weighing 660 g in the ratio 2:5:3.
   Find the largest share.
5. To make concrete you can mix 3 parts sand to 1 part cement.
   How much sand do you need to make 8 tonnes of concrete?
6. To make grey paint you can mix 3 parts black paint with 7 parts white paint. How much of each colour paint do you need to make 20 litres of grey paint?
7. Two squares are shown with their perimeters.
   (a) Write down the ratio of the lengths of their sides.
   (b) Work out the ratio of their areas.

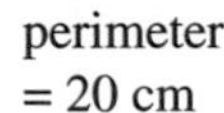

perimeter
= 28 cm

8. An object weighing 210 g consists of copper, zinc and iron. There is three times as much copper as zinc and one and a half times as much zinc as iron. How much zinc is there?

In questions 9 to 14 write the ratios in a more simple form.

9 20 cm : 1 m

10 20 mm : 5 cm

11 400 g : 2 kg

12 200 ml : 2 litres

13 0.5 m : 60 cm : 3 m

14 300 g : 0.7 kg : 3 kg

15 

Here is a square array of cubes. There is one red cube and the rest are black. There are 13 cubes along each side of the square. Write down the ratio,

red cubes : black cubes.

16 The angles in a triangle are in the ratio 3:1:2.
Find the sizes of the three angles.

17 The angles in a quadrilateral are in the ratio 2:2:3:2.
Find the largest angle in the quadrilateral.

18 The sides of a rectangle are in the ratio 3:1. The area of the rectangle is 48 cm^2.
Find the sides of the rectangle.

Find n if $n:4 = 3:7$

We can write $\frac{n}{4} = \frac{3}{7}$

$$n = \frac{3}{7} \times 4 = \frac{12}{7} = 1\tfrac{5}{7}$$

Exercise 2E

1 Find n in each case.

(a) $n:5 = 2:3$ (b) $n:3 = 3:4$

2 The ratio of squash to water in a drink is 3:8. How much squash is used with 4 litres of water?

3 A photo of a barbecue was enlarged in the ratio 2:5.
The enlarged photo was 6.5 cm long.
How long was the original?

4 Find x.

(a) $x : 4 = 9 : x$

(b) $x : 20 = 50 : x^2$

5 A pond contains carp and trout. If $\frac{5}{9}$ of the fish are carp, what is the ratio of carp to trout?

6 Lee, Mike and Neil formed a syndicate to enter a giant lottery. They agreed to share their winnings in the ratio of their contribution. Lee paid £1, Mike paid 60p and Neil paid 25p. Together they won £1 480 000. How much did Neil get?

7 Antifreeze is put into a car's radiator to prevent the water freezing. A mixture of antifreeze to water of 1:3 is a 25% mix.

(a) What would a $33\frac{1}{3}$% mix be?

(b) How much antifreeze is needed to make 12 litres of the 25% mix?

(c) How much antifreeze is needed to make 12 litres of the $33\frac{1}{3}$% mix?

8 The number of pages in a magazine was increased from 48 to 60. What will the new price be if the price, which was 36p, is increased in the same ratio?

9 The ratio of Lucy's age to Helen's age is 3:4. How old is Helen if she is 7 years older than Lucy?

10 The sum of two numbers p and q is 66 and p is 6 less than q. Find the ratio $p{:}q$.

11 The ratio $x{:}y = 1{:}2$ and the ratio $y{:}z = 4{:}5$

What is the ratio $x{:}z$?

12 In the diagram, $\frac{4}{5}$ of the circle is shaded and $\frac{2}{3}$ of the triangle is shaded.

What is the ratio of the area of the circle to the area of the triangle?

13 In a Fibonacci sequence, each successive term is obtained by adding the two previous terms. A Fibonacci sequence starts

1, 1, 2, 3, 5, 8, 13, 21, 34, 55, …

(a) Write down the next four numbers in the sequence.

(b) The ratio of successive pairs of terms can be found:

$\frac{1}{1} = 1$, $\frac{2}{1} = 2$; $\frac{3}{2} = 1.5$ etc.

Find the next ten ratios of successive pairs of terms. [ie $\frac{5}{3}, \frac{8}{5}, \frac{13}{8}$ etc]

What do you notice?

Map scales

On a map of scale 1:2000 000, two points appear 3 cm apart. What is the actual distance between the points?

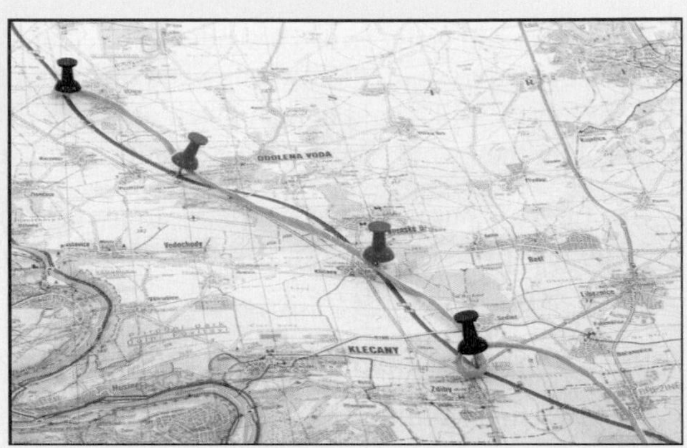

1 cm on map = 2000 000 cm on land.

3 cm on map = 3 × 2000 000 cm on land.

6 000 000 cm = 60 000 m

= 60 km

The two points are 60 km apart.

Exercise 3M

1. On a map whose scale is 1:1000, the distance between two houses is 3 cm. Find the actual distance between the two houses, giving your answer in metres.

2. The distance on a map between two points is 8 cm. Find the actual distance in metres between the two points, given that the scale of the map is 1 : 100.

3. The scale of a certain map is 1:10 000. What is the actual distance in metres between two churches which are 4 cm apart on the map?

4. On a map whose scale is 1:100 000, the distance between two villages is 7 cm. What is the actual distance in kilometres between the two villages?

5. The distance on a map between two towns is 9 cm. Find the actual distance in kilometres between the two towns, given that the scale of the map is 1:1 000 000.

6. The photo shows a football pitch and running track. Which of the following is nearest to the actual scale of this photo:

   1.2500 1:10 000 1:25000?

7. Find the actual distance in metres between two towers which are 5 cm apart on a map whose scale is 1:10 000.

8 A river is 5 cm long on a map whose scale is 1:20 000. Find the actual length of the river.

9 Andrew finds that the distance between two cities on a map whose scale is 1:1 000 000 is 12 cm. What is the actual distance in kilometres between the two cities?

Exercise 3E

1 The distance between two points is 30 km. How far apart will they be on a map of scale 1:50 000?

2 The length of a section of motorway is 15 km. How long will it be on a map of scale 1:100 000?

3 The scale of a map is 1:200 000. What is the actual distance between two villages given that they are 8.5 cm apart on the map?

4 

The diameter of a globe is 60 cm.
The *circumference* of the earth is about 40000 km.
Estimate the scale of this globe.
Give your answer in the form. 1: n.

5 If two towns are 5.4 cm apart on a map and the scale of the map is 1:3 000 000, what is the actual distance between the two towns?

6 A world map is drawn to a scale of 1:80 000 000, while a map of Great Britain is drawn to a scale of 1: 3 000 000. On the map of Great Britain, the ditance from Land's End to John o'Groats is 36 cm. How far apart are the two places on the world map?

7 The scale used in a motoring atlas is '1 inch to 3 miles' Write this in the form 1: n
[1 mile = 1760 yards]

8 Five men ride for 3 hours at an average speed of 6 km/h. On their map they have travelled 12 cm. What is the scale of their map?

9 The area of a lake on a map is 12 cm^2. Work out the actual area of the lake if the scale of the map is 1:10000.

10 The actual area of a large farm is 4000 hectares. Calculate the area of the farm on a map of scale 1:20 000.

5.7 Congruent shapes, tessellation

In section 5.7 you will learn about:

- congruent shapes
- tessellation

Congruent shapes are exactly the same in shape and size. Shapes are congruent if one shape can be fitted exactly over the other.

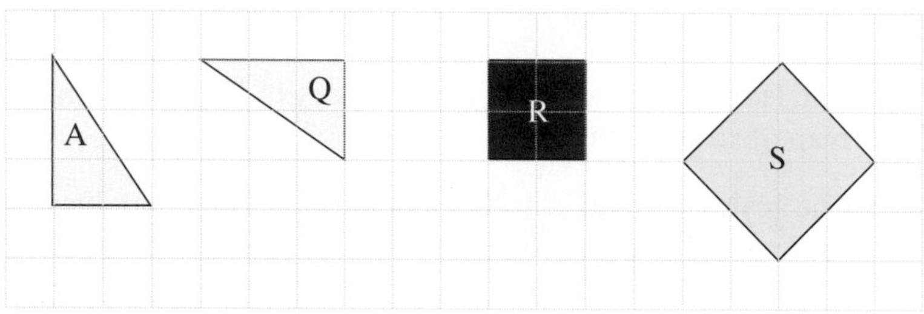

P and Q are congruent R and S are not congruent

Exercise 1M

1 Decide which shapes are congruent pairs. [You can use tracing paper]

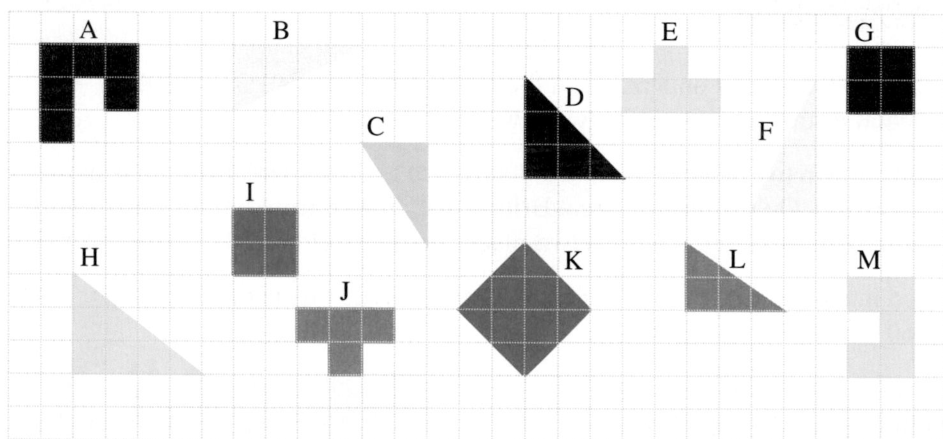

2 Copy the diagram and colour in congruent shapes with the same colour.

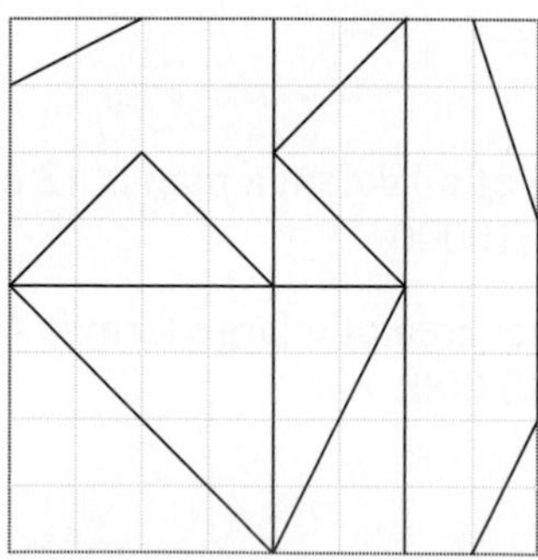

3 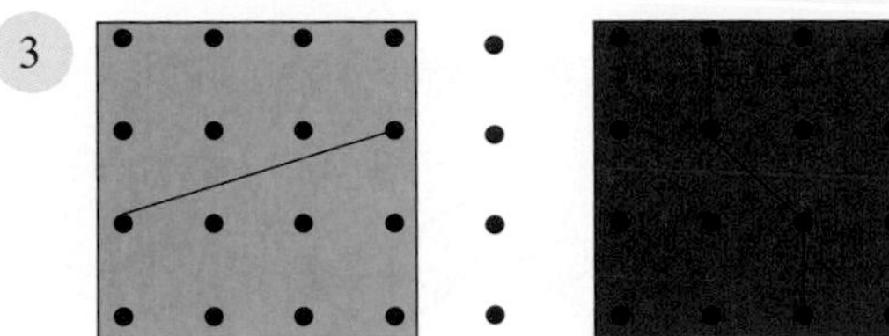

The 4 × 4 grids are divided into two congruent shapes.
Do this in as many different ways as possible.

4 Two congruent right angled triangles are joined together along equal sides

(a) How many shapes are possible?
(b) How many shapes are possible if the congruent triangles are scalene or equilateral?

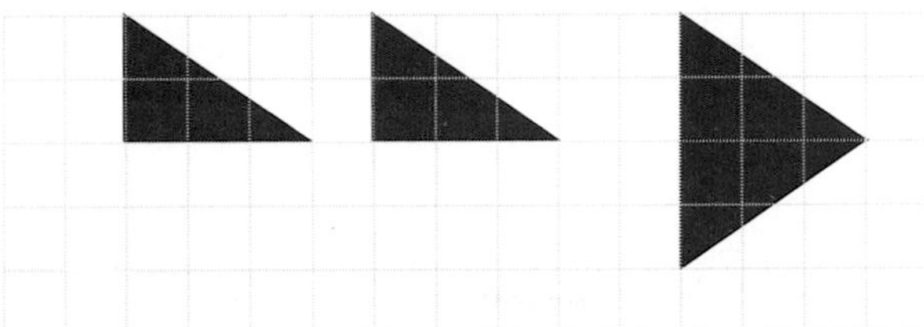

5 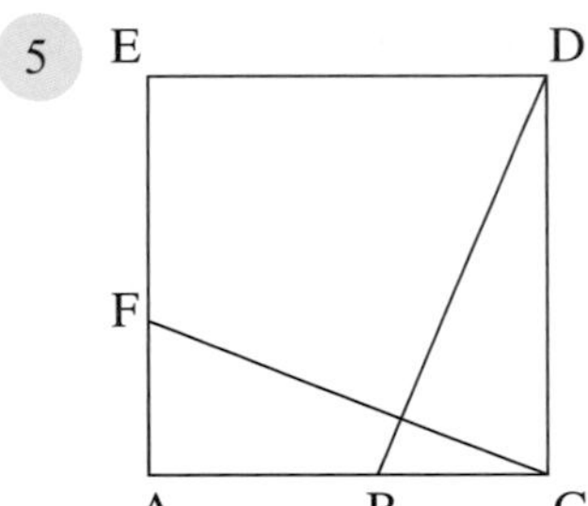

You are told that triangles DBC and CFA are congruent. Copy and complete.

(a) side AF = side ☐
(b) side CF = side ☐
(c) angle CFA = angle ☐
(d) angle ☐ = angle CDB.

Tessellation

- in tessellation we study the different ways we can regularly tile any flat surface, no matter how large. The examples below show tessellation using quadrilaterals:

(Rectangles)

(Kites)

- Draw *any* quadrilateral on card and make a tessellation.

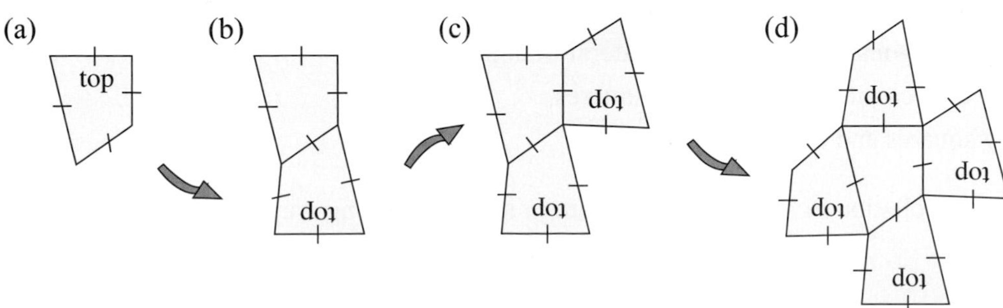

Interesting tessellations may be formed using sets of different shapes, provided the lengths of their sides are compatible

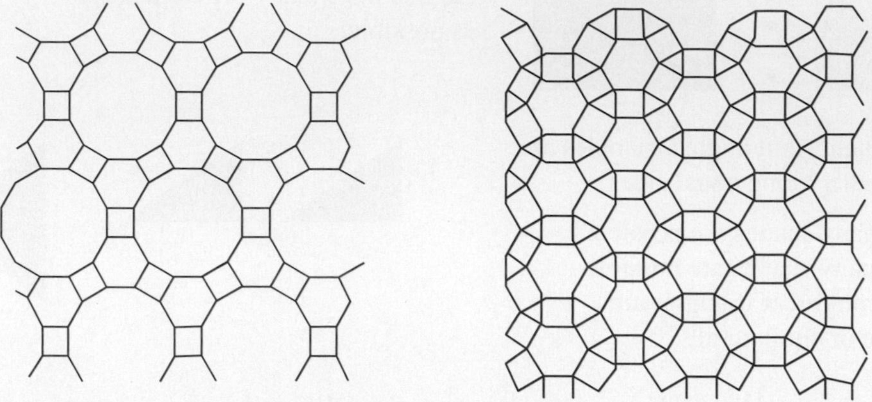

Exercise 2M

1 Draw and cut out a template on card for each of the shapes below:
(You can trace the shapes below to save time: All their sides are compatible).

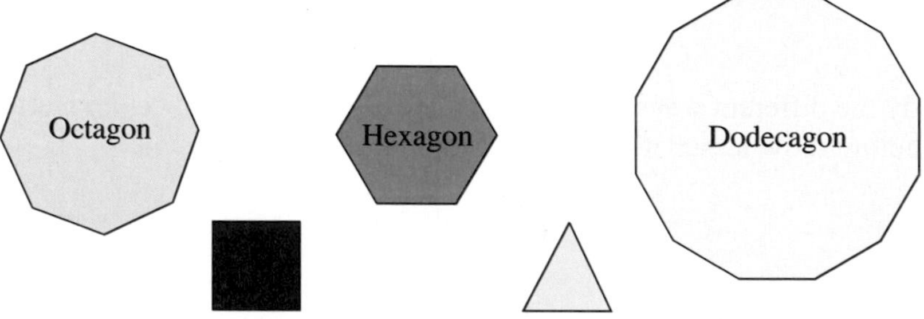

2 Either (i) draw a tessellation on plain paper or (ii) draw a tessellation directly onto tracing paper, using:

(a) only hexagons

(b) only octagons and squares

(c) only dodecagons and equilateral triangles.

(d) only hexagons, squares and equilateral triangles.

(e) only dodecagons, hexagons and squares.

(f) only squares and equilateral triangles.

3 For each tessellation in 2, colour the pattern in an interesting way.

CHECK YOURSELF ON SECTIONS 5.5 AND 5.6

1 Straight line graphs

(a) Draw the graph of $y = 2x - 3$ for values of x from 0 to 4.

(b) Find the equation of the line which passes through the following points:
(1, 5) (2, 7) (3, 9) (4, 11)

2 Curved graphs

Draw the graph of $y = x^2 - 2$ for values of x from –3 to 3.

Use a scale of 2 cm to 1 unit on the x axis and 1 cm to 1 unit on the y axis.

From your graph estimate the value of y when $x = 1.5$.

3 Using graphs

The conversion graph for pints and litres is shown.

Use the graph to convert

(a) 1 litre to pints

(b) 1.5 pints to litres

(c) 1.2 litres to pints

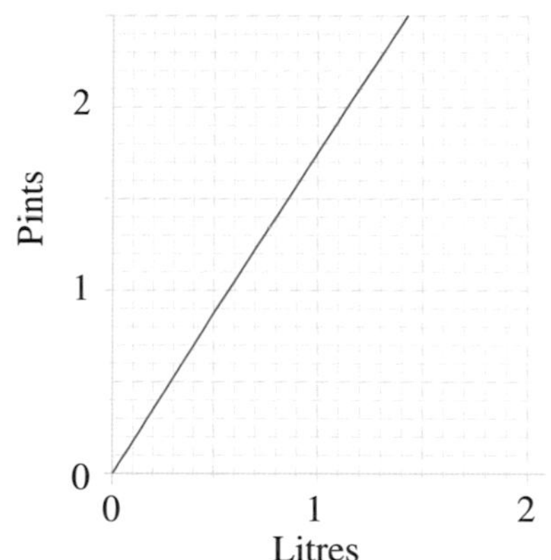

4 Using ratio

(a) Write these ratios in a more simple form.

(i) 6:12:15 (ii) 18:45:63

(b) Share £220 between two people in the ratio 4:7

(c) Find n if $n:3 = 3:2$

(d) In a box the ratio of white dice to coloured dice is 2:5. There are 560 dice in the box. How many dice are coloured?

(e) A road is 4 cm long on a map of scale 1:50 000. Find the actual length of the road.

UNIT 5 MIXED REVIEW

Part one

1 Look at the five dice. Of the numbers thrown, write down the ratio
odd numbers : even numbers.

2 (a) Draw the graph of $y = 3x - 1$, taking values of x from –3 to +3.
(b) Write down the coordinates of the point where the line cuts the x axis.

3 (a) Draw the graph of $y = x^2 - 3$, taking values of x from –3 to +3.
(b) Write down the coordinates of the two points where the curve cuts the x axis.

4 Work out the lengths of the sides marked with letters. All lengths are in cm.

(a)
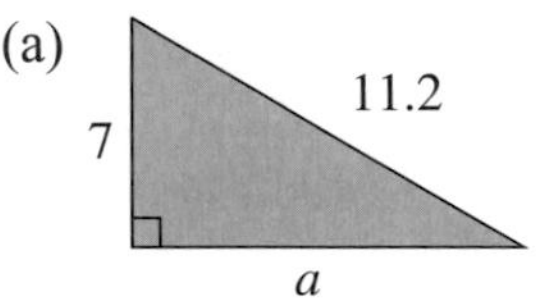

(b)
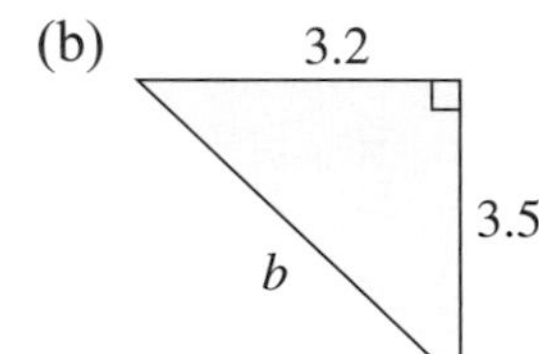

(c)
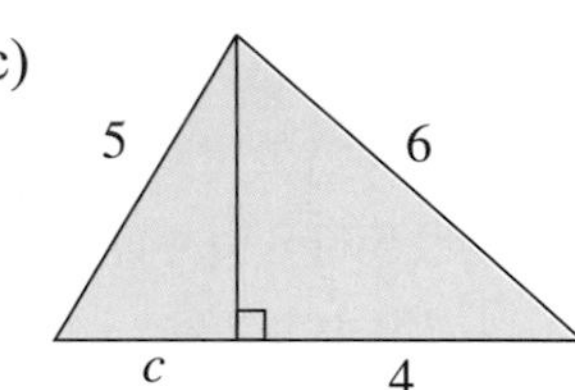

5 Different shapes can be drawn on a grid of nine dots. The vertices of each shape are drawn at any dot.
Here are two examples:
a rectangle and a trapezium.

Draw four grids and label them A, B, C, D. [You can use dotty paper but it is not necessary].
(a) On grid A draw any parallelogram.
(b) On grid B draw any isosceles triangle.
(c) On grid C draw another isosceles triangle, different to the one you drew on grid B.
(d) On grid D draw a trapezium, different to the one in the example above.

6 (a) Write each of the following as decimals
(i) 22% (ii) $\frac{5}{8}$ (iii) 7%
(b) Simon got 52 out of 80 in science test. What was his mark as a percentage?
(c) Write these numbers in order of size, smallest first:
0.11, $\frac{1}{9}$, 10%, 0.01.
(d) Share £108 between Steve and Phil in the ratio 2:7.

7 Describe fully each of the following transformations.

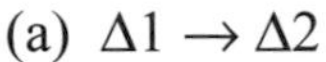

(a) $\Delta 1 \rightarrow \Delta 2$
(b) $\Delta 1 \rightarrow \Delta 3$
(c) $\Delta 1 \rightarrow \Delta 4$
(d) $\Delta 4 \rightarrow \Delta 5$

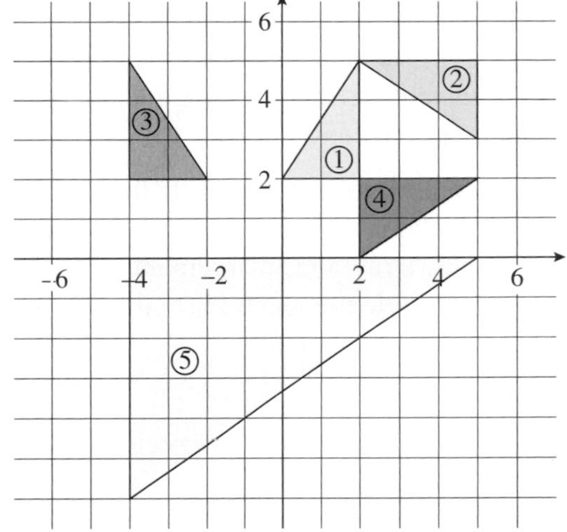

8 A farmer found that the daily milk produced by each of his cows was only 2.3 litres so he decided to put them through of course of hypnotherapy. Unfortunately the consequence was that production fell by 5.5% There were 70 cows in his herd. By how much did his daily milk production fall?

9 Black and white tiles are used to make 'mini' chess boards of various sizes. As white tiles are more expensive there are never more white tiles than black tiles on any size board.

(a) How many white tiles are there on the 6×6 board?
(b) How many black tiles are there on the 7×7 board?

10 In these diagrams a letter 'V' is drawn across each rectangle.

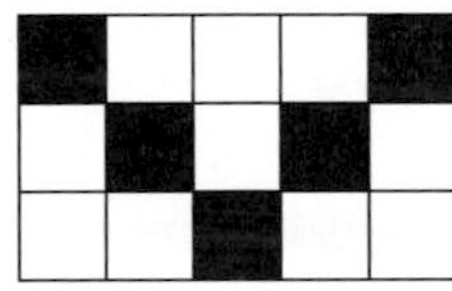

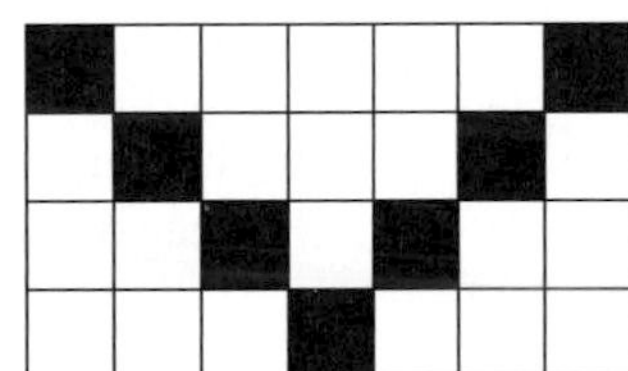

(a) Count the black squares, b, and the white squares, w, in each diagram and write the results in a table.

b	w
3	3

(b) Draw the next diagram in the sequence. Count the black squares and the white squares and add the results to your tables.
(c) *Predict* the number of white squares in the next diagram (that is the fifth diagram) in the sequence.
(d) In a later diagram, there are 136 white squares. How many black squares are there in that diagram?

11 (a) Copy the shape S inside the rectangle as shown. Shape S is enlarged so that it just fits inside the rectangle. Draw the enlargement of S and mark the centre of enlargement.

(b) Draw the same shape S inside the same rectangle but translate it 1 square to the right and 1 square upwards. Draw the enlargement of S so that it just fits inside the rectangle and mark the centre of enlargement.

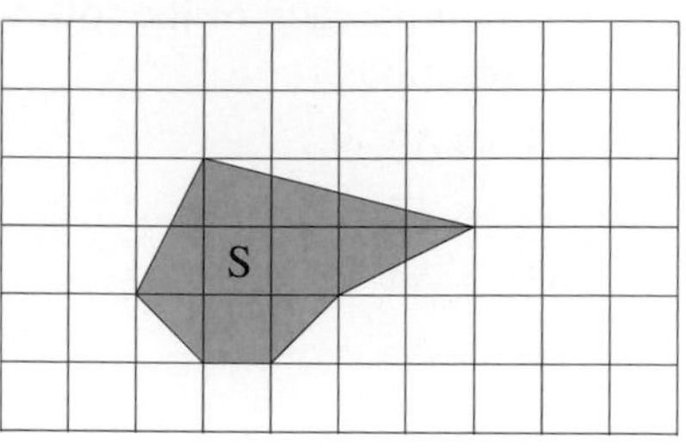

Part two

1 The graph shows the journeys of Mark and Meera, who drove from their home to an hotel 120 km away.

(a) What was Meera's speed?
(b) What was Mark's speed after his short stop?
(c) How far apart were they at 1030?
(d) What was Mark's *average* speed for the whole journey?

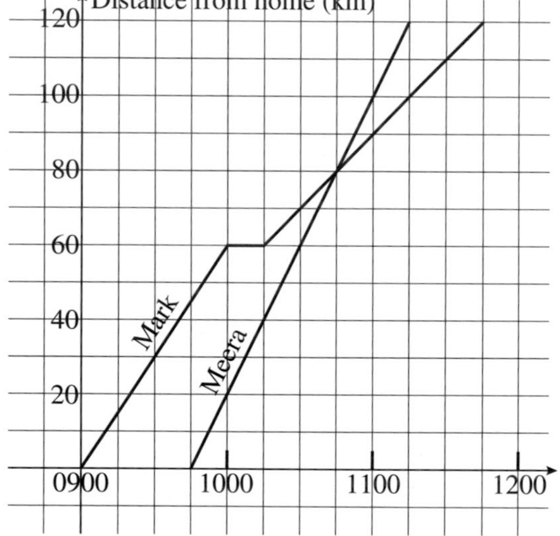

2 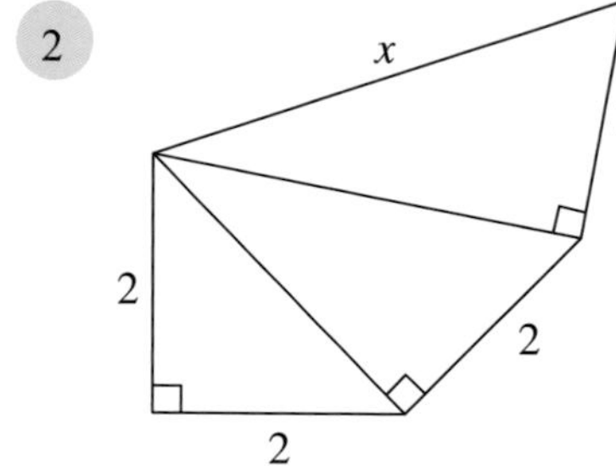

Find the length x.
All dimensions are in cm.

3 The angles in a triangle are in the ratio 2:3:5.
Find the three angles.

4 Find the value of x in each case.
(a) $x:4 = 3:10$
(b) $x:4 = 16:x$

5

(a) For this set of bricks write down the ratio red bricks: non-red bricks

(b) A shop orders 250 sets of these bricks. How many red bricks will there be altogether?

6 Draw x and y axes with values from –8 to +8. Plot and label $\Delta 1$ at (–4, –3), (–4, –6), (–2, –3).

(a) Draw the triangles $\Delta 2$, $\Delta 3$, $\Delta 4$, $\Delta 5$ as follows:
   (i) $\Delta 1 \rightarrow \Delta 2$ rotation, 180°, centre (0, –3)
   (ii) $\Delta 2 \rightarrow \Delta 3$ rotation, 180°, centre (3, 1)
   (iii) $\Delta 1 \rightarrow \Delta 4$ enlargement scale factor 3, centre (–5, –7)
   (iv) $\Delta 1 \rightarrow \Delta 5$ reflection in $y = 1$

(b) Describe fully each of the following transformations:
   (i) $\Delta 2 \rightarrow \Delta 3$ (ii) $\Delta 3 \rightarrow \Delta 4$.

7 At a mental arithmetic test Lucy scored 14 out of 20. She concentrates better when she stands on her head and when doing so she scored 24 out of 30 in a similar test. By how much did her percentage mark improve?

8 The diagram shows an equilateral triangle of side 8 cm with a line of symmetry drawn through A.

(a) Calculate the vertical height of the triangle.

(b) Calculate the area of the triangle.

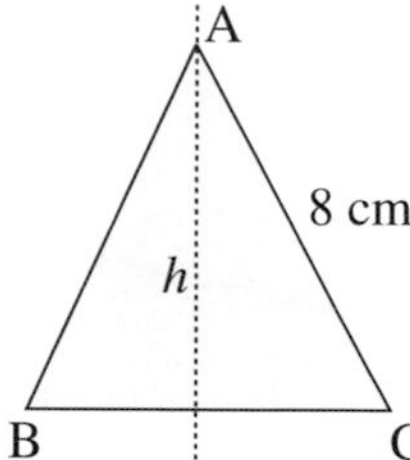

9 Find the equations of the lines which pass through the following points.

(a)

x	3	4	5	6	7
y	6	7	8	9	10

(b)

x	2	3	4	5	6
y	7	9	11	13	15

10 A wooden cube has sides of length 20 cm.

(a) Calculate the length of the diagonal of each face of the cube.

(b) Calculate the length of the diagonal from point A to point B.

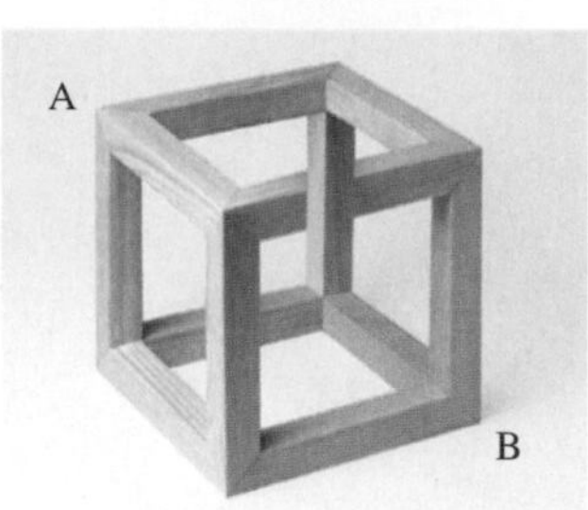

11 A car driver can take one of two routes from A to C:
Route 1. From A to B and then B to C. This route is along main roads and he travels at 50 mph. The angle between AB and BC is 90º.

Route 2. From A straight to C along a shortcut. This is a minor road and he drives at only 30 mph.

(a) Which route takes the shorter length of time?
(b) By how much in hours is it shorter?

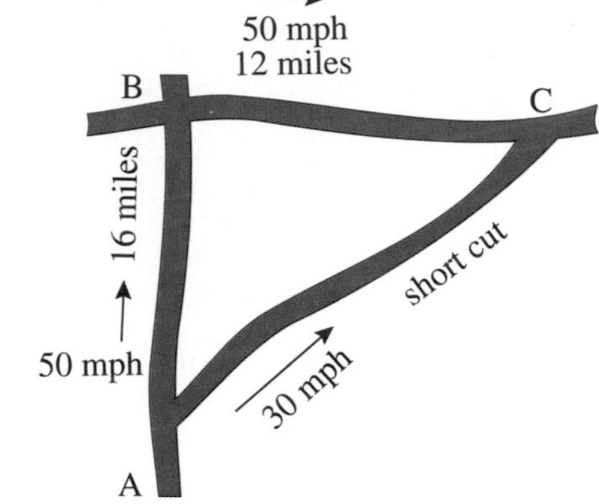

12

(a) In this picture of chess pieces what is the ratio of pawns : other pieces?

(b) In a complete chess set what is the ratio of pawns : other pieces?

13 Which of the measurements below is the best estimate when 100 yards is converted into metres?

A 90 m **B** 110 m **C** 1100 m **D** 0.9 m

Puzzles and Problems 5

Cross numbers without clues

Here are cross number puzzles with a difference. There are no clues, only answers, and you have to find where the answers go.

(a) Copy out the cross number pattern.
(b) Fit all the given numbers into the correct spaces. Work logically and tick off the numbers from lists as you write them in the squares.

1

<table>
<tr><td></td><td></td><td></td><td>■</td><td></td><td></td></tr>
<tr><td></td><td></td><td></td><td>■</td><td></td><td></td></tr>
<tr><td></td><td></td><td>■</td><td></td><td></td><td></td></tr>
<tr><td></td><td>■</td><td></td><td></td><td></td><td></td></tr>
<tr><td></td><td></td><td>■</td><td></td><td></td><td></td></tr>
<tr><td>■</td><td></td><td>9</td><td></td><td>■</td><td>■</td></tr>
</table>

2 digits	*3 digits*	*4 digits*	*5 digits*
23	146	2708	25404
26	235	2715	25814
42	245		37586
57	337		
59	539		
87	695		

2

<table>
<tr><td></td><td></td><td></td><td></td><td>■</td><td></td><td></td><td></td></tr>
<tr><td></td><td></td><td>■</td><td></td><td></td><td></td><td></td><td>■</td></tr>
<tr><td></td><td></td><td></td><td></td><td></td><td>■</td><td></td><td></td></tr>
<tr><td></td><td>■</td><td></td><td>0</td><td></td><td>■</td><td></td><td></td></tr>
<tr><td></td><td></td><td></td><td></td><td>■</td><td></td><td>■</td><td></td></tr>
<tr><td>■</td><td></td><td></td><td>■</td><td></td><td></td><td></td><td></td></tr>
<tr><td></td><td></td><td></td><td></td><td>■</td><td></td><td></td><td></td></tr>
<tr><td></td><td>■</td><td>■</td><td></td><td></td><td></td><td>■</td><td>■</td></tr>
</table>

2 digits	*3 digits*	*4 digits*	*5 digits*
18	244	2163	36918
21	247	4133	46514
31	248	4213	54374
33	332	4215	54704
47	333	4283	87234
63	334	4317	
64	608	4394	
77			

3

<table>
<tr><td></td><td>■</td><td></td><td></td><td></td><td></td><td></td><td>■</td></tr>
<tr><td></td><td></td><td></td><td></td><td></td><td></td><td></td><td>■</td></tr>
<tr><td></td><td></td><td>■</td><td>■</td><td></td><td></td><td></td><td></td></tr>
<tr><td>■</td><td></td><td></td><td></td><td>■</td><td></td><td>■</td><td></td></tr>
<tr><td></td><td></td><td></td><td></td><td></td><td>■</td><td></td><td></td></tr>
<tr><td></td><td>■</td><td></td><td></td><td></td><td></td><td></td><td>■</td></tr>
<tr><td></td><td></td><td></td><td>■</td><td></td><td></td><td></td><td>■</td></tr>
<tr><td></td><td></td><td></td><td></td><td></td><td>■</td><td></td><td>0</td></tr>
</table>

2 digits	*3 digits*	*4 digits*	*5 digits*	*7 digits*
36	145	2286	16145	4235824
52	185	5235	66145	
56	245	5248	66152	
63	246	5249	66272	
65	374	5452	91671	
77	437	6241		
90	646			
	896			

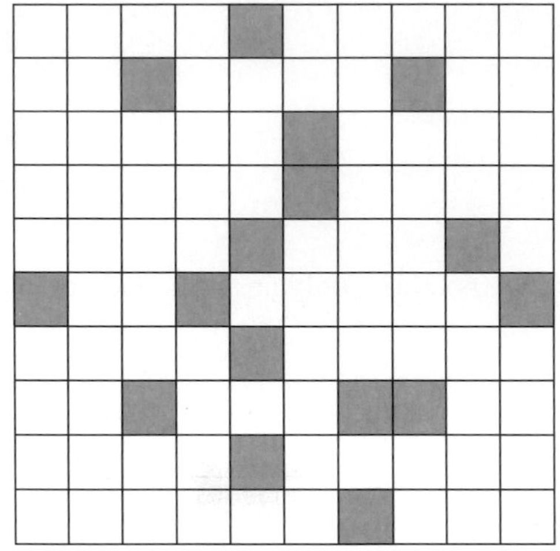

2 digits	*3 digits*	*4 digits*	*5 digits*
14	123	1325	14251
22	231	1478	29163
26	341	1687	29613
43	439	1976	29872
65	531	2523	34182
70	670	4798	54875
81		5601	63712
82		5611	67358
		5621	82146
		6109	84359
		8171	97273

6 digits	*7 digits*
145026	9354234
740136	
983514	

5 This one is more difficult.

2 digits	*3 digits*	*4 digits*	*5 digits*
15	137	2513	29666
19	206	3048	31873
21	276	3214	40657
22	546	3244	43104
28	592	3437	43158
31	783	3514	54732
77		3517	60783
90		3544	62114
		4122	80751
		4127	82614
		6934	93654

6 digits	*7 digits*
235785	9733764
235815	
452705	

Diagonals

Look at the squares below.

4 × 4

1			8
	2	7	
	6	3	
5			4

8 squares along the diagonals

5 × 5

1				9
	2		8	
		3		
	7		4	
6				5

9 squares along the diagonals

6 × 6

1					12
	2			11	
		3	10		
		9	4		
	8			5	
7					6

12 squares along the diagonals

(a) Draw a similar diagram for a 7 × 7 square and count the squares along the two diagonals.

(b) How many squares are there along the diagonals of
(i) a 10 × 10 square? (ii) a 15 × 15 square?

(c) A square wall is covered with square tiles. There are 33 tiles altogether long the two diagonals. How many tiles are there on the whole wall?

(d) Another square wall has 40 tiles altogether along the two diagonals. How many tiles are there on the whole wall?

(e) A square wall is covered by 900 square tiles. How may tiles are there along the two diagonals?

A long time ago! 5

The Tower of Hanoi

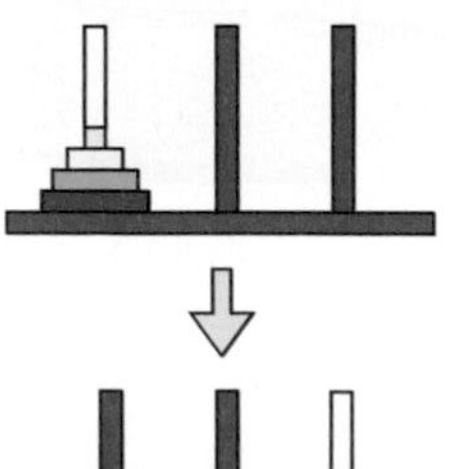

This puzzle was created by Eduard Lucas in the 19th century. The task is to move a pile of different sized discs from one post to another.

There are 3 posts. Only one disc may be moved at any time and must be moved directly onto another post. A larger disc may never be placed onto a smaller disc.

The aim is to move all the discs to another post using the least number of moves.

Exercise

1 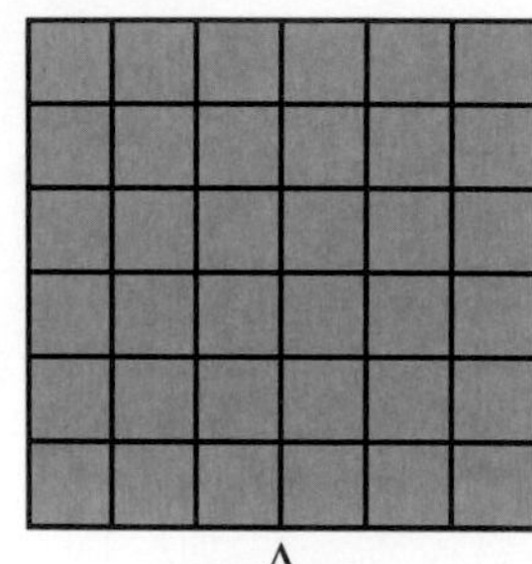

A

B

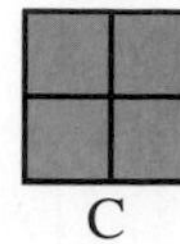

C

Cut out 3 squares as shown.

Use them in place of 3 discs.

Place C on top of B on top of A.

Place 3 crosses on a piece of paper in place of posts.

Move A, B and C from one post onto another post using the Tower of Hanoi rules above.

What are the least number of moves needed?

Discuss with a partner. Could they do any better than you?

2 Now repeat with 4 discs.

3 Try with just 2 discs.

4 One disc would need one move.

Look at your answers for 1 disc, 2 discs, 3 discs and 4 discs.

Can you see a pattern for the least number of moves so far?

If you can see a pattern, what will be the least number of moves needed for 5 discs?

Now move 5 discs for real.

5 What is the least number of moves needed for 7 discs?

6 Some people say: 'At the great temple of Benares, there is a brass plate on which 3 vertical diamond pins are attached. On one of these pins there are 64 golden discs with the smallest on the top and so on down to the largest on the bottom. The god Brahma placed these discs on this pin at the time of creation. The temple priests transfer the discs from pin to pin, one at a time. They never place a larger disc on a smaller one. It is said that when all the discs have been transferred to the last pin, the universe will end!'

Assuming that the priests take one second to move a disc from one pin to another, use your pattern or rule from questions 1 to 5 to work out how long it takes to move all 64 discs from one pin to another.

7 **RESEARCH:**

Find out more about the Tower of Brahma problem. Did you get close to the correct answer?

Mental Arithmetic Practice

Here is a set of mental arithmetic questions. Ideally a teacher will read out each question twice, with pupils books closed. The test of 30 questions should take about 20 minutes.

Test 1

1. I am thinking of a number. If I double it, add five and then double, the result the answer is 14. What number am I thinking of?
2. Work out $\frac{3}{4}$ plus $\frac{1}{2}$ and give the answer as a decimal.
3. Divide one billion by 100.
4. A rectangle has area 20 cm^2. What is the area of a rectangle whose sides are twice as long as those of this rectangle?
5. In a quiz, Joe got 16 out of 20. What percentage is that?
6. Increase a price of £1000 by 4%.
7. Work out 15% of 200 m.
8. I think of a number, subtract 2 and then divide by 10. The result is 10. What number am I thinking of?
9. Which is largest: $\frac{1}{26}$ or 4%?
10. A bar of chocolate costs 80p. I buy as many as I can for £3. How much change will I receive?
11. Add together 2, 3, 4, 5, 6 and 10.
12. Write down 100 million millimetres in kilometres.
13. Work out 1000 – 434.
14. Name the date which is 3 months before the 2nd of October.
15. Write down the next prime number after 47.
16. Write $\frac{1}{20}$ as a percentage.
17. In May, James weighs 50 kg. By July his weight is reduced by 10%. What does he weigh in July?
18. Find the total surface area of a cube of side 2 cm.
19. Work out 98 + 100 + 102.
20. Find the length of the perimeter of a regular octagon of side 12 cm.
21. Find the change from £2 when you buy two items for 28p each.
22. Give a rough estimate for the square root of 960.
23. Find the cost of 48 eggs at £4 per dozen.
24. A car is travelling at a steady speed of 50 m.p.h. How far does it go in 30 minutes?
25. Sam has one of each of the coins from 2 p to 2 pounds. What is their total value?
26. Three angles of a quadrilateral are 40°, 50° and 60°. What is the fourth angle?
27. How many inches are there in a yard?
28. A pie chart has a pink sector representing 5% of the whole chart. What is the angle of the sector?
29. A film started at 9.15 and finished at 11.40. How long was the film in hours and minutes?
30. Which has the longer perimeter: a square of side 7 cm or a regular hexagon of side 5 cm?

UNIT 6

6.1 More Algebra

In this section you will learn how to:

- solve equations involving fractions
- solve equations involving brackets
- solve word problems by forming equations
- use algebra to explain connections

Solving equations

Remember the rule : '*Do the same thing to both sides.*'

Solve the equations

(a) $3x - 7 = 50$

$3x = 57$ (Add 7)

$x = \frac{57}{3}$ (Divide by 3)

$x = 19$

(b) $4x - 1 = 2x + 9$

$4x = 2x + 10$ (Add 1)

$2x = 10$ (Subtract $2x$)

$x = 5$ (Divide by 2)

Exercise 1M

Solve the equations.

1 $3x - 2 = 13$

2 $4x + 1 = 25$

3 $7x - 2 = -1$

4 $5 + 2x = 6$

5 $7 + 3x = 22$

6 $3 = 4x + 1$

7 $5 = 3x - 1$

8 $7 = 15 - 2x$

9 $10 = 12 - 3x$

10 $4 = 6x + 5$

11 $7x - 1 = -8$

12 $3 - x = 10$

In questions 13 to 24, begin by putting the x terms on one side of the equation.

13 $4x + 3 = 2x - 5$

14 $7x - 5 = 2x + 8$

15 $3x + 7 = 8x + 2$

16 $6x + 1 = 2 - 3x$

17 $7x - 2 = 1 - 3x$

18 $5 - x = 2x - 7$

19 $2x - 8 = 11x + 12$

20 $3x - 9 = 4x + 4$

21 $2 + 8x = 5 - x$

22 $16x + 9 = 12x - 3$

23 $1 - 10x = 6 - 5x$

24 $4 - 5x = 4 + 7x$

Equations with fractions

(a) $\frac{2x}{3} = 5$

$2x = 15$ [Multiply by 3]

$x = \frac{15}{2}$ [Divide by 2]

$x = 7\frac{1}{2}$

(b) $\frac{4}{x} = -2$

$4 = -2x$ [Multiply by x]

$\frac{4}{-2} = x$ [Divide by –2]

$-2 = x$

(c) $\frac{x}{2} + 3 = 7$

$\frac{x}{2} = 4$ [Subtract 3 from both sides.]

$\cancel{2} \times \frac{x}{\cancel{2}} = 4 \times 2$ [Multiply both sides by 2.]

$x = 8$

(d) $\frac{4}{x} - 1 = 14$

$\frac{4}{x} = 15$ [Add 1 to both sides.]

$\cancel{x}\frac{4}{\cancel{x}} = 15x$ [Multiply both sides by x.]

$4 = 15x$

$\frac{4}{15} = x$

Exercise 1E

Solve the equations.

1 $\frac{x}{3} = 4$

2 $\frac{x}{5} = 2$

3 $5 = \frac{x}{4}$

4 $\frac{x}{7} = -2$

5 $\frac{x}{5} = -5$

6 $\frac{2x}{3} = 1$

7 $\frac{3x}{4} = 2$

8 $\frac{5x}{2} = 2$

9 $\frac{6}{x} = 7$

10 $\frac{4}{x} = 9$

11 $\frac{2}{x} = 11$

12 $\frac{3}{x} = \frac{1}{4}$

13 $3 = \frac{8}{x}$

14 $\frac{2}{3} = \frac{10}{x}$

15 $\frac{8}{x} = -11$

16 $-2 = \frac{100}{x}$

Questions 17 to 32 are more difficult.

17 $\frac{x}{3} + 1 = 5$

18 $\frac{x}{2} - 1 = 8$

19 $\frac{x}{5} + 9 = 8$

20 $6 + \frac{x}{3} = 10$

21 $\frac{1}{2}x + 9 = 20$

22 $\frac{1}{3}x - 6 = 11$

23 $\frac{2}{3}x + 8 = 10$

24 $\frac{4}{5}x - 1 = 0$

25 $x - 3 = \frac{1}{2}x$

26 $7 - \frac{x}{4} = 1$

27 $3 - \frac{x}{4} = \frac{x}{2}$

28 $\frac{9}{x} - \frac{1}{2} = 1$

29 $\frac{3}{x} - 2 = 4$

30 $\frac{4}{x} + 2 = 1$

31 $7 - \frac{5}{x} = 5$

32 $\frac{3}{2x} + 1 = 4$

Equations with brackets

Many of the more difficult problems which appear later in this section involve forming equations with brackets. Once the brackets have been removed the method of solution is similar to that for the equations dealt with earlier.

(a) $3(2x - 1) = 2(5 - x)$

$$6x - 3 = 10 - 2x$$
$$6x + 2x = 10 + 3$$
$$8x = 13$$
$$x = 1\tfrac{5}{8}$$

(b) $2(3x - 1) - (x - 2) = 5$

$$6x - 2 - x + 2 = 5$$
$$5x = 5$$
$$x = 1$$

Exercise 2M

Solve the equations.

1 $3(x + 4) = 2(x + 5)$

2 $7(x + 2) = 4(x + 6)$

3 $6(x - 4) = 2(x - 1)$

4 $3(x + 5) = 2(4 - x)$

5 $4(1 - 3x) = 9(3 + x)$

6 $7(2x + 1) = 2(5 + 4x)$

7 $8(x - 3) = 2x$

8 $2(x + 1) + x = 7$

9 $7(x - 2) - 3 = 2(1 - x)$

10 $5(x - 1) - (x + 2) = 0$

11 $2(3x - 1) - 3(x + 1) = 0$

12 $4(x + 1) + 2(1 - x) = x$

13 $6 - 2x = 5(1 - x)$

14 $8 + 3(2x + 1) = 9$

15 $3(1 - x) - (3 + x) = 0$

16 $3x + 2(2x + 1) = 4(3 + x)$

17 $6x - 2(3x - 1) = 4x$

18 $(5 - x) - (x - 10) = 15$

Problem solving with equations

Many mathematical problems are easier to solve when an equation is formed. In general it is a good idea to start by introducing a letter like 'x' or 'h' to stand for the unknown quantity.

Steven is thinking of a number. When he doubles the number, adds 4 and then multiplies the result by 3, the answer is 13. What number is he thinking of?

Let the number he is thinking of be x.
He doubles it, adds 4, multiplies the result by 3.
We have, $3(2x + 4) = 13$

Solving this equation we obtain $x = \frac{1}{6}$.

Exercise 2E

In each question, I am thinking of a number. Use the information to form an equation and then solve it to find the number.

1. If I subtract 2 from the number and then multiply the result by 5, the answer is 11.
2. If I double the number and then subtract 7, the answer is 4.
3. If I multiply the number by 4, add 3 and then double the result, the answer is –2.
4. If I treble the number, add 2 and then double the result, the answer is 9.
5. If I add 4 to the number and then multiply the result by 7, I get the same answer as when I subtract 1 from the number and then double the result.
6. If I multiply the number by 7 and subtract 10, I get the same answer as when I add 2 to the number and then double the result.
7. If I multiply the number by 5, subtract 2, and then multiply the result by 4, the answer I get is the same as when I double the number and then subtract 3.
8. If I double the number, add 3 and then multiply the result by 5, I get the same answer as when I double the number and then add 21.
9. If I subtract 2 from the number and then multiply the result by 9, I get the same answer as when I take the number *away from* 3 and then double the result.
10. If I subtract the number *from* 2 and then multiply the result by 4, I get the same answer as when I add 1 to the number and then multiply the result by 5.
11. If I treble the number, add 5 and then double the result, I get the same answer as when I double the number and then subtract from 11.
12. If I double the number, add 4 and then divide the result by 3, I get the same answer as when I subtract the number from 10 and then double the result.

Ebony had saved £54 and Hayley had saved £14. After both girls have been babysitting, for which they each receive the same amount of money, Ebony has three times as much as Hayley.

How much did they each receive for babysitting?

[P.T.O]

Let the amount they each received be £x.

To help 'see' the problem, draw a table to show their money.

	Ebony	Hayley
Before:	£54	£14
After:	£54 + x	£14 + x

Ebony now has three times as much as Hayley.

$$54 + x = 3(14 + x)$$

$$54 + x = 42 + 3x$$

$$12 = 2x \qquad 6 = x$$

They each received £6 for babysitting.

Exercise 3M

Answer these questions by forming an equation and then solving it.

1 (a) Find x if perimeter is 18 cm.

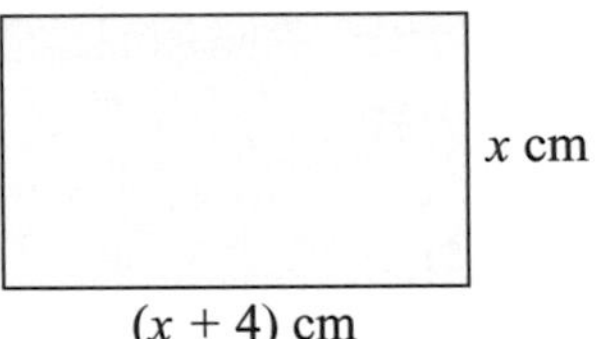

(b) Find x if the area is 6 cm^2.

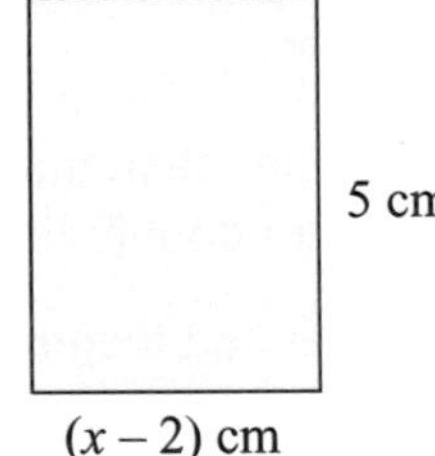

2 Sally has 5 times as many sweets as her brother Paul, but, as she is feeling generous, she gives him 10 of hers so that they now each have the same number. How many did Paul have originally?

3 The diagram shows two angles in an isosceles triangle. Find the angles in the triangle.

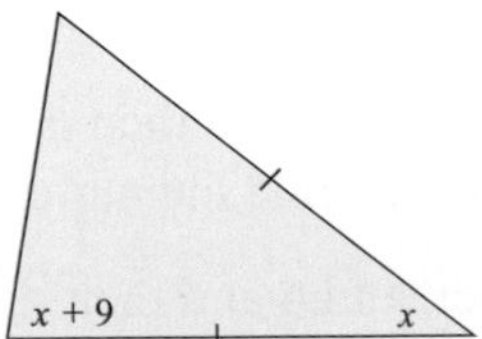

4 In the quadrilateral, AB = x cm, BC is 2 cm less than AB and CD is twice as long as BC. AD is 1 cm longer than CD. If the perimeter of the quadrilateral is 33 cm, find the length of AB.

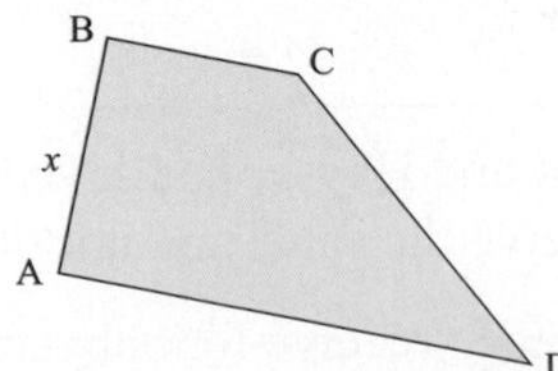

5 

Jeans cost £x and hats cost £$(2x - 1)$.
Three pairs of jeans and five hats cost £138 altogether.
Find the cost of the jeans.

6 Sam has £71 and Tim has £30. They are both paid the same money for a paper round. Now Sam has twice as much as Tim. How much were they each paid?

7 The diagram shows a road from P to T.
P to Q is 3 km more than S to T.
R to S is twice the distance from P to Q.
Q to R is 7 km less than R to S.
If the total distance from P to T is 44 km, find the distance from P to Q.

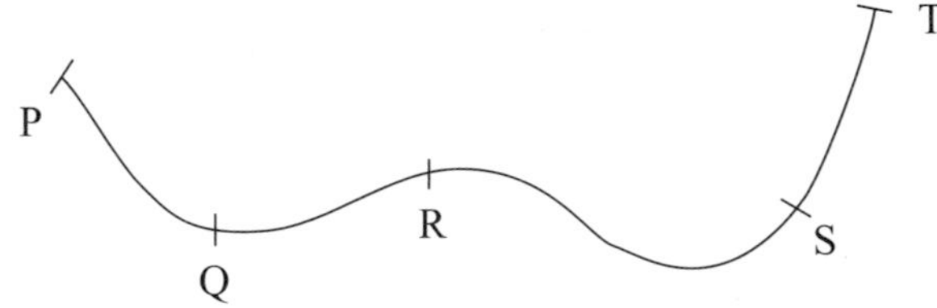

8 The sum of four consecutive whole numbers is 250. Let the first number be x and write down the other three numbers in terms of x.
Find the four numbers.

9 The sum of four consecutive *odd* numbers is 144. Find the numbers.

10 Seven years after her son is born a mother is five times as old as he is.
How old was the mother when her baby was born?

Exercise 3E

1 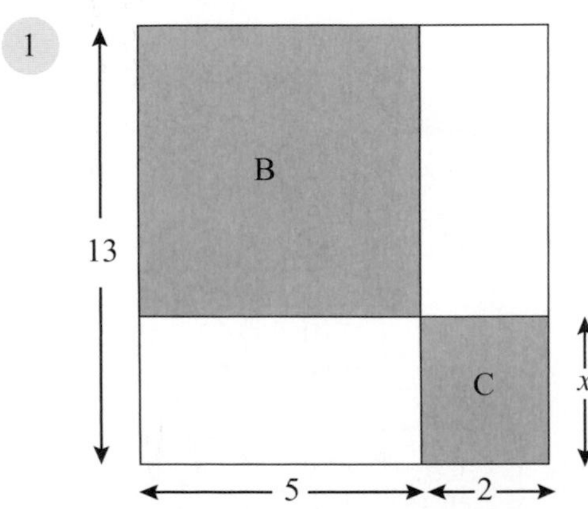

The area of rectangle B is four times the area of rectangle C.
Find x.

2 There were x people on a bus when it left A. It then stopped only at B, C and D.
At B 5 people got on and nobody got off.
After leaving C, there were three times as many people on the bus as when it arrived there.
There were 42 people on the bus when it arrived in D.
Form an equation in x and solve it to find the number of people on the bus when it left A.

3 Dan pours 5 barrels of water into an empty tank and his sister Meg pours in a further 12 litres through a hose. Later on, their father fills 2 barrels *from* the tank.
There are 45 litres of water still in the tank.
Use x for the number of litres in a barrel.
Make an equation and solve it to find x.

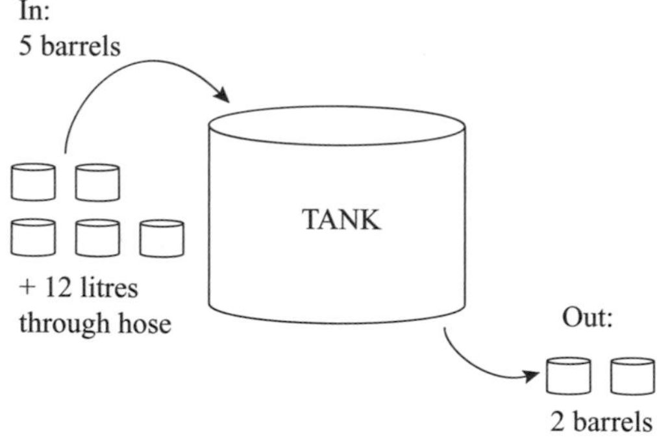

4 Rafa concentrates better with a box on his head. He worked out that in 34 years he will be three times as old as he is now. How old is he now?

5 Arsenal played 38 games in the premiership. They won n games and lost 5 games.
They got 3 points for each win, 1 point for each draw and 0 points for each defeat.
Altogether they got 89 points. How many games did they win?

6 The width of a rectangle is $(x + 7)$ cm and its perimeter is $(8x + 12)$cm. The length of the rectangle is 20 cm. Find the area of the rectangle.

7 In these number walls the number in each brick is found by adding the numbers in the two bricks below. Find n in each wall.

(a)

17

3 | n | 10

(b)

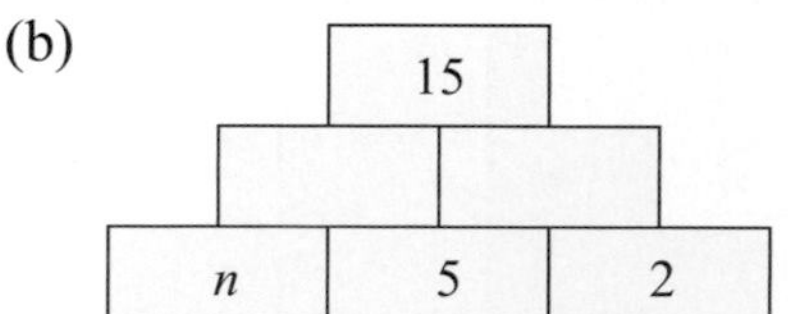

(c)

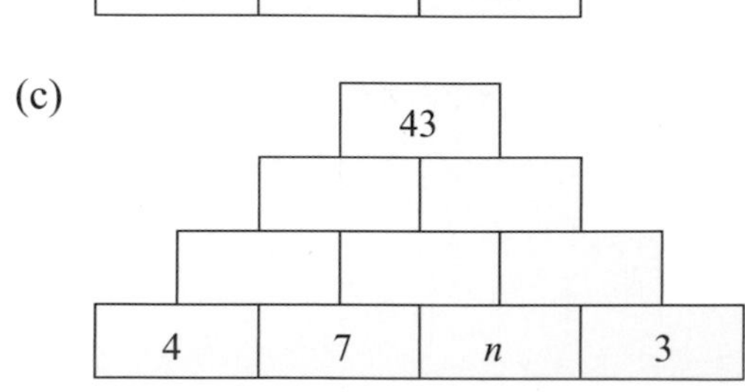

(d)

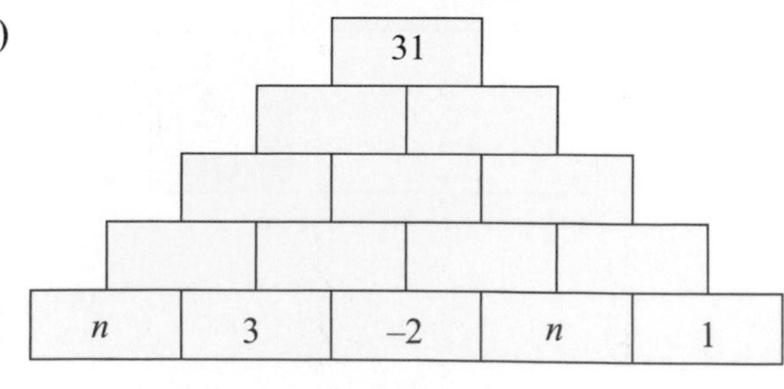

8 The diagram shows a rectangular pond ABCD surrounded by a uniform path of width 2m. AB is three times as long as BC and WX is twice as long as XY.
Find the dimensions of the pond.

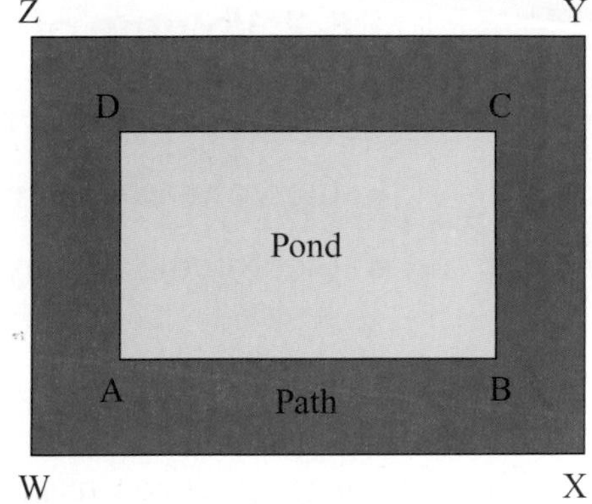

9

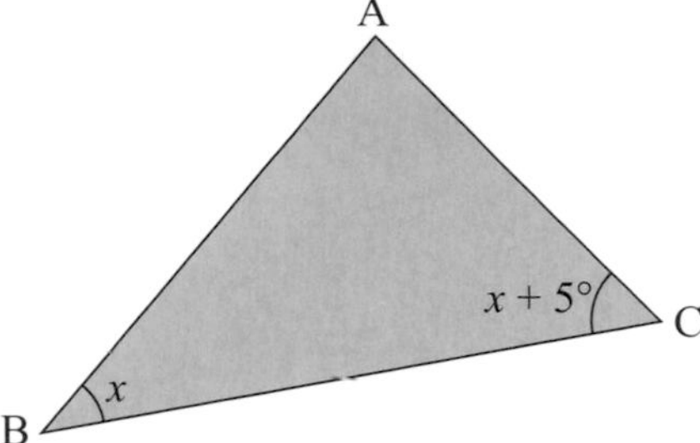

Angle A is 30° more than the sum of angles B and C.
Find the three angles of the triangle.

10 The chain 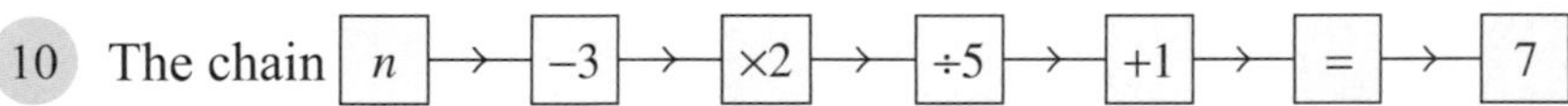

can be written as the equation

$$\frac{2(n-3)}{5} + 1 = 7.$$

Solve the equation to find n.

11 Form an equation for each chain below and then solve it to find n.

(a) 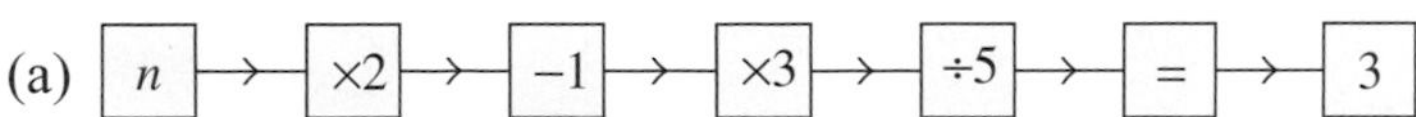

(b) 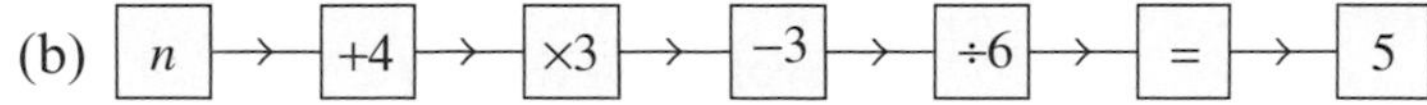

6.2 Volume of objects

In section 6.2 you will learn about

- the volume of a cuboid and other prisms
- the volume of a cylinder.

Cuboids

- Volume is a measure of how much physical space an object takes up.

  Blocks A and B are each made from eight cubes, measuring 1cm × 1cm × 1cm. They each have a volume of 8 cubic cm, which is written 8 cm^3.

  Rectangular blocks like these are called *cuboids*. A cube, like block B, is a special kind of cuboid.

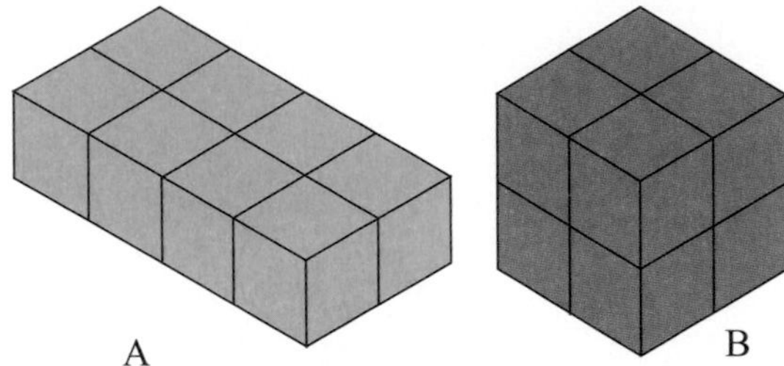

- The volume of a cuboid is given by the formula,

Volume = (length) × (width) × (height)

(a) Find the volume of the cuboid

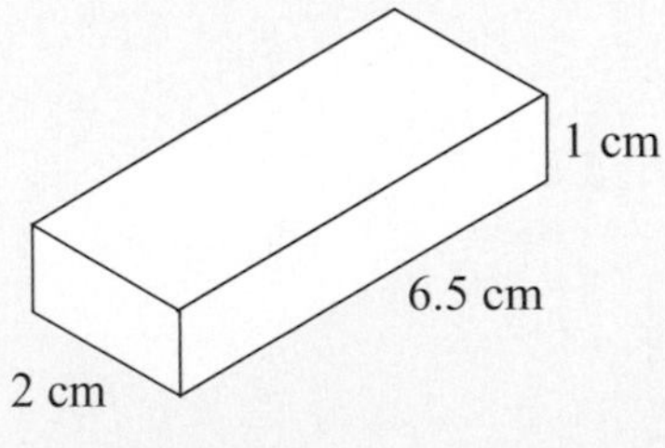

Volume = 2 × 6.5 × 1

= 13 cm^3

(b) Find the volume of the cuboid

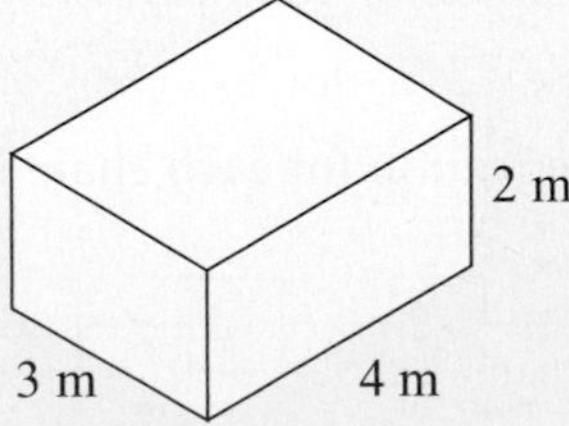

Volume = 3 × 4 × 2

= 24 m^3 (note the units)

Exercise 1M

In questions 1 to 6 work out the volume of each cuboid. Give your answer in the correct units

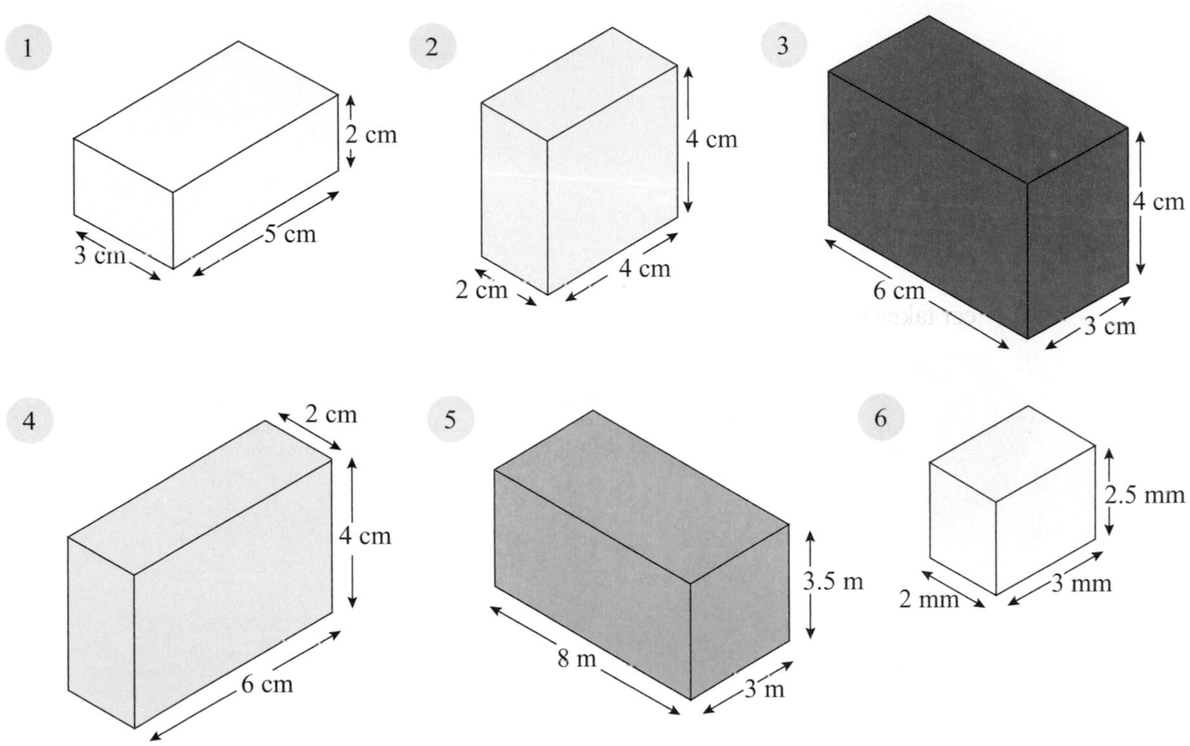

In questions 7 to 9 write down the volume of the object. All the objects are made from centimetre cubes.

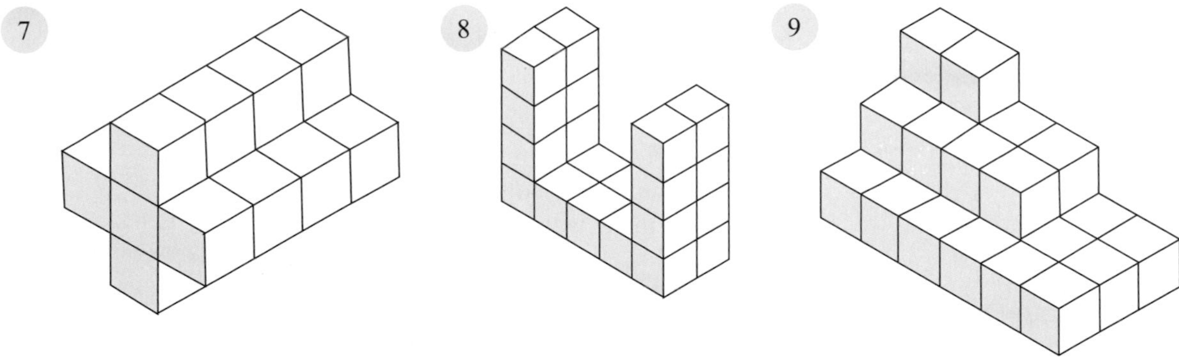

10 (a) Draw a sketch of a 4 m by 4 m by 2 m cuboid.
(b) Calculate the volume of the cuboid.
(c) Calculate the total surface area of the cuboid.

11 Calculate the volume of each girder by splitting them into cuboids. All lengths are in cm.

(a)

(b)

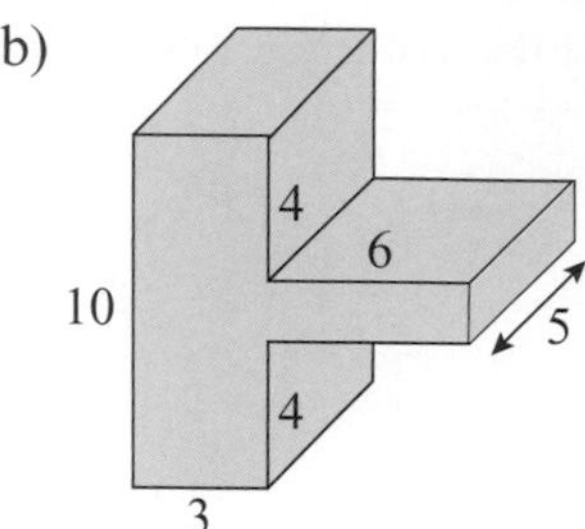

12 Farmers were asked to redesign their melons so that they could fit more melons into delivery boxes. They grew melons as cubes of side 16 cm.

The melons were delivered in cubical boxes of side 1.28 m.

How many melons could go in each box?

Exercise 1E

1 The large cube is cut into lots of identical small cubes as shown. Calculate the volume of each small cube.

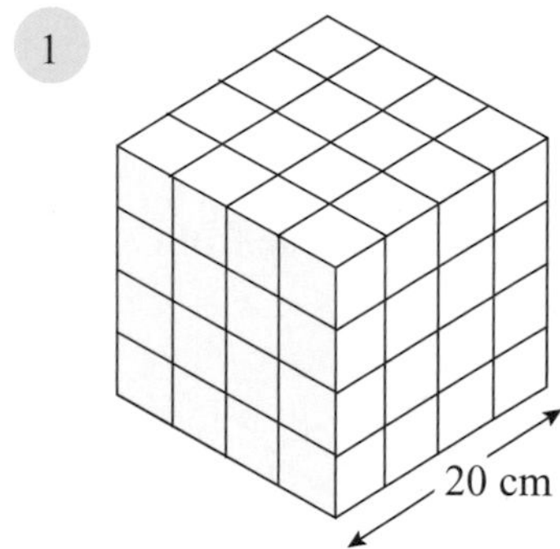

2 A mine shaft 400 m long is dug with the cross-section shown. Calculate the volume of earth which must be removed to make way for the shaft.

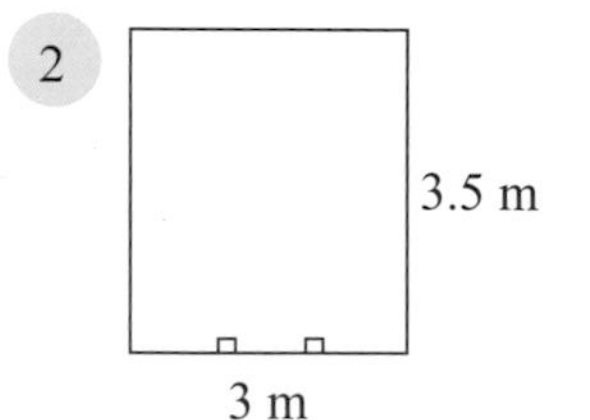

3 The diagram shows an empty swimming pool. Water is pumped into the pool at a rate of 2 m^3 per minute. How long will it take to fill the pool?

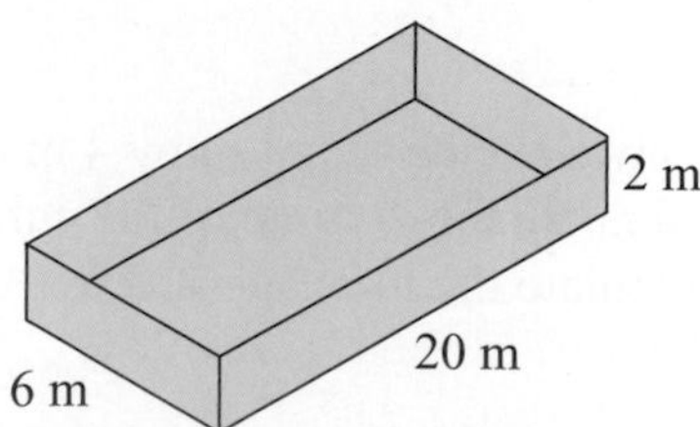

4 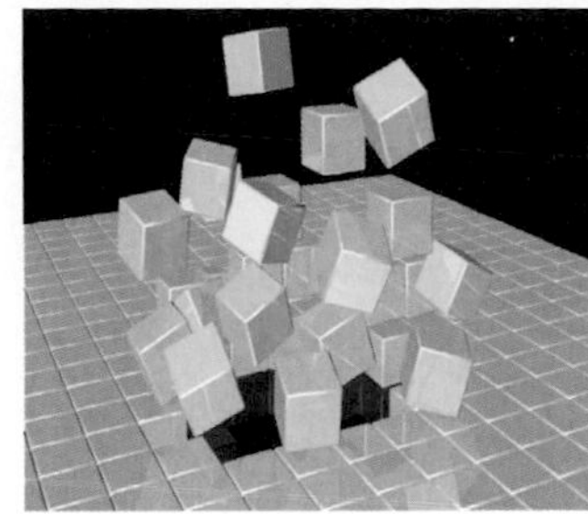

Gold cubes of side 3 cm are placed together in a flat square measuring 210 cm by 210 cm.

The cubes are used to make a square-based column with a side of 15 cm.

How tall is the column?

5 The shapes below are nets for closed boxes. Work out the volume of the box in each case, giving your answer in cubic cm.

(a) 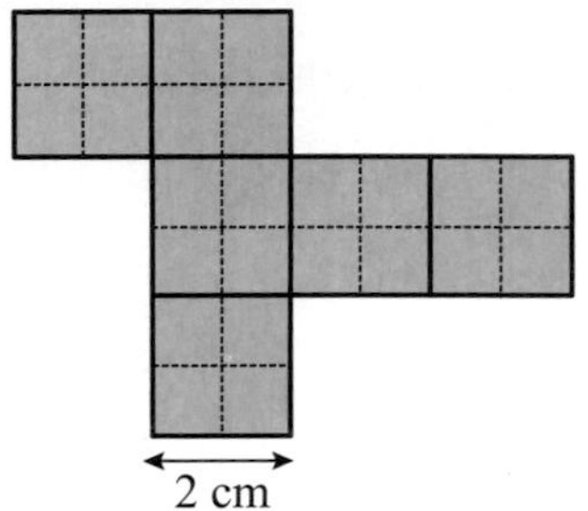

(b) 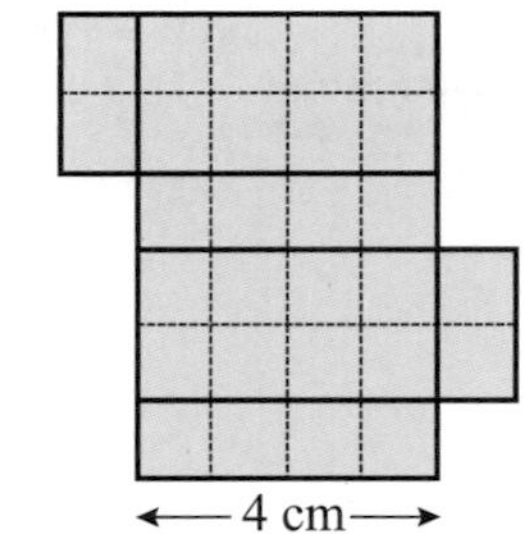

(c) 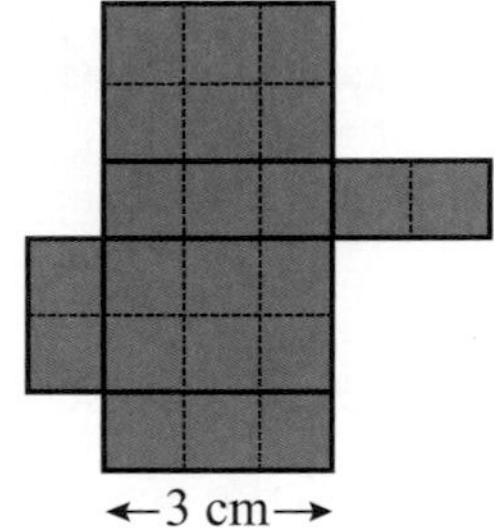

6 In a storm 2 cm of rain fell in 1 hour. Calculate the volume of water, in cm^3, which fell on the roof of the garage shown.

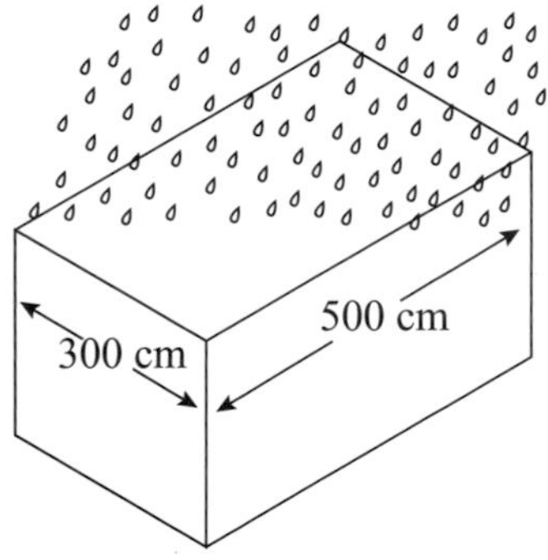

7 The inside of a spaceship orbiting the earth is a cuboid measuring 3 m by 4 m by 2 m. Unfortunately air is leaking from the spaceship at a rate of 1000 cm^3/sec. How long will it take for all the air to leak out?

8 Find the length x.

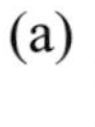

(a) 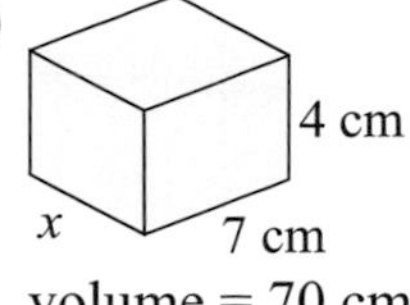

volume = 70 cm^3

(b) 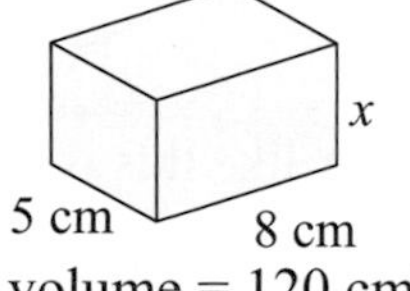

volume = 120 cm^3

(c) 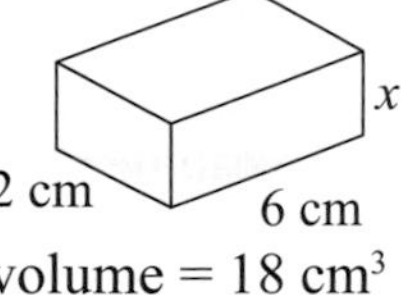

volume = 18 cm^3

(d) 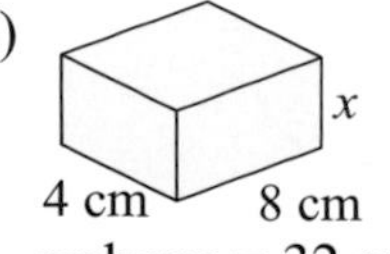

volume = 32 cm^3

(e) 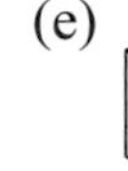

volume = 27 cm^3

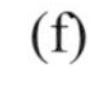

(f) 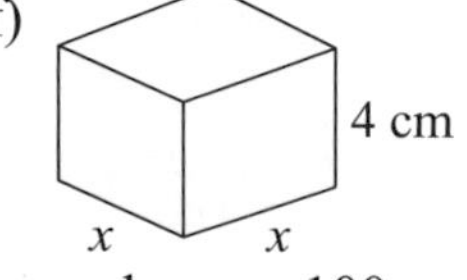

volume = 100 cm^3

9 The diagram shows an object of volume 7 cm^3. Use isometric paper to draw the following objects:
(a) a cuboid with volume 45 cm^3
(b) a T-shaped object with volume 15 cm^3
(c) an L-shaped object with volume 20 cm^3
(d) any object with a volume of 23 cm^3.

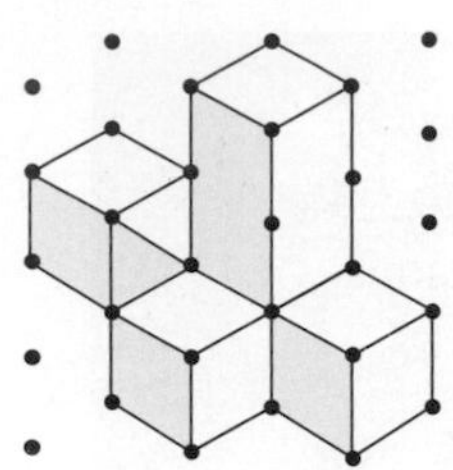

10 

The internal dimensions of the container with this lorry are 7 m by 4.2 m by 2.8 m.

It carries a number of boxes each measuring 100 cm by 98 cm by 85 cm.

What is the largest number of boxes which can be loaded?

11 Sketch a cuboid a cm b cm by c cm.

(a) Write an expression for the volume of the cuboid.
(b) Write an expression for the total surface area of the cuboid.

12 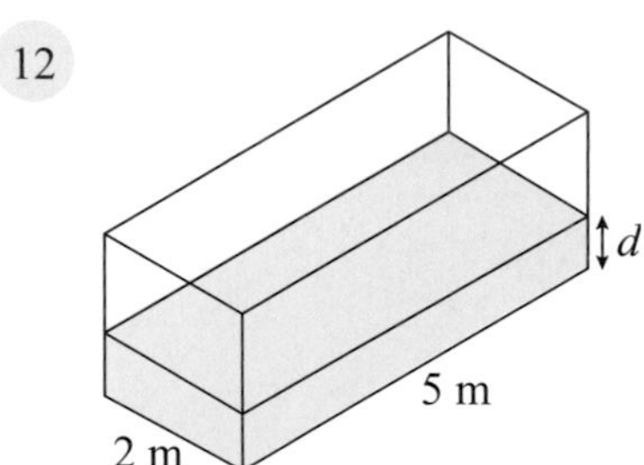

A children's paddling pool has a base 2 m by 5 m. There is 5 m^3 of water in the pool.

Calculate the depth of water d in the pool, stating the units clearly.

Prisms

The volume of the object shown can be found by dividing the object into layers. Each layer contains 6 cubes and there are 4 layers. The volume of the object is 24 cm^3.

An object which can be cut into identical layers like this is called a *prism*.

A prism has the same cross section throughout its length.

Volume of a prism = (Area of cross section) × (length)

Any cuboid is a prism since it has the same cross section throughout its length.

Find the volume of the prism shown.

All the angles are right angles and the dimensions are in cm.

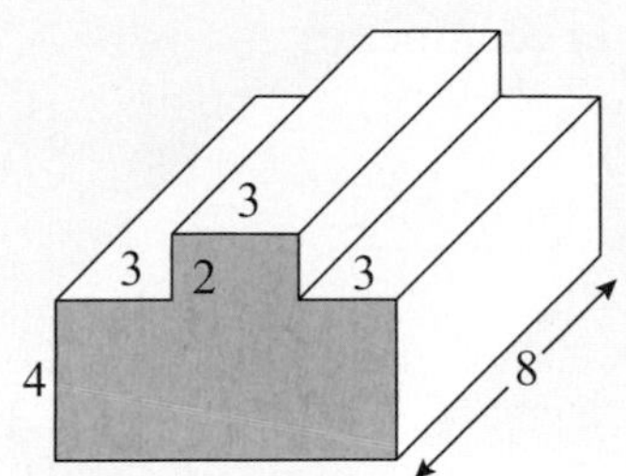

Area of cross section = $4 \times (3 + 3 + 3) + (3 \times 2)$
$= 42 \text{ cm}^2$.

Volume of prism = 42×8
$= 336 \text{ cm}^3$

Liquids

The volume of a liquid is usually given in litres or millilitres (ml)

1000 ml = 1 litre

and 1 ml is the same as 1 cm^3.

The diagram shows a cubic metre of water.

$1 \text{ m}^3 = 100 \times 100 \times 100 \text{ cm}^3$

$= 1\,000\,000 \text{ cm}^3$

So $1 \text{ m}^3 = 1\,000\,000$ ml = 1000 litres

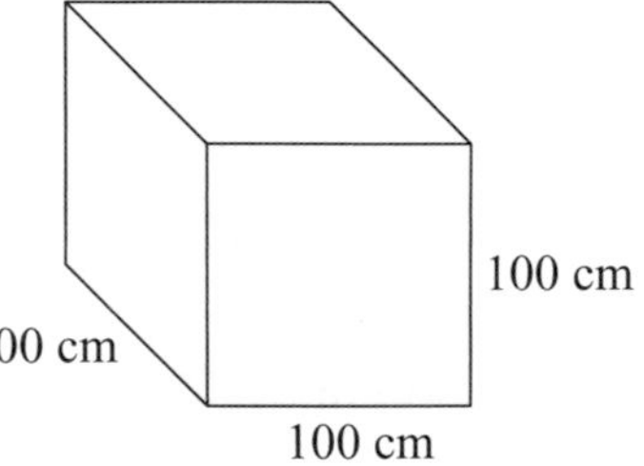

Exercise 2M

Find the volume of each prism.

1 Area of end = 3 cm^2

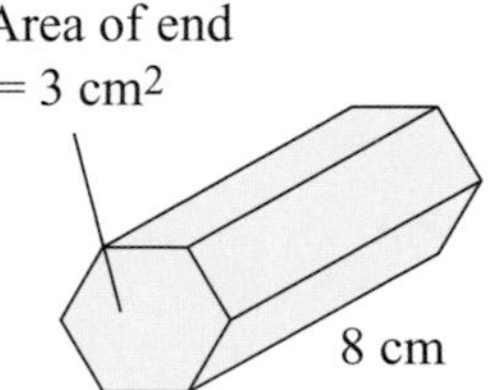

2 Area of end = 7 m^2

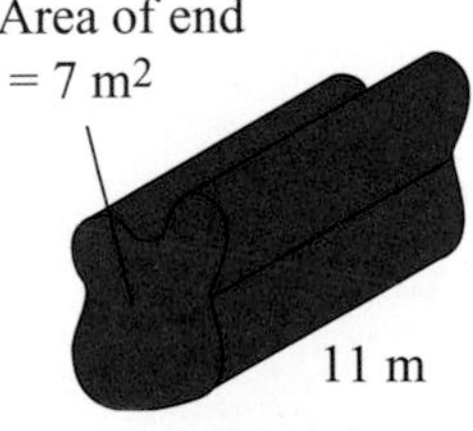

3

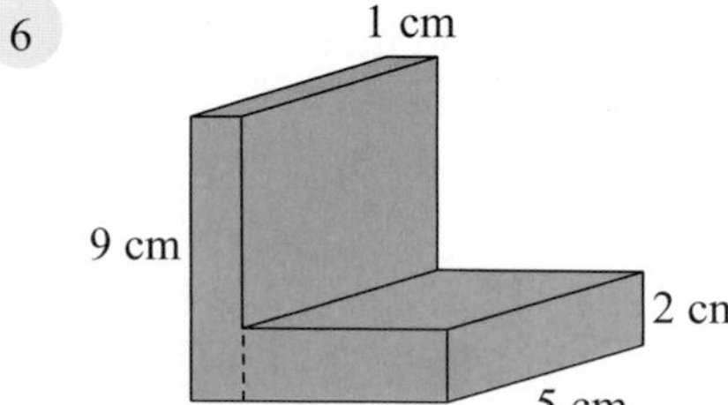

4

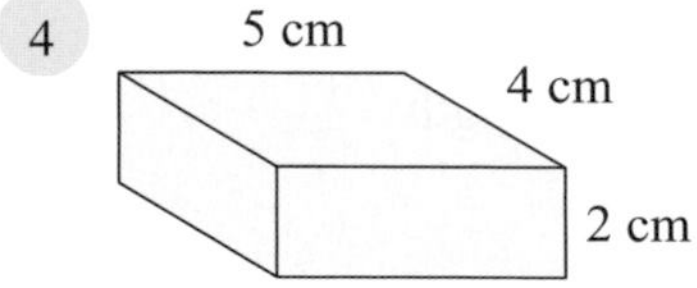

5

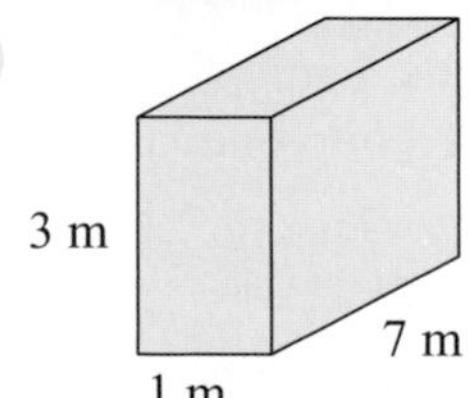

6

In questions 7 to 9 find the volume of each prism. All the angles are right angles and the dimensions are in centimetres.

7

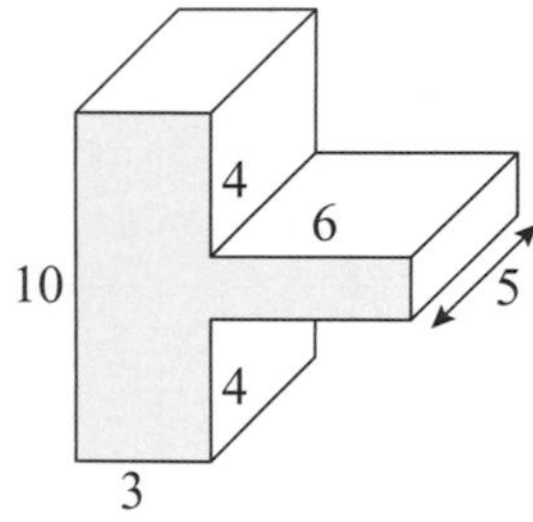

8

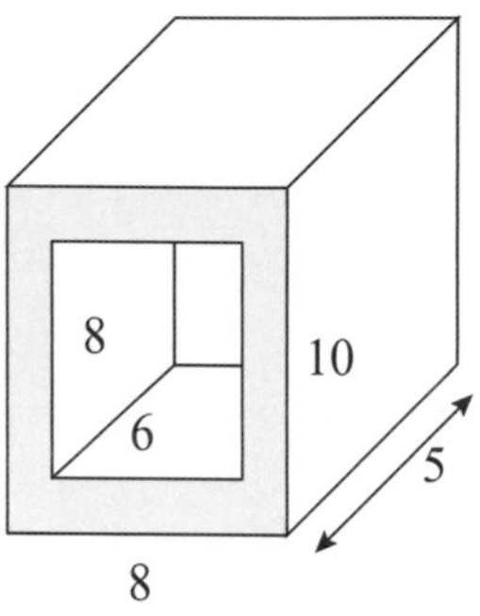

9

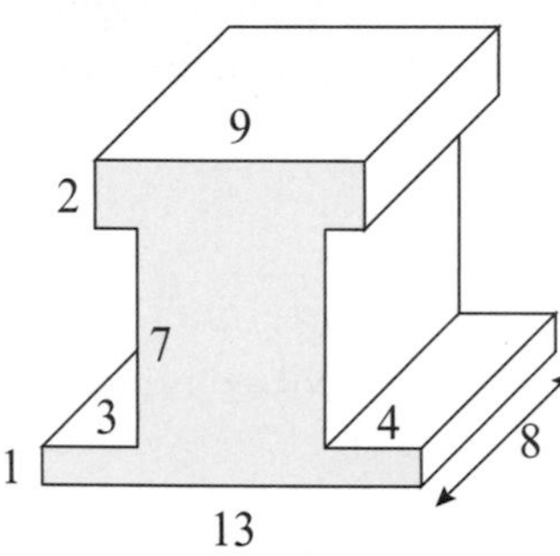

Exercise 2E

1 A uniform metal rod of length 5 m has a volume of 3750 cm^3. Find the area of the cross-section of the rod.

2 A vertical tower of height 32 m has a square cross-section. Find the length of a side of the square if the volume of the tower is 4608 m^3.

3 Find the volume, in litres, of the water trough shown.

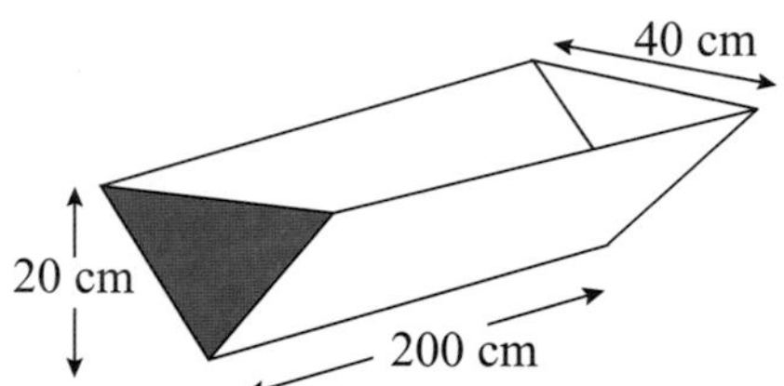

4 Find the capacity, in litres, of a rectangular tank with internal dimensions 60 cm by 20 cm by 1 m. [1 litre = 1000 cm^3]

5

A tray contains 200 ice cubes of side 2 cm. When ice melts its volume expands by 3%. Calculate the volume of water you will have when all the ice cubes melt.

6 Liquid is poured into the can shown at a rate of 20 ml/sec. How long will it take to fill the can?

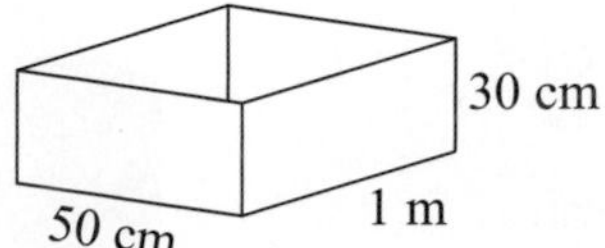

7 Two solid metal cuboids have dimensions, in cm, $2 \times 4 \times 10$ and $3 \times 3 \times 5$. The cuboids are melted down and formed into one large cube. Find the length of one side of the cube.

8 A cuboid has dimensions, in cm, $a \times b \times c$. The total volume of n of these cuboids is 3640 cm^3. Find the value of n if $a = 5$, $b = 7$ and $c = b + 1$.

9 The cross section of a plaster moulding for ceilings is a quarter circle cut from a square. 1 cm^3 of the plaster weighs 1.2 g. Calculate the weight of a 4 m length of this moulding.

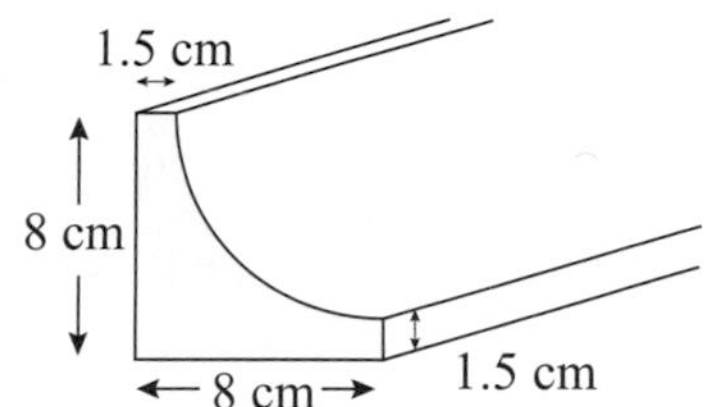

10 The diagram shows the cross section of a swimming pool. Water is pumped into the pool at a rate of 20 litres/sec. How long, in hours and minutes, will it take to fill the pool?

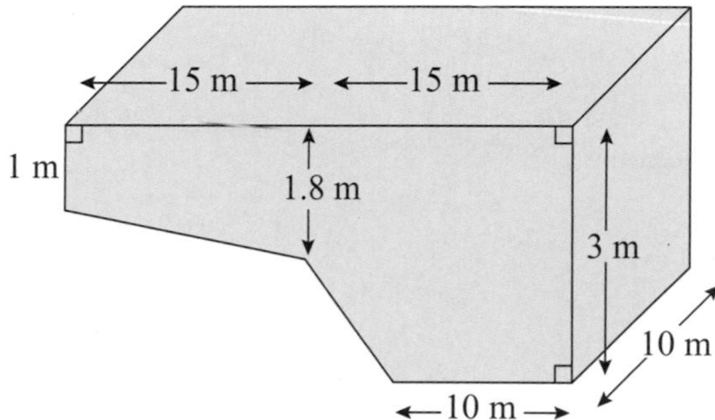

Cylinders

A cylinder is a prism because it has the same cross section throughout its length.

Volume = (area of cross section) × (length)

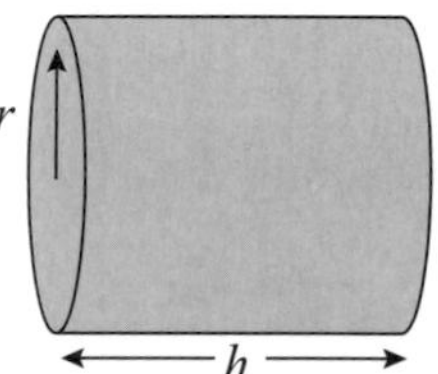

Volume = $\pi r^2 h$

(a) A cylinder has radius 3 cm and length 10 cm. Find the volume of the cylinder.

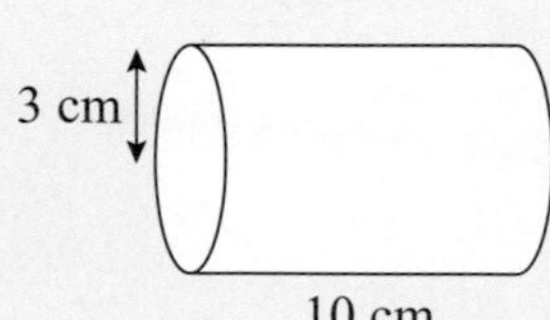

$V = \pi r^2 h$

$V = \pi \times 3^2 \times 10$

$V = 283$ cm^3 (to 3 s.f.)

(b) Find the capacity, in litres, of the oil drum shown

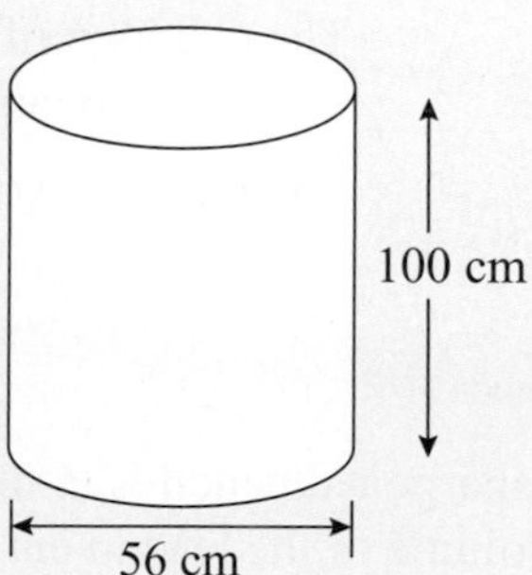

The oil drum is a cylinder.

Volume of oil drum = $\pi \times 28^2 \times 100$

= 246 000 cm^3 (to 3 s.f.)

Capacity of oil drum = 246 litres (to 3 s.f.)

Exercise 3M

Give answers correct to 3 significant figures, where necessary.

1 Find the volume of each cylinder.

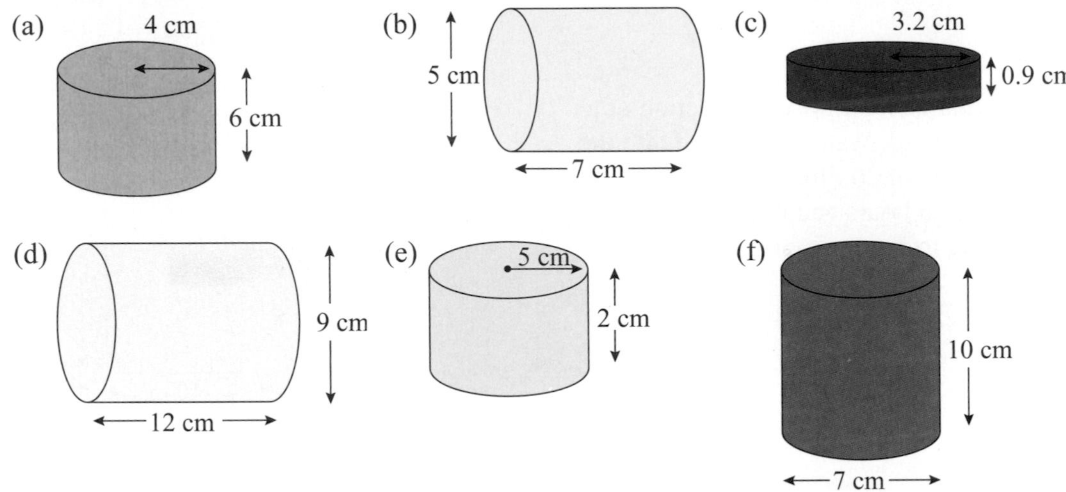

2 Cylinders are cut along the axis of symmetry. Find the volume of each object.

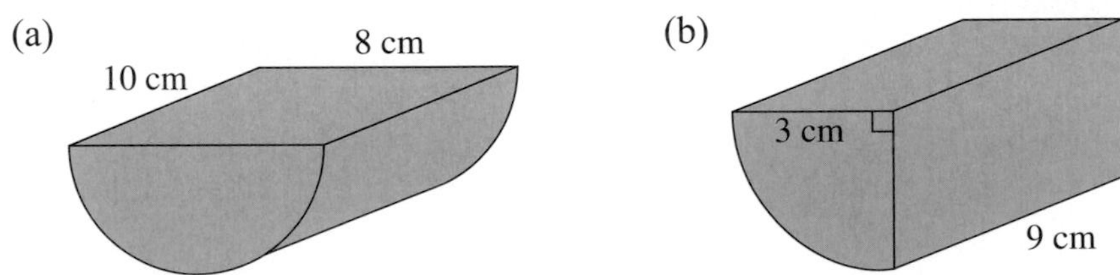

3 Find the volume in litres of a cylindrical tank of radius 40 cm and height 35 cm.

4 

The diameter of a CD is 12 cm and the hole in the middle has diameter 1.6 cm. The thickness of the CD is 1.3 mm.

Calculate the volume of plastic in the CD.

5 The lead in an unsharpened pencil is in the shape of a cylinder of diameter 2 mm and length 16 cm. Find the volume of the lead in cm^3.

6 A mine shaft 200 m long is dug with the cross-section shown. Calculate the volume of earth which must be removed to make way for the shaft.

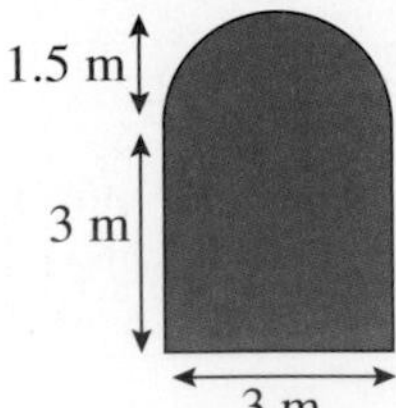

7 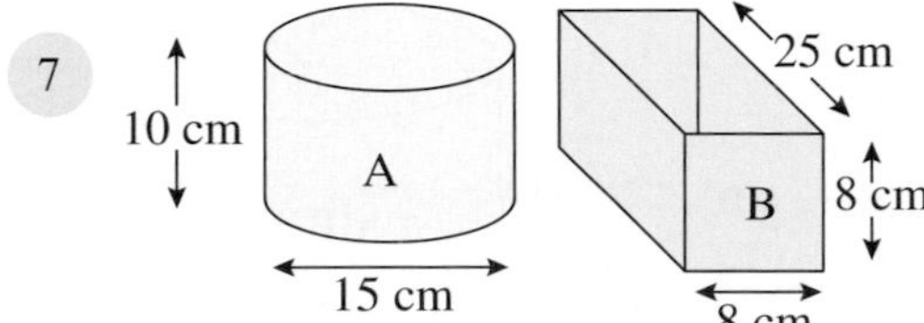

Water is poured from the full cylinder A into the empty tank B. Will all the water go in?

8 An empty cylindrical tank of height 70 cm and diameter 1 metre is to be filled from a tap which delivers water at the rate of 150 ml per second. How long will it take to fill the tank? Give your answer to the nearest minute.

9 The sector angle of the red piece of this pie graph is 40°. The radius and thickness of the graph are 20 cm and 4 cm respectively. Calculate the volume of the red piece.

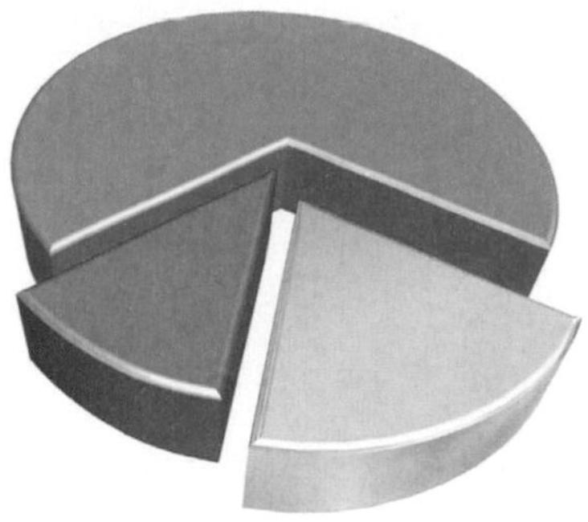

Exercise 3E

1 

The can shown has a capacity of 385 ml. Its internal diameter is 7 cm. Calculate the internal height of the can, correct to the nearest tenth of a cm.

2 A solid sculpture weighing 5.7 kg is made of metal and 1 cm^3 of the metal weighs 7.8 grams. The sculpture is to be melted down into solid cylinders of diameter and height 4 cm. How many complete cylinders can be made?

3 The cross-section of a metal pipe is shown below. Calculate the volume of metal used to make a pipe of length 10 m.

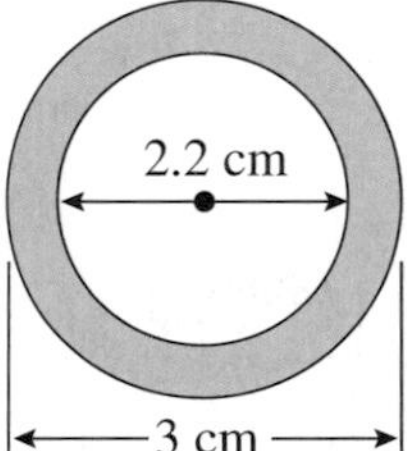

4 Rain water from a garage roof is collected in a cylindrical water butt which is initially empty. The roof measures 6 m by 2.5 m and the diameter of the water butt is 60 cm. In a storm 1.2 cm of rain fell on the roof. What will be the depth of the water in the butt?

5 How many times can the cylindrical glass be filled from the large drum which is full of milk?

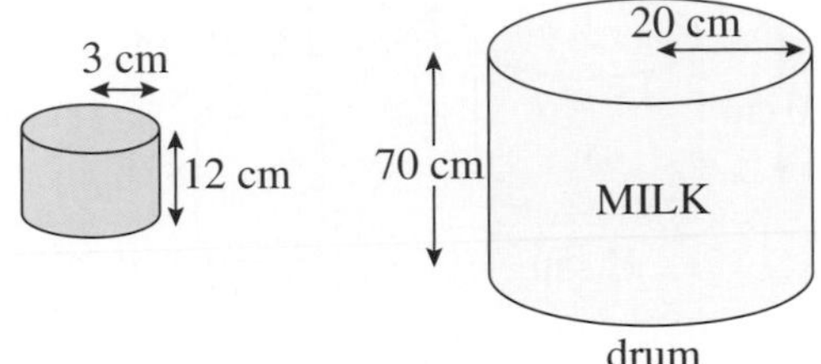

6 'Vache qui rit' cheese portions are packed in circular boxes. Each portion is 1.4 cm thick and has a top surface which is a sector of a circle of radius 5 cm.

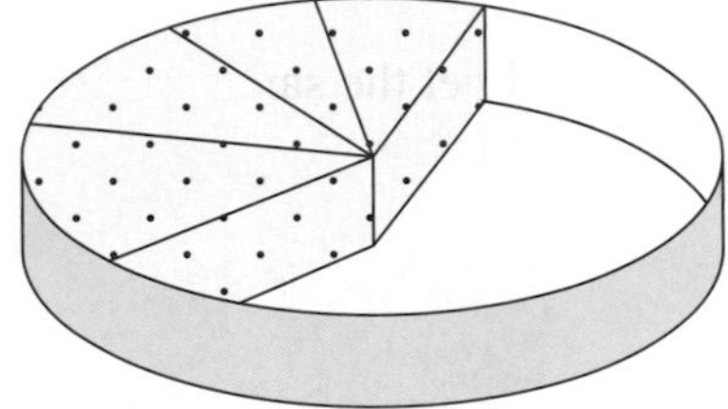

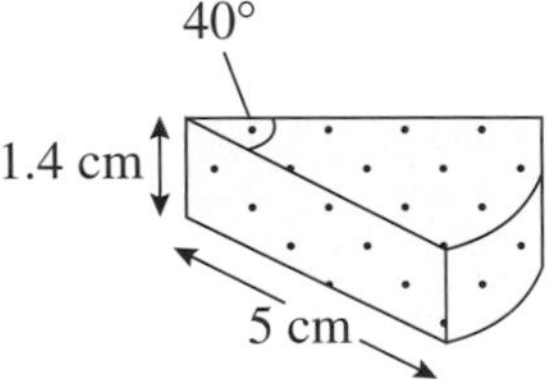

(a) Calculate the volume of the cheese in a full box and hence the volume of one portion.

(b) 100 cm^3 of 'Vache qui rit' weighs 113 grams. Find the weight of one portion of cheese.

7 A solid rectangular block has dimensions 35 cm × 28 cm × 18 cm. Calculate the volume of the largest cylinder which can be cut from this block.

8 A cylindrical can of internal radius 20 cm stands upright. It contains water to a depth of 30 cm. Calculate the rise in the level of the water when a brick of volume 1800 cm^3 is immersed in the water.

9 Six chrome balls, each of volume 35 cm^3, are melted down and made into a solid cylinder. The diameter and height of the new cylinder are equal. Calculate the height of the cylinder.

CHECK YOURSELF ON SECTIONS 6.1 AND 6.2

1 More algebra

(a) Solve the equations

(i) $5 = 3x + 4$ (ii) $13 - 4x = 8 + x$ (iii) $3(x + 1) + x = 9$

(b) Find the number I am thinking of.

(i) If I add 5 to the number and then multiply the result by 3, the answer is 19.

(ii) If I add 6 to the number and then multiply the result by 4, I get the same answer as when I subtract 2 from the number and then multiply the result by 6.

(c) The height of this picture is $(x + 4)$ cm and its perimeter is $(6x + 14)$ cm. The width of the picture is 15 cm. Find the area of the picture.

2 Volume of objects

(a) Find the volume of each object. All lengths are in cm

(i)

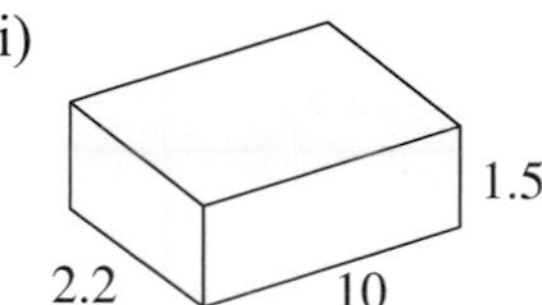

(ii)

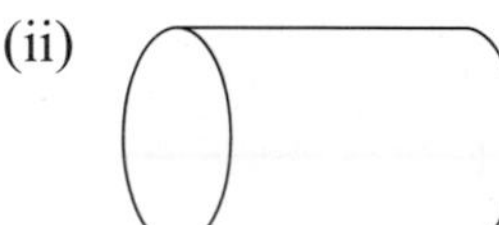

cylinder of radius 6 cm and length 8 cm

(b)

The box shown has a square base. The height of the box is 60 cm. Find the length of each side of the base if the volume of the box is 181500 cm^3.

6.3 Percentages 2

In this section you will:

- review interchanging between percentages, decimals and fractions
- find percentages of quantities
- increase and decrease quantities by a percentage

Percentages, decimals and fractions

Exercise 1M Hidden words

(a) Start in the top left box.
(b) Change the number to a fraction, decimal or % as required.
(c) Find this answer in the top corner of another box.
(d) Write down the letter in that box.
(e) Repeat step (b), (c) and (d) until you arrive back at the top left box.
(f) Write down the message.

26% 30% → fraction	0.3% S (1 − 0.94) → %	32% A (0.1 + 0.05) → fraction	$33\frac{1}{3}$% N $\left(\frac{1}{2} - 0.4\right)$ → decimal	0.75 Y 80% → fraction
$\frac{3}{20}$ G (10 ÷ 1000) → %	35% E (0.1 − 0.01) → fraction	5% S $\frac{3}{5}$ → decimal	0.15 Q 45% → fraction	$\frac{11}{25}$ I $\frac{3}{1000}$ → %
95% A half of 0.1 → %	$\frac{3}{10}$ P $\frac{3}{4}$ → decimal	0.125 H 44% → fraction	6% S (10% of 1.5) → decimal	1% O $\left(\frac{3}{8} - \frac{1}{8}\right)$ → %
0.1 E 3% → fraction	$\frac{9}{20}$ U 2% → decimal	0.02 A $\frac{2}{3}$ → %	$\frac{4}{5}$ T 16% → decimal	$\frac{3}{100}$ W $\frac{1}{8}$ → decimal
0.16 H $\frac{8}{25}$ → %	$66\frac{2}{3}$% R $\left(\frac{1}{4} + 0.1\right)$ → %	0.6 K $\frac{1}{3}$ → %	$\frac{9}{100}$ S $\frac{13}{50}$ → %	25% R 0.95 → %

Finding a percentage

(a) Work out 18% of £5600

Either: 18% of £5600

$= \frac{18}{100} \times \frac{5600}{1}$

$= £1008$

Or: 18% of £5600

$= 0.18 \times 5600$

$= £1008$

(b) Change a mark of 17 out of 40 into a percentage.

To change a fraction to a percentage, multiply by 100.

$\therefore$ Answer $= \frac{17}{40} \times 100$

$= 42.5\ \%$

Exercise 2M

1 Work out the following. Give your answer correct to the nearest penny, where necessary.

(a) 11% of £265 (b) 3.5% of £2450

(c) 16% of £1.95 (d) 8.2% of £16.50

2 Write down the missing number, as a *decimal*

(a) 62% of 241 = ■ × 241 (b) 6% of 3000 = ■ × 3000

(c) 8% of 425 = ■ × 425 (d) 3.2% of 780 = ■ × 780

(e) 17.5% of 600 = ■ × 600 (f) 125% of 399 = ■ × 399

3 In a spelling test Ayesha got 52 out of 80. What was her mark as a percentage?

4 

What percentage of these shoes are green?

5 What percentage of the letters in the box are

(a) vowels?

(b) the letter R?

Give your answers correct to 1 d.p.

S	M	O	K	I	N	G	I	S
N	O	T	P	A	R	T	I	C
U	L	A	R	L	Y	G	O	O
D	F	O	R	Y	O	U	O	K

6 A breakfast cereal contains the following ingredients by weight:
Toasted Oat Flakes 720 g, Raw Sugar 34 g, Oat Bran 76 g,
Honey 26 g, Banana 57 g, Hazelnuts 12 g.
What percentage of the packet is Oat Bran?
Give your answer correct to one decimal place.

7 The table shows the results when three makes of car were tested for a particular fault in the ventilation system.

(a) What percentage of the cars which failed were Fords?

(b) What percentage of the Rolls Royce cars failed?

	Rolls Royce	Renault	Ford
Failed	2	13	25
Passed	17	474	1756
Total			

8

	Men	Women	Total
colour blind	55	37	92
not colour blind	473	394	867
Total	528	431	959

The tables shows the results of a test for colour blindness conducted on 959 people.

(a) What percentage of the men were colour blind?

(b) What percentage of the colour blind people were women?

9 The table gives details of the ages of children in a school with 884 pupils.

(a) What percentage of the under-15s are boys?

(b) What percentage of the pupils in the whole school are girls?

(c) What percentage of the girls are 15 and over?

[Give your answers correct to 1 d.p.]

	Boys	Girls
Under 15	215	184
15 and over	223	262

10 At a disco there were x boys and 72 girls. Find x if approximately 45% of the people at the disco were boys.

11 Find the odd one out in each list.

(a) 2% $\quad \frac{10}{50} \quad 0.2 \quad \frac{3}{15} \quad \frac{9}{45}$

(b) $\frac{2}{5} \quad 0.4 \quad 40\% \quad \frac{8}{20} \quad \frac{0.2}{0.5} \quad \frac{1}{2.5} \quad \frac{45}{120}$

(a) Increase a price of £6800 by 17%

New price = 117% of £6800

$= 1.17 \times 6800$

= £7956

(b) Decrease a price of £584 by 2%

New price = 98% of £584

$= 0.98 \times 584$

= £572.32

Exercise 2E

1 Find the missing number as a decimal

[For example: To increase £480 by 4%, work out 480 × **1.04**].

(a) To increase £840 by 8%, work out 840 × (?).
(b) To increase £56.50 by 10%, work out 56.5 × (?).
(c) To decrease 660 kg by 3%, work out 660 × (?).
(d) To decrease 4400 m² by 15%, work out 4400 × (?).

2 The 2009 price of a diving holiday is £860.
Calculate the 2010 price, which is 5% higher.

3 Find the new price of a necklace costing £85, after the price is reduced by 7%.

4 (a) Increase a price of £12.95 by 15%.
(b) Increase a price of £2560 by 10%.
(c) Decrease a price of £249.99 by 5%.
(d) Decrease a price of £6.3 million by 2%.

5 During the 2009 season the average home crowd watching Manchester United was 77600 and the average price paid for admission was £45.
For the 2010 season the average crowd was 3% less but the average admission price was increased by 8%.
How much money was paid for admission for the 19 home games in the 2010 season? Give your answer correct to the nearest thousand pounds.

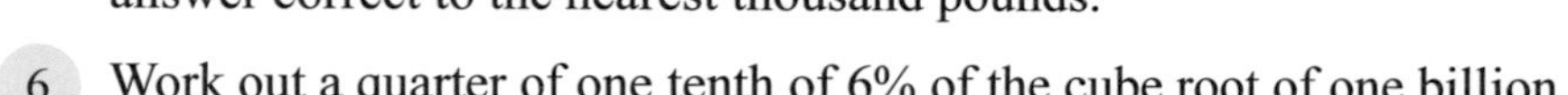

6 Work out a quarter of one tenth of 6% of the cube root of one billion.

7 (a) Calculate the volume of the cuboid shown.
(b) Calculate the new volume when the length width and height of the cuboid are each increased by 10%

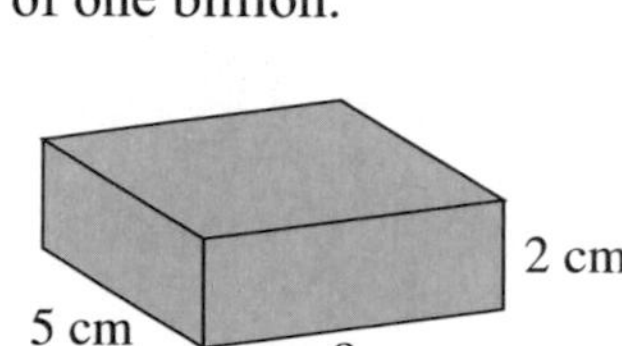

8 The island state of Gandia is divided between 3 tribes A, B and C as shown. Tribe A subsequently starts a war and increases its land area by 15%. The area controlled by tribe B is reduced by 5% and the area controlled by tribe C is reduced by $13\frac{1}{3}$%. Draw a possible new map of the country and state the area now controlled by each tribe.

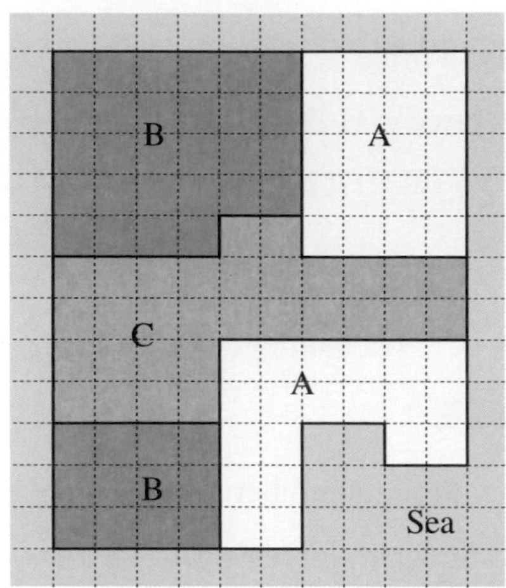

9 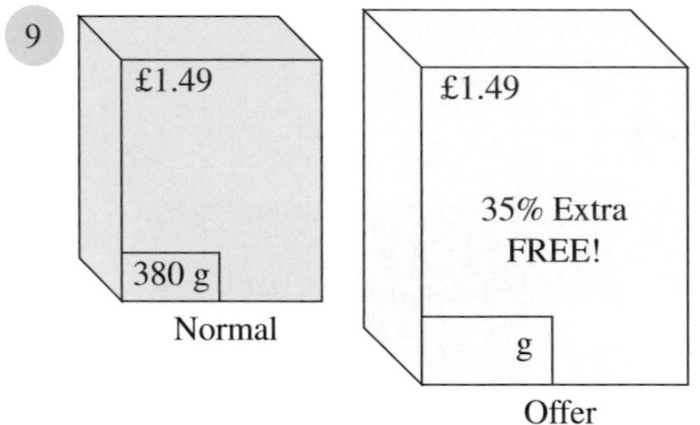

As part of a special promotion, the weight of Corn Flakes sold in a packet is increased by 35%, while the price remains the same. Calculate the weight of Corn Flakes in the special 'offer' size.

10 The cost of printing a book depends on two factors: paper costs (32%) and manufacturing costs (68%).
In 2010 it cost £95 000 to print 100 000 copies of Philip Pullman's latest book. By 2011 the paper costs had increased by 27% and the manufacturing costs had increased by 4%. Find the cost of printing 100 000 copies of the book in 2011.

11 The formula connecting z, a, b and n is $z = a(b^n)$.

(a) Calculate, to 3 s.f., the value of z when $a = 100$, $b = 1.8$ and $n = 3$.
(b) Calculate the new value of z after both a and b are increased by 20%, while n remains the same.

12 The new balance on Mr Roe's credit card account is £967.60 (i.e. he *owes* £967.60). He cannot afford to pay the bill in full and on March 1 he repays only the minimum allowed, which is 5% of the balance. Interest, at 1.6% per month, is charged on the remaining debt [i.e. £967.60 – (5% of £967.60)].

(a) How much does Mr Roe pay on March 1?
(b) How much does Mr Roe owe the credit card company on April 1? [Assume he makes no further purchases with the card].

6.4 Probability

In section 6.4 you will learn about:

- the probability of events not occurring
- the expected number of times an event will occur
- probability involving two events
- experimental probability

Events occurring or not occurring

- If the probability of an event occurring is p, then the probability of it not occurring is $1 - p$.
- Ten identical discs numbered 1, 2, 3, 4, 5, 6, 7, 8, 9, 10 are put into a bag. One disc is selected at random.

  In this example there are 10 possible equally likely outcomes of a trial.

  (a) The probability of selecting a '2' $= \frac{1}{10}$

  This may be written p(selecting a '2') $= \frac{1}{10}$

  (b) p (not selecting a 2) $= 1 - \frac{1}{10}$

  $= \frac{9}{10}$

  (c) p (selecting a number greater than 7) $= \frac{3}{10}$

  (d) p (not selecting a number greater than 7) $= 1 - \frac{3}{10} = \frac{7}{10}$

Exercise 1M

1 One card is picked at random from a pack of 52.
Find the probability that it is

(a) a diamond (b) not a diamond

(c) the King of hearts (d) not the King of hearts

2 Seven discs numbered 3, 4, 5, 7, 9, 11, 12 are placed in a bag. One disc is selected at random.
Find the probability that it is

(a) a 5 (b) not a 5

(c) an odd number (d) an even number

3 4 5 7

9 11 12

3 With this spinner find the probability of getting:

(a) a 7 (b) not a 7 (c) a prime number

(d) a number greater than 6

4 The probability of a drawing pin landing 'point up' is 0.61. Find the probability of the drawing pin landing 'point down'.

5 A South Seas diver collected 965 oysters. Just one of the oysters contained a pearl. One oyster is chosen at random. Find the probability that

(a) it contains a pearl

(b) it does not contain a pearl.

6 A dice has its faces numbered 2, 3, 3, 3, 4, 7. Find the probability of rolling

(a) a '7'

(b) an even number.

7 One card is selected at random from the eight cards shown.

Find the probability of selecting

(a) the ace of diamonds (b) a king

(c) an ace (d) a red card

8 If Mala throws a 3 or a 5 on her next throw when playing 'Snakes and Ladders' she will slide down a snake on the board. What is the probability that she will avoid a snake on her next throw?

9 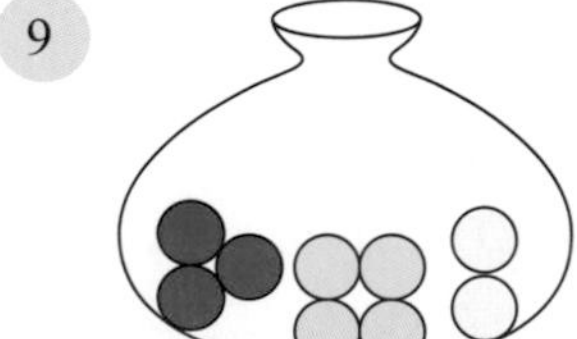

A bag contains 9 balls: 3 red, 4 blue and 2 yellow.

(a) Find the probability of selecting a red ball.

(b) The 2 yellow balls are replaced by 2 blue balls. Find the probability of selecting a blue ball now.

10 Nicole has 3 kings and 1 ace. She shuffles the cards and takes one without looking.

Nicole asks two of her friends about the probability of getting an ace.

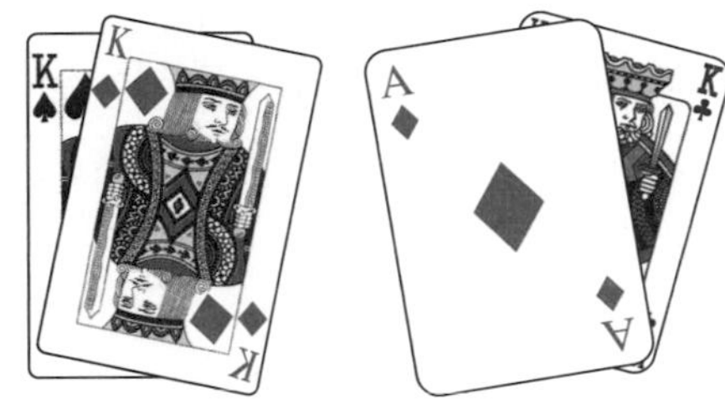

Angie says:

'It is $\frac{1}{3}$ because there are 3 kings and 1 ace.'

Syline says

'It is $\frac{1}{4}$ because there are 4 cards and only 1 ace.'

Which of her friends is right?

11 A field contains 10 cows, 5 horses and 1 lion. The lion is thought to be tame and half of the cows are mad. One animal is chosen at random. Find the probability that the animal:

(a) is mad

(b) enjoys eating grass

(c) might eat you.

Expected number of successes

When an experiment (like rolling a dice or tossing a coin) is repeated several times, we can calculate the number of times we expect an event to occur. Call the event in which we are interested a 'success'.

Expected number of successes = (probability of a success) × (number of trials)

(a) A fair dice is rolled 540 times. How many times would you expect to roll a '2'.

$p(\text{rolling a } 2) = \frac{1}{6}$

Expected number of 2s $= \frac{1}{6} \times 540$

$= 90$

(b) On a spinner the probability of getting a 7 is $\frac{2}{9}$. How many times would you expect to spin a 7 if you make 225 spins?

Expected number of 7s $= \frac{2}{9} \times 225$

$= 50$

Exercise 1E

1. A fair dice is rolled 480 times. How many times would you expect to roll:
   (a) a 'two'
   (b) an odd number?

2. A spinner, with 12 equal sectors, is spun 600 times. How often would you expect to spin:
   (a) a coloured sector
   (b) an even number
   (c) a vowel
   (d) a prime number?
   [a prime number is divisible only by itself and by one]

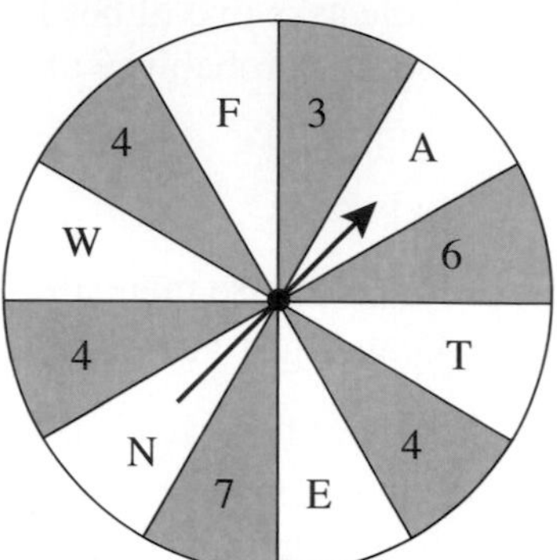

3. A coin is biased so that the probability of tossing a 'head' is 0.58.
   (a) How many 'heads' would you expect when the coin is tossed 200 times?
   (b) How many 'tails' would you expect when the coin is tossed 1000 times?

4. One ball is selected at random from the bag shown and then replaced. This procedure is repeated 400 times. How many times would you expect to select:
   (a) a blue ball,
   (b) a green ball?

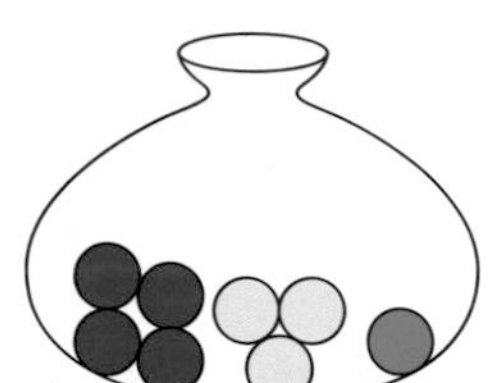

5. Mo puts these numbered balls in a bag.
   (a) He shakes the bag and takes one ball without looking. What is the probability of getting a '2'?
   (b) Mo wants to put more balls in the bag so that the chance of getting a '4' is *twice* the chance of getting a '3'. What balls could he put in the bag?

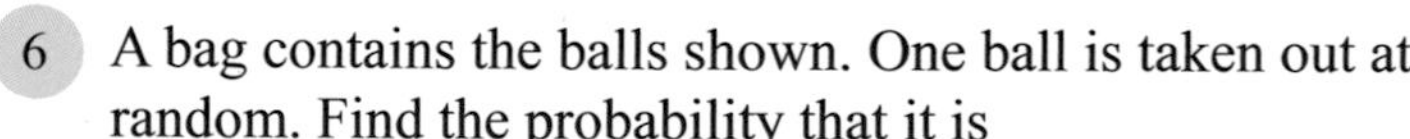

6. A bag contains the balls shown. One ball is taken out at random. Find the probability that it is
   (a) red (b) not red (c) blue
   One more red ball and one more blue ball are added to the bag.
   (d) Find the new probability of selecting a red ball from the bag.

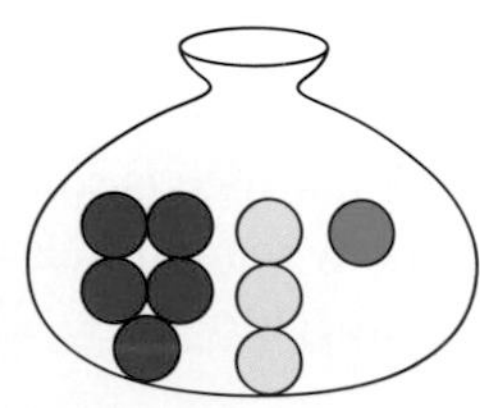

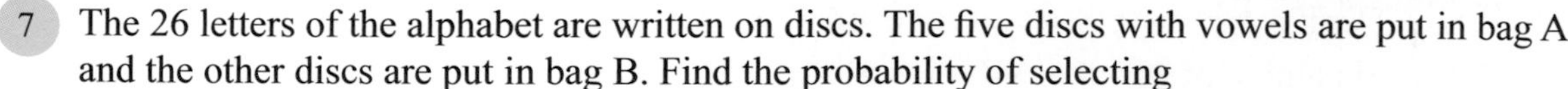

7. The 26 letters of the alphabet are written on discs. The five discs with vowels are put in bag A and the other discs are put in bag B. Find the probability of selecting
   (a) an 'o' from bag A
   (b) a 'z' from bag B
   (c) a 'w' from bag A

8 Mark played a card game with Paul. The cards were dealt so that both players received two cards. Mark's cards were a five and a four. Paul's first card was a six.

Find the probability that Paul's second card was

(a) a five (b) a picture card [a King, Queen or Jack].

9 A shopkeeper is keen to sell his stock of left-handed scissors. He has read that 9% of the population is left-handed. What is the probability that the next person to enter his shop is right-handed?

10 (a) Steve has taken a number of cards at random from a pack. The probability of picking a red card from Steve's cards is $\frac{3}{5}$. What is the probability of picking a black card?
(b) How many cards of each colour *could* there be in Steve's cards?
(c) Write down another possibility for the number of cards of each colour that are in Steve's cards.

11 One person is selected at random from a group of 2175 tourists visiting Big Ben. What is the probability that the person chosen will have his or her birthday that year on a Sunday?

12 One ball is selected at random from a bag containing m white balls and n green balls. What is the probability of selecting a green ball?

13 A dice has its six faces marked

0p, 0p, 0p, 0p, 5p, 20p.

In a game at a school fair players pay 5p to roll the dice and they win the amount shown on the dice.

During the afternoon the game is played 540 times.

(a) How much money would be paid by the people playing the game?
(b) How many times would you expect the dice to show '20p'?
(c) How many times would you expect the dice to show '5p'?
(d) How much profit or loss would you expect the stall to make?

14 At another stall at the fair players pay 20p to spin the pointer on the board shown. Players win the amount shown by the pointer.

The game is played 800 times.

Work out the expected profit or loss on this game.

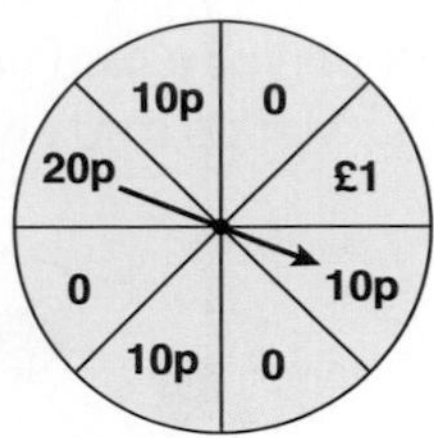

15 A dice is biased so that the probability of rolling a 'six' is x [x is a fraction].

(a) How many sixes would you expect when the dice is rolled 360 times?

(b) How many times would you expect not to get a six when the dice is rolled 200 times?

Two events : listing possible outcomes

When an experiment involves two events, it is usually helpful to make a list of all the possible outcomes. When there is a large number of outcomes, it is important to be systematic in making the list.

- Coins

(a) Using H for 'head' and T for 'tail', two coins can land as:

H H
H T
T H
T T

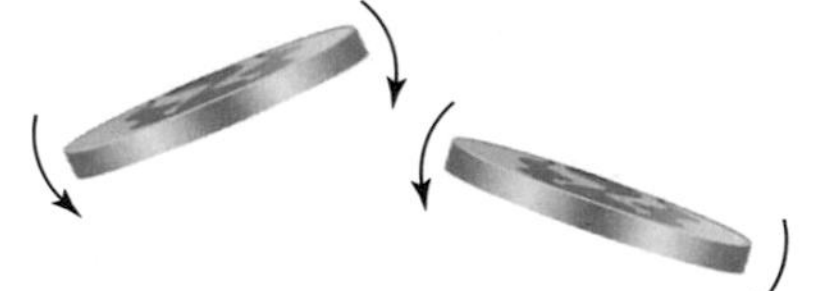

(b) Three coins can land as:

Notice that the outcomes in the boxes are the outcomes for two coins, as above.

H	H	H	T	H	H
H	H	T	T	H	T
H	T	H	T	T	H
H	T	T	T	T	T

- Two dice

When a red dice is thrown with a white dice, the outcomes are (red dice first):
(1, 1), (1, 2), (1, 3), (1, 4), (1, 5), (1, 6), (2, 1), (2, 2), (2, 3).....(6, 6).

The 36 equally likely outcomes can be shown on a grid. Point A shows a 4 on the red dice and a 5 on the white dice. Point B shows a 2 on the red dice and a 4 on the white dice.

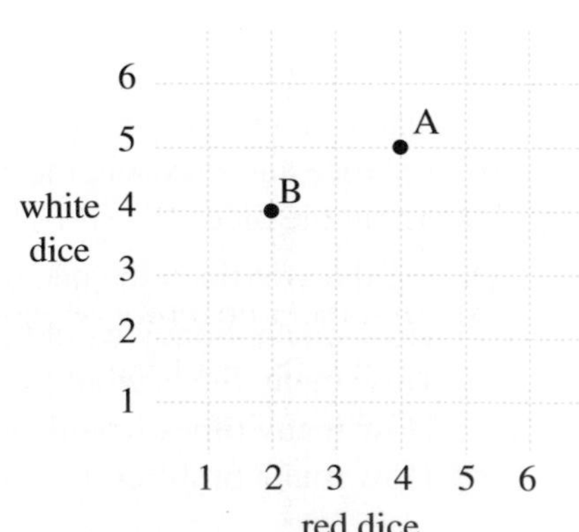

The probability of getting a total of 10 on two dice can be found:

$$p(\text{total is } 10) = \frac{(\text{number of ways of getting a total of } 10)}{(\text{number of possible outcomes})}$$

$$= \frac{3}{36}$$

Exercise 2M

1 Roll a pair of dice 108 times and in a tally chart record the frequency of obtaining the totals from 2 to 12.

Total	Frequency
2	
3	
⋮	
⋮	
12	

2 (a) Work out the expected probability of getting a total of 5 when two dice are rolled together.

Compare your answer with the experimental probability of getting a total of 5 obtained in the experiment in question 1.

(b) Work out the expected probability of other totals and compare them with the experimental results.

3 A red dice is thrown first and then a blue dice is thrown.

(a) Find the probability that the score on the blue dice is the same as the score on the red dice.

(b) Find the probability that the score on the blue dice is one more than the score on the red dice.

4 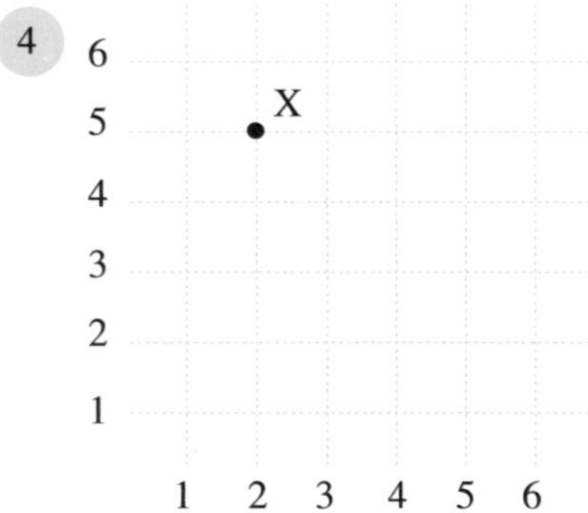

Two dice are rolled together and the *difference* is found. In the grid the point X has a difference of 3 obtained by rolling a 2 and a 5.

Find the expected probability of obtaining a difference of (a) 3

(b) 0

5 (a) List all the outcomes when three coins are tossed together.

(b) Find the probability of getting

(i) exactly one head

(ii) three tails.

6 (a) List all the outcomes when four coins are tossed together.
(b) Find the probability of getting
(i) exactly two heads
(ii) exactly one tail
(iii) four heads

7 (a) How many outcomes are possible when one coin is tossed five times?
(b) In a soccer knock-out competition, Barcelona won the toss five times in a row. What is the probability of this happening?

Exercise 2E

1 A bag contains a 1p coin, a 10p coin and a 20p coin. Two coins are selected at random.
(a) List all the possible combinations of two coins which can be selected from the bag.
(b) Find the probability that the total value of the two coins selected is
(i) 11p
(ii) 30p

2 The four cards shown are shuffled and placed face down on a table.

Two cards are selected at random.

(a) List all the possible pairs of cards which could be selected.
(b) Find the probability that the total of the two cards is
(i) 5
(ii) 9

3 The spinner shown has six equal sections on the outside and three equal sections in the middle. The spinner shows a '5' and an 'A'.

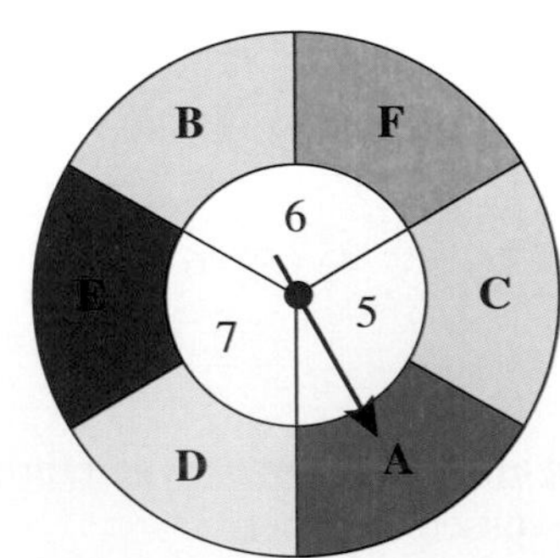

Find the probability of spinning
(a) a 'C'
(b) a '7'
(c) a '6' and an 'F' at the same time

4 A coin and a dice are tossed together.

(a) List all the possible outcomes.
(b) Find the probability of getting
(i) a head on the coin and a 6 on the dice
(ii) a tail on the coin and an even number on the dice.

5 Two bags contain numbered discs as shown. One disc is selected at random from each bag.

(a) Draw a grid to show all the possible outcomes.

(b) Find the probability that

(i) the total of the two numbers is 6

(ii) the total of the two numbers is less than 5.

6 Two spinners, with equal sectors, are numbered 0, 1, 2, ….9. The two spinners are spun together and the difference between the scores is recorded. So a '5' and a '9' gives a difference of 4.

(a) Draw a grid to show all the possible outcomes and write the difference for each outcome.

(b) Find the probability of obtaining

(i) a difference of 4 (ii) a difference of 9

(c) What is the most likely number for the difference?

Experiment: Calculator simulation of two spinners

We can simulate two 10-sided spinners by using the RAN# button on a calculator.

When the RAN# button is pressed (possibly after 'SHIFT') the display shows a *random* 3 digit decimal number between 0.000 and 0.999.

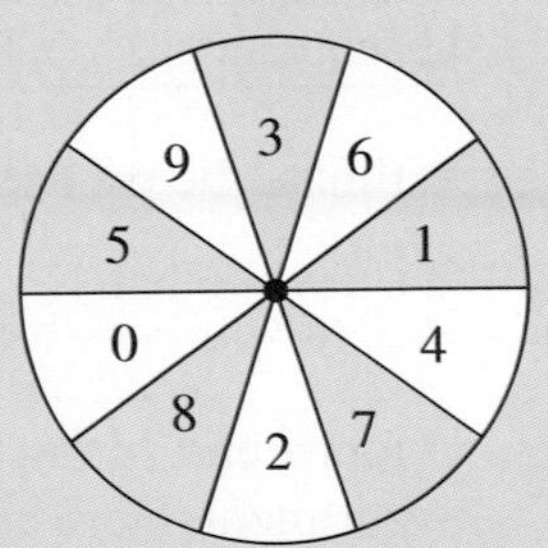

We can ignore the first digit after the point and use the last 2 digits to represent imaginary random scores on two spinners.

E.g. 0.~~9~~27 shows a '2' and a '7' 0.~~8~~13 shows a '1' and a '3'

↑ ignore the 9

In question (6) of the last exercise you calculated the theoretical probability of getting a difference of 4 and a difference of 9, using two 10-sided spinners.

You can now use a calculator to see how closely the experimental results agree with the predicted results.

Difference	Tally
0	
1	
2	
⋮	
9	

(a) Make a tally chart, recording the difference in the last two digits for every number you get using the RAN# button. Perform about 100 or 200 trials.

(b) Collect together the results for the whole class. [Pass a sheet around the class].

(c) Work out the totals for each difference and also the total number of trials.

(d) Find the experimental probability of getting a difference of 4. Find the experimental probability of getting a difference of 9.

(e) Compare you experimental results with the results you predicted in question (6) of the last exercise.

Experimental probability

Exercise 3M

1 A bag contained coloured balls. Rajiv randomly selects a ball from the bag and then replaces it. Here are the results.

Colour	White	Green	Blue
Frequency	10	31	19

Estimate the probability that on his next draw he will select

(a) a white ball (b) a green ball.

2 Dimpna and Jenny both did the 'dropping a drawing pin' experiment. Here are their results.

Dimpna

Trials	20
'Point up'	10

Jenny

Trials	150
'Point up'	61

Another drawing pin is dropped.

(a) For Dimpna, what is the probability of getting 'point up'?

(b) For Jenny, what is the probability of getting 'point up'?

(c) Whose result is likely to be more reliable? Why?

3 Sean collected the results of 40 Liverpool home games.
Estimate the probability that in their next home game:
(a) they will win
(b) they will lose.

Won	18
Lost	10
Drawn	12

For Liverpool's next 40 games, the results were:

Won	23
Lost	11
Drawn	6

Using all 80 results, estimate the probability of
(c) winning their next game.
(d) drawing their next game.

Would you expect these probabilities to be more accurate than those based on the first 40 matches? If so, why?

4 Roll a fair dice 60 times. How many 'ones' would you expect to roll?
Compare your experimental result with the theoretical one.
Suppose you do the experiment again (i.e. roll the dice another 60 times.)
Would you expect to get the same result?

CHECK YOURSELF ON SECTIONS 6.3 AND 6.4

1 Percentages

(a) Work out (i) 16% of £213 (ii) 5.4% of £1650

(b) (i) Calculate the area of the picture.
(ii) Calculate the new area when the length of each side is increased by 5%.

(c) A man earns £10400 and pays £1768 in tax.
What percentage of his earnings does he pay in tax?

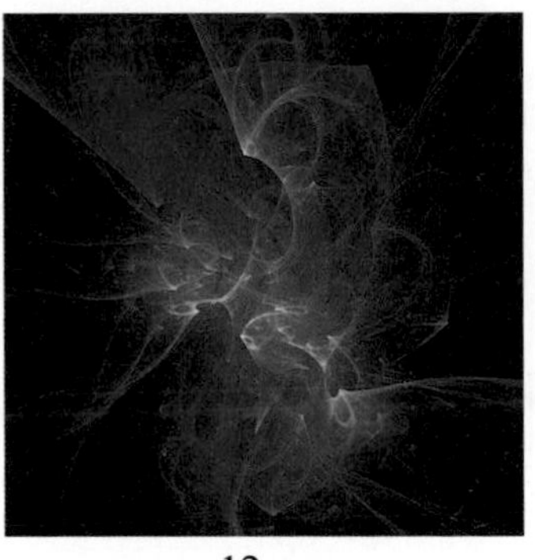

2 Probability

1 A box contains 12 balls: 3 red, 2 yellow, 4 green and 3 black.

(a) Find the probability of selecting
(i) a red ball (ii) a yellow ball.

(b) The 3 black balls are replaced by 3 yellow balls.
Find the probability now of selecting
(i) a red ball (ii) a yellow ball.

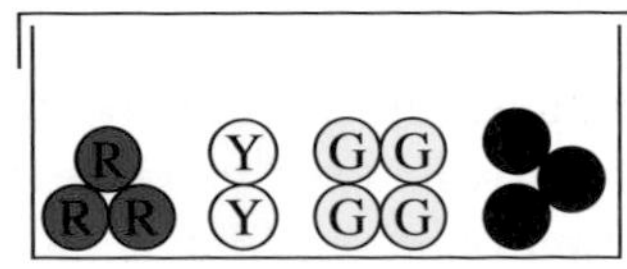

2 A spinner and a dice are spun and rolled at the same time.

(a) List all the possible outcomes.

(b) What is the probability of getting a total score which is
(i) equal to 22 (ii) greater than 22?

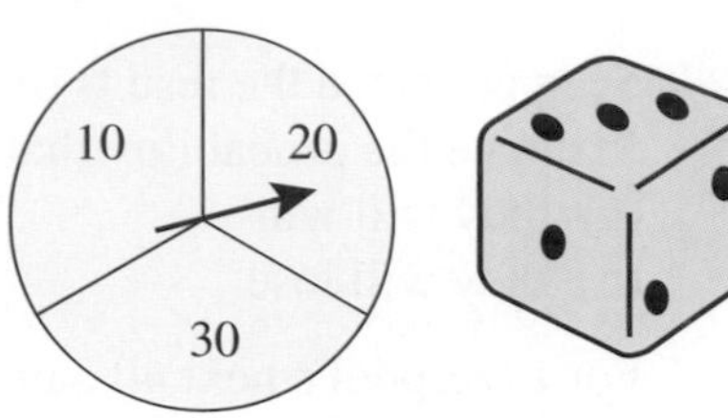

6.5 Drawing three dimensional objects

In section 6.5 you will:

- draw three dimensional objects on isometric paper
- solve problems with objects
- learn about drawing three views of an object

Isometric paper

A drawing of a solid is a 2-D representation of a 3-D object. Below are two pictures of the same object.

(a) On squared paper.

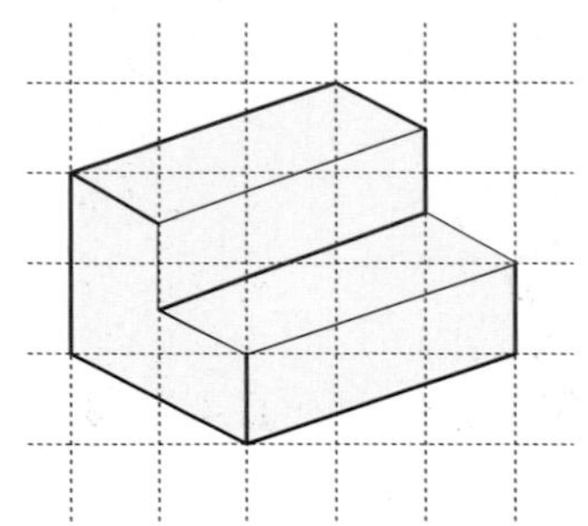

(b) On isometric dot paper.

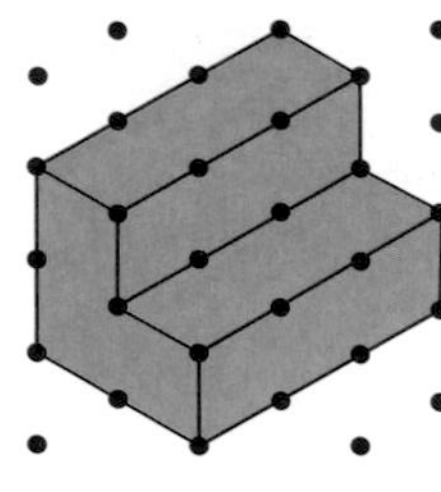

The dimensions of the object cannot be taken from the first picture but they can be taken from the second. Isometric paper can be used either as dots (as above) or as a grid of equilateral triangles. Either way, the paper must be the right way round (as shown here).

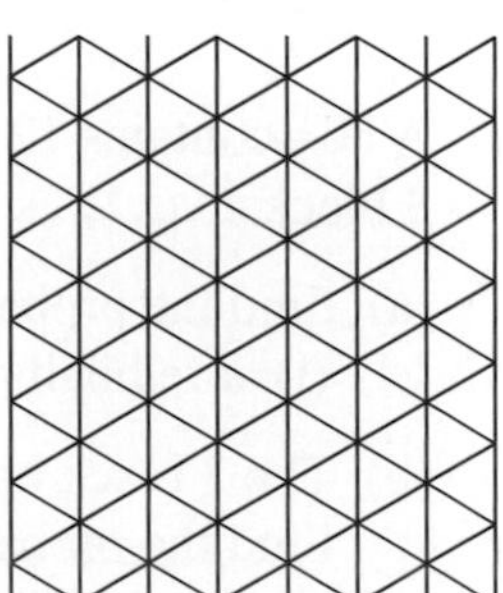

N.B. Most of the questions in this section are easier, and more fun to do, when you have an ample supply of 'unifix' or 'multilink' cubes.

Exercise 1M

1 On isometric paper make a copy of each object below. Underneath each drawing state the number of 'multilink' cubes needed to make the object. (Make sure you have the isometric paper the right way round!)

(a)

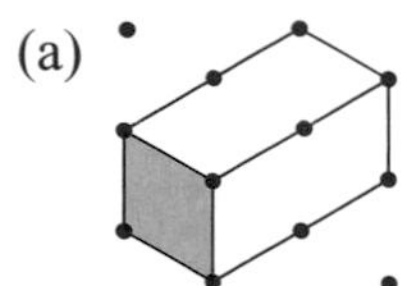

(b)

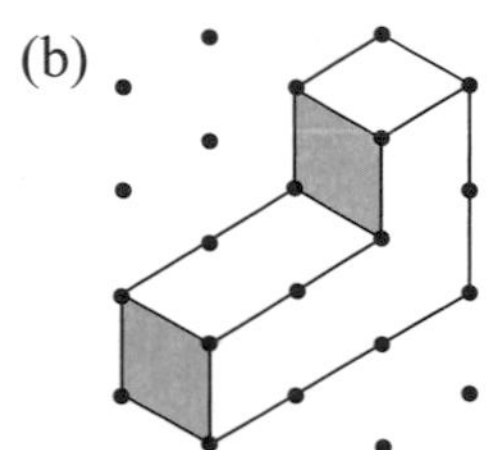

(c)

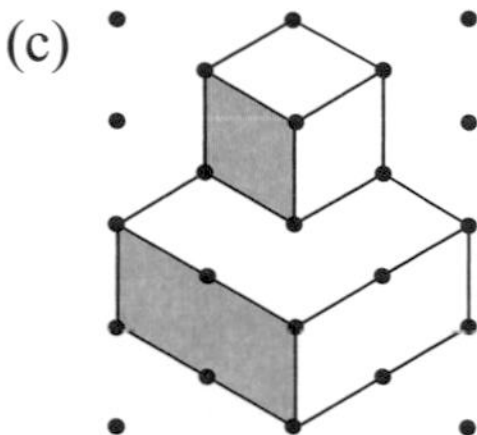

2 Using four cubes, you can make several different shapes. A and B are different shapes but C is the same as A.

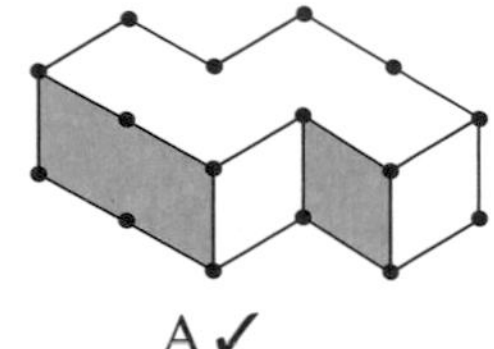

A ✓

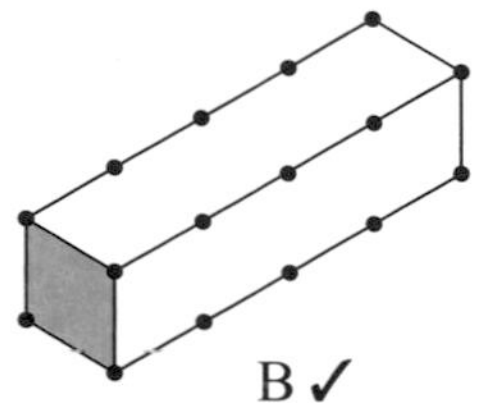

B ✓

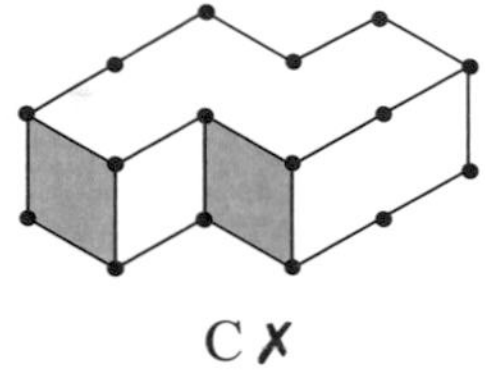

C ✗

Make as many different shapes as possible, using four cubes, and draw them all (including shapes A and B above) on isometric paper.

3 Make the object shown using cubes. Now draw the object *from a different view*.

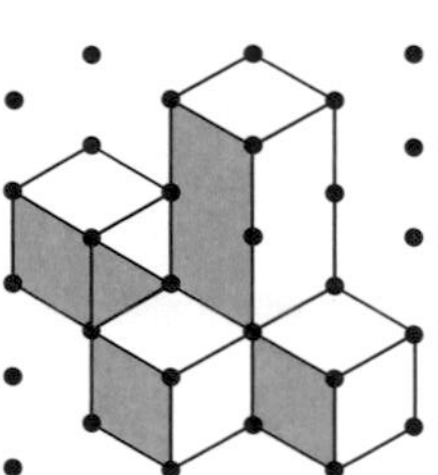

4 Build your own 3-D models of shapes A, B, C and D below. If possible use a different colour for each one.

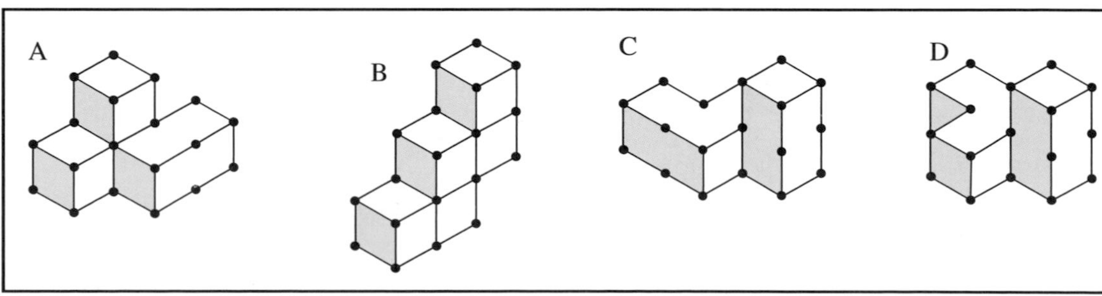

Decide which of the shapes below are the same as shape A on the previous page.
Repeat for shapes B, C and D.

Which shape is neither A, B, C nor D?

1.

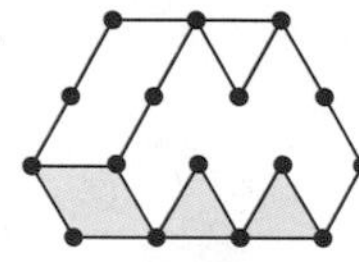

2.

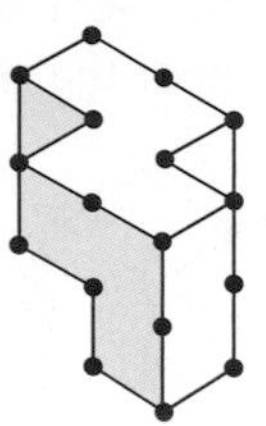

3.

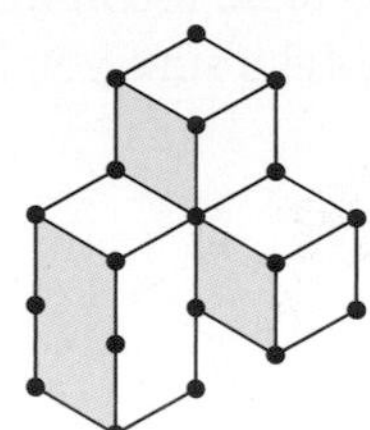

4.

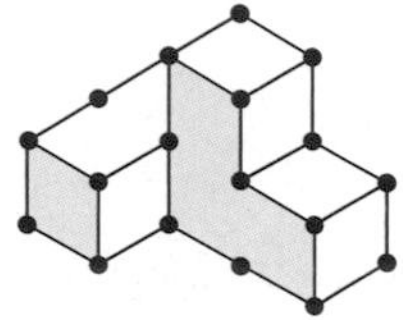

5.

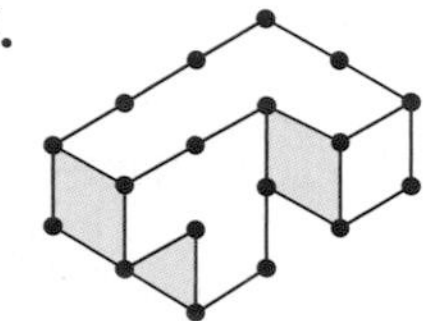

6.

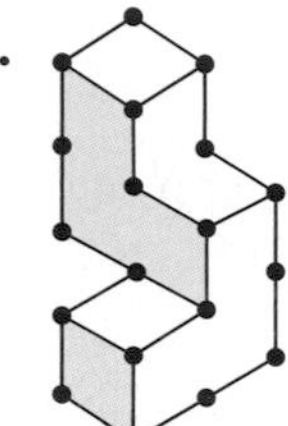

7.

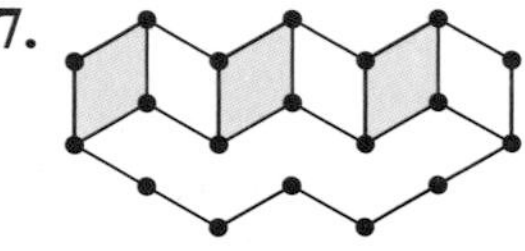

8.

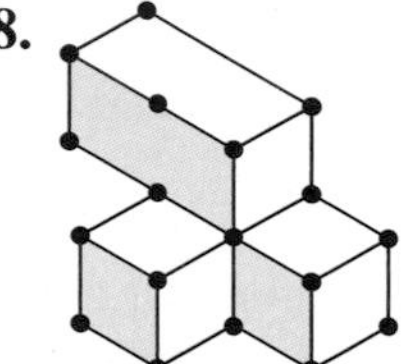

9.

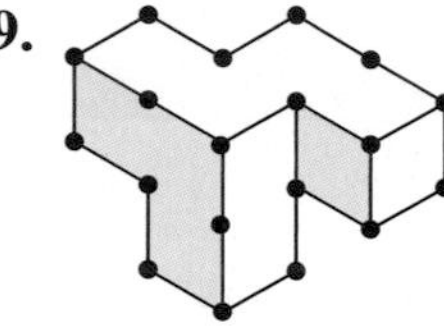

10.

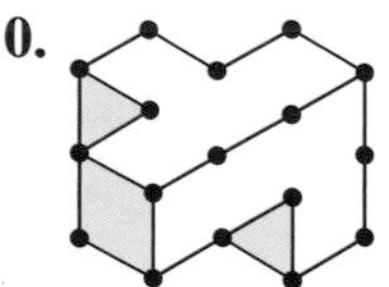

11.

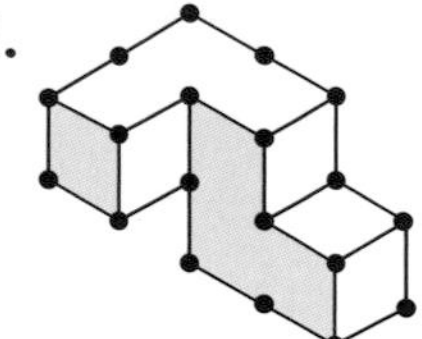

12.

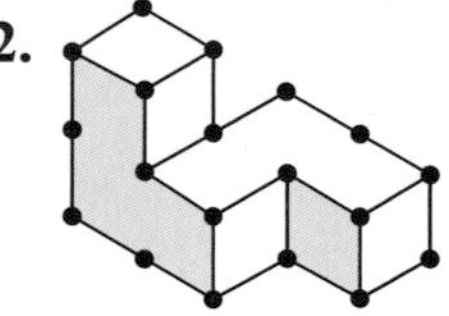

5 You need 18 cubes. Make the two shapes below. Arrange them to make a $3 \times 3 \times 2$ cuboid by adding a third shape, which you have to find. Draw the third shape on isometric paper.

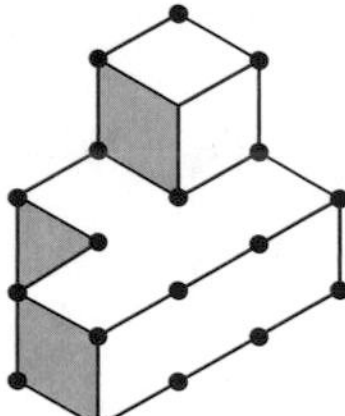

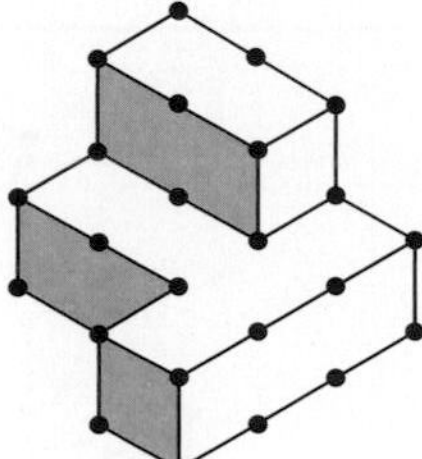

6 You need 27 small cubes for this question. Make the four shapes below and arrange them into a $3 \times 3 \times 3$ cube by adding a fifth shape, which you have to find. Draw the fifth shape on isometric paper. (The number next to each shape indicates the number of small cubes in that shape).

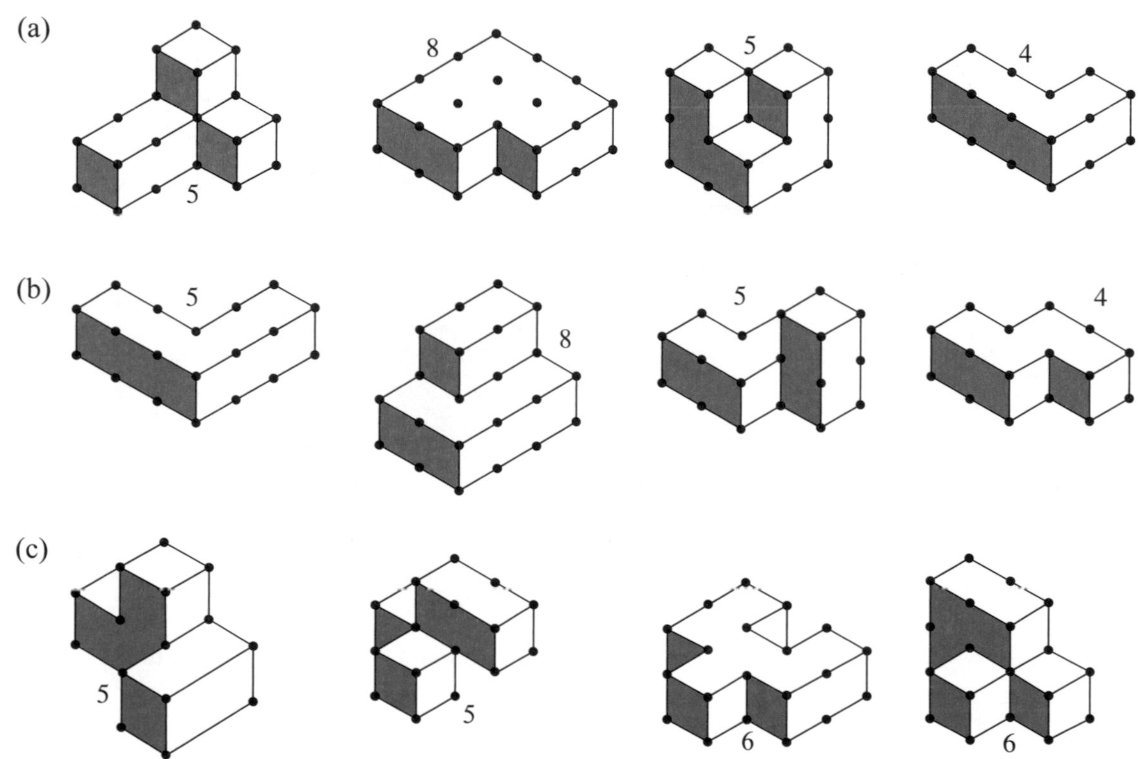

Three views of a shape

Here is a 3-D object made from centimetre cubes. We can draw 3 views of the object on squared paper.

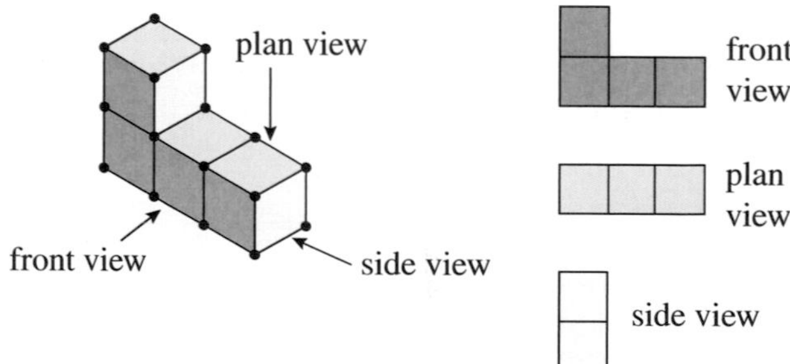

Exercise 2M

In questions 1 to 6 draw the plan view, the front view and the side view of the object

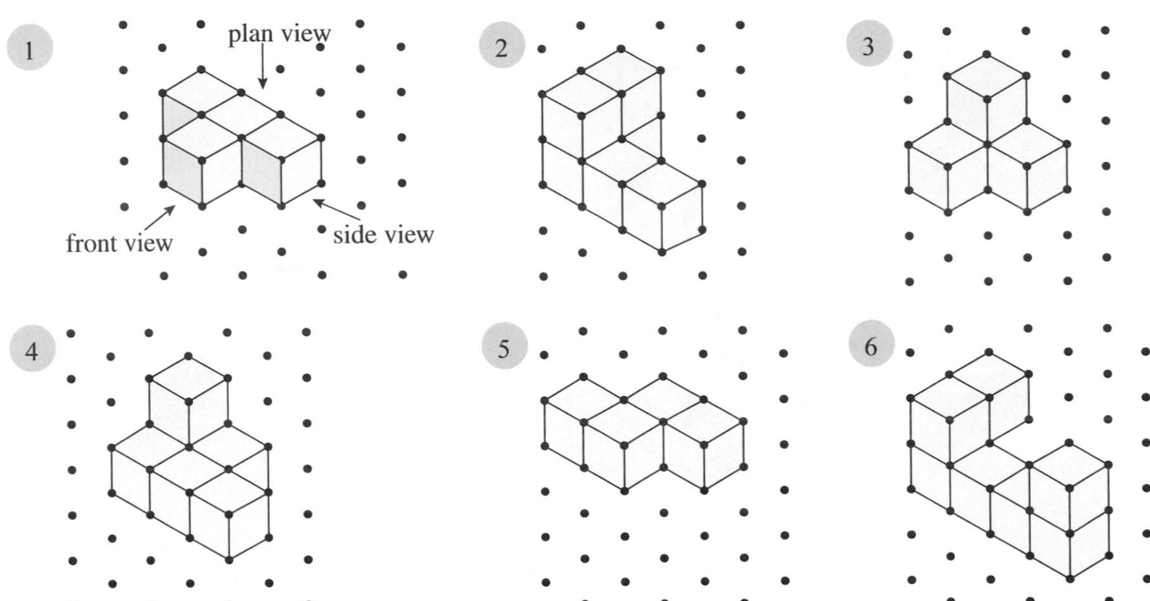

In questions 7 to 14 you are given three views of a shape. Use the information to make the shape using centimetre cubes.

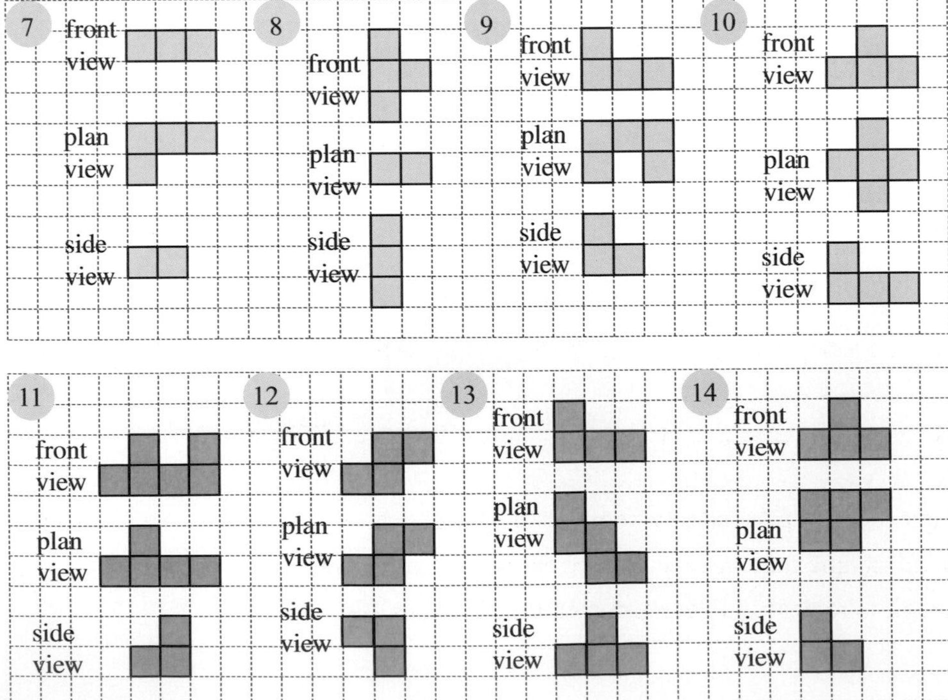

6.6 Statistical methods

In section 6.6 you will:

- discuss a statistical problem, collect relevant data and then present the data in an effective way

Statistical methods

In general, problems that can be answered by statistical methods are complicated! At the start you need to think carefully about questions which may be related.

It is helpful to go through the following procedure.

A Discuss the problem. Identify related questions

B Decide which data to collect

C Decide how to collect the data

D Present the data.

A Discuss the problem. Here is an example.

'*Do parents watch more TV than their children*?'

What counts as 'active TV watching'?
Does it count if you are just in the room?
If you conduct a survey, how can you make sure the data is accurate?
Can people remember accurately what they watched 24 hours ago?
Are people going to answer honestly?
Suppose one or both parents arrive home late every day. How would this affect the survey?
What about watching videos or CDs?

B Which data to collect.

For different problems you might obtain data from:

- a questionnaire or survey of a sample of people.
- secondary sources like newspapers, reference books, websites or Google.

You should realise that data which you collect might be time consuming. On the other hand, you can decide exactly what questions to ask and to whom you ask them.

Realise also that a small sample may not accurately represent a large group.

Is a sample of 10 enough to represent a year group of 180? Perhaps you should join with others to make a group effort.

C How to collect the data.

- You need to design a data collection sheet or questionnaire like those below.

data collection sheet

Name	Height (cm)	Distance to school	Transport to school	Hours of T.V.	Favourite day	
Emma						
Lynne						
Bjorn						
Lars						
Narishta						
David						

Questionnaire

- Your name: ....
- Height (cm) ....
- Distance to school (nearest mile) ....
- How do you get to school? ....
- Hours of T.V.watched each week (estimate) ....
- Favourite day of the week at school ....
-

- For continuous data (like heights) you could use a frequency table.

height	frequency
151–160	11
161–170	8
171–180	5

D Present the data.

- Remember 'A picture paints a thousand words.' Use bar charts, pie charts, scatter graphs……

Suppose you get 20 different answers to the question: 'What is your favourite T.V. program?'
A bar chart with a bar for each program will look very dull!
You could try putting the programs into groups like 'comedy', 'soaps', 'sports', 'drama' etc.
The choice is yours.

- Write a short report, interpreting results and write a clear *conclusion* to say what you found.

Collecting your own data

- For many people the most interesting data is the data *they* decide to find because it is what interests *them*. Below are some suggestions for the sort of problem you could attempt.

1 Are you more accurate at throwing with your writing hand than with your other hand?

Class activity: Each person throws a screwed-up ball of paper into a rubbish bin from a fixed distance. Throw five with each hand and collect results for the whole class.

On target	Writing hand	Other hand
0		
1		
2		
3		
4		
5		

2 Are absences from school equally likely on any day of the week?
Are Mondays and Fridays more frequent than other days for absences?
Are days when PE is taught more often chosen?
Do year 11 pupils take more days off school than year 7 pupils?
Where could information be obtained to answer these questions?

3 'More babies are born in the spring than at any other time of year.'
What exactly do we mean by 'the spring'?
Investigate your year group to see if this is a true statement for your generation.

4

Test the following theory:

'To find a child's potential height take the mean height of the parents, then add 8 cm for a boy and subtract 8 cm for a girl.'

What would be a suitable age group on which to test this theory? Collect data and draw two separate scatter graphs. Plot the mean height of parents on the horizontal axis and height of son or daughter on the vertical axis.

MIXED REVIEW UNIT 6

Part one

1. One card is picked at random from a pack of 52.

   Find the probability that it is

   (a) the Queen of diamonds
   (b) a ten
   (c) a diamond.

2. Ten discs numbered 1, 3, 3, 3, 4, 7, 8, 9, 11, 11 are placed in a bag. One disc is selected at random.

   Find the probability that it is

   (a) an even number
   (b) a three
   (c) less than 6.

3. How many times can the small box be filled from the large container which is full of fertilizer?

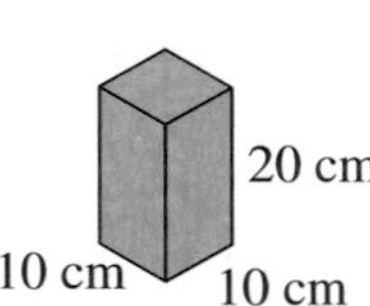

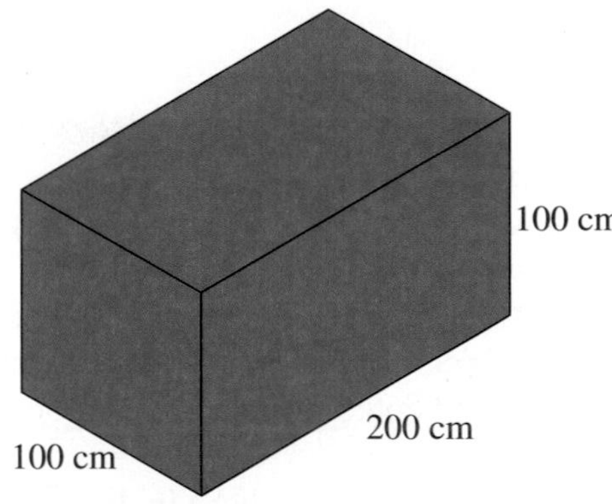

4.

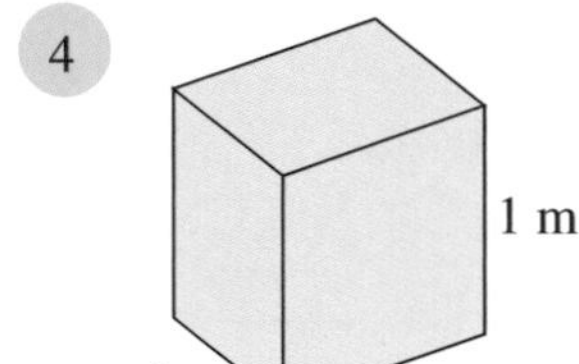

(a) Work out the volume of this cube (i) in m^3
(ii) in cm^3

(b) Copy and complete: $1\text{ m}^3 = \square\text{ cm}^3$

$2.4\text{ m}^3 = \square\text{ cm}^3$

$1\text{ m}^3 = \square\text{ mm}^3$

5. Find the value of each expression when $n = 3$.

   (a) $n^2 - n$ (b) $5(2n - 1)$ (c) $(n - 5)^2$ (d) $3n^2$

   (e) $10 - 4n$ (f) $\frac{(n+1)^2}{4}$ (g) $\frac{6}{n} + \frac{n}{3}$ (h) $n + n^2 + n^3$

6. The value of each brick in the wall is found by adding the values in the two bricks below.

   (a) Copy and complete this wall.

   (b) If the top number is 46, find the value of x.

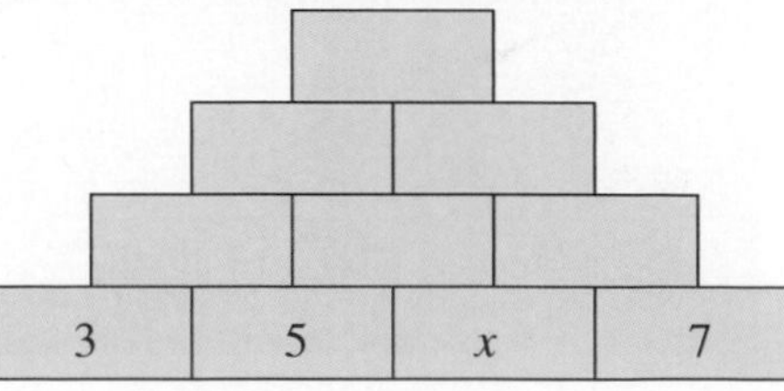

7 This object is made from 8 cubes.

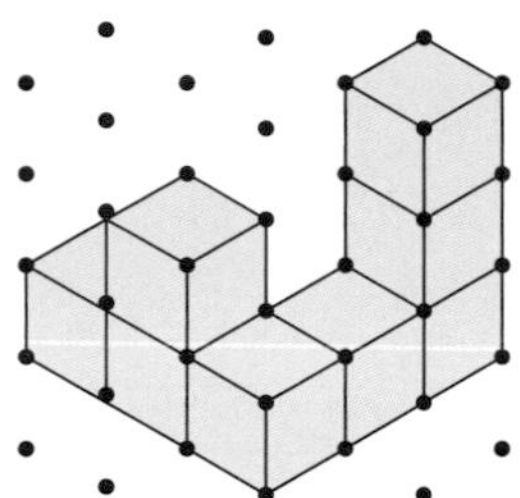

The plan view is drawn showing the number of cubes on that base.

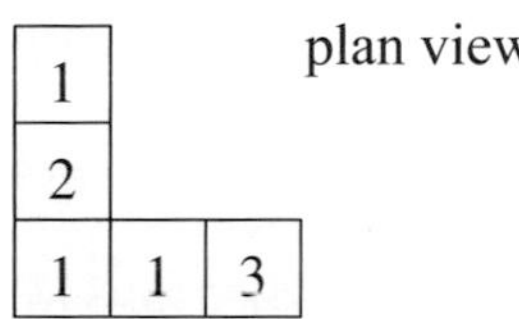

Use isometric paper to draw each of these shapes where the number of cubes on the base are shown.

(a)

1		1
2	1	3

(b)

3	2	1
1		
4	2	

(c)

1	2	4	2
2	3		1
2			

8 The number of people visiting the Taj Mahal one day was 11,249. How many of these people would you expect to celebrate their birthdays on a Tuesday in the year 2011?

9 When playing Monopoly, Philip knows that the probability of throwing a 'double' with two dice is $\frac{1}{6}$. What is the probability that he does *not* throw a double with his next throw?

10 Calculate the volume of each of the prisms shown below. All lengths are in cm.

(a)

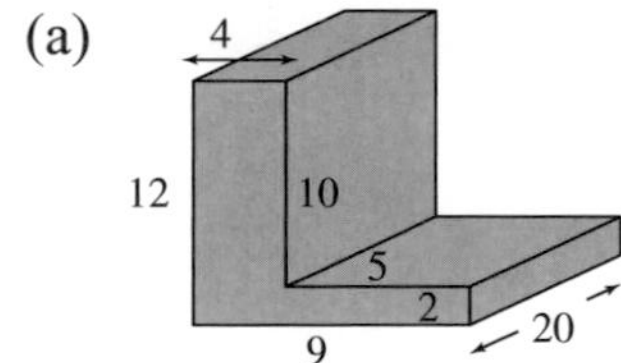

(b)

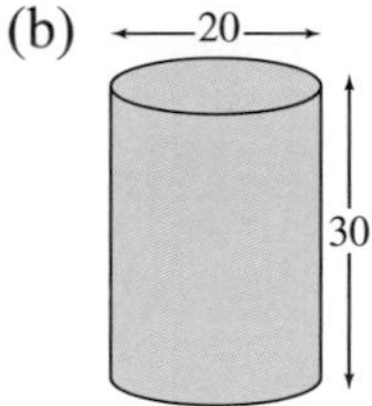

(c)

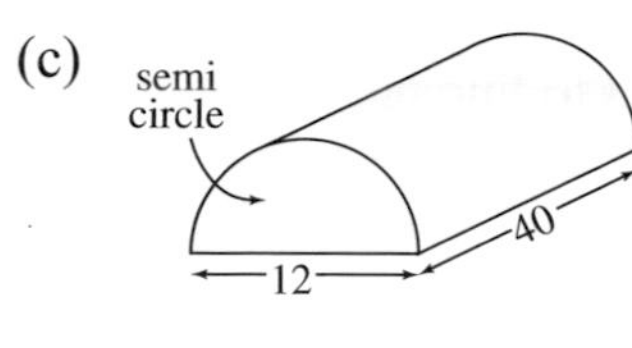

11 Oil from the large drum is used to fill many of the small cans.

How many cans may be filled from the drum?

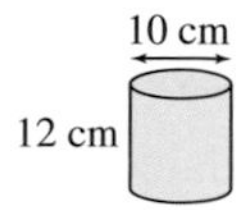

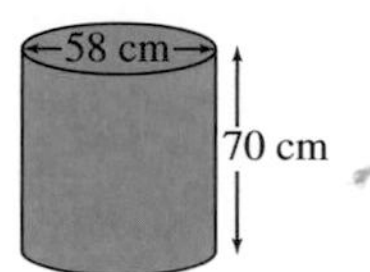

12 Elton sold one of his cars for £15000. He made a profit of 20%. At what price did he buy the car?

Part two

1 Solve the equations

(a) $19 = 11 + 10n$ (b) $5(2x - 3) = 3(3x + 4)$

(c) $3(6 - 2y) = y + 2$ (d) $\frac{z}{4} + 1 = 10$

2 Sam thinks of a number. He multiplies it by 3, adds 4 and then doubles the result. The answer is 11.

Form an equation and then solve it to find the number.

3 Loni is thinking of a number. Three times the number plus 5 gives the same answer as when the number is added to 4 and then the result is doubled. Find the number she is thinking of.

4 The cylinder and the cuboid shown have the same volume. Calculate the height h of the box.

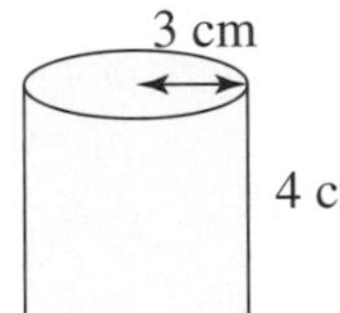

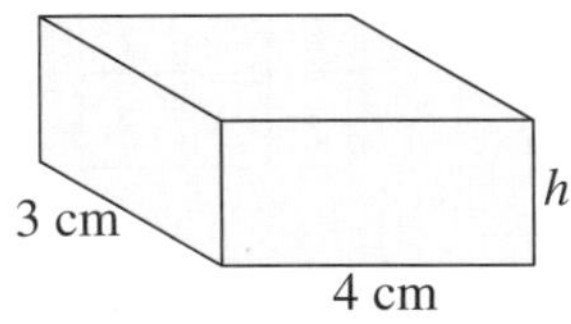

5 

The internal and external diameters of a pipe are 2 cm and 2.6 cm respectively. The length of the pipe is 3 m. The pipe is made from material of density 8g/cm^3. Calculate the mass of the pipe.

6 The diagram shows two angles in an isosceles triangle. Form an equation involving x and solve it to find the angles of the triangle.

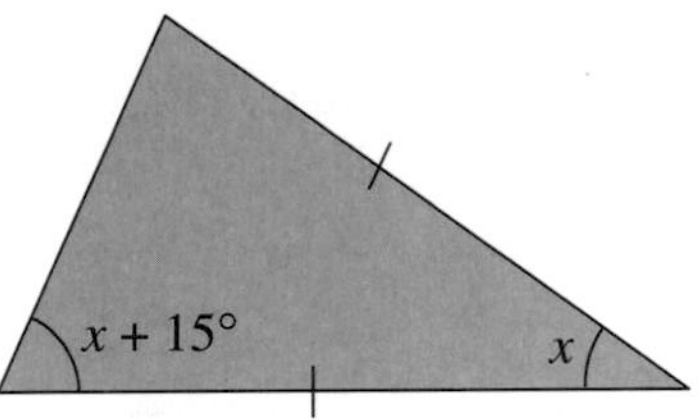

7 (a) 13 out of 80 cars failed their annual MoT test. What percentage failed?

(b) Increase a mass of 4100 kg by 2.5%

8 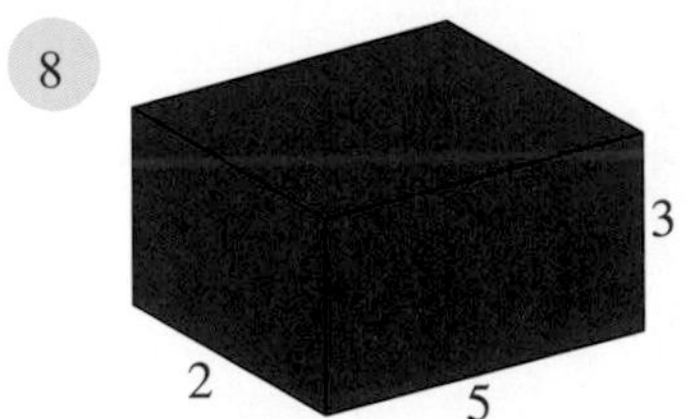

The dimensions of the cuboid are in cm.

(a) Calculate the volume of this cuboid.

(b) Calculate the volume of the cuboid when each of the dimensions is increased by 10%.

(c) By what percentage has the volume increased?

9 Some steps are to be made in concrete.

(a) Calculate, in cubic metres, the volume of concrete needed.

(b) The concrete is mixed, by volume, from cement, sand and stones, in the ratio 2:3:6
What volume of sand is required for the steps?

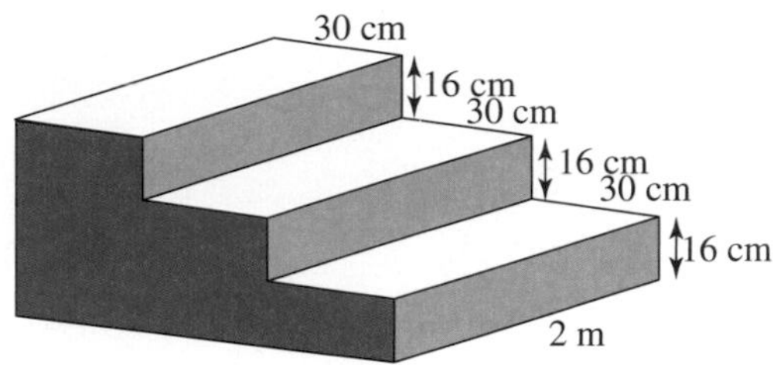

10 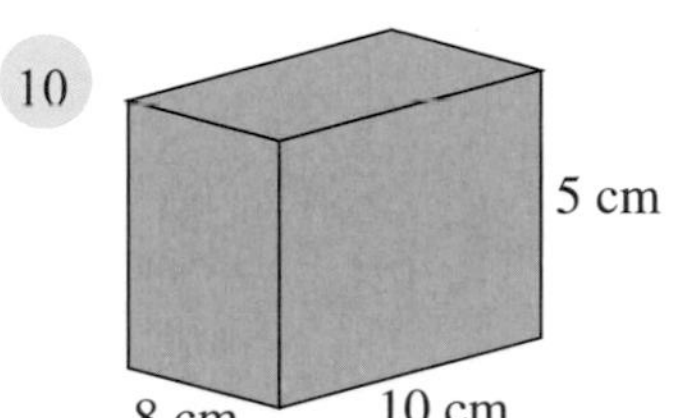

Twenty of the cuboids shown are melted down and cast into one large cube.

Find the length of each side of the cube.

11 (a) Draw a grid to show the 36 equally likely outcomes when two dice are thrown together. [Like the grid in the question below.]

(b) Find the probability of getting
  (i) a total of 4
  (ii) a total of 7
  (iii) the same number on both dice.

12 The grid shows the outcomes when two dice are thrown together.

Copy the grid and write down the difference between the two scores for each outcome. Two differences are shown, as examples.

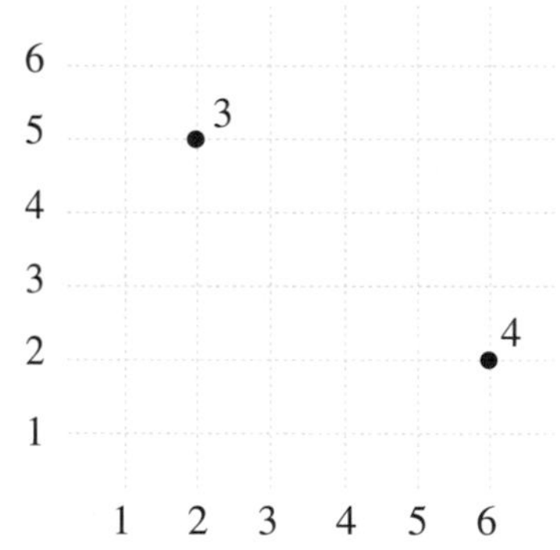

(a) Find the probability of obtaining a difference of
  (i) 4 (ii) 1

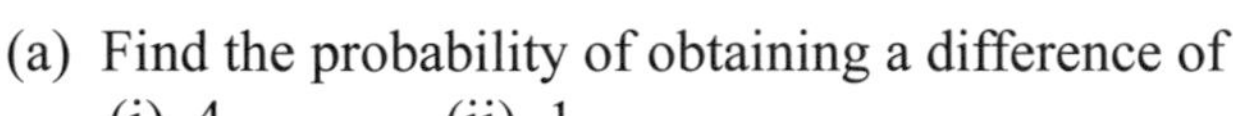

(b) What number is the most likely difference?

13 Simplify the following.

(a) $5(c-2)+8-3c$ (b) $m(5+m)-3m$ (c) $xy+yx+xy$

(d) $m \times m^2 \times m^3$ (e) $c\,(c+2c)-c^2$ (f) $x(2x+1)-x(x-1)$

(g) $\frac{a^4}{a}$ (h) $\frac{3}{t}-\frac{1}{t}$ (i) $\frac{a}{b} \times \frac{2b}{a}$

Answers to 'check yourself' questions

Page 23 sections 1.1, 1.2 and 1.3

1.1 (a) 2, 3, 5, 7, 11, 13, 17, 19, 23

(b) 2 + 3 = 5 (many others) (c) 28 (others)

(d) 1, 2, 3, 4, 5, 6, 8, 10, 12, 15, 20, 24, 30, 40, 60, 120

(e) 7, 14, 21, 28, 35 (f) (i) 9 + 36 (ii) 25 + 81

(iii) 9 + 64 (g) (i) 9 (ii) 32

(iii) 10 000 (iv) 1 000 000

1.2 (a) (i) $\frac{13}{14}$ (ii) $\frac{7}{24}$ (iii) $1\frac{1}{12}$

(b) (i) $1\frac{2}{45}$ (ii) $3\frac{1}{3}$ (iii) $\frac{1}{4}$

1.3 (a) (i) 54 cm^2, 36 cm (ii) 21 cm^2, 21.5 cm

(b) base 5 cm, ht. 12 cm (c) 900 m

Page 42 sections 1.4 and 1.5

1. (a) (i) –10 (ii) –14 (iii) –13 (iv) 50 (v) 81 (vi) –0.8 (vii) –7 (viii) –40

(b)

1	6	–1
0	2	4
5	–2	3

2. (a) (i) 30 (ii) 48 (iii) 6

(b) (i) –3 (ii) –28 (iii) 11

3. (a) (i) 53 (ii) 1 (iii) 0.034 (b) (i) 2, 10, 18, 26, 34

(ii) 240, 120, 60, 30, 15, 7.5 (c) (i) 31, 39 (ii) 49, 71

Page 51 section 1.6

1. 1. 18 2. 70 3. 9 4. 80 5. 5 6. 44

2. (a) 0.8 (b) 43.1 (c) $2\frac{17}{30}$ (d) 10.8 (e) 4.1

(f) 1.9 (g) 1.2 (h) 252.6

Page 78 sections 2.1 and 2.2

1. (a) 1480 (b) 22.172 (c) 638 (d) 7613 (e) 0.162

2. (a) 1.9 (b) 0.07 (c) 12 (d) 21.6 (e) 0.0096 (f) 22.4

3. (a) (i) 800 (ii) 1200 (iii) 200

(iv) 180 (v) £600 (vi) 30

(b) 2500 km (c) (i) 16.4 (ii) 8.5 (iii) 0.3

Page 95 sections 2.3 and 2.4

1. (a) 142° (b) $b = 106°$, $c = 78°$

(c) $d = 40°$, $e = 60°$ (d) $x = 26°$

(e) $p = 68°$, $q = 56°$, $r = 68°$

2. (a) $4n - 6$ (b) $4c - 2$

(c) $3n^2 - 2n$ (d) $3xy$ (e) m^3 (f) $6e^2$ (g) n

(h) t (i) $\frac{3}{m}$

Page 114 section 2.6

1. (a) 32.7 cm (b) 19.4 cm (c) 28.6 cm

2. (a) 84.9 cm^2 (b) 26.1 cm^2 (c) 50.3 cm^2

Page 140 sections 3.1 and 3.2

1. (b) vertices at: (i) (–3, 1) (–3, 4) (–5, 4)

(ii) (1, 1) (1, –2) (3, –2)

(c) (i) $y = \frac{-1}{2}$ (ii) $y = x$

2. (a) 11 (b) 5.75 m

Page 154 sections 3.3 and 3.4

1. (a) 1600 (b) 120 (c) 78 (d) 103

(e) 178 (f) 217 (g) 4545 (h) 1400

(i) 0.26 (j) 150° (k) £10.50

2. (a) (i) 25 (ii) 53 (iii) 58 (b) (i) 5

(ii) 30 (iii) 23 (iv) –40

(c) $\frac{4n}{n}$, $\frac{12}{n}$, $10^n - 996$, $\frac{(n+1)^2}{4}$

Page 192 sections 4.1 and 4.3

1. (a) 045° (b) 090° (c) 135°

(d) 180° (e) 225° (f) 270°

2. (a) (ii) strong negative correlation

(b) A positive, B none, C none, D strong negative

Page 207 sections 4.4 and 4.5

1. (a) (i) 40% (ii) 0.02 (iii) $0.\dot{2}$ (iv) 62%

(b) £21.28 (c) €4.18, £122.93

2. events in order: IJ, BC, JK, CD, DE and/or HI, AB, EF

Page 228 sections 4.6 and 4.7

1. (a) (i) rotation 90° CW, centre (–1, –1)

(ii) rotation 90° ACW, centre (3, –1)

(iii) reflection in $y = -1$

(iv) reflection in $y = x$

(v) rotation 90° CW, centre (–1, –1)

(b) various e.g. rotation 180°, centre (1, 0) then reflection in $y = 3$

2. (a) (i) $4n - 12$ (ii) $7n + 1$ (iii) $n - 2$ (b) (i) 6

(ii) $\frac{7}{5}$ (iii) 3 (c) sides 11

Page 256 sections 5.1 and 5.2

2. (a) (i) $4n$ (ii) $2n + 1$ (iii) $n + 2$ (iv) $\frac{n}{n+1}$

(b) (i) 26 (ii) 10001 (c) (i) $3n - 1$ (ii) $7n + 3$

(iii) $4n - 1$

Page 270 section 5.4

1. (a) $\sqrt{41}$ (b) $\sqrt{45}$ (c) $\sqrt{51}$ (d) $\sqrt{504}$

2. (a) 31.2 cm^2 (b) 7.35 cm

Page 291 sections 5.5 and 5.6

1. (b) $y = 2x + 3$

2. 0.25

3. (a) 175 litres (b) 0.85 litres (c) 2.1 pints

4. (a) (i) 2:4:5 (ii) 2:5:7
(b) £80, £140 (c) 4.5
(d) 400 (e) 2 km

Page 321 sections 6.1 and 6.2

1. (a) (i) $\frac{1}{3}$ (ii) 1 (iii) 1.5
(b) (i) $1\frac{1}{3}$ (ii) 18 (c) 150 cm^2

2. (a) (i) 33 cm^3 (ii) 905 cm^3 (b) 55 cm

Page 337 sections 6.3 and 6.4

Part 1 **1.** (a) (i) £34.08 (ii) £89.10 (b) (i) 144 cm^2
(ii) 158.76 cm^2 (c) 17%

Part 2 **1.** (a) (i) $\frac{1}{4}$ (ii) $\frac{1}{6}$ (b) (i) $\frac{1}{4}$ (ii) $\frac{5}{12}$
2. (b) (i) $\frac{1}{18}$ (ii) $\frac{5}{9}$

INDEX